W9-BVD-297

# Mathematics

## Applying the Concepts

**AUTHORS**

**Chris Dearling**
B.Sc., M.Sc.
Burlington, Ontario

**Wayne Erdman**
B.Math, B.Ed.
Toronto District School Board

**Brian McCudden**
M.A., M.Ed., Ph.D.
Toronto, Ontario

**Roland W. Meisel**
B.Sc., B.Ed., M.Sc.
Port Colborne, Ontario

**Tess Miller**
B.Sc., B.Ed.
Durham District School Board

**Jacob Speijer**
B.Eng., M.Sc.Ed., P.Eng.
District School Board of Niagara

**ASSESSMENT CONSULTANTS**

**Chris Dearling**
B.Sc., M.Sc.

**Brian McCudden**
M.A., M.Ed., Ph.D.

**TECHNOLOGY CONSULTANT**

**Roland W. Meisel**
B.Sc., B.Ed., M.Sc.

**PEDAGOGY CONSULTANT**

**Jeff Irvine**
B.Math, B.Ed., M.A., M.B.A., C.F.P.

Toronto Montréal Boston Burr Ridge, IL Dubuque, IA Madison, WI New York San Francisco St. Louis Bangkok Bogotá Caracas Kuala Lumpur Lisbon London Madrid Mexico City Milan New Delhi Santiago Seoul Singapore Sydney Taipei

COPIES OF THIS BOOK MAY BE OBTAINED BY CONTACTING:
McGraw-Hill Ryerson Ltd.

WEB SITE:
*http://www.mcgrawhill.ca*

E-MAIL:
*orders@mcgrawhill.ca*

TOLL-FREE FAX:
1-800-463-5885

TOLL-FREE CALL:
1-800-565-5758

OR BY MAILING YOUR ORDER TO:
McGraw-Hill Ryerson
Order Department
300 Water Street
Whitby, ON L1N 9B6

Please quote the ISBN and title when placing your order.

Student text ISBN:
0-07-092242-X

McGraw-Hill
Ryerson

*Mathematics: Applying the Concepts 9*



ISBN 0-07-092242-X

*http://www.mcgrawhill.ca*

1 2 3 4 5 6 7 8 9 10 TRI 0 9 8 7 6 5 4 3

Printed and bound in Canada

Care has been taken to trace ownership of copyright material contained in this text. The publishers will gladly accept any information that will enable them to rectify any reference or credit in subsequent printings.

*The Geometer's Sketchpad*®, Key Curriculum Press, 1150 65th Street, Emeryville, CA 94608, 1-800-995-MATH.

CBR™ is a trademark of Texas Instruments Incorporated.

**National Library of Canada Cataloging in Publication Data**

Erdman, Wayne, [date]

Mathematics: applying the concepts 9/authors, Wayne Erdman, Tess Miller, Jacob Speijer; assessment consultants, Chris Dearling, Brian McCudden; technology consultant: Roland W. Meisel; pedagogical consultant: Jeff Irvine.

Includes index.
For use in grade 9.
ISBN 0-07-092242-X

1. Mathematics—Textbooks. I. Miller, Tess II. Speijer, Jacob III. Title.

QA39.3.E73 2003 510 C2003-901442-8

Publisher: Diane Wyman
Project Manager: Maggie Cheverie
Developmental Editors: Jean Ford, Tom Gamblin, Julia Cochrane
Supervising Editor: Cathy Deak
Copy Editors: Mary Agnes Challoner, Julia Cochrane, Angela Chan, Dianne Brassolotto
Permissions Editor: Jacqueline Donovan
Editorial Assistant: Erin Parton
Junior Editor: Tara Quach
Production Supervisor: Yolanda Pigden
Production Coordinators: Paula Brown, Jennifer Wilkie
Cover Design: Dianna Little
Interior Design: Tom Dart/First Folio Resource Group, Inc.
Art Direction: Tom Dart/First Folio Resource Group, Inc.
Electronic Page Make-Up: Tom Dart, Claire Milne/First Folio Resource Group, Inc.
Cover Image: SCOTT MARKEWITZ/Getty Images, LARRY PROSOR/SUPERSTOCK

# Acknowledgements


## Reviewers of *Mathematics: Applying the Concepts 9*

*The authors and editors of* Mathematics: Applying the Concepts 9 *wish to thank the advisors and reviewers listed below for their thoughtful comments and suggestions. Their input has been invaluable in ensuring that this text meets the needs of the students and teachers taking this course.*

### Advisors

Steve Etienne
District School Board of Niagara

Donna Kotsopoulos
Thames Valley District School Board

Lillian Kovachis Perivolaris
Toronto District School Board

John Gardiner
Trillium Lakelands District School Board

### Reviewers

Mary Card
Toronto District School Board

Cathy Dunne
Peel District School Board

John Ferguson
Lambton-Kent District School Board

Fred Ferneyhough
Peel District School Board

David Furlong
Toronto District School Board

Kara Gilby
Ottawa-Carleton District School Board

Judi Hanta
Hamilton-Wentworth Catholic District School Board

Kaethe Imbert
Ottawa-Carleton District School Board

Mike Jacobs
Durham Catholic District School Board

Donna Loster
Kawartha Pine Ridge District School Board

Louis Lim
York Region District School Board

Giovanni Quartarone
Toronto District School Board

Larry Romano
Toronto Catholic District School Board

Carl Stewart
Durham District School Board

Natasha Sudy
York Region District School Board

Angela Van Kralingen
Niagara Catholic District School Board

Bill Virtue
Dufferin Peel District School Board

Steve Wight
Upper Canada District School Board

*The authors and editors would also like to extend special thanks to the students and teachers of the following schools for providing us with feedback and suggestions during the development of the content and design for this text. Their input was invaluable in making decisions on the design and lesson structure of this text that we believe have improved the quality of this learning resource.*

A.B. Lucas Secondary School, Thames Valley District School Board

Central Peel Secondary School, Peel District School Board

Neil McNeil Catholic Secondary School, Toronto Catholic District School Board

Nepean High School, Ottawa-Carleton District School Board

# Contents

## Chapter 1

### Applying Number Sense



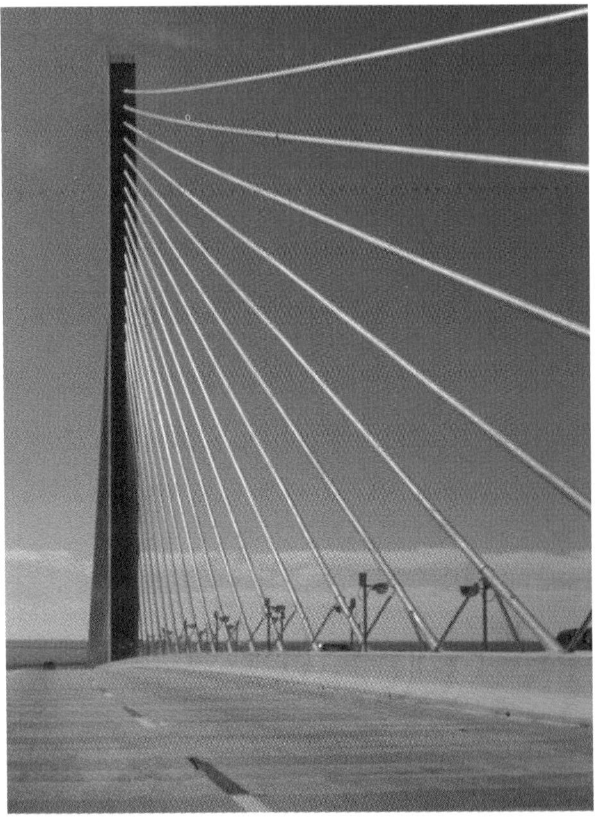

## Chapter 2

### Perimeter and Area Relationships



## Chapter 3

### Surface Area and Volume Relationships

## CHAPTER 4

### ANALYSING RELATIONSHIPS WITH DATA



## CHAPTER 5

### EXPLORING INTEGERS AND RATIONAL NUMBERS

# Chapter 6

## Linear and Non-Linear Relations



# Chapter 7

## Analysing Linear Relations



# Chapter 8

## Applying Exponents

## CHAPTER 9

### EXPLORING POLYNOMIALS



## CHAPTER 10

### MODELLING WITH EQUATIONS



## CHAPTER 11

### EXPLORING GEOMETRIC RELATIONSHIPS



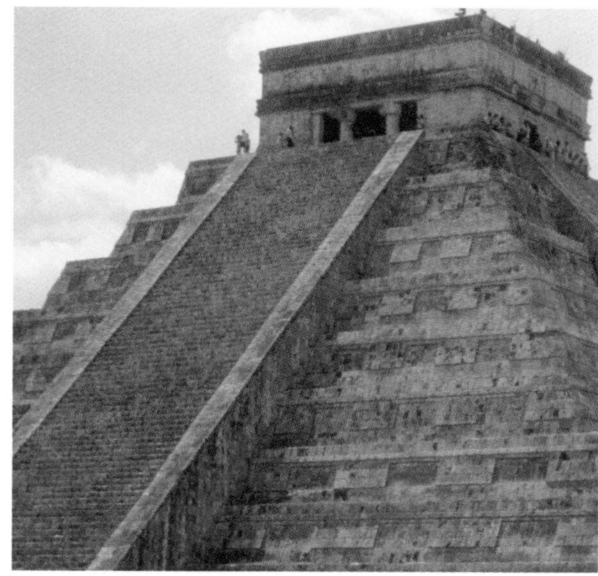

# A Tour of Your Textbook

## CHAPTER OPENER

- This two-page spread introduces what you will learn in the chapter.
- The **Chapter Problem** is introduced. Questions related to the chapter problem occur throughout the chapter and are identified by a chapter problem logo.

CHAPTER

8

Applying Exponents

An optic fibre can be as thin as a human hair, yet long enough to lay across a city. In this chapter, you will

- study exponents
- combine exponents in calculations
- use exponents to handle very large and very small numbers, such as the dimensions of optic fibres

Chapter Problem

In Canada, as in most countries, we recycle a lot of material. We also produce a large amount of garbage. In 2000, Canadians generated 25 200 000 000 000 kg of waste. Of that, only 1 280 000 000 000 kg was recycled. In this chapter, you will learn quick ways to calculate with large numbers like these.

## GET READY

Examples and questions review key skills from previous mathematics courses that are needed for success with the new concepts of the chapter.

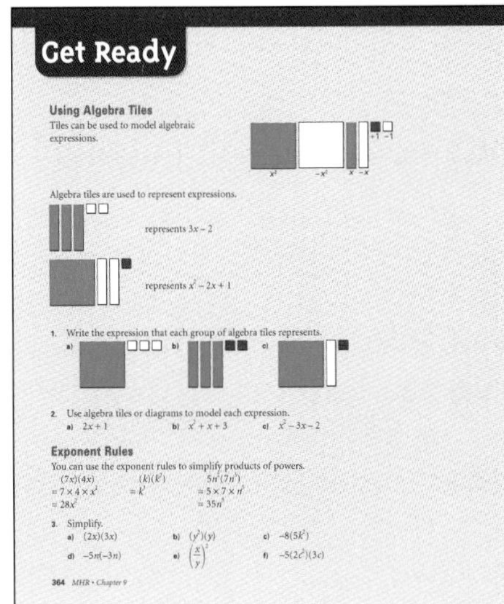

Get Ready

**Using Algebra Tiles**

Tiles can be used to model algebraic expressions.



Algebra tiles are used to represent expressions.

represents $3x - 2$

represents $x^2 - 2x + 1$

1. Write the expression that each group of algebra tiles represents.
   a) b) c)

2. Use algebra tiles or diagrams to model each expression.
   a) $2x + 1$ b) $x^2 + x + 3$ c) $x^2 - 3x - 2$

**Exponent Rules**

You can use the exponent rules to simplify products of powers.

$(7x)(4x) = 7 \times 4 \times x^2 = 28x^2$ $(k)(k^2) = k^3$ $5n^2(7n^3) = 5 \times 7 \times n^5 = 35n^5$

3. Simplify.
   a) $(2x)(3x)$ b) $(y^3)(y)$ c) $-8(5k^2)$
   d) $-5n(-3n)$ e) $\left(\frac{x}{y}\right)^2$ f) $-5(2c^2)(3c)$

364 MHR • Chapter 9

# NUMBERED SECTIONS

## LESSON OPENER

Often lessons start with a real-world setting to which the mathematical concepts relate.

## DISCOVER

These are step-by-step activities, leading you to build your own understanding of the math concepts of the lesson.

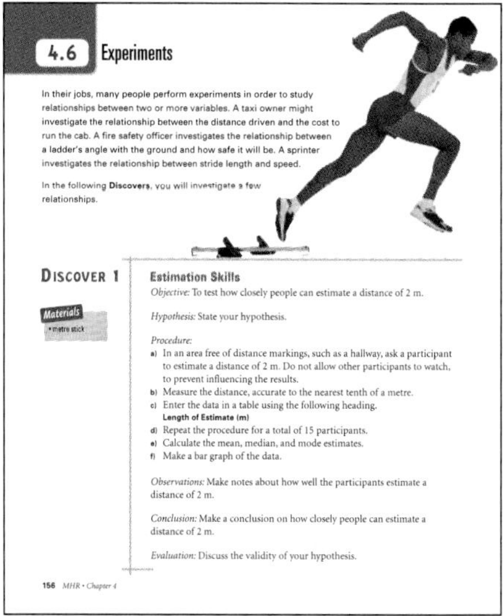
4.6 Experiments

In their jobs, many people perform experiments in order to study relationships between two or more variables. A taxi owner might investigate the relationship between the distance driven and the cost to run the cab. A fire safety officer investigates the relationship between a ladder's angle with the ground and how safe it will be. A sprinter investigates the relationship between stride length and speed.

In the following **Discovers**, you will investigate a few relationships.

DISCOVER 1

Materials
• metre stick

**Estimation Skills**

*Objective:* To test how closely people can estimate a distance of 2 m.

*Hypothesis:* State your hypothesis.

*Procedure:*
a) In an area free of distance markings, such as a hallway, ask a participant to estimate a distance of 2 m. Do not allow other participants to watch, to prevent influencing the results.
b) Measure the distance, accurate to the nearest tenth of a metre.
c) Enter the data in a table using the following heading.
**Length of Estimate (m)**
d) Repeat the procedure for a total of 15 participants.
e) Calculate the mean, median, and mode estimates.
f) Make a bar graph of the data.

*Observations:* Make notes about how well the participants estimate a distance of 2 m.

*Conclusion:* Make a conclusion on how closely people can estimate a distance of 2 m.

*Evaluation:* Discuss the validity of your hypothesis.

156 MHR • Chapter 4

## EXAMPLES

- Worked examples provide model solutions that show how the new concepts are used.
- You can refer to these examples as you work on the exercises.

## KEY CONCEPTS

- This feature summarizes the concepts learned in the lesson.
- Your can refer to this summary when you are studying or doing homework.

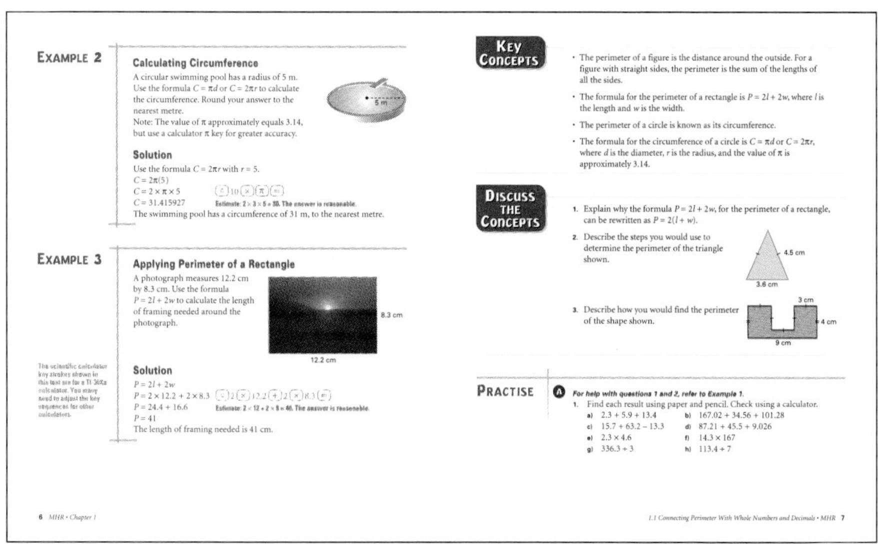
EXAMPLE 2 **Calculating Circumference**

A circular swimming pool has a radius of 5 m. Use the formula $C = \pi d$ or $C = 2\pi r$ to calculate the circumference. Round your answer to the nearest metre.
Note: The value of $\pi$ approximately equals 3.14, but use a calculator $\pi$ key for greater accuracy.



**Solution**

Use the formula $C = 2\pi r$ with $r = 5$.
$C = 2\pi(5)$
$C = 2 \times \pi \times 5$
$C = 31.415927$
Estimate: $2 \times 3 \times 5 = 30$. The answer is reasonable.
The swimming pool has a circumference of 31 m, to the nearest metre.

EXAMPLE 3 **Applying Perimeter of a Rectangle**

A photograph measures 12.2 cm by 8.3 cm. Use the formula $P = 2l + 2w$ to calculate the length of framing needed around the photograph.



**Solution**

$P = 2l + 2w$
$P = 2 \times 12.2 + 2 \times 8.3$
$P = 24.4 + 16.6$
Estimate: $2 \times 12 + 2 \times 8 = 40$. The answer is reasonable.
$P = 41$
The length of framing needed is 41 cm.

KEY CONCEPTS

- The perimeter of a figure is the distance around the outside. For a figure with straight sides, the perimeter is the sum of the lengths of all the sides.
- The formula for the perimeter of a rectangle is $P = 2l + 2w$, where $l$ is the length and $w$ is the width.
- The perimeter of a circle is known as its circumference.
- The formula for the circumference of a circle is $C = \pi d$ or $C = 2\pi r$, where $d$ is the diameter, $r$ is the radius, and the value of $\pi$ is approximately 3.14.

DISCUSS THE CONCEPTS

1. Explain why the formula $P = 2l + 2w$, for the perimeter of a rectangle, can be rewritten as $P = 2(l + w)$.
2. Describe the steps you would use to determine the perimeter of the triangle shown.
3. Describe how you would find the perimeter of the shape shown.



PRACTISE

A *For help with questions 1 and 2, refer to Example 1.*

1. Find each result using paper and pencil. Check using a calculator.
a) $2.3 + 5.9 + 13.4$ b) $167.02 + 34.56 + 101.28$
c) $15.7 + 63.2 - 13.3$ d) $87.21 + 45.5 + 9.026$
e) $2.3 \times 4.6$ f) $14.3 \times 167$
g) $336.3 \div 3$ h) $113.4 \div 7$

6 MHR • Chapter 1

1.1 Connecting Perimeter With Whole Numbers and Decimals • MHR 7

## DISCUSS THE CONCEPTS

These questions allow you to reflect on and discuss the concepts you have just learned.

## Practise

- These questions provide an opportunity to practise your knowledge and understanding of the concepts you have just learned.
- To help you, questions are referenced to the worked examples.

## Apply the Concepts

- These questions allow you to use what you learned to solve problems.
- There are many opportunities to use technology. If a specific tool or materials are needed, it is stated.
- Many questions begin with a **blue descriptor** to give connections to topics of interest, or a **red descriptor** to identify the Achievement Chart category that the question addresses.

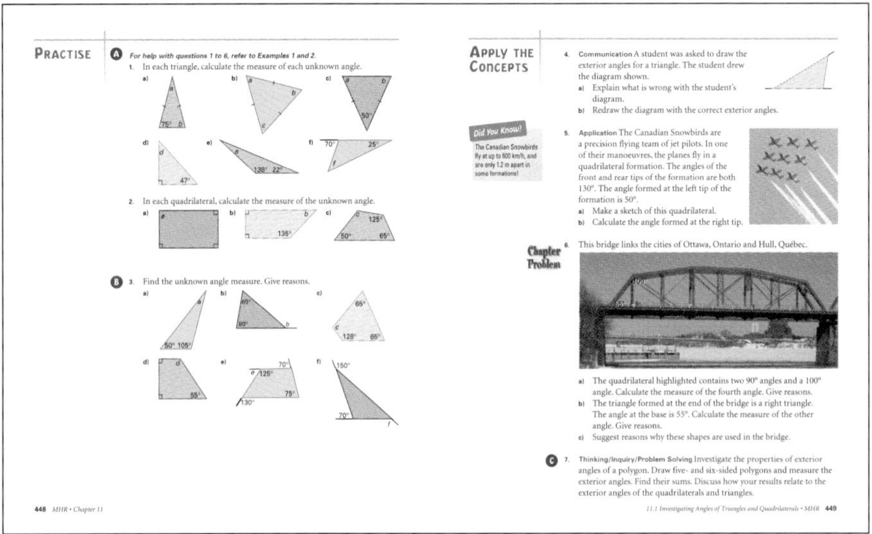

PRACTISE

A *For help with questions 1 to 6, refer to Examples 1 and 2.*

1. In each triangle, calculate the measure of each unknown angle.

a) b) c) d) e) f)

2. In each quadrilateral, calculate the measure of the unknown angle.

a) b) c)

B 3. Find the unknown angle measure. Give reasons.

a) b) c) d) e) f)

448 MHR • Chapter 11

APPLY THE CONCEPTS

4. **Communication** A student was asked to draw the exterior angles for a triangle. The student drew the diagram shown.
   a) Explain what is wrong with the student's diagram.
   b) Redraw the diagram with the correct exterior angles.

Did You Know?

The Canadian Snowbirds fly at up to 600 km/h, and are only 1.2 m apart in some formations!

5. **Application** The Canadian Snowbirds are a precision flying team of jet pilots. In one of their manoeuvres, the planes fly in a quadrilateral formation. The angles of the front and rear tips of the formation are both 130°. The angle formed at the left tip of the formation is 50°.
   a) Make a sketch of this quadrilateral.
   b) Calculate the angle formed at the right tip.

Chapter Problem

6. This bridge links the cities of Ottawa, Ontario and Hull, Québec.
   a) The quadrilateral highlighted contains two 90° angles and a 100° angle. Calculate the measure of the fourth angle. Give reasons.
   b) The triangle formed at the end of the bridge is a right triangle. The angle at the base is 55°. Calculate the measure of the other angle. Give reasons.
   c) Suggest reasons why these shapes are used in the bridge.

C 7. **Thinking/Inquiry/Problem Solving** Investigate the properties of exterior angles of a polygon. Draw five- and six-sided polygons and measure the exterior angles. Find their sums. Discuss how your results relate to the exterior angles of the quadrilaterals and triangles.

*11.1 Investigating Angles of Triangles and Quadrilaterals* • MHR 449

## Levels

**A** questions are knowledge and understanding questions. They require straightforward use of the concepts.

**B** questions require a little more. You may need to use what you have learned in the lesson in an applied setting, or make a decision about what tool to use to solve a problem, or communicate your understanding of a concept, or use various problem solving strategies.

**C** questions are provided in some sections. These are more challenging and thought-provoking.

# Technology

- Scientific calculators are useful for many sections. Key-stroke sequences are provided for techniques that may be new to you.
- A graphing calculator is useful for some sections, particularly for graphing relations.

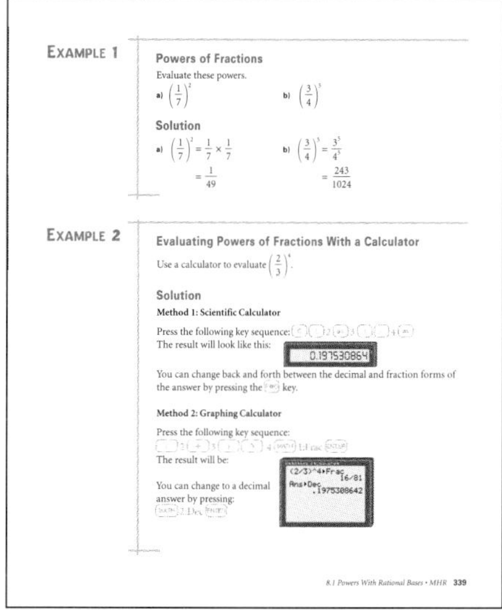

**Example 1** Powers of Fractions

Evaluate these powers.

a) $\left(\frac{1}{7}\right)^2$ b) $\left(\frac{3}{4}\right)^5$

Solution

a) $\left(\frac{1}{7}\right)^2 = \frac{1}{7} \times \frac{1}{7} = \frac{1}{49}$ b) $\left(\frac{3}{4}\right)^5 = \frac{3^5}{4^5} = \frac{243}{1024}$

**Example 2** Evaluating Powers of Fractions With a Calculator

Use a calculator to evaluate $\left(\frac{2}{3}\right)^4$.

Solution

Method 1: Scientific Calculator

Press the following key sequence:

The result will look like this: 0.197530864

You can change back and forth between the decimal and fraction forms of the answer by pressing the key.

Method 2: Graphing Calculator

Press the following key sequence:

The result will be:

You can change to a decimal answer by pressing:

(2/3)^4▸Frac 16/81
Ans▸Dec .1975308642

8.1 Powers With Rational Bases • MHR 339

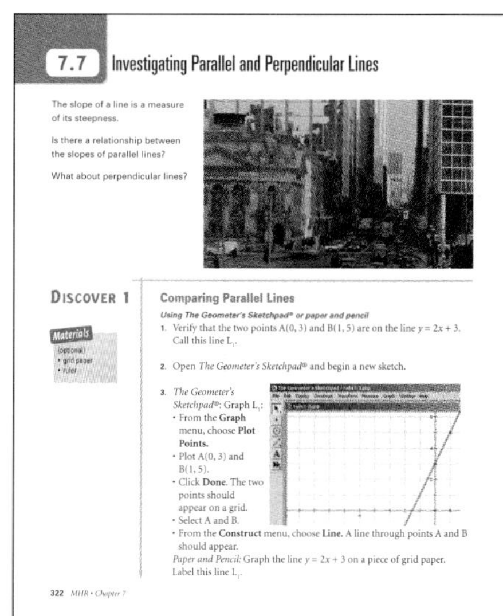

7.7 Investigating Parallel and Perpendicular Lines

The slope of a line is a measure of its steepness.

Is there a relationship between the slopes of parallel lines?

What about perpendicular lines?

**Discover 1** Comparing Parallel Lines

*Using The Geometer's Sketchpad® or paper and pencil*

Materials (optional) • grid paper • ruler

1. Verify that the two points A(0, 3) and B(1, 5) are on the line $y = 2x + 3$. Call this line $L_1$.
2. Open *The Geometer's Sketchpad®* and begin a new sketch.
3. *The Geometer's Sketchpad®*: Graph $L_1$:
   - From the **Graph** menu, choose **Plot Points.**
   - Plot A(0, 3) and B(1, 5).
   - Click **Done.** The two points should appear on a grid.
   - Select A and B.
   - From the **Construct** menu, choose **Line.** A line through points A and B should appear.

   *Paper and Pencil:* Graph the line $y = 2x + 3$ on a piece of grid paper. Label this line $L_1$.

322 MHR • Chapter 7

- *The Geometer's Sketchpad®* is used in several sections for investigating concepts related to measurement and geometry.
- Alternative steps for doing investigations using pencil and paper are provided for those who do not have access to this computer software.

- The **Technology Appendix**, on pages 484–497, provides detailed help for some basic functions of *The Geometer's Sketchpad®* and the TI-83 or TI-83 Plus graphing calculator. These pages will be particularly helpful to anyone who has not used these tools before.
- Margin notes refer you to relevant parts of the Technology Appendix for help with particular techniques used in the Discovers, Examples, or questions.

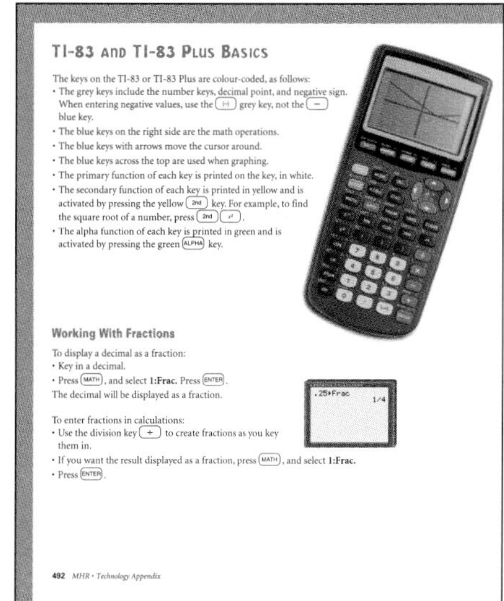

TI-83 and TI-83 Plus Basics

The keys on the TI-83 or TI-83 Plus are colour-coded, as follows:

- The grey keys include the number keys, decimal point, and negative sign. When entering negative values, use the (-) grey key, not the − blue key.
- The blue keys on the right side are the math operations.
- The blue keys with arrows move the cursor around.
- The blue keys across the top are used when graphing.
- The primary function of each key is printed on the key, in white.
- The secondary function of each key is printed in yellow and is activated by pressing the yellow 2nd key. For example, to find the square root of a number, press 2nd √.
- The alpha function of each key is printed in green and is activated by pressing the green ALPHA key.

Working With Fractions

To display a decimal as a fraction:

- Key in a decimal.
- Press MATH, and select 1:Frac. Press ENTER.

The decimal will be displayed as a fraction.

.25▸Frac 1/4

To enter fractions in calculations:

- Use the division key ÷ to create fractions as you key them in.
- If you want the result displayed as a fraction, press MATH, and select 1:Frac.
- Press ENTER.

492 MHR • Technology Appendix

# ASSESSMENT

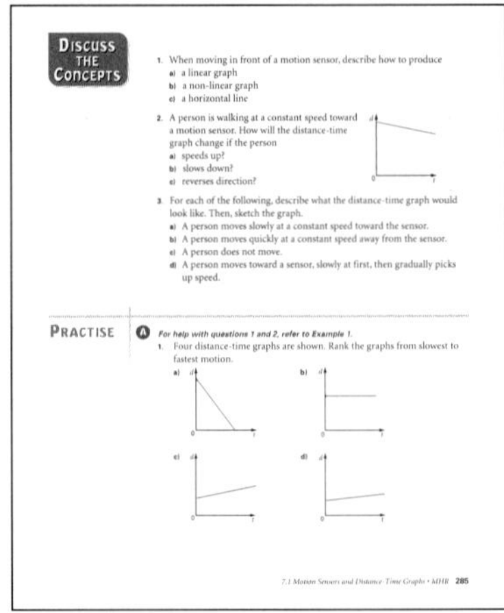

DISCUSS THE CONCEPTS

1. When moving in front of a motion sensor, describe how to produce
   a) a linear graph
   b) a non-linear graph
   c) a horizontal line
2. A person is walking at a constant speed toward a motion sensor. How will the distance-time graph change if the person
   a) speeds up?
   b) slows down?
   c) reverses direction?
3. For each of the following, describe what the distance-time graph would look like. Then, sketch the graph.
   a) A person moves slowly at a constant speed toward the sensor.
   b) A person moves quickly at a constant speed away from the sensor.
   c) A person does not move.
   d) A person moves toward a sensor, slowly at first, then gradually picks up speed.

PRACTISE

A *For help with questions 1 and 2, refer to Example 1.*

1. Four distance-time graphs are shown. Rank the graphs from slowest to fastest motion.

7.1 Motion Sensors and Distance-Time Graphs • MHR 285

## DISCUSS THE CONCEPTS

- These questions provide an opportunity to communicate your understanding of the concepts before proceeding to use your skills in the Practise and Apply the Concepts questions.
- Through this discussion you can identify any concepts or areas you need to study further.

## PRACTICE TEST

Each chapter ends with a practice test. The test has three styles of question: multiple choice, short answer, and extended response. Practising these types of question will help you prepare for provincial testing.

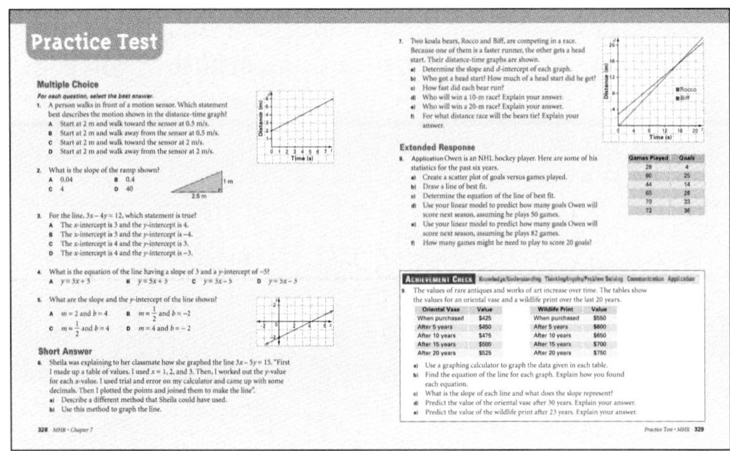

Practice Test

**Multiple Choice**

*For each question, select the best answer.*

1. A person walks in front of a motion sensor. Which statement best describes the motion shown in the distance-time graph?
   A Start at 2 m and walk toward the sensor at 0.5 m/s.
   B Start at 2 m and walk away from the sensor at 0.5 m/s.
   C Start at 2 m and walk toward the sensor at 2 m/s.
   D Start at 2 m and walk away from the sensor at 2 m/s.
2. What is the slope of the ramp shown?
   A 0.04 B 0.4
   C 4 D 40
3. For the line, $3x - 4y = 12$, which statement is true?
   A The $x$-intercept is 3 and the $y$-intercept is 4.
   B The $x$-intercept is 3 and the $y$-intercept is −4.
   C The $x$-intercept is 4 and the $y$-intercept is 3.
   D The $x$-intercept is 4 and the $y$-intercept is −3.
4. What is the equation of the line having a slope of 3 and a $y$-intercept of −5?
   A $y = 3x + 5$ B $y = 5x + 3$ C $y = 3x - 5$ D $y = 5x - 3$
5. What are the slope and the $y$-intercept of the line shown?
   A $m = 2$ and $b = 4$ B $m = \frac{1}{2}$ and $b = -2$
   C $m = \frac{1}{2}$ and $b = 4$ D $m = 4$ and $b = -2$

**Short Answer**

6. Sheila was explaining to her classmate how she graphed the line $3x - 5y = 15$. "First I made up a table of values. I used $x = 1, 2,$ and 3. Then, I worked out the $y$-value for each $x$-value. I used trial and error on my calculator and came up with some decimals. Then I plotted the points and joined them to make the line".
   a) Describe a different method that Sheila could have used.
   b) Use this method to graph the line.

328 MHR • Chapter 7

7. Two koala bears, Rocco and Biff, are competing in a race. Because one of them is a faster runner, the other gets a head start. Their distance-time graphs are shown.
   a) Determine the slope and $d$-intercept of each graph.
   b) Who got a head start? How much of a head start did he get?
   c) How fast did each bear run?
   d) Who will win a 10-m race? Explain your answer.
   e) Who will win a 20-m race? Explain your answer.
   f) For what distance race will the bears tie? Explain your answer.

**Extended Response**

8. **Application** Owen is an NHL hockey player. Here are some of his statistics for the past six years.
   a) Create a scatter plot of goals versus games played.
   b) Draw a line of best fit.
   c) Determine the equation of the line of best fit.
   d) Use your linear model to predict how many goals Owen will score next season, assuming he plays 50 games.
   e) Use your linear model to predict how many goals Owen will score next season, assuming he plays 82 games.
   f) How many games might he need to play to score 20 goals?

| Games Played | Goals |
|---|---|
| 28 | 4 |
| 60 | 25 |
| 44 | 14 |
| 65 | 28 |
| 70 | 33 |
| 72 | 36 |

ACHIEVEMENT CHECK Knowledge/Understanding Thinking/Inquiry/Problem Solving Communication Application

9. The values of rare antiques and works of art increase over time. The tables show the values for an oriental vase and a wildlife print over the last 20 years.

| Oriental Vase | Value |
|---|---|
| When purchased | \$425 |
| After 5 years | \$450 |
| After 10 years | \$475 |
| After 15 years | \$500 |
| After 20 years | \$525 |

| Wildlife Print | Value |
|---|---|
| When purchased | \$550 |
| After 5 years | \$600 |
| After 10 years | \$650 |
| After 15 years | \$700 |
| After 20 years | \$750 |

   a) Use a graphing calculator to graph the data given in each table.
   b) Find the equation of the line for each graph. Explain how you found each equation.
   c) What is the slope of each line and what does the slope represent?
   d) Predict the value of the oriental vase after 30 years. Explain your answer.
   e) Predict the value of the wildlife print after 23 years. Explain your answer.

Practice Test • MHR 329

## ACHIEVEMENT CHECK

The last question on the practice test provides an opportunity to demonstrate your knowledge and understanding, your ability to apply what you have learned, your problem-solving skills, and your communication skills.

## TASKS

Tasks are presented at the end of chapters 3, 5, 7, and 11. These are more involved problems that require you to use several concepts from the preceding chapters. Each task has multi-part questions and may take about 15 min to complete. Experience with this type of task will also help you prepare for provincial testing.

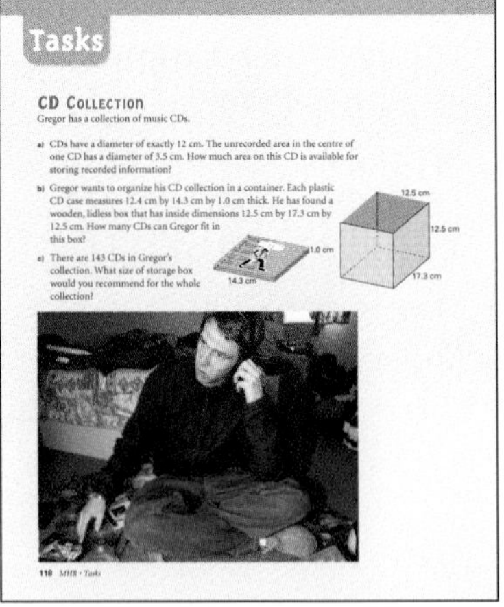

Tasks

CD COLLECTION

Gregor has a collection of music CDs.

a) CDs have a diameter of exactly 12 cm. The unrecorded area in the centre of one CD has a diameter of 3.5 cm. How much area on this CD is available for storing recorded information?

b) Gregor wants to organize his CD collection in a container. Each plastic CD case measures 12.4 cm by 14.3 cm by 1.0 cm thick. He has found a wooden, lidless box that has inside dimensions 12.5 cm by 17.3 cm by 12.5 cm. How many CDs can Gregor fit in this box?

c) There are 143 CDs in Gregor's collection. What size of storage box would you recommend for the whole collection?



118 MHR • Tasks

# Chapter Review

- This feature appears at the end of each chapter.
- By working through these questions, you will identify areas where you may need more review or study before doing the Practice Test.

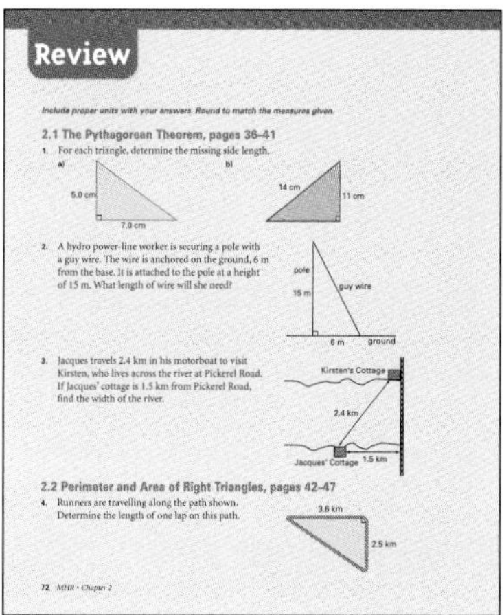
Review

*Include proper units with your answers. Round to match the measures given.*

**2.1 The Pythagorean Theorem, pages 36–41**

1. For each triangle, determine the missing side length.
   a) 
   b) 



2. A hydro power-line worker is securing a pole with a guy wire. The wire is anchored on the ground, 6 m from the base. It is attached to the pole at a height of 15 m. What length of wire will she need?



3. Jacques travels 2.4 km in his motorboat to visit Kirsten, who lives across the river at Pickerel Road. If Jacques' cottage is 1.5 km from Pickerel Road, find the width of the river.



**2.2 Perimeter and Area of Right Triangles, pages 42–47**

4. Runners are travelling along the path shown. Determine the length of one lap on this path.



72 MHR • Chapter 2

# Cumulative Review

- A cumulative review occurs at the end of chapters 3, 5, 7, and 10. These questions allow you to review concepts you learned in the chapters since the last cumulative review. They also help to prepare you for the **Tasks**.
- The course review following chapter 11 provides a selection of questions from throughout the whole course.

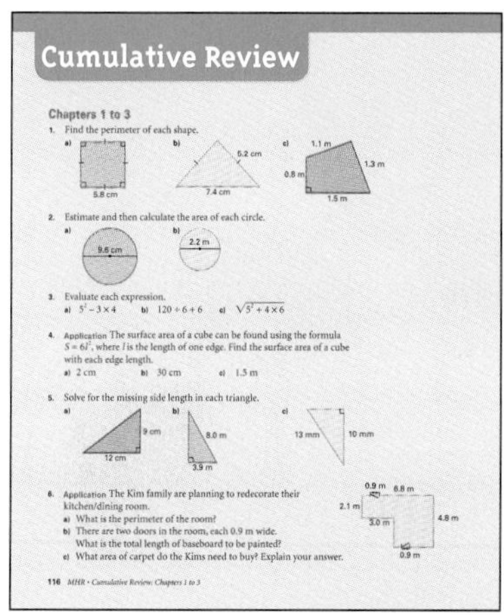
Cumulative Review

**Chapters 1 to 3**

1. Find the perimeter of each shape.
   a) b) c)



2. Estimate and then calculate the area of each circle.
   a) b)



3. Evaluate each expression.
   a) $5^2 - 3 \times 4$ b) $120 \div 6 + 6$ c) $\sqrt{5^2 + 4 \times 6}$

4. Application The surface area of a cube can be found using the formula $S = 6l^2$, where $l$ is the length of one edge. Find the surface area of a cube with each edge length.
   a) 2 cm b) 30 cm c) 1.5 m

5. Solve for the missing side length in each triangle.
   a) b) c)



6. Application The Kim family are planning to redecorate their kitchen/dining room.
   a) What is the perimeter of the room?
   b) There are two doors in the room, each 0.9 m wide. What is the total length of baseboard to be painted?
   c) What area of carpet do the Kims need to buy? Explain your answer.



116 MHR • Cumulative Review: Chapters 1 to 3

# Other Features

## Internet Links

This logo is shown beside questions in which it is suggested that you use the Internet to help solve the problem or to research or collect information. Some direct links are provided via our web site: *www.school.mcgrawhill.ca/links/MATC9.*

## Did You Know?

This feature appears in the margin of some pages. It provides interesting facts related to the topics.

**Did You Know?**

The highest flight of a kite on a single string took place in Ontario, in 2000. Richard Synergy flew his 9-m kite to an altitude of 4422 m!

## Make Connections

This margin feature points out some of the connections between topics in the course.

**Make Connections**

**Scatter plots** were introduced in section **4.5 Data Analysis: Trends and Relationships**.

## Math Tip

This feature appears at the end of some numbered sections. It provides helpful hints or alternative strategies.

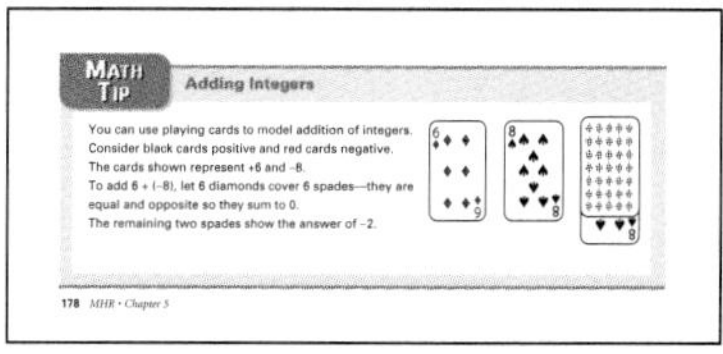
Math Tip — Adding Integers

You can use playing cards to model addition of integers. Consider black cards positive and red cards negative. The cards shown represent +6 and -8. To add 6 + (-8), let 6 diamonds cover 6 spades—they are equal and opposite so they sum to 0. The remaining two spades show the answer of -2.

178 MHR • Chapter 5

# CHAPTER 1
# Applying Number Sense

In this warm-up chapter, you will
- review your skills with whole numbers and decimals
- practise some estimation techniques
- apply these skills to work with some simple formulas

**Chapter Problem**

Jeff keeps the water in his swimming pool at 28°C. On a typical summer day, water evaporates from the pool at an average rate of 0.48 L/h/m$^2$ (litres per hour per square metre) of surface area of the water. How much water will evaporate from the pool in one day?

# Get Ready

## Mental Arithmetic—Regrouping Numbers

Find the sum mentally.

24 + 18 + 16 + 12
= 70

**Regroup mentally looking for numbers that add to 10.**
**(24 + 16) + (18 + 12) = 40 + 30**

Find the difference mentally.

64 – 5
= 59

**Regroup mentally to make the subtraction easier.**
**(64 – 4) – 1 = 60 – 1**

**1.** Add or subtract using mental arithmetic.

**a)** 26 + 19 **b)** 197 + 13 **c)** 22 + 15 + 8
**d)** 84 – 5 **e)** 184 – 15 **f)** 201 – 98
**g)** 25 + 33 + 75 **h)** 236 – 38 **i)** 123 + 457 – 50

**2.** Use mental arithmetic to find each result.

**a)** 5 + 8 + 12 + 3 + 15 **b)** 15 + 20 – 5 – 10 + 25
**c)** 1508 + 501 – 202 **d)** 347 – 50 + 123
**e)** 21 – 17 + 32 + 8 **f)** 750 + 250 + 500 – 1500

## Rounding

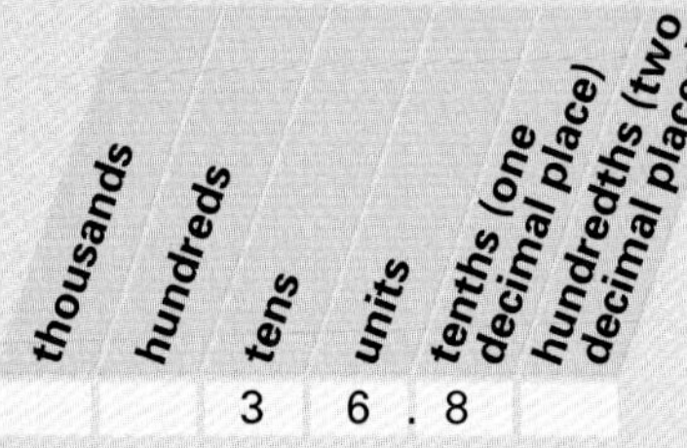


Round 36.8 to the nearest unit.
To the nearest unit, 36.8 is 37.

**The digit 6 is in the units place.**
**The digit to the right of 6 is 5 or greater, so round up.**

Round 5024 to the nearest ten.
To the nearest ten, 5024 is 5020.

**The digit 2 is in the tens place.**
**The digit to the right of 2 is less than 5, so do not round up. Use a 0 placeholder to keep 2 in the tens column.**

**3.** Round to the nearest unit.

**a)** 12.3 **b)** 15.98 **c)** 100.2 **d)** 5467.09

**4.** Round to the nearest tenth.

**a)** 25.32 **b)** 176.086 **c)** 0.069 **d)** 0.183

**5.** Round to the nearest hundred.

**a)** 1267 **b)** 54 309 **c)** 1 993 567 **d)** 89.2

## Converting Among Metric Units

Convert each measure to the indicated unit.

5400 m to kilometres

1000 m = 1 km

$5400 \text{ m} = \frac{5400}{1000} \text{ km}$

5400 m = 5.4 km

0.38 kg to grams

1 kg = 1000 g

$0.38 \text{ kg} = 0.38 \times 1000 \text{ g}$

038 kg = 380 g

| Length | Mass |
|---|---|
| 10 mm = 1 cm | 1000 mg = 1 g |
| 100 cm = 1 m | 1000 g = 1 kg |
| 1000 m = 1 km | 1000 kg = 1 t |

**6.** Convert each measure to the indicated unit.

**a)** 120 m to centimetres
**b)** 15 km to metres
**c)** 4.1 cm to millimetres
**d)** 65 cm to metres
**e)** 800 m to kilometres
**f)** 1.34 g to milligrams
**g)** 0.0042 kg to grams
**h)** 1.02 L to millilitres
**i)** 7500 mL to litres

## Estimating Area

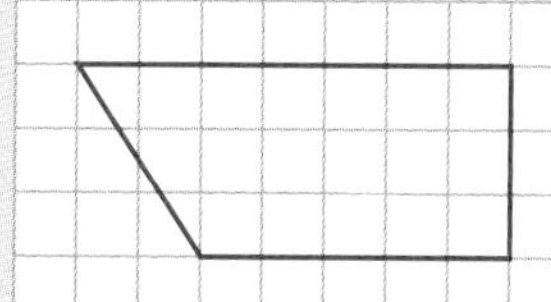

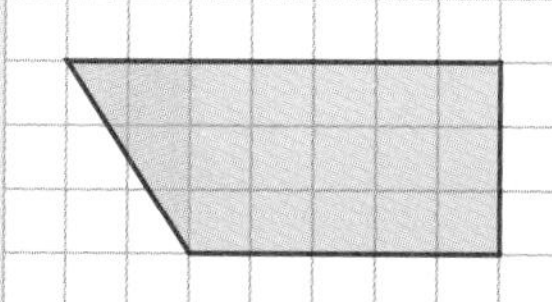

Estimate the area of the figure in square units.
The shape can be thought of as a rectangle and a triangle.
The rectangle contains 15 squares.
The triangle contains 1 complete square, and 4 part squares.
Count each part square as half a square.
Add the pieces.

$$15 + 1 + 4 \times \frac{1}{2} = 15 + 1 + 2$$
$$= 18$$

The area of the figure is about 18 square units.

**7.** Estimate the area of each figure in square units. Describe the method you used.

**a)**

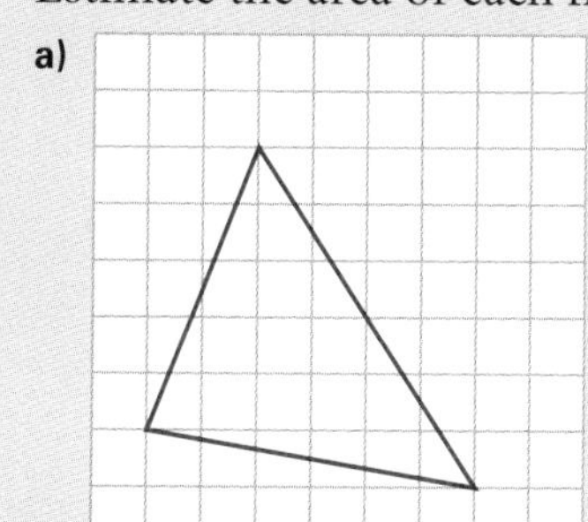

**b)**

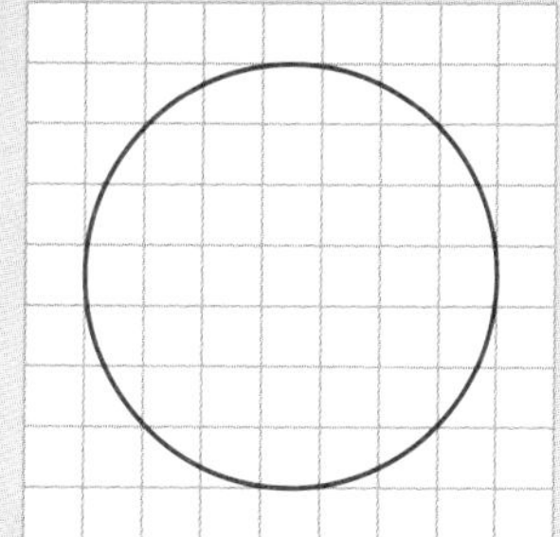

**c)**

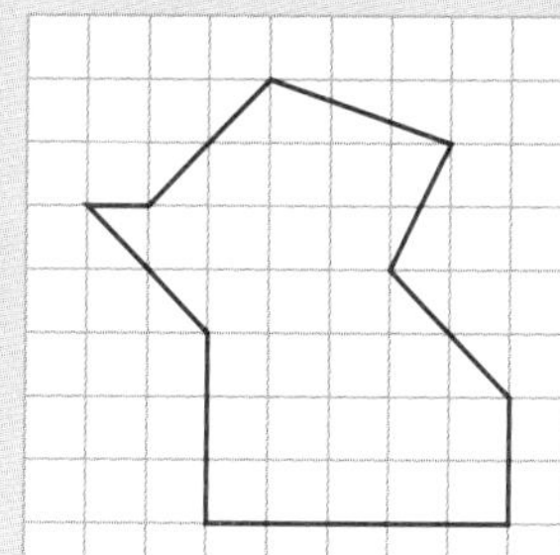

# 1.1 Connecting Perimeter With Whole Numbers and Decimals

In many situations and careers, you will need to know how to measure objects and calculate their perimeter. This section explores these skills.

The **perimeter** of a shape is the distance around the outside. The perimeter of a shape with straight sides can be found by adding the lengths of all the sides. The perimeter of a circle is known as its **circumference**.

## Discover

**Materials**

- flexible tape measure
- circular objects such as paper cups, pop cans

### Investigating the Relationship Between Circumference and Diameter

1. In your notebook, set up a chart with the headings shown. Include six blank rows one for each object you will measure.

| Object | Circumference | Diameter | Circumference ÷ Diameter |
|---|---|---|---|
| | | | |

2. Measure the diameter and the circumference of your first object, to the nearest tenth of a centimetre. Record the measures in your chart. Make sure to measure the widest part of the circle for the diameter.

3. Divide the circumference by the diameter. Enter the result, rounded to two decimal places, in your chart.

4. Repeat steps 2 and 3 for your second object.

5. Copy the results from two classmates into your chart.

6. Compare all six results in your chart. What do you notice?

## Did You Know?

The number $\pi$ has fascinated people for ages. The ancient Egyptians, around 1700 BCE, approximated $\pi$ as $\frac{256}{81}$. By 220 BCE the Greeks were using $\frac{22}{7}$ for its value. Computers can now give $\pi$ to billions of decimal places. To four decimal places, $\pi$ is 3.1416.

7. How important is it to be accurate?

8. Write a conclusion about the result when the circumference of a circle is divided by its diameter.

9. How do the results of this investigation relate to the formula for the circumference of a circle, $C = \pi d$?

## EXAMPLE 1

### Perimeter of Geometric Shapes

Find the perimeter of each shape.

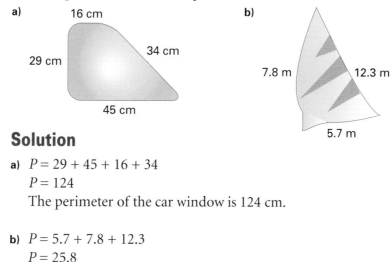

a)

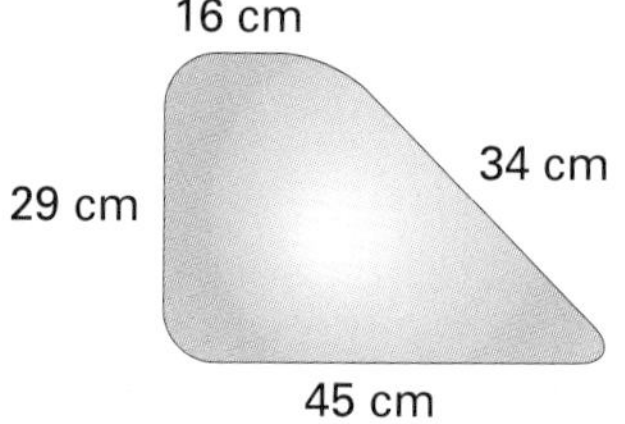


b)

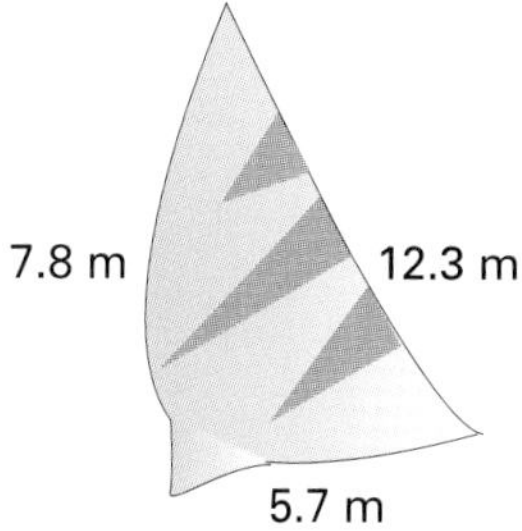


### Solution

a) $P = 29 + 45 + 16 + 34$
$P = 124$
The perimeter of the car window is 124 cm.

b) $P = 5.7 + 7.8 + 12.3$
$P = 25.8$
The perimeter of the sail is 25.8 m.

## EXAMPLE 2

### Calculating Circumference

A circular swimming pool has a radius of 5 m. Use the formula $C = \pi d$ or $C = 2\pi r$ to calculate the circumference. Round your answer to the nearest metre.

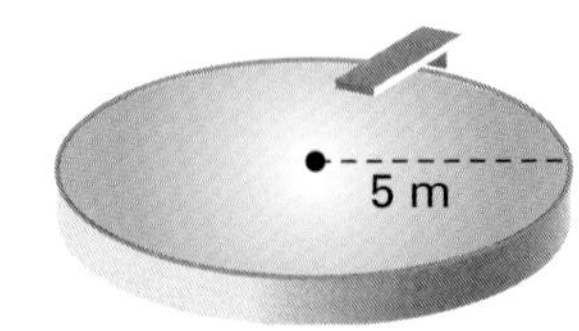


Note: The value of $\pi$ approximately equals 3.14, but use a calculator $\pi$ key for greater accuracy.

### Solution

Use the formula $C = 2\pi r$ with $r = 5$.

$C = 2\pi(5)$

$C = 2 \times \pi \times 5$    (C) 10 (×) (π) (=)

$C = 31.415927$    **Estimate: $2 \times 3 \times 5 = 30$. The answer is reasonable.**

The swimming pool has a circumference of 31 m, to the nearest metre.

## EXAMPLE 3

### Applying Perimeter of a Rectangle

A photograph measures 12.2 cm by 8.3 cm. Use the formula $P = 2l + 2w$ to calculate the length of framing needed around the photograph.

**The scientific calculator key strokes shown in this text are for a TI-30Xa calculator. You many need to adjust the key sequences for other calculators.**

### Solution

$P = 2l + 2w$

$P = 2 \times 12.2 + 2 \times 8.3$    (C) 2 (×) 12.2 (+) 2 (×) 8.3 (=)

$P = 24.4 + 16.6$    **Estimate: $2 \times 12 + 2 \times 8 = 40$. The answer is reasonable.**

$P = 41$

The length of framing needed is 41 cm.

- The perimeter of a figure is the distance around the outside. For a figure with straight sides, the perimeter is the sum of the lengths of all the sides.
- The formula for the perimeter of a rectangle is $P = 2l + 2w$, where $l$ is the length and $w$ is the width.
- The perimeter of a circle is known as its circumference.
- The formula for the circumference of a circle is $C = \pi d$ or $C = 2\pi r$, where $d$ is the diameter, $r$ is the radius, and the value of $\pi$ is approximately 3.14.

## Discuss the Concepts

1. Explain why the formula $P = 2l + 2w$, for the perimeter of a rectangle, can be rewritten as $P = 2(l + w)$.
2. Describe the steps you would use to determine the perimeter of the triangle shown.

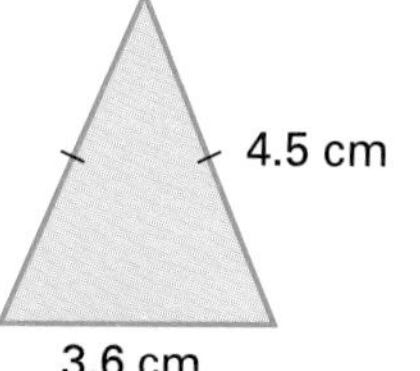


3. Describe how you would find the perimeter of the shape shown.

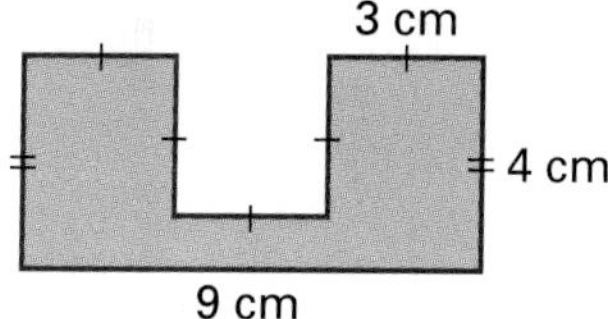


## Practise

**A** ***For help with questions 1 and 2, refer to Example 1.***

1. Find each result using paper and pencil. Check using a calculator.

   **a)** $2.3 + 5.9 + 13.4$ **b)** $167.02 + 34.56 + 101.28$

   **c)** $15.7 + 63.2 - 13.3$ **d)** $87.21 + 45.5 + 9.026$

   **e)** $2.3 \times 4.6$ **f)** $14.3 \times 167$

   **g)** $336.3 \div 3$ **h)** $113.4 \div 7$

2. Calculate the perimeter of each figure.

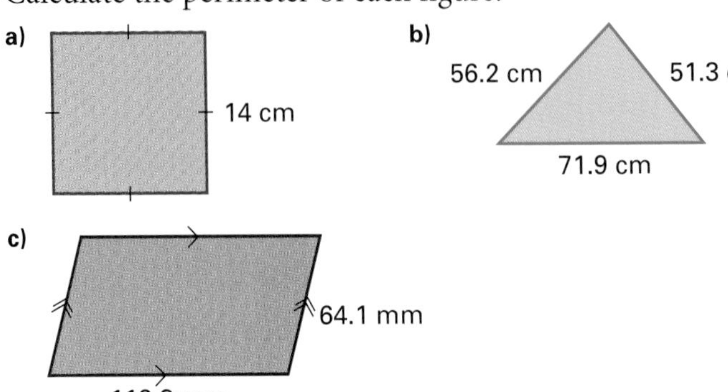


***For help with question 3, refer to Example 2.***

3. Calculate the circumference of each circle. Round your answers to one decimal place.

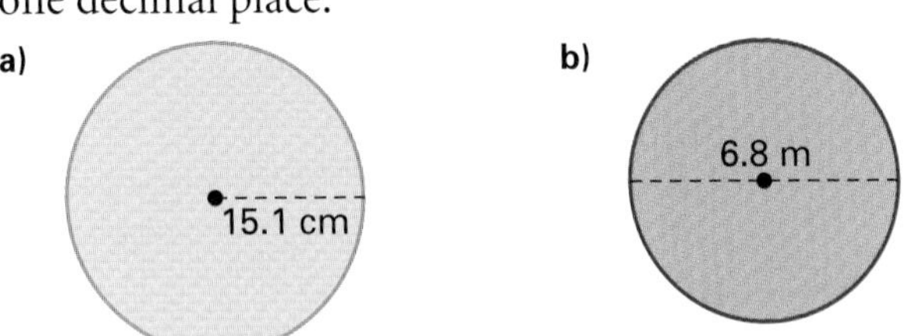


4. Determine the lengths of the unknown sides. Then, calculate the perimeter of the figure.

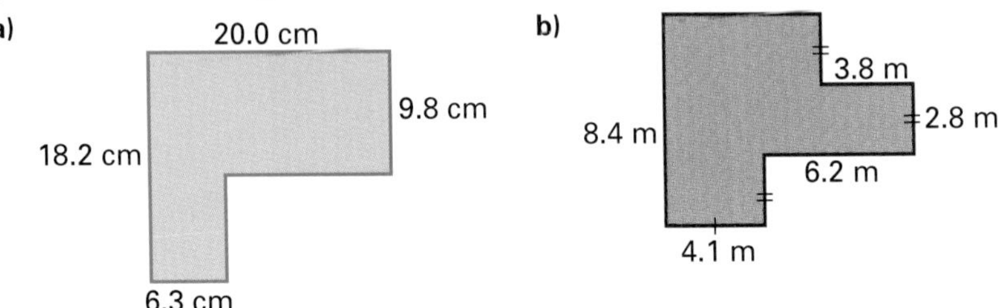


## Apply the Concepts

**B**

5. **Application** The floor of a rectangular room measures 4.2 m by 3.1 m. The doorway is 0.9 m wide. Baseboard is to be installed around the perimeter of the room, except in the doorway.

0.9 m
3.1 m
4.2 m

   **a)** What length of baseboard needs to be bought?

   **b)** How much will the baseboard cost, at $1.85 per metre?

6. **Thinking/Inquiry/Problem Solving** A square mirror has a perimeter of 1.20 m.
   a) Describe how to find the side length of the mirror.
   b) Determine the side length.

7. An equilateral triangle has a perimeter of 4.5 cm. What is the length of each side?

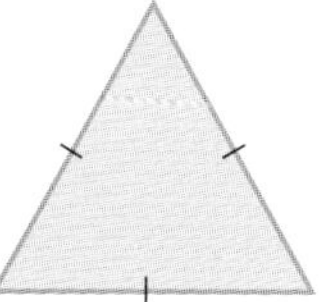

8. **Rug making** Shana is hooking a semi-circular rug. The diameter of the rug is 110 cm. What length of binding tape will she need to go around the edge of the rug? Round your answer to the nearest centimetre.

9. **Application** One fitness club has a circular track with a diameter of 12 m. A second fitness club has a circular track with a diameter of 18 m. How much longer is the track at the second club? Round your answer to the nearest metre.

10. **Thinking/Inquiry/Problem Solving** A shelving unit is to be built with five shelves, each 1.5 m long. The two vertical supports will each be 1.8 m tall. The boards come in 2.0 m, 3.0 m, and 4.0 m lengths and will need to be cut to the appropriate size. How many boards of each length need to be bought in order to minimize waste? Explain your solution.

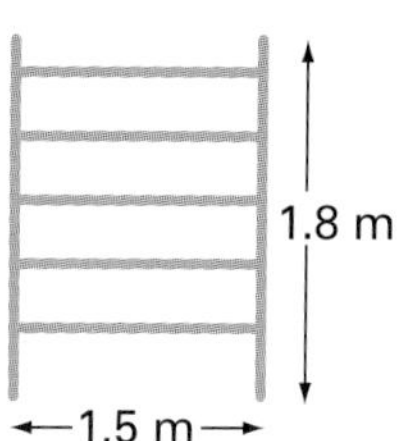

# 1.2 Estimation

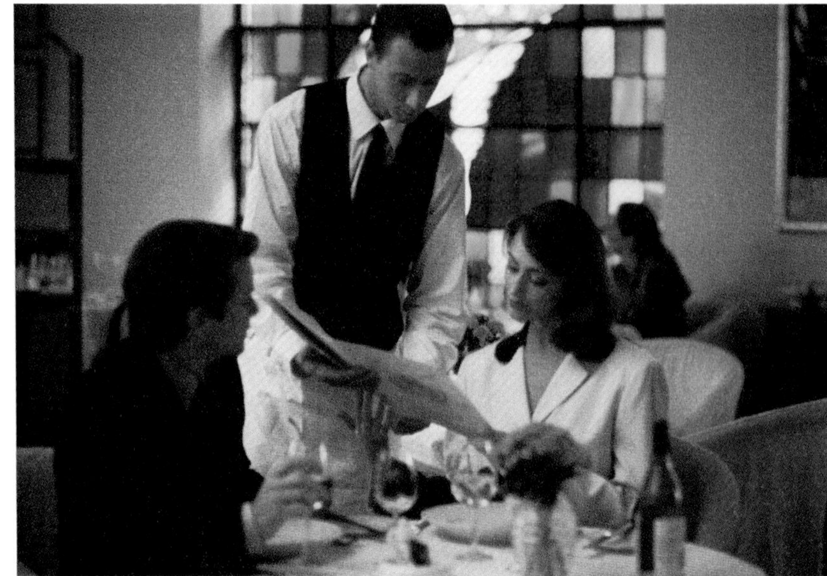

People tip to reward good service. In restaurants, they usually tip 10% to 15% of the bill. People do not always carry a calculator with them. Neither do they want to perform long multiplication by hand in order to calculate the tip. Good estimation skills help solve this type of problem.

## DISCOVER

- Metre sticks or measuring tapes

### Estimating Measurements

1. a) Estimate the width of the top of your desk. Write down how wide you think the desk is, in centimetres.
   b) Measure a ten-centimetre long part of your hand. Use your 10-cm hand part to find the approximate width of your desk.
   c) Use a ruler to measure the width of your desk.
   d) By how much was your estimate in part a) off? Was your estimate in part b) closer to the actual width?

2. a) Estimate the length of the classroom. Write down how long you think the classroom is, in metres.
   b) Measure a one-metre walking stride. Use your 1-m walking stride to find the approximate length of the classroom.
   c) Use a metre stick or measuring tape to measure the exact length of the classroom.
   d) By how much was your estimate in part a) off? Was your estimate in part b) closer to the actual width?

3. Comment on how reasonable your estimates were.

4. Give an example of when you might need to use this type of estimation skill.

The **Discover** illustrates how to use estimation skills in measurement problems. It is also important to be able to judge if your calculator results are reasonable. Then, if you press the wrong calculator key, you can judge whether the answer makes sense. The result can often be estimated mentally by using rounded numbers. You need to decide what is reasonable when rounding.

## Example 1

### Using Rounding to Estimate a Sum

Sarah is buying five items, priced at \$34.95, \$8.50, \$19.78, \$12.34, and \$10.67. Approximately how much is her total bill, before taxes?

### Solution

Round the prices to the nearest dollar and add.

$35 + 9 + 20 + 12 + 11 = 87$

Sarah's bill is approximately \$87, before taxes.

## Example 2

### Calculating Then Rounding

Wei Lim runs 8 km every day to train for a cross-country meet. She measured her stride to be 1.3 m long. Approximately how many strides (to the nearest 100) does she need to run 8 km?

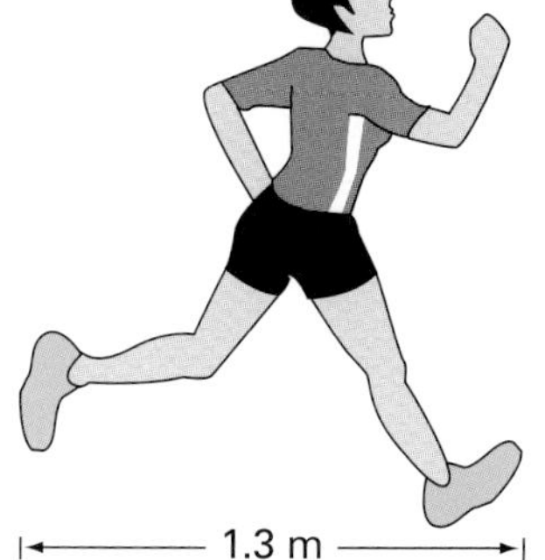


### Solution

Rounding Wei Lim's stride to the nearest metre would result in a very inaccurate answer. In a situation such as this, divide for accuracy. Then, round the result.

$8 \text{ km} = 8000 \text{ m}$
$8000 \div 1.3 \doteq 6153.846$

Wei Lim needs approximately 6200 strides to run 8 km.

## EXAMPLE 3

### Estimating a Tip

People usually tip 10% to 15% of the bill when paying a restaurant bill. Determine an appropriate 15% tip for a $14.35 restaurant bill.

### Solution

One method is the following:

| | |
|---|---|
| • take 10% of the total; | 10% of \$14.35 = \$1.435 |
| • round to the nearest half dollar for small amounts; | Round to \$1.50 |
| • round to the nearest dollar for large amounts; | |
| • add half of the 10% amount. | Half of \$1.50 = \$0.75 |
| | \$1.50 + \$0.75 = \$2.25 |

For this restaurant bill, an appropriate tip is $2.25.

## KEY CONCEPTS

- When only approximate answers are needed, round first, then calculate using mental arithmetic.
- When more accuracy is needed, use accurate calculations, then round the answer to an appropriate number of places.
- To consider how reasonable an answer is, use mental arithmetic with rounded numbers to check.

1. Describe an appropriate method for estimating the 15% taxes (PST and GST) on a bill of $34.17.
2. Describe a method of estimating whether you need a 250-sheet, 500-sheet, or 750-sheet package of notepaper for the rest of the year in this math class.
3. Lightbulbs are often sold as "1000-hour bulbs". How might lightbulb manufacturers arrive at such a figure?
4. Suzie was given the job of evaluating $25.1 + 17.3 \times 45.7$. She used her scientific calculator and read in the display 1937.68.
   a) Use estimation to tell whether this answer is reasonable.
   b) What mistake did she most likely make?

## PRACTISE

*For help with questions 1 to 3, refer to Example 1.*

1. Round to the nearest unit.
   - a) $138.65
   - b) 30.1 km
   - c) 569.9 mm
   - d) 7.2 cents
   - e) 2100.692 L
   - f) 34.5 m

2. Round to the nearest hundred.
   - a) 13 459 km
   - b) 99.99 cm
   - c) $245.21
   - d) 64 years
   - e) 561.2 m
   - f) 83.8 L

3. Round to the nearest tenth.
   - a) 1.46 kg
   - b) 12.349 mm
   - c) 612.79 L
   - d) 53.01 cm
   - e) 6.13 mL
   - f) 1.002 km

4. Match the items with the most appropriate unit of measure. Some units may be used more than once.

| | | | |
|---|---|---|---|
| a) | volume of a glass of drinking water | A) | millilitres (mL) |
| b) | area of an apartment room | B) | litres (L) |
| c) | length of a cell phone | C) | grams (g) |
| d) | mass of a calculator | D) | kilograms (kg) |
| e) | area of a country | E) | milligrams (mg) |
| f) | volume of water in a reservoir | F) | metres (m) |
| g) | mass of an automobile | G) | millimetres (mm) |
| h) | diameter of a shoe lace | H) | centimetres (cm) |
| i) | area of a desk top | I) | square metres ($m^2$) |
| j) | mass of a piece of paper | J) | square kilometres ($km^2$) |
| | | K) | square centimetres ($cm^2$) |

5. Use estimation to match the calculations with the most appropriate estimate from this list: 10, 20, 30, 40, 50, 60, 70, 80.
   - a) $12.3 \times 5.7$
   - b) $88.91 - 3.2 - 5.9 - 1.1$
   - c) $15.27 + 14.5 + 1.16 + 0.9$
   - d) $698 \div 72$

6. Use estimation to decide whether each calculator screen shows a reasonable answer.
   a) 2.3 + 7.1 + 6.48 + 4.56 + 8.8 + 3.672 + 12.309

   b) 58.13 × 21.46

   c) 1256.3 ÷ 9.7

   d) 120.3 + 28.2 – 15.01 – 36.4

## APPLY THE CONCEPTS

7. **Shopping** The prices of food items to be bought in a grocery store are:

   $1.25, $2.38, $4.78, $5.00, $2.95, $4.05, $6.19, $8.87

   a) Round each price to the nearest dollar.
   b) Find the approximate total cost of the groceries (there is no tax on food).
   c) What is the approximate change back from two $20 bills?

*For help with questions 7 and 8, refer to Example 3.*

8. **Tipping** What is an appropriate 10% tip on each taxi fare?
   a) $12.70 b) $23.15
   c) $6.75 d) $29.30

9. Estimate an appropriate 15% tip for each restaurant bill.
   a) $12.59 b) $8.30
   c) $56.75 d) $37.82

10. **Thinking/Inquiry/Problem Solving** Describe a method that could be used to estimate the thickness of one sheet of paper.

11. **Walking Speed** Most days, it takes Rohan 20 to 22 min to walk 1.8 km to school. Estimate Rohan's usual walking speed, to the nearest kilometre per hour. Remember: speed = distance ÷ time.

12. **Application** Gasoline is sold by the litre. Prices are listed to the nearest tenth of a cent. At one gasoline station, regular gasoline is selling for 72.9 ¢ per litre, or $0.729/L.

   **a)** What is the approximate cost of 50 L, to the nearest dollar?

   **b)** What is the approximate cost of 23 L, to the nearest dollar?

   **c)** If you have $40, approximately how much of this gasoline can you buy, to the nearest litre?

**Chapter Problem**

13. Jeff keeps the water in his swimming pool at 28°C. On a typical summer day, water evaporates from the pool at an average rate of 0.48 L/h/$m^2$ (litres per hour per square metre) of surface area of the water. The surface area of Jeff's pool is 36 $m^2$. How much water will evaporate from the pool in 10 h?

**Did You Know?**

1 L of water has a mass of 1 kg, which is approximately 2.2 lb (pounds).

C

14. **Thinking/Inquiry/Problem Solving** The following are known as Fermi problems, after the Italian-American physicist Enrico Fermi. This type of problem requires estimation skills and numerical reasoning. The problems are open-ended: answers will vary.
   - How many pennies would cover the floor of your classroom?
   - How many jelly beans fill a 3-L jar?
   - How many pizzas will be ordered by students at your school this school year?
   - How many basketballs would it take to fill your classroom?

   **a)** Select one problem and answer it. Explain your reasoning and any assumptions you make.

   **b)** Make up your own Fermi question. Remember, it must be solvable through estimation and numerical reasoning.

**MATH TIP**

### Test for Divisibility by 4

The summer Olympics take place every four years. For this century, the years are 2004, 2008, 2012, ... If the last two digits of a number are divisible by 4, then the whole number is divisible by 4.

# 1.3 Exponents and the Order of Operations

In geography, you work with areas expressed in square kilometres. For example, the area of Ontario is 1 068 580 km$^2$. In science, you work with volumes expressed in cubic centimetres. For example, the volume of one beehive is 15 500 cm$^3$. Exponents are seen in these units of measurement.

## DISCOVER

### Paper Folding to Model Powers of 2

1. Take a piece of scrap paper of any size. Fold it in half. You now have 2 layers.

2. Fold it in half again. You now have $2 \times 2$ or 4 layers.

3. Continue folding it in half until you are unable to continue.

4. Copy the following table into your notebook. Complete the table up to your total number of folds.

| Folds | Layers | Exponential Form |
|---|---|---|
| 0 | 1 | $2^0$ |
| 1 | 2 | $2^1$ |
| 2 | $2 \times 2 = 4$ | $2^2$ |

5. Check with your classmates. What was the maximum number of folds? Can you explain why, even with large sheets of paper, the maximum number of folds is so small?

6. Predict how many layers there would be after 10 folds.

7. Predict how many layers there would be after 20 folds.

8. What does the first row of entries in the table tell you?

Repeated multiplication of the same number by itself can be expressed as a **power**. The number is said to be in **exponential form**.

$$64 = \underbrace{2 \times 2 \times 2 \times 2 \times 2 \times 2}_{\text{6 factors}}$$

$$= 2^6$$

exponent
Power
base

As you may have discussed in step 8 of the **Discover**, when a base is raised to an exponent of 0, the result is 1.

$2^0 = 1$

## EXAMPLE 1

### Writing and Evaluating Powers

Express each as a power. Then, evaluate using a calculator.

**a)** $3 \times 3 \times 3 \times 3$ **b)** $5 \times 5 \times 5$

### Solution

**a)** $3 \times 3 \times 3 \times 3 = 3^4$
$= 81$

C 3 $y^x$ 4 =

**Note: The exponent key may vary.**

**b)** $5 \times 5 \times 5 = 5^3$
$= 125$

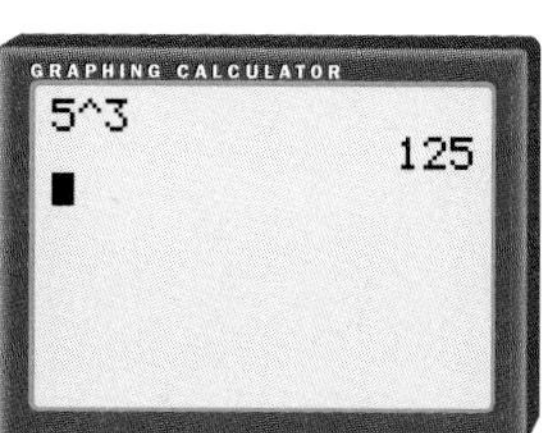


**Refer to the Technology Appendix for an introduction to the graphing calculator.**

Finding a **square root** is the inverse operation of squaring. Since $3^2 = 9$, $\sqrt{9} = 3$. To calculate the square root of a number, express the number as a squared power. Then, the base is the square root.

**EXAMPLE 2**

## Finding Square Roots

Evaluate each square root mentally. Check using a calculator.

**a)** $\sqrt{25}$ **b)** $\sqrt{10\,000}$

### Solution

**a)** $\sqrt{25} = \sqrt{5^2}$
$= 5$

Using a calculator:

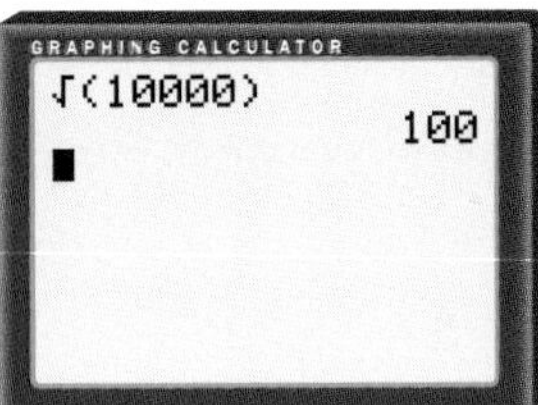


**b)** $\sqrt{10\,000} = \sqrt{100^2}$
$= 100$

Using a graphing calculator:



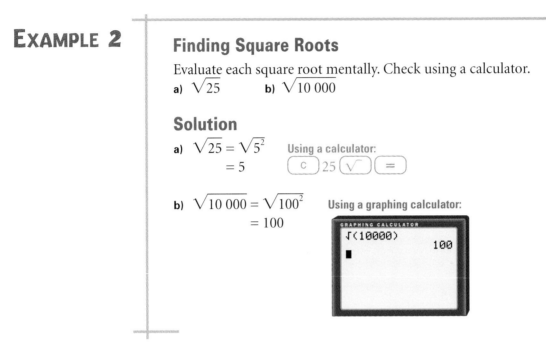

When several operations occur in expressions, you need to use the correct **order of operations** as follows:

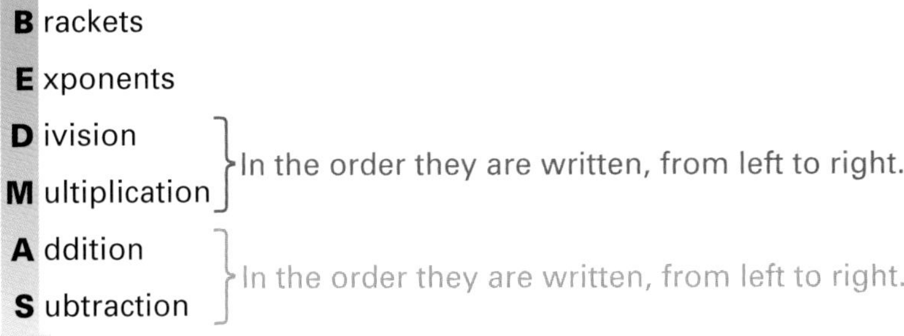

B rackets
E xponents
D ivision
M ultiplication
In the order they are written, from left to right.
A ddition
S ubtraction
In the order they are written, from left to right.

## EXAMPLE 3

### Using the Order of Operations

Use the order of operations to evaluate each expression.

**a)** $3(4 + 1)^2$  **b)** $7^3 - 2(3^2 - 5)$  **c)** $\sqrt{25 - 16}$

### Solution

**a)**
$$\begin{aligned} & 3(4 + 1)^2 \\ &= 3(5)^2 && \text{Brackets} \\ &= 3(25) && \text{Exponent} \\ &= 75 && \text{Multiplication} \end{aligned}$$

**b)**
$$\begin{aligned} & 7^3 - 2(3^2 - 5) \\ &= 343 - 2(9 - 5) && \text{Within brackets — exponents} \\ &= 343 - 2(4) && \text{Within brackets — subtraction} \\ &= 343 - 8 && \text{Multiplication} \\ &= 335 && \text{Subtraction} \end{aligned}$$

**c)**
$$\begin{aligned} & \sqrt{25 - 16} && \text{Treat a square root sign as a kind of bracket.} \\ &= \sqrt{9} && \text{Complete the operations inside the square root.} \\ &= 3 \end{aligned}$$

- A power represents repeated multiplication of the same number.
- In the power $x^y$, $x$ is the base and $y$ is the exponent. For example, $2^5$ is a power. The base is 2 and the exponent is 5. The value of the power is $2 \times 2 \times 2 \times 2 \times 2$, or 32.
- The order of operations in expressions is:

## Discuss the Concepts

1. In the **Discover**, you started with 1 and continuously doubled the previous number. Explain why this is the same as having a power with a base of 2.

2. Describe, in order, the operations required to evaluate each of the following. Do not evaluate.
   a) $5 \times 3^7$
   b) $2 + 8(9 - 2^2)$
   c) $\sqrt{6^2 + 8^2}$

3. The word "Brackets" is used as the first step in the order of operations. Explain what this means when you are evaluating an expression.

## Practise

*For help with question 1, refer to Example 1.*

1. Write each expression as a power. Do not evaluate.
   a) $6 \times 6 \times 6 \times 6$
   b) $9 \times 9 \times 9 \times 9$
   c) 12
   d) $15 \times 15$
   e) $8 \times 8 \times 8 \times 8 \times 8$
   f) $5 \times 5 \times 5 \times 5 \times 5 \times 5 \times 5$

*For help with question 2, refer to Example 2.*

2. Find each square root without using a calculator.
   a) $\sqrt{4}$
   b) $\sqrt{9}$
   c) $\sqrt{100}$
   d) $\sqrt{49}$
   e) $\sqrt{1}$
   f) $\sqrt{144}$

*For help with question 3, refer to Example 1.*

3. Evaluate each power using a scientific or graphing calculator.
   a) $7^5$
   b) $3^8$
   c) $12^4$
   d) $6^5$
   e) $1.4^2$
   f) $5.7^3$

B

4. **Communication** Each of the following sequences has a pattern. Describe the pattern. Then, write each sequence in exponential form.
   a) 3, 9, 27, 81, 243
   b) 1, 4, 9, 16, 25, 36, 49
   c) 1, 10, 100, 1000, 10 000
   d) 1, 2, 4, 8, 16, 32
   e) 1, 8, 27, 64
   f) $1, \frac{1}{4}, \frac{1}{16}, \frac{1}{64}, \frac{1}{256}$

*For help with question 5, refer to Example 3.*

5. Use the order of operations to evaluate each expression.
   a) $100 \times 3^2$
   b) $6^2 + 4^2$
   c) $(6 + 4)^2$
   d) $\sqrt{13^2 - 5^2}$
   e) $\sqrt{13^2} - \sqrt{5^2}$
   f) $8 + 5(4 - 1)^3$
   g) $(7 - 2^2)(3 + 5)^2$
   h) $5.2^2 - 4.2^2$
   i) $2.9 - 5.6^2$
   j) $(21 - 12) \div 3^2$
   k) $1.2^2 \div 0.2^3$
   l) $4 + \sqrt{11 + (2 + 3)^2}$

6. Copy each equation. Insert brackets to make each statement true.

a) $3 + 2 \times 15 - 7 \stackrel{?}{=} 19$  b) $4^2 - 7^2 \stackrel{?}{=} 81$

c) $10 \div 2.3 + 7.7 \stackrel{?}{=} 1$  d) $3^2 - 1 \div 5 \stackrel{?}{=} 1.6$

## APPLY THE CONCEPTS

7. **Application** A bacterial culture began with 1000 bacteria. The number of bacteria doubled every 12 h. How many bacteria were present after

a) 1 day?  b) 2 days?

c) 1 week?

8. **Prize Choices** On a TV game show, you are offered three choices for a prize, in dollars.

**A** double your age, squared

**B** 2 to the exponent of your age

**C** the square root of your age, cubed

Which offer should you take, and why?

9. Every person has 2 birth parents, 4 birth grandparents, and so on. These people are known as your ancestors. How many ancestors does a person have in each generation? Write each of your answers in exponential form.

a) the 3rd generation, their great-grandparents

b) the 4th generation

c) the 10th generation

10. **Communication** Use a calculator to evaluate each pair and to help establish a pattern or rule for square roots of some decimals. Describe the rule.

a) $\sqrt{25}, \sqrt{0.25}$  b) $\sqrt{36}, \sqrt{0.36}$

c) $\sqrt{81}, \sqrt{0.81}$  d) $\sqrt{4}, \sqrt{0.04}$

11. **Application** For a vacation, a family rented a van at $72.95 per day, plus $2.50 insurance per day, plus $0.25 per kilometre driven. Their vacation lasted 8 days and they travelled 1572 km.

a) Write an expression that represents the cost of the rental, without using brackets.

b) Write another expression that represents the cost of the rental, using brackets.

c) Evaluate both expressions to find the exact cost of the rental.

# 1.4 Working With Area and Other Formulas

You have used area and perimeter formulas before. Formulas are also used in many other areas such as finance, farming, fitness, and travel.

## Example 1

### Using Area Formulas

Use the formulas provided to determine the area of each figure. Round to one decimal place, where necessary.

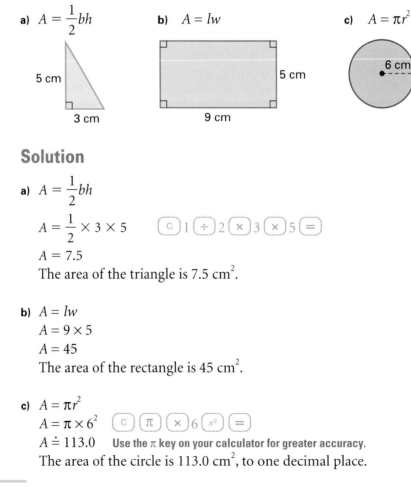

**a)** $A = \frac{1}{2}bh$

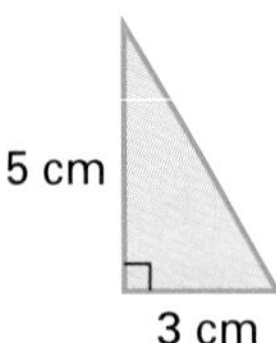


**b)**  $A = lw$

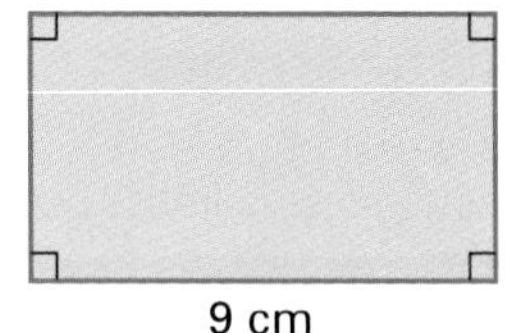


**c)** $A = \pi r^2$

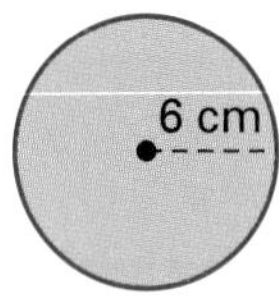


### Solution

**a)** $A = \frac{1}{2}bh$

$A = \frac{1}{2} \times 3 \times 5$  C 1 ÷ 2 × 3 × 5 =

$A = 7.5$

The area of the triangle is 7.5 cm$^2$.

**b)** $A = lw$

$A = 9 \times 5$

$A = 45$

The area of the rectangle is 45 cm$^2$.

**c)** $A = \pi r^2$

$A = \pi \times 6^2$  C π × 6 $x^2$ =

$A \doteq 113.0$  **Use the π key on your calculator for greater accuracy.**

The area of the circle is 113.0 cm$^2$, to one decimal place.

## EXAMPLE 2

### Using the Simple Interest Formula

The simple interest payable on $\$P$ invested for $t$ years, at an interest rate $r\%$ is given by the formula $I = Prt$. How much interest is payable after 5 years on a $400 investment earning 4% simple interest?

### Solution

$P = 400$

$r = 4\%$ or $0.04$

$t = 5$

Substitute into the formula $I = Prt$

$I = 400 \times 0.04 \times 5$

$I = 80$

The interest payable after 5 years is $80.

## EXAMPLE 3

**Did You Know?**

The first known lighthouse was the Pharos of Alexandria, Egypt. Constructed around 300 BCE, it was 137 m tall. This lighthouse was one of the Seven Wonders of the Ancient World. It was destroyed, by invaders and earthquakes, by the 1300's. The oldest existing lighthouse is La Coruna in Spain. It was built in 20 BCE.

### Using a Science Formula

The distance, $d$, in kilometres, to the horizon can be calculated using the formula $d = 3.6\sqrt{h}$, where $h$ is the height, in metres, above the surface of Earth. The lookout on a sailing ship is 20 m above water level. How far away is the horizon, to the nearest kilometre?

### Solution

$d = 3.6\sqrt{h}$ — **Substitute $h = 20$ into the formula.**

$d = 3.6 \times \sqrt{20}$ — C 3.6 × 20 √ =

$d \doteq 16$

The horizon is 16 km away, to the nearest kilometre.

## Key Concepts

- To evaluate a formula when some values are known, substitute the known values. Then, use the correct order of operations to evaluate the expression.

## Discuss the Concepts

1. There are two formulas for the circumference of a circle. Describe when you would use each one.
   $C = \pi d$ $\qquad$ $C = 2\pi r$

2. On a test, the formula $P = 2(l + w)$ was provided, with $l = 4$ and $w = 7$. One student gave this incorrect solution:
   $P = 2(4 + 7)$
   $P = 8 + 7$
   $P = 15$
   Where did the student go wrong?

## Practise

***For help with question 1, refer to Example 1.***

1. Calculate the area of each shape. Round to one decimal place where necessary.

a)

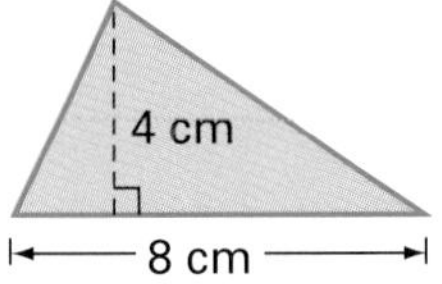


b)

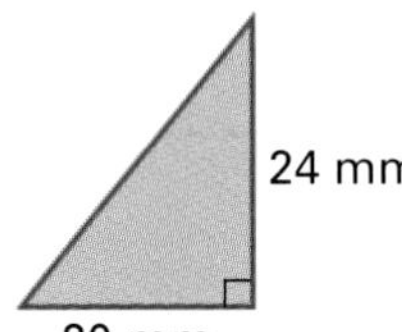


c)

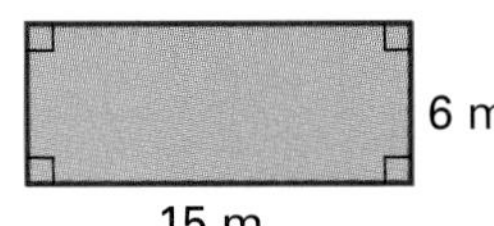


d)

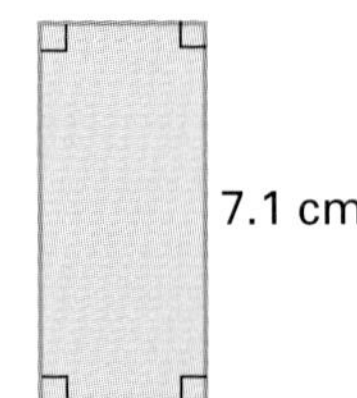


e)

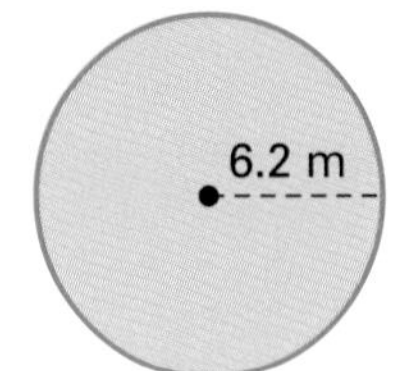


f)

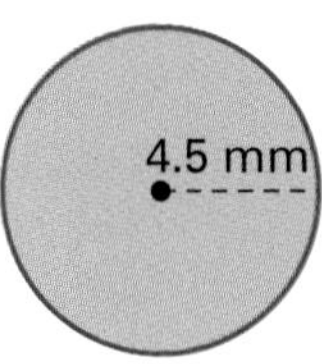

***For help with question 2, refer to Examples 2 and 3.***

**2.** Substitute the given value(s) and evaluate.

| | | |
|---|---|---|
| **a)** | $C = 10 + 5t$ | $t = 2$ |
| **b)** | $C = \pi d$ | $d = 10$ |
| **c)** | $P = 2(l + w)$ | $l = 50, w = 30$ |
| **d)** | $y = mx + b$ | $x = 10, m = 3, b = 4$ |
| **e)** | $s = \dfrac{d}{t}$ | $d = 120, t = 4$ |
| **f)** | $I = Prt$ | $r = 0.02, P = 1000, t = 0.5$ |
| **g)** | $d = \sqrt{2s^2}$ | $s = 3$ |
| **h)** | $r = \sqrt{x^2 + y^2}$ | $x = 5, y = 13$ |

## APPLY THE CONCEPTS

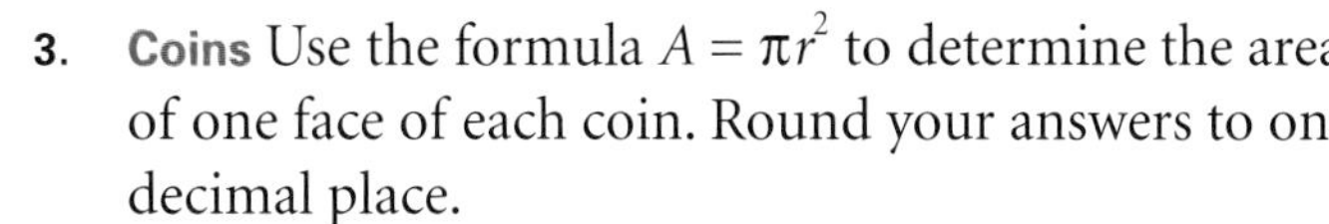

**B**

**3.** **Coins** Use the formula $A = \pi r^2$ to determine the area of one face of each coin. Round your answers to one decimal place.

**a)** Penny: $r = 9.5$ mm **b)** Nickel: $r = 1.0$ cm
**c)** Dime: $r = 9.0$ mm **d)** Quarter: $r = 1.2$ cm
**e)** Loonie: $r = 1.3$ cm **f)** Toonie: $r = 1.4$ cm

**4.** **Bills** All Canadian paper money has the same dimensions.

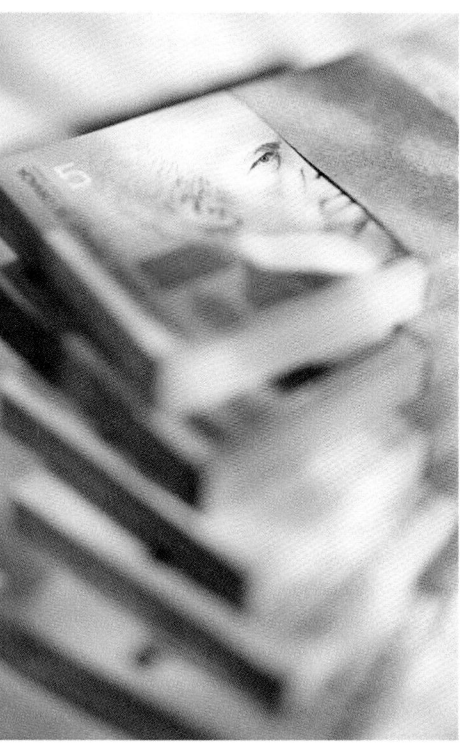

**a)** Measure the dimensions, to the centimetre, of a \$5 or a \$10 bill. Then, calculate the area of the bill.

**b)** When the Bank of Canada orders printed money, such as \$10 bills, it is printed in sheets of 40 bills. How many sheets of \$10 bills are needed to print a total of \$1 000 000?

**c)** What is the area of one sheet of bills?

**d)** What is the total area of paper needed to print \$1 000 000 in \$10 bills?

5. **Communication** A stone is thrown upward at a speed of 20 m/s. The height, $h$ in metres, of the stone after $t$ seconds, is approximated by the formula $h = 20t - 5t^2$.
Determine the height of the stone after each time.

**a)** 1 s **b)** 2 s **c)** 2.5 s **d)** 4 s

**e)** Describe the path of the stone as time goes from zero to four seconds.

6. **Application** The area of a trapezoid can be calculated using the formula $A = \frac{1}{2}h(a + b)$.
Calculate the area of each trapezoid.

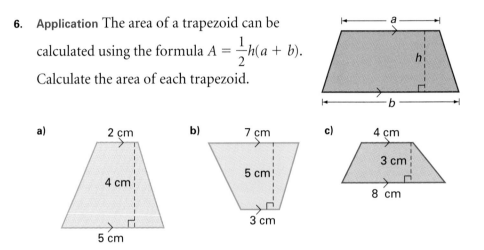

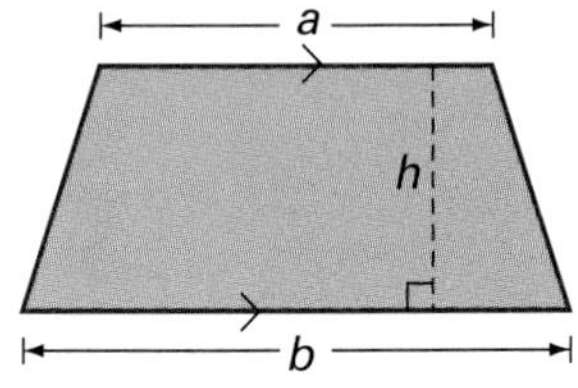


**a)**

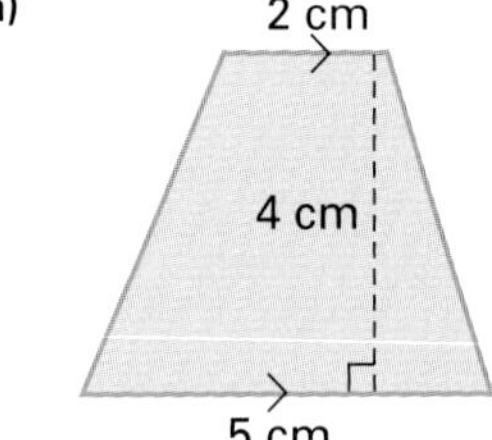

**b)**

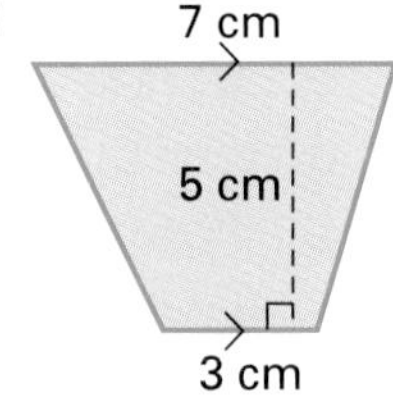


**c)**

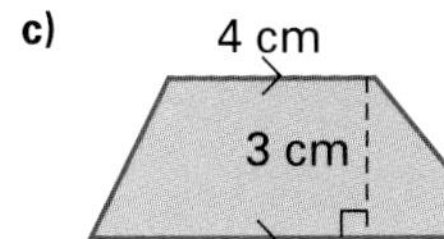


7. Shallow water waves travel at an estimated speed, $s$, in kilometres per hour, given by the formula $s = 0.2\sqrt{d}$, where $d$ is the depth of the water, in metres. How fast are the waves travelling if the water has each of the following depths? Round your answers to the nearest tenth of a kilometre per hour.

**a)** 1 m **b)** 4 m **c)** 12 m

8. **Heart Rate** During exercise, the maximum recommended heart rate, $H$, in beats per minute, for adults, age $A$ years, is modelled by the formula $H = 230 - 1.2A$.
What is the maximum recommended heart rate for an adult of each age?

**a)** 18 years

**b)** 30 years

**c)** 60 years

**d)** Why does the maximum recommended heart rate decline as you get older?

**Chapter Problem**

9. Jeff's neighbours keep the water in their swimming pools at 28°C. On a typical summer day, water evaporates at an average rate of 0.48 L/h/$m^2$ (litres per hour per square metre) of surface area of the pool. Determine the volume of water that would evaporate from each pool in one day. Round your answers to the nearerst ten litres.

a) b)

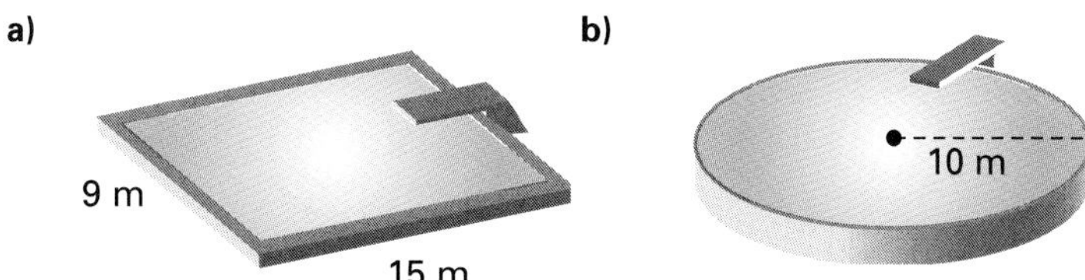


10. **Simple Interest** The future amount of an investment that pays simple interest can be found using the formula $A = P(1 + rt)$, where $A$ is the future amount in dollars, $P$ is the principal in dollars, $r$ is the interest rate as a decimal, and $t$ is the time in years. Find the future amount of each investment.
    a) \$500 invested at 4% simple interest, after 5 years
    b) \$1000 invested at 3.5% simple interest, after 4 years

C 11. **Flying** In order to turn an airplane, the pilot raises one wing and lowers the other. This is called "banking the plane". The plane turns in the direction of the lower wing. For example, to turn left, the left wing is lowered, and the right one is raised. The angle between the wings and the horizontal is called the *angle of bank*. If a pilot banks too far, the plane stalls and falls out of the sky. The maximum angle of bank, $A$, in degrees, allowed for a small airplane depends on the flying speed $v$, in kilometres per hour, according to the formula $A = 0.015v^2 - 0.218v + 104$. At a speed of 120 km/h, what is the maximum angle of bank allowed?

# Review

## 1.1 Connecting Perimeter With Whole Numbers and Decimals, pages 4–9

1. Calculate the perimeter of each shape. Round to one decimal place where necessary.

**a)**

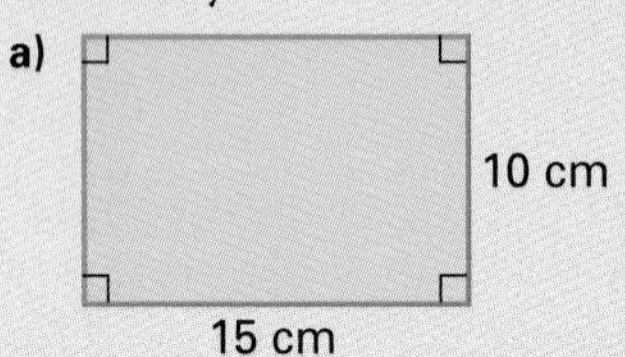


**b)**

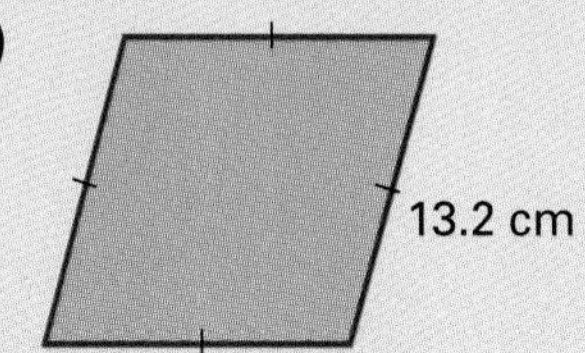


**c)**

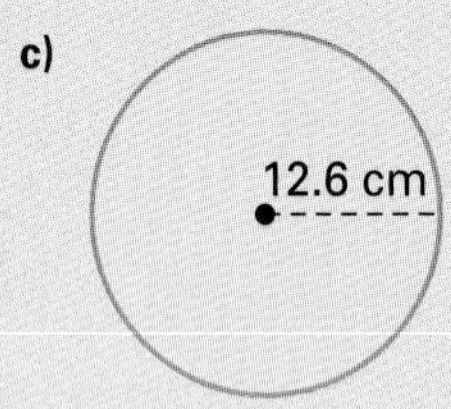


**d)**

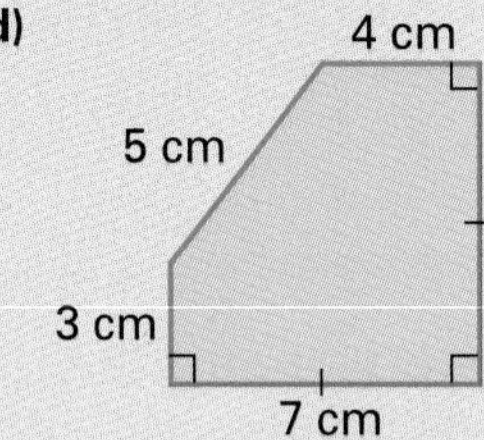


2. **Problem Solving** A boat has six circular portholes, each with a radius of 24 cm. Each porthole needs sealant around its circumference. What is the total length that needs sealant? Round your answer to the nearest metre.

## 1.2 Estimation, pages 10–15

3. Use estimation to determine whether each scientific calculator screen shows a reasonable answer.

**a)** $15.2 \times 9.5$

**b)** $698.2 \div 7.2$

**c)** $761.33 - 438.12 + 122.41$

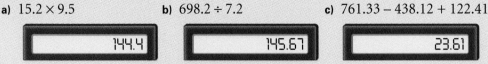

4. In a science class activity, each pair of students was asked to measure the length of a green bean. The lengths, in centimetres, were as follows:

6.7, 12.4, 15.1, 9.8, 7.0, 7.7, 10.2, 18.5, 12.6, 3.9, 8.9, 13.2

a) Estimate the total length of the green beans, to the nearest centimetre.
b) Estimate the average length, to the nearest tenth.

## 1.3 Exponents and the Order of Operations, pages 16–21

5. Write each expression as a power. Do not evaluate.
a) $8 \times 8 \times 8 \times 8 \times 8 \times 8$ b) $17 \times 17 \times 17$ c) 9

6. Evaluate each square root without the use of a calculator.
a) $\sqrt{36}$ b) $\sqrt{100}$ c) $\sqrt{49}$

7. Use the order of operations to evaluate each expression.
a) $(9 + 2)^2$ b) $(15 - 6) \div 3^2$ c) $\sqrt{6^2 + 8^2}$
d) $68 - 2(2 + 1)^3$ e) $2^0 + \sqrt{24 + (9 - 4)^2}$

8. **Application** In a rumour-passing experiment, you told a rumour to 3 friends. Each friend told the rumour to 3 friends. Each of those friends told the rumour to 3 friends, and so on. Assuming all friends are different people, how many friends will be told the rumour in
a) the next round?
b) the sixth round?
c) the twentieth round?

## 1.4 Working With Area and Other Formulas, pages 22–27

9. The formula for the area of a rectangle is $A = lw$. Calculate the area of a rectangle with length 8.2 cm and width 3.5 cm.

10. The formula for the area of a triangle is $A = \frac{1}{2}bh$. Calculate the area of a triangle with base 134 mm and height 78 mm.

11. Use the formula $A = \pi r^2$ to determine the area of a compact disc with radius of 6 cm. Round your answer to one decimal place.

12. Use the formula $A = \frac{1}{2}h(a + b)$ to calculate the area of the trapezoid.

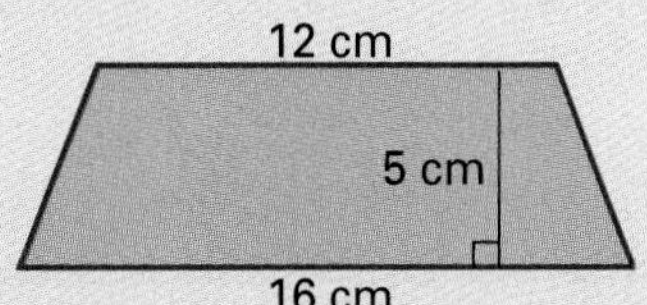

# Practice Test

## Multiple Choice

***For questions 1 to 5, select the correct answer.***

**1.** $12.4 - 3.7 \times 2$

**A** 5 **B** 17.4 **C** 21.1 **D** 1.29

**2.** $9 \times 9 \times 9 \times 9 \times 9 \times 9 \times 9$ expressed as a power is

**A** $7 \times 9$ **B** $7^9$ **C** $9^7$ **D** $81^7$

**3.** Which expression gives an answer of 61?

**A** $(5 + 6)^2$ **B** $5 + 6^2$ **C** $6 + 5^2$ **D** $5^2 + 6^2$

**4.** When substituting $s = 9$ into the formula $d = \sqrt{4s^2}$, the result is

**A** 36 **B** 18 **C** 324 **D** 6

**5.** The mass of an ant is most appropriately measured in

**A** grams **B** millimetres **C** milligrams **D** litres

## Short Answer

**6.** You use centimetres (cm) as a unit of length and square centimetres ($cm^2$) as a unit of area. Explain why.

**7.** Describe how to round the length 23.47 cm to the nearest tenth.

**8.** In the mathematical statement $2^3 = 8$, state the word used to identify

**a)** 2

**b)** 3

**c)** 8

**9.** Calculate the perimeter and the area of the rectangle shown.

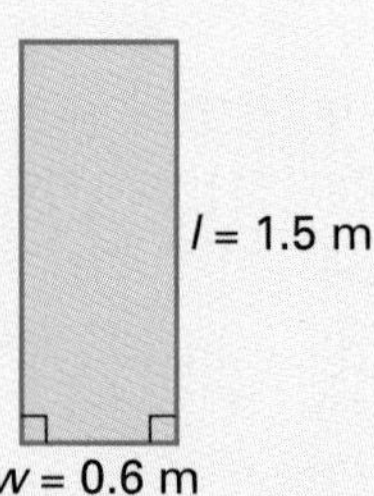


**10.** Describe a method that you could use to measure the thickness of a dime.

## Extended Response

**11.** **Thinking/Inquiry/Problem Solving, Communication** The dimensions of a poster board are 40 cm by 60 cm. A second poster board measures 80 cm by 120 cm, double the dimensions of the first poster board. The price of the first poster board is $1.50. Is $6.00 an appropriate price for the second poster board? Give reasons for your answer.

**12.** **Thinking/Inquiry/Problem Solving, Communication** The cost, $C$, in dollars, of producing a school yearbook is given by the formula $C = S + 5n$, where $S$ is the set-up cost and $n$ is the number of yearbooks printed.

**a)** Find the cost to produce 1000 yearbooks, with a setup cost of $12 000.

**b)** When more than 1500 yearbooks are printed, the printer reduces the set-up cost to $11 000. If a school estimates that they need 1400 yearbooks, would they be better to increase their order to 1500? Explain your answer.

**ACHIEVEMENT CHECK** Knowledge/Understanding Thinking/Inquiry/Problem Solving Communication Application

**13.** Beth and Jared built a two-level wooden deck at the back of their home. It is shown in the diagram. They decide to insert a large circular hot tub that has a diameter of 2.0 m.

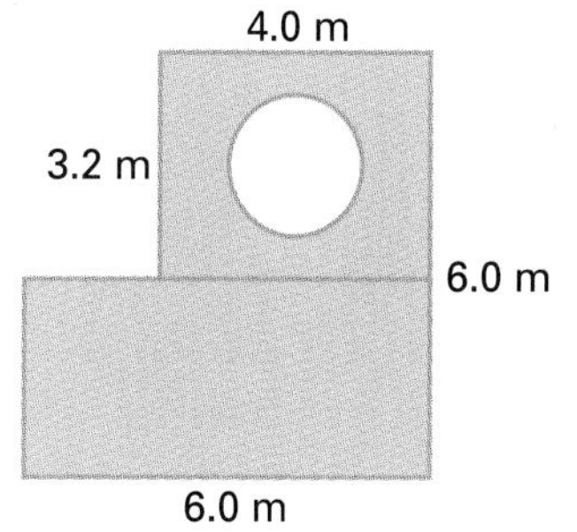


**a)** Calculate the area of the remaining exposed wooden floor of the deck, on both levels.

**b)** They want to stain the wood. The local building supply store sells cans of stain for $16.95 (before tax) that will each cover 7.0 m$^2$ of wood. Beth and Jared have budgeted $75 for the purchase of stain. Is this sufficient? Explain your reasoning.

**c)** A building inspector says that the deck must have a safety railing around its perimeter. A contractor gives them an estimate of $75/m (including all labour, materials, and taxes). What will this railing cost?

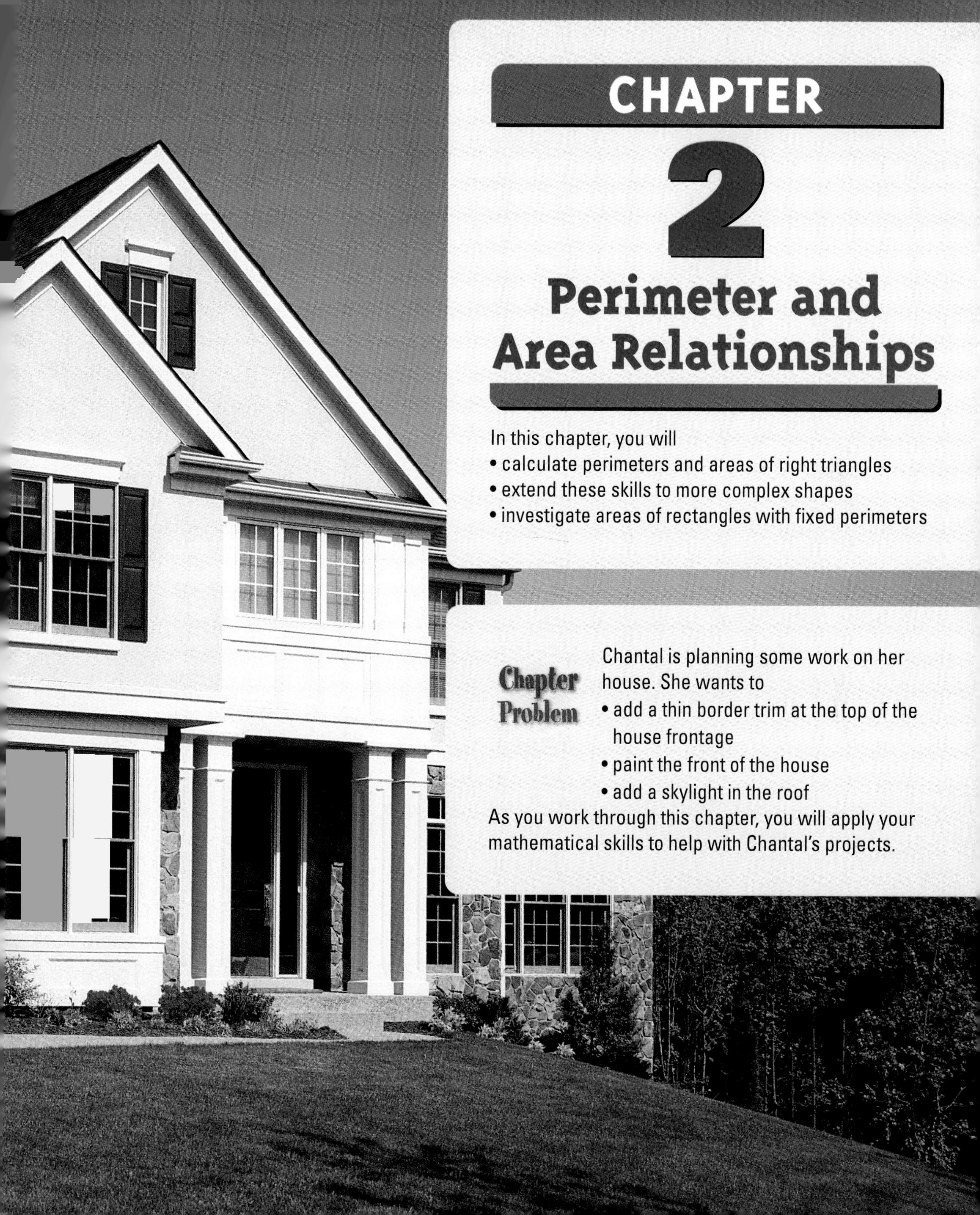

# CHAPTER 2

# Perimeter and Area Relationships

In this chapter, you will
- calculate perimeters and areas of right triangles
- extend these skills to more complex shapes
- investigate areas of rectangles with fixed perimeters

**Chapter Problem**

Chantal is planning some work on her house. She wants to
- add a thin border trim at the top of the house frontage
- paint the front of the house
- add a skylight in the roof

As you work through this chapter, you will apply your mathematical skills to help with Chantal's projects.

# Get Ready

## Substituting Into Formulas

The area of a rectangle with length $l$ and width $w$ is given by the formula $A = lw$.
Substitute the values $l = 13.5$ and $w = 7.3$ into $A = lw$. Then, evaluate the expression.

$A = lw$
$A = 13.5 \times 7.3$
$A = 98.55$

1. Substitute the given values into each formula and evaluate the expression.

**a)** $P = a + b + c$ $\quad a = 3.5, b = 4, c = 5.5$
**b)** $P = 2l + 2w$ $\quad l = 5.2, w = 3.5$
**c)** $c = a - 2b$ $\quad a = 6, b = 8$
**d)** $C = 2\pi r$ $\quad r = 2.6$
**e)** $A = \frac{1}{2}bh$ $\quad b = 4, h = 8$

## Solving Simple Equations

To solve the equation below, rearrange to get $s$ by itself.

$$s + 10 = 15$$
$$s + 10 - 10 = 15 - 10$$
$$s = 5$$

2. Solve these equations.

**a)** $a + 7 = 25$ **b)** $28 + b = 36$ **c)** $43 = 17 + c$

## Calculating Perimeters

Determine the perimeter of the shape shown.
The shape is a rectangle, with two sides of length 3 m and two sides of length 7 m.

perimeter = 3 + 7 + 3 + 7
= 20

The perimeter is 20 m.

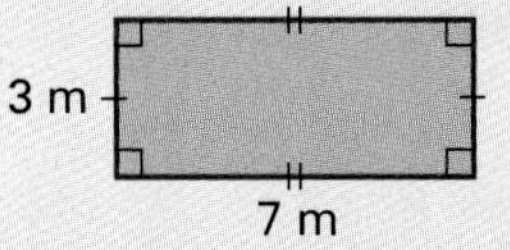


**The small single and double lines tell you which sides measure the same length.**

*Remember to include proper units with your answers.*

3. Determine the perimeter of each rectangle.

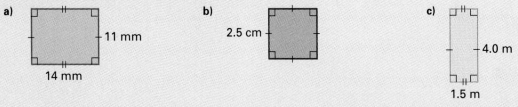

**a)**

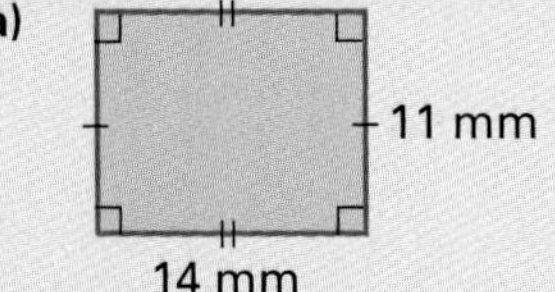


**b)** 2.5 cm

**c)**

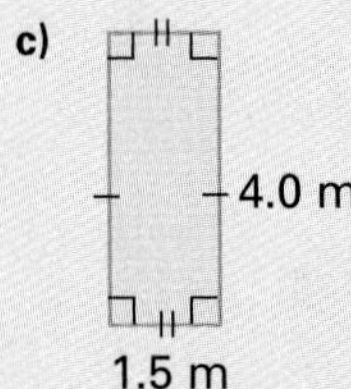

4. Determine the perimeter of each triangle.

a)

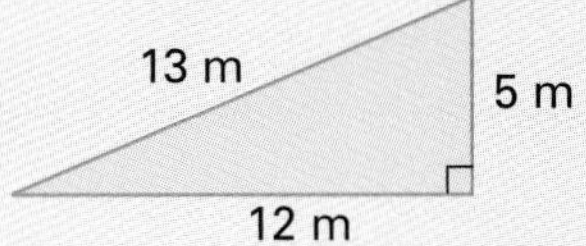


b)

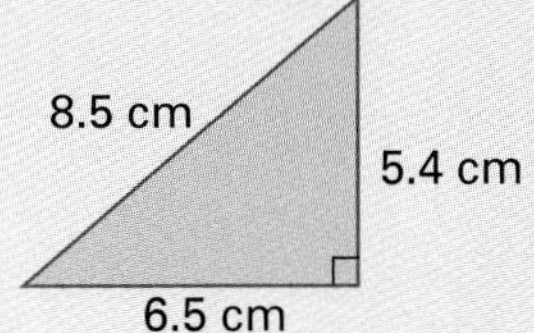


c)

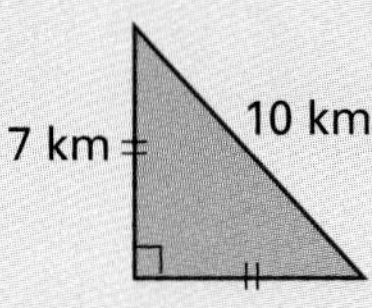


5. Determine the perimeter of each shape.

a)

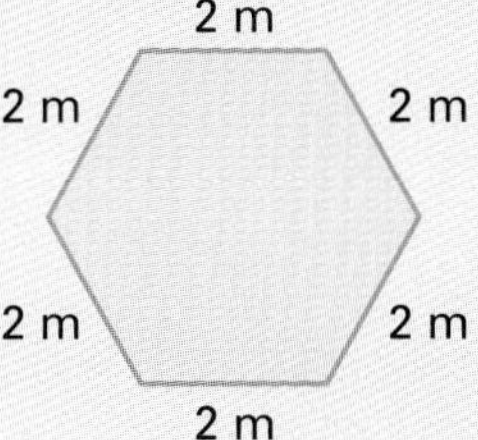


b)

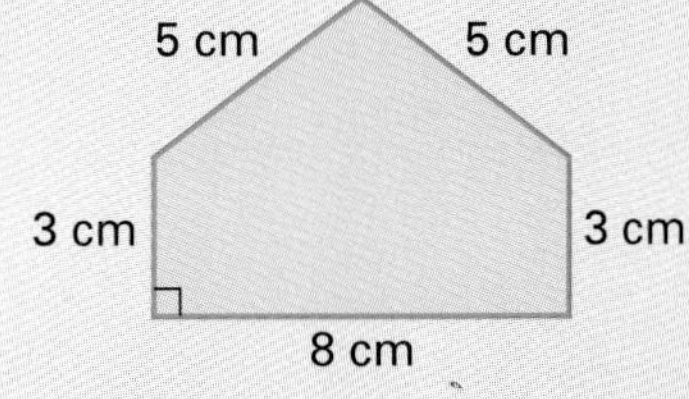


c)

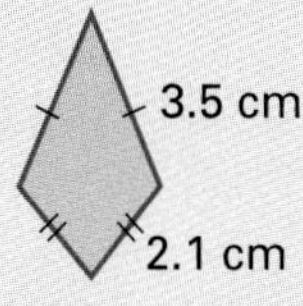


## Calculating Areas

Determine the area of each shape.

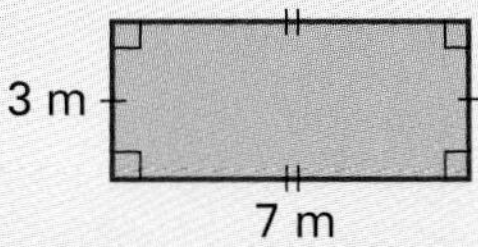


The shape is a rectangle, with length 7 m and width 3 m. Substitute $l = 7$ and $w = 3$ into the formula $A = lw$.

$A = lw$

$A = 7 \times 3$

$A = 21$

The area of the rectangle is 21 $m^2$.

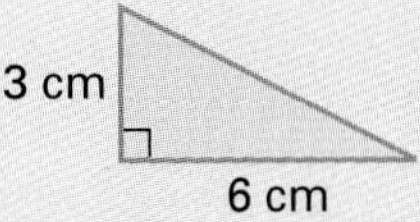


The shape is a triangle, with base 6 cm and height 3 cm. Substitute $b = 6$ and $h = 3$ into the formula $A = \frac{1}{2}bh$.

$A = \frac{1}{2}bh$

$A = \frac{1}{2} \times 6 \times 3$

$A = \frac{6 \times 3}{2}$ C 6 × 3 ÷ 2 =

$A = 9$

The area of the triangle is 9 $cm^2$.

6. Determine the area of each rectangle in question 3.

7. Determine the area of each triangle in question 4.

# 2.1 The Pythagorean Theorem

A **right triangle** is a triangle with one angle equal to 90° (a right angle). Right triangles often occur in measurement problems. Think of how a right triangle fits each of these situations:

- a ladder leaning against a wall
- throwing a baseball from home plate to second base
- measuring the diagonal of a computer screen
- looking at the top of a cliff from the ground below

There is a special relationship between the side lengths of right triangles: the Pythagorean relationship.

## Discover

**Materials**
- centimetre grid paper
- pencil and paper

### The Pythagorean Relationship

1. On a piece of grid paper, draw the right triangle shown.

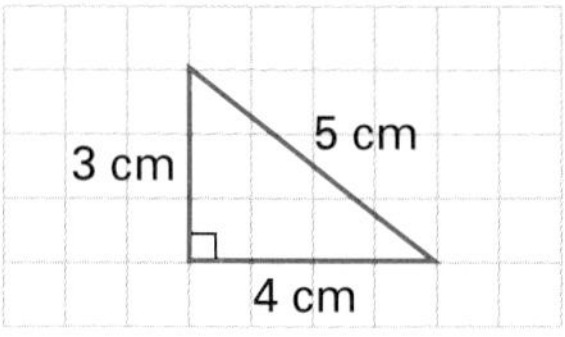


2. a) Construct a 3 cm by 3 cm square using one side of the triangle. Call this Square A.
   b) Construct a 4 cm by 4 cm square on another side of the triangle. Call this Square B.
   c) Construct a 5 cm by 5 cm square on the third side of the triangle. Call this Square C. Your triangle should now be surrounded by three squares.

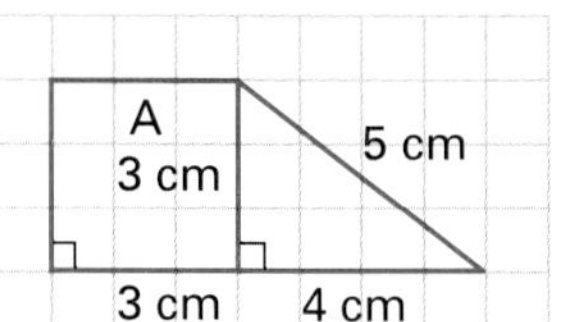

3. a) Find the areas of Squares A and B. Add them.
   b) Find the area of Square C (count or estimate part-squares carefully).

4. Compare your answers to questions 3a) and b). What do you notice?

5. Enter measurements and areas for the triangle in a table such as the one shown here.

| $a$ | $b$ | $c$ | $a^2$ | $b^2$ | $a^2 + b^2$ | $c^2$ |
|---|---|---|---|---|---|---|
| 3 | 4 | 5 | | | | |
| | | | | | | |

6. Create a new right triangle with different measurements. Repeat questions 1 through 5. (Count or estimate part-squares carefully.) Add the data to your table. Continue until you have data for at least four triangles.

7. a) Make a statement about the relationship you notice.
   b) Compare your data with your classmates' data. Is your statement confirmed?
   c) Explain why the results may not have worked out perfectly in every case.

The results of the **Discover** illustrate the important relationship known as the Pythagorean theorem. This theorem, or mathematical truth, is named after a famous Greek mathematician, Pythagoras (580–500 B.C.E.).

The longest side of a right triangle, labelled $c$ in this diagram, is called the **hypotenuse**. It is the side opposite the small box that marks the 90° angle. The two smaller sides are labelled $a$ and $b$.

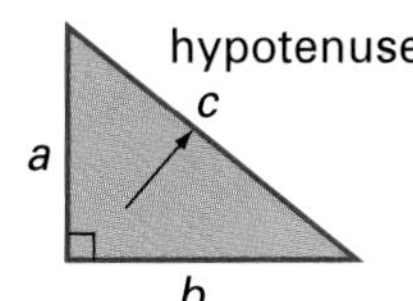


The **Pythagorean theorem** says that, in a right triangle, the square of the length of the hypotenuse is equal to the sum of the squares of the two shorter side lengths. In symbols,

$$c^2 = a^2 + b^2$$

## Example 1

### Calculating the Hypotenuse

When Laurie swims laps in her rectangular swimming pool, she decides to swim along the diagonal, so that she does not have to turn around as often. Find the distance Laurie travels by swimming once along the diagonal.

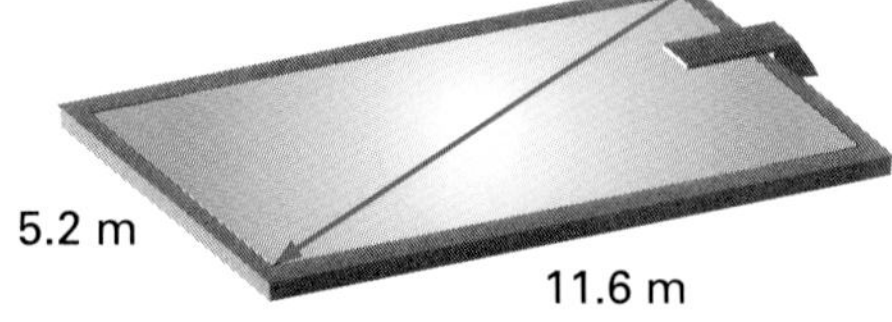


### Solution

Identify the hypotenuse. In the diagram, the diagonal, *d*, is the hypotenuse.

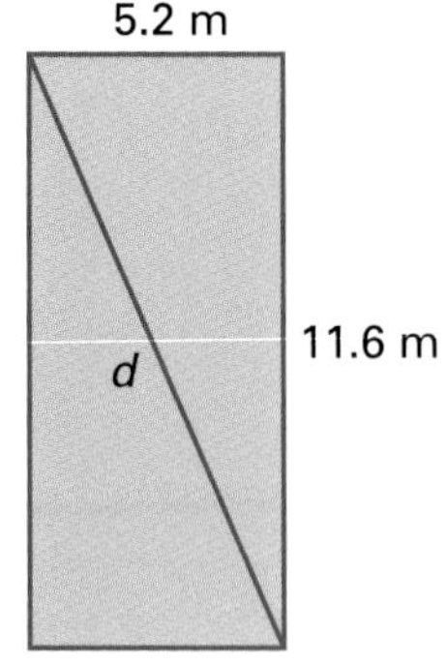


Now apply the Pythagorean theorem.

$d^2 = 5.2^2 + 11.6^2$

$d^2 = 27.04 + 134.56$ **Square the side lengths.**

$d^2 = 161.6$

$\sqrt{d^2} = \sqrt{161.6}$ **Take the square root of both sides.**

$d \doteq 12.7$ **Use the (√) key on a calculator.**

Laurie swims 12.7 m along the diagonal, to the nearest tenth of a metre.

## Example 2

### Finding One of the Shorter Sides

Alysia wants to determine how high her kite is flying. With the 125-m string fully extended, she pulls the kite so that it is directly above a tree. She estimates the tree to be 85 m from where she is standing. How high is the kite?

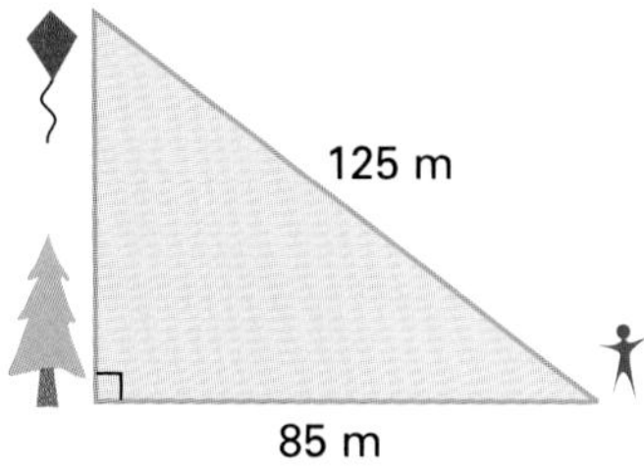

## Solution

First, identify the hypotenuse.
Then, label the sides.

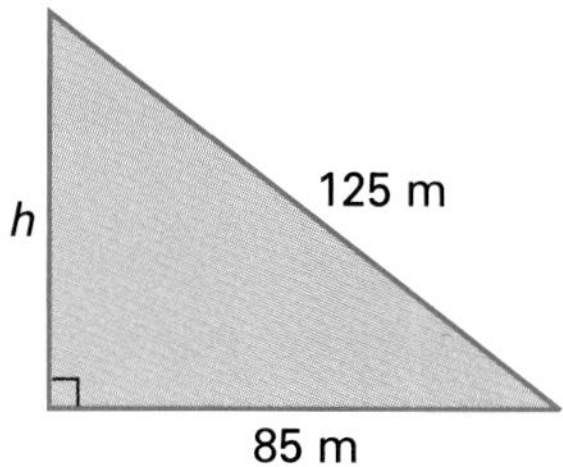


The length of the hypotenuse is 125 m. Let $h$ be the unknown height.

$$125^2 = 85^2 + h^2$$

$$15\,625 = 7225 + h^2$$ **Square the side lengths.**

$$15\,625 - 7225 = h^2$$ **Subtract 7225 from both sides.**

$$8400 = h^2$$

$$\sqrt{8400} = \sqrt{h^2}$$

$$h \doteq 92$$ **The original measures are in whole metres, so round the answer to the nearest metre. The "≐" symbol shows that you are rounding.**

Alysia's kite is approximately 92 m above the ground.

**Did You Know?**

The highest flight of a kite on a single string took place in Ontario, in 2000. Richard Synergy flew his 9-m kite to an altitude of 4422 m!

## Key Concepts

- The Pythagorean theorem is used to calculate the unknown side of a right triangle. Note: it does not work for triangles without a right angle.
- The longest side of a right triangle is the hypotenuse.
- The Pythagorean theorem states that the square of the length of the hypotenuse is equal to the sum of the squares of the two shorter side lengths.
- The Pythagorean theorem can be stated as the formula $c^2 = a^2 + b^2$, where $c$ is the hypotenuse.

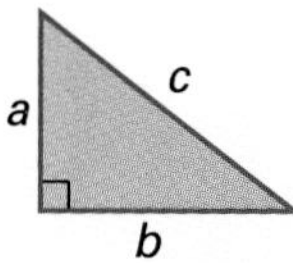


## Discuss the Concepts

1. Describe two ways to identify the hypotenuse in a right triangle.
2. State the Pythagorean theorem in everyday language.

## PRACTISE

*Include proper units with your answers. Round to match the measures given.*

1. In each triangle, which side is the hypotenuse?

a) 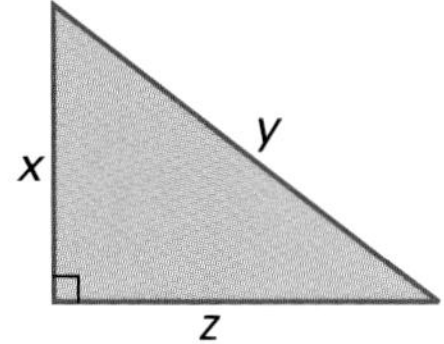


b) 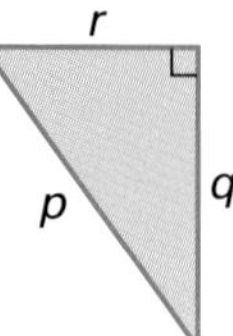


c) 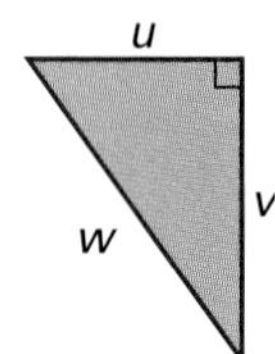

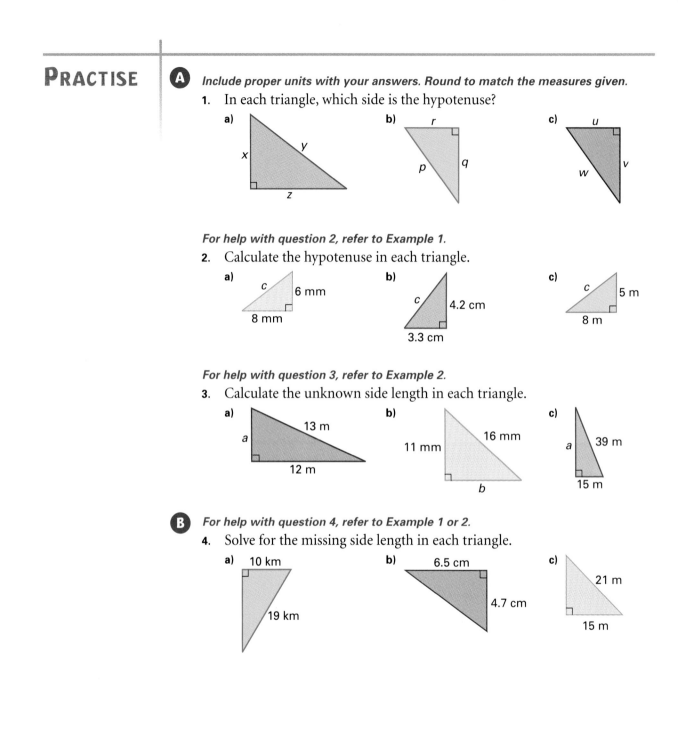


*For help with question 2, refer to Example 1.*

2. Calculate the hypotenuse in each triangle.

a) 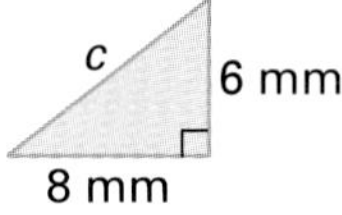


b) 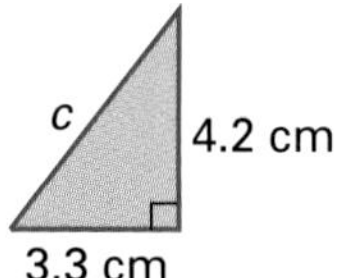


c) 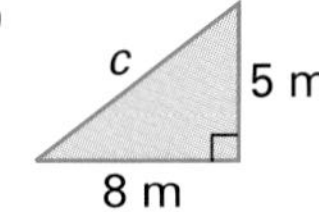


*For help with question 3, refer to Example 2.*

3. Calculate the unknown side length in each triangle.

a) 13 m, a, 12 m

b) 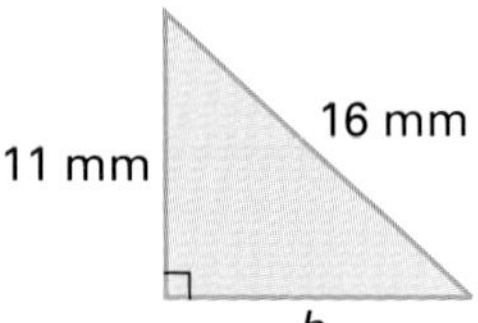


c) 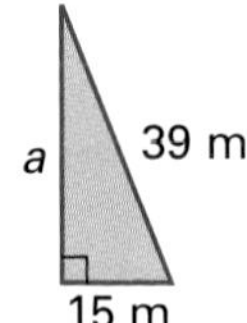


**B** *For help with question 4, refer to Example 1 or 2.*

4. Solve for the missing side length in each triangle.

a) 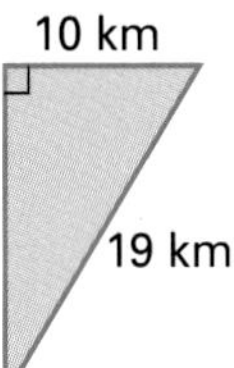


b) 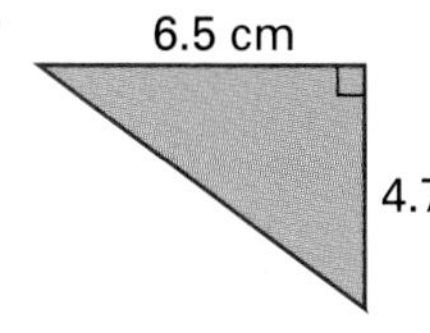


c) 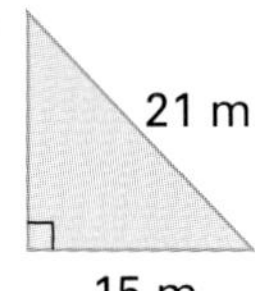

## Apply the Concepts

5. **Application** Zeke drives from his house in Geometropolis to his cottage in Decimal Point. He drives 64 km east and then 135 km north. How much travel distance will he save when he can drive along the new Square Route Expressway?

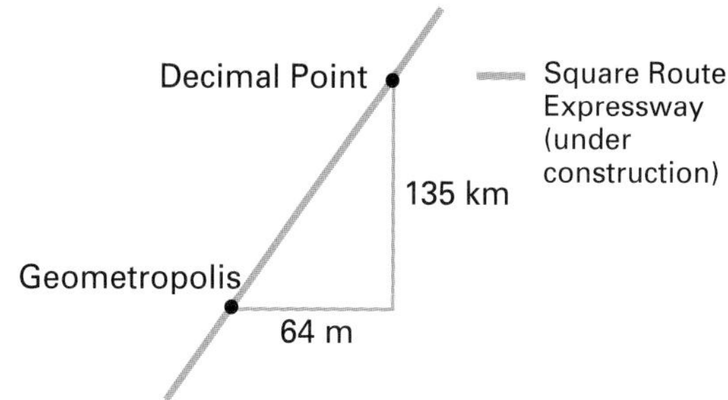


**Did You Know?**

Another way of writing 12 inches is 12″. One inch is the same length as 2.54 cm.

6. **Screen measurements** TV and computer screens are described by the measure along their diagonal, typically in inches. What is the height of a 12″ computer screen, if its width is 8″?

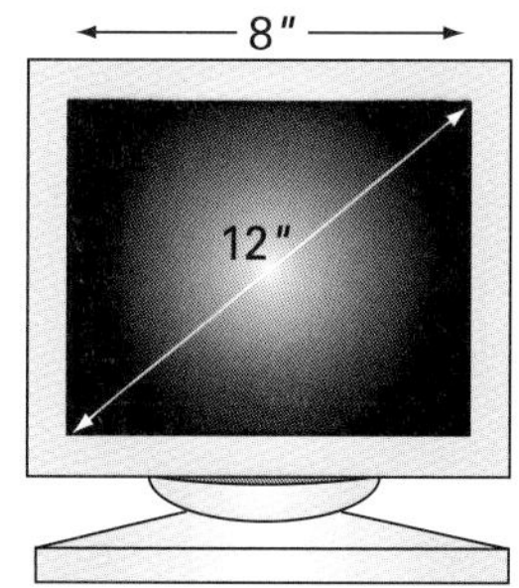


7. **Baseball** A catcher at home plate is trying to throw out a runner at second base.
   a) **Communication** Explain how you can calculate the distance of the throw, if you know the distance between bases.
   b) The distance between bases is approximately 27 m. How far is the ball thrown, to the nearest metre?

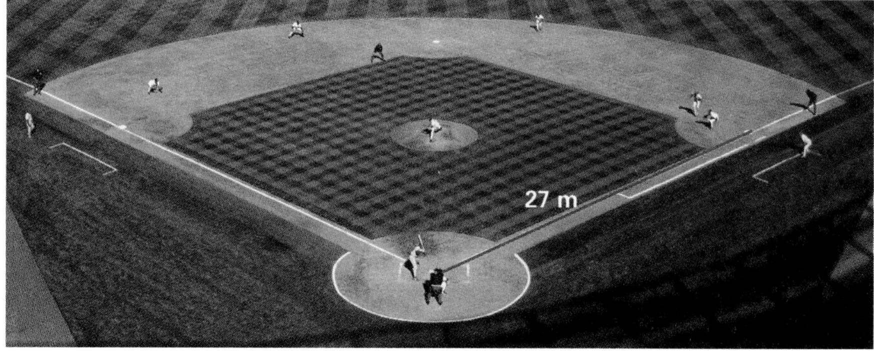


8. **Application** A surveyor is finding the height of a vertical cliff. She measures the base of the cliff to be 100 m away, and the top of the cliff to be 125 m away. How high is the cliff?

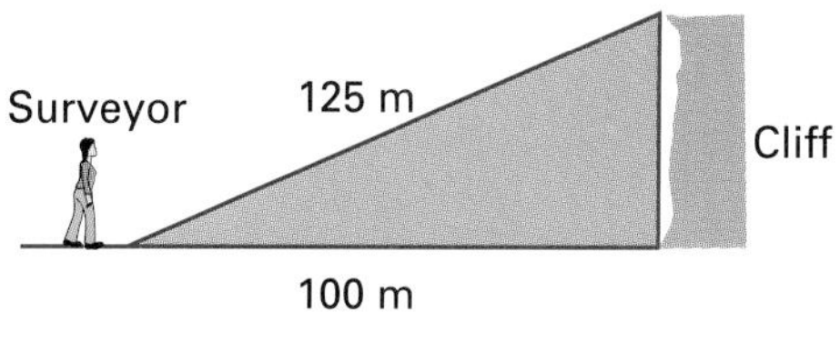

# 2.2 Perimeter and Area of Right Triangles

Imagine you are planning a hiking trail around the tip of Point Pelee, shown in the photograph. The trail is in the shape of a right triangle, and you know the distances of the two parts along the coast. To find the length of the whole trail, you need to determine the length of the overland part. The Pythagorean theorem can be a useful tool when finding the perimeters and the areas of right triangles.

## Example 1

### Perimeter of a Right Triangle

A city park, shown in this plan, is bordered by two roads and a river. An in-line skating path goes just inside the park perimeter. How long is the path?

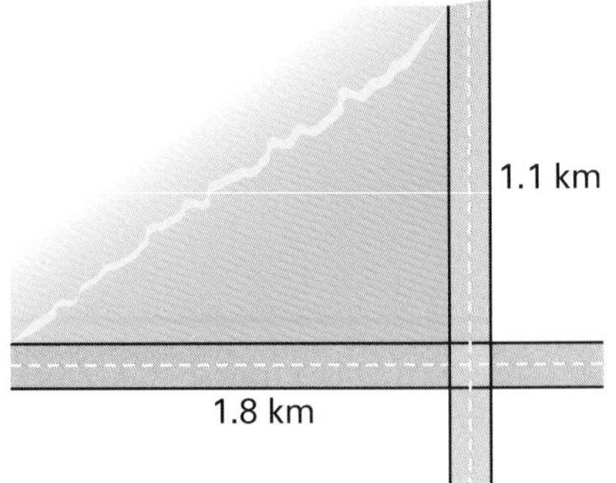


### Solution

The unknown side length, along the river, is the hypotenuse of a right triangle. Apply the Pythagorean theorem.

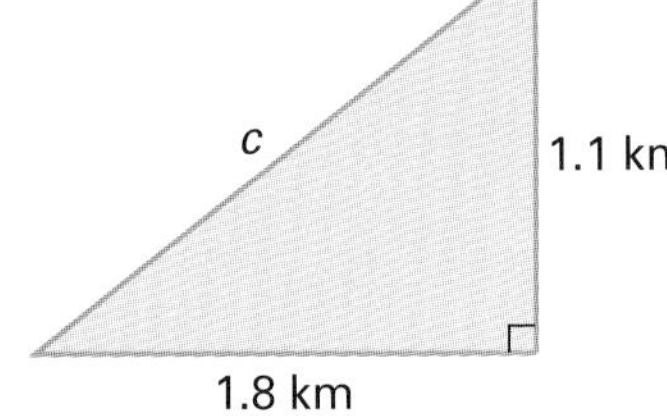


$c^2 = 1.8^2 + 1.1^2$

$c^2 = 3.24 + 1.21$ **Square the side lengths.**

$c^2 = 4.45$

$\sqrt{c^2} = \sqrt{4.45}$

$c \doteq 2.1095$

The perimeter of the path is the sum of the three side lengths.

$P = 1.8 + 1.1 + 2.1095$

$P \doteq 5.0$ **When adding, round to match the precision of the measures given.**

The in-line skating path is 5.0 km long, to the nearest tenth of a kilometre.

## Example 2

### Area of a Right Triangle

Sven wants to buy top soil for a triangular flower bed in one corner of his back yard. He measures 7.4 m along the lawn edge and 4.3 m along the flagstones, but can not easily measure along the rose bushes. Determine the area of Sven's flower bed.

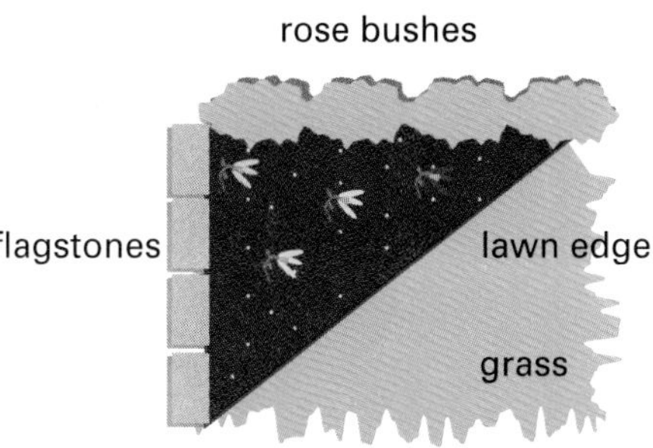


### Solution

To calculate the area of a triangle, you need to know its base and height. For a right triangle, the base and height are the lengths of the two shorter sides.

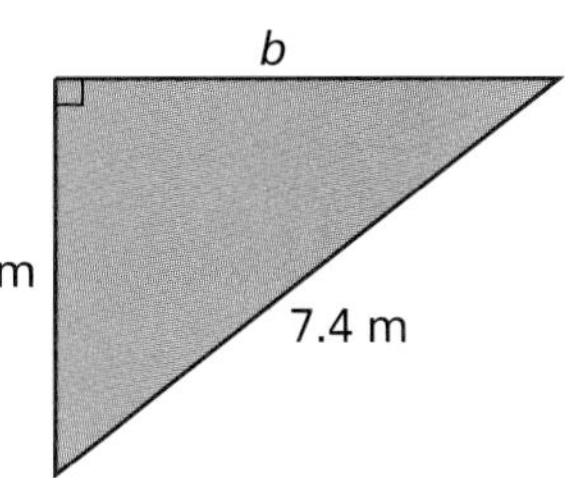


Apply the Pythagorean theorem.

$$7.4^2 = 4.3^2 + b^2$$
$$54.76 = 18.49 + b^2$$
$$54.76 - 18.49 = b^2$$
$$36.27 = b^2$$
$$\sqrt{36.27} = \sqrt{b^2}$$
$$b \doteq 6.022$$

Now apply the formula for area of a triangle.

$$A = \frac{1}{2}bh$$
$$A = \frac{1}{2} \times 6.022 \times 4.3$$

C 6.022 × 4.3 ÷ 2 =

$$A \doteq 13$$

**When multiplying, round to match the number of digits in the given measures. Both given measures, 4.3 m and 7.4 m, have two digits of accuracy.**

The area of Sven's flower bed is 13 $m^2$, to two digits of accuracy.

**Area is measured in square units, such as square metres ($m^2$).**

## Key Concepts

- The perimeter of a right triangle is the sum of the lengths of the three sides. The Pythagorean theorem can be applied if one of the sides is unknown.
- To calculate the area of a right triangle, use the formula $A = \frac{1}{2}bh$, with the lengths of the two shorter sides as the base $b$ and the height $h$.

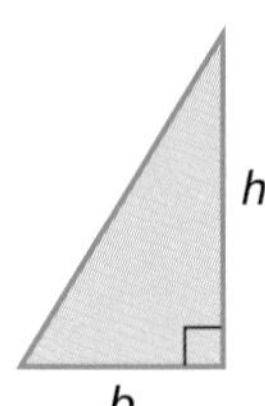


## Discuss the Concepts

1. In each case, do you need to calculate the perimeter or the area of a right triangle? Explain.
   a) Sven is putting a small picket fence around his flower bed.
   b) Manjinder is trimming the slanting roof edges at the top of his house with aluminum siding.
   c) Chi-An is buying paint for the side panels of her go-kart.
   d) Chi-An is finding the length of chain needed to connect three sprockets on her go-kart.
2. A soccer coach has her players run the length, width, and diagonal of the field during practice. Suppose you know the length and width of the field. Describe how to determine the distance of one lap.

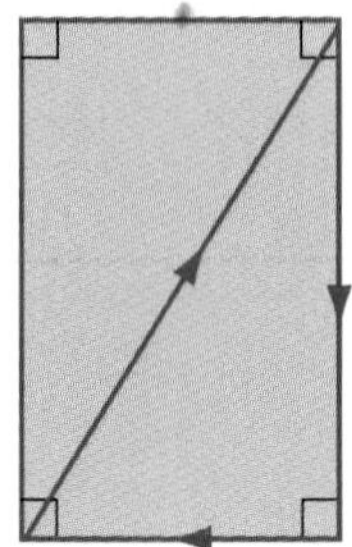

3. If you know any two side lengths of a right triangle, can you determine its area? If yes, explain how. If no, explain why not.
4. For the triangle shown, the side lengths are given
   • with precision to the nearest tenth, and
   • each have three digits
   Describe how you would round the answer when calculating
   a) the perimeter
   b) the area

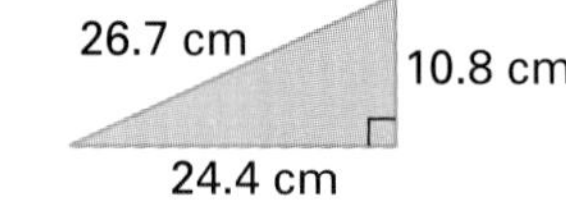

## PRACTISE

***Include proper units with your answers. Round your answers appropriately.***

***For help with question 1, refer to Example 1.***

**1.** Determine the perimeter of each triangle.

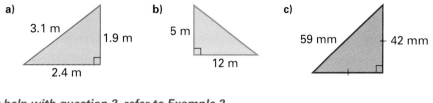

**a)**

3.1 m
1.9 m
2.4 m

**b)**

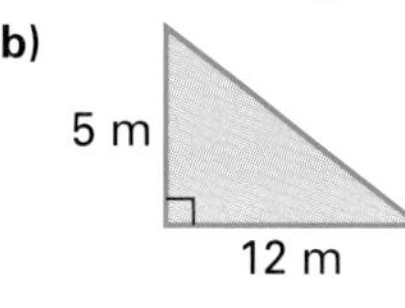


**c)**

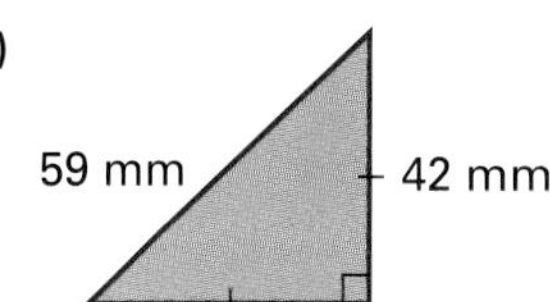


***For help with question 2, refer to Example 2.***

**2.** Determine the area of each triangle.

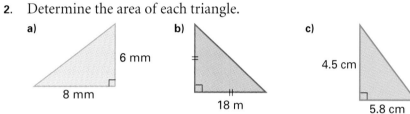

**a)**

6 mm
8 mm

**b)**

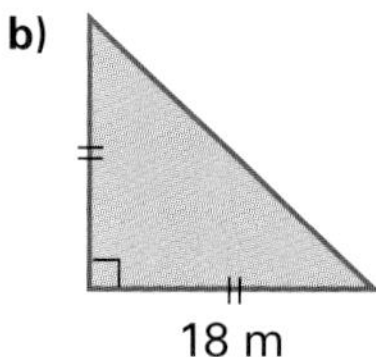


**c)**

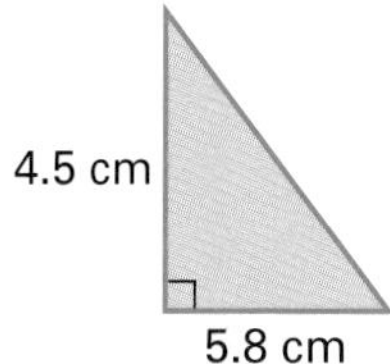


***For help with questions 3, 4, and 5, refer to Examples 1 and 2.***

**3.** Solve for the unknown side in each triangle.

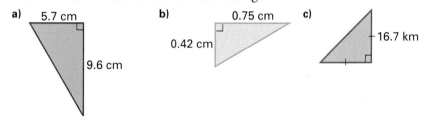

**a)**

5.7 cm
9.6 cm

**b)**

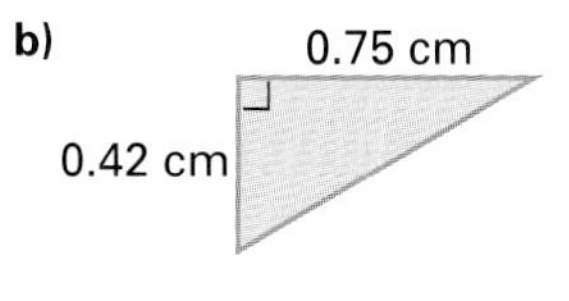


**c)**

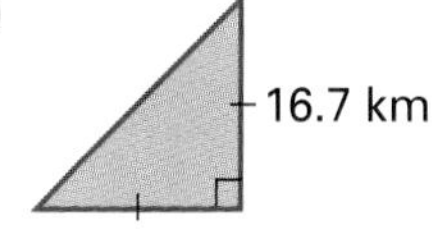


**4.** Find the perimeter of each triangle in question 3.

**5.** Calculate the area of each triangle in question 3.

**B**

**6.** Calculate the perimeter of each triangle.

**a)**

5.7 cm
2.6 cm

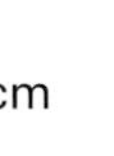

**b)**

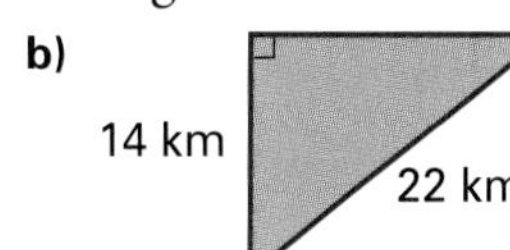

7. Calculate the area of each triangle.

a) 

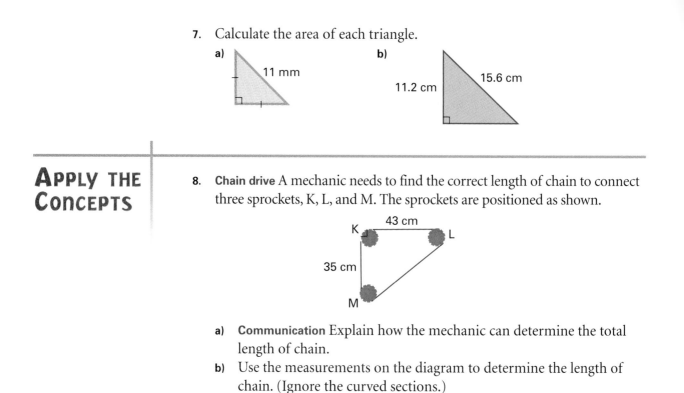

b) 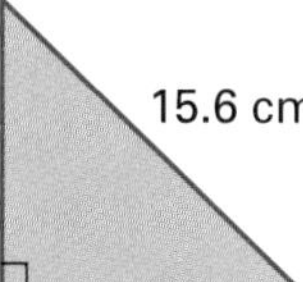


## Apply the Concepts

8. **Chain drive** A mechanic needs to find the correct length of chain to connect three sprockets, K, L, and M. The sprockets are positioned as shown.

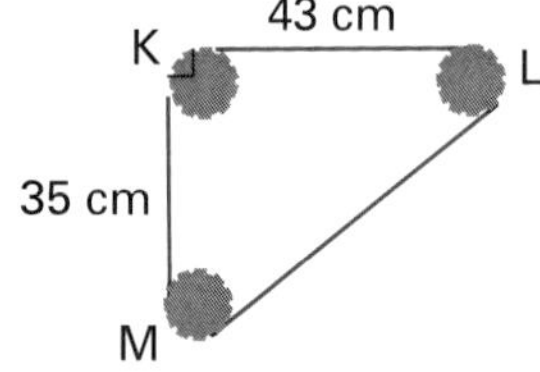


a) **Communication** Explain how the mechanic can determine the total length of chain.

b) Use the measurements on the diagram to determine the length of chain. (Ignore the curved sections.)

## Math Tip

### Body Measures

You can use yourself to get a sense of some common measures. For example, your fingernails are about 1 cm, or 10 mm, wide.

Measure your handspan (tip of little finger to tip of thumb, with fingers spread), or your outstretched arm length, to get a sense of other measures.

9. a) It is difficult for Chantal to measure the slant height of the roof of her house. Apply the Pythagorean theorem to calculate this length.
   b) Determine the length of trim Chantal needs to go around the top triangular front region. She needs trim for the two sloping sides and the base of the triangle.
   c) The trim that Chantal likes costs \$2.95/m, plus 8% PST and 7% GST. How much will it cost Chantal for her material? (Hint: If you add PST and GST, you will find that the total tax is 15%.)

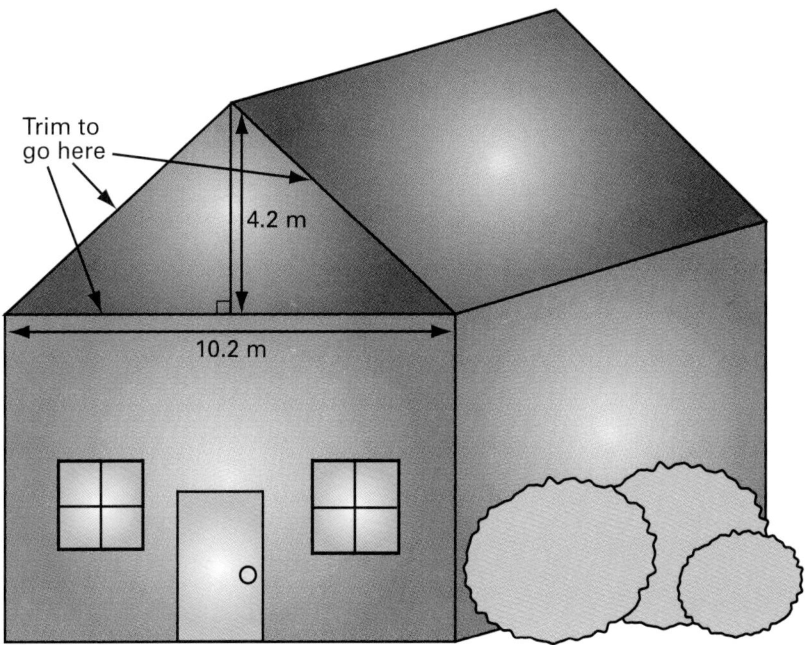


**C** 10. **Application** A park is bordered by a river and two fences. A trail that runs right along the river is 2.4 km long. Determine the perimeter of the park.

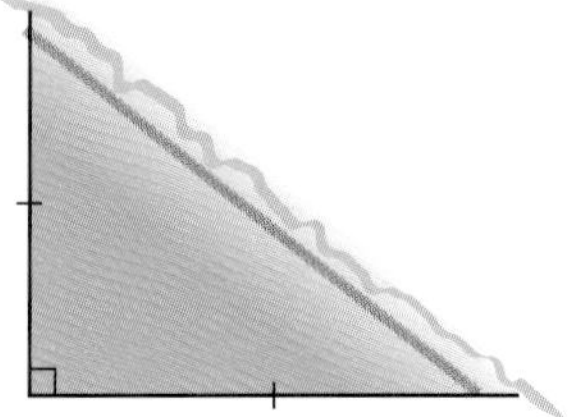

# 2.3 Using *The Geometer's Sketchpad*® to Confirm the Pythagorean Theorem

*The Geometer's Sketchpad*® is a computer program for exploring geometry and measurement. In this section, you will:

- learn how to use several basic tools and commands
- construct simple geometric shapes
- perform various measurements
- apply a special Custom Tool
- confirm the Pythagorean theorem

Open *The Geometer's Sketchpad*®. Here is a summary of the basic tools and their commands:

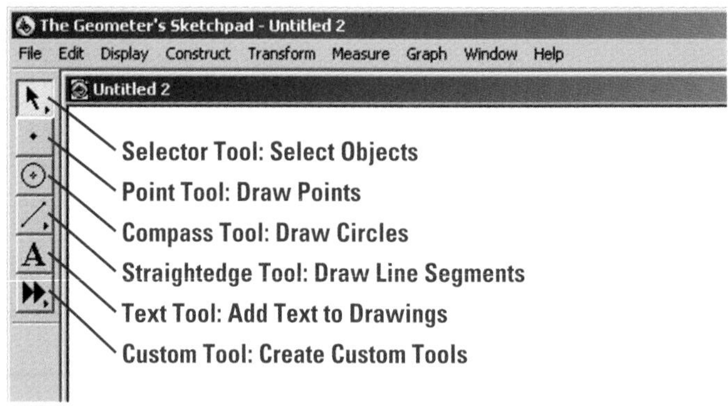


## Discover

### Part A: Setting Up

1. Go to the **Edit** pull-down menu and choose **Preferences**. You should see this dialog box:

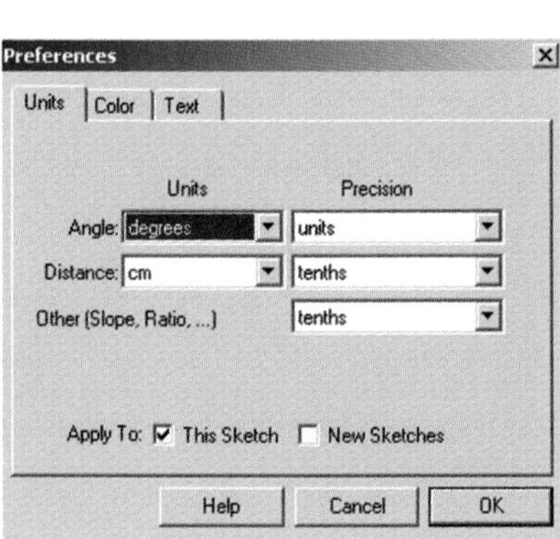


   Set the following preferences.

   a) Choose the **Units** tab and set the **Angle Unit** to be "**degrees,**" using the pull-down menu.
   b) Choose the **Angle Precision** to be "**units.**"
   c) Choose the **Distance Unit** to be "**cm.**"
   d) Choose the **Distance Precision** to be "**tenths.**"
   e) Choose the **Slope and Calculation Precision** to be "**tenths.**"
   f) Choose the Text tab and check **For All New Points** and **As Objects Are Measured**.
   g) Click on **OK**.

If this custom tool is not visible, your teacher can help you with **Loading Custom Tools** (see Technology Appendix).

2. You will need to add to the **Custom Tools** a special tool called **4/Square (By Edge).** Click on the **Custom Tool** button and choose **Tool Options...**. Choose **Copy Tool**, then **Polygons**, and then **4/Square (By Edge)**. Click on **OK**.

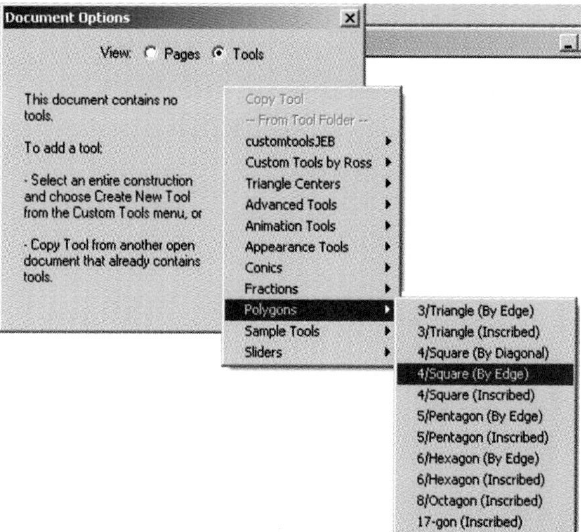

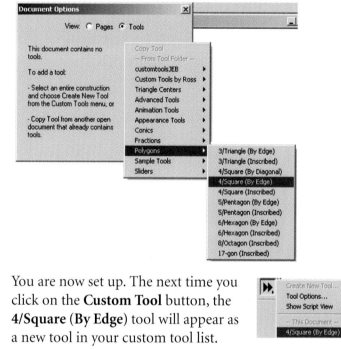

You are now set up. The next time you click on the **Custom Tool** button, the **4/Square (By Edge)** tool will appear as a new tool in your custom tool list.

## Part B: Constructing a Triangle

3. Follow these steps to construct a triangle.
   a) Click on the **Point Tool** and click in three random places in the workspace. Three points should appear, labelled A, B, and C.

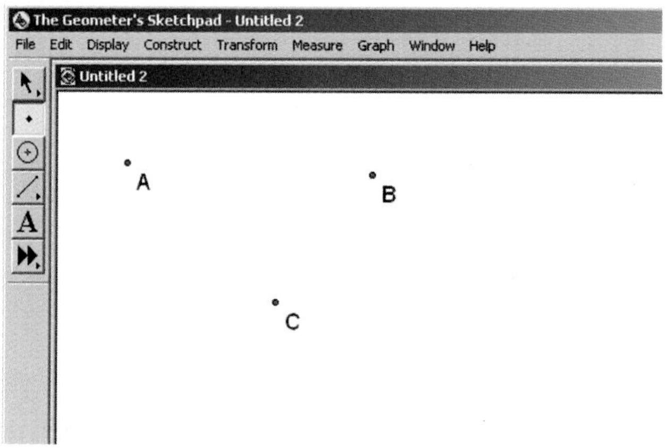

b) Click on the **Selector Tool.** Click and drag a dashed box that surrounds the three points. When you release the mouse, the box will disappear and the three points will change in appearance. These points are now "selected."

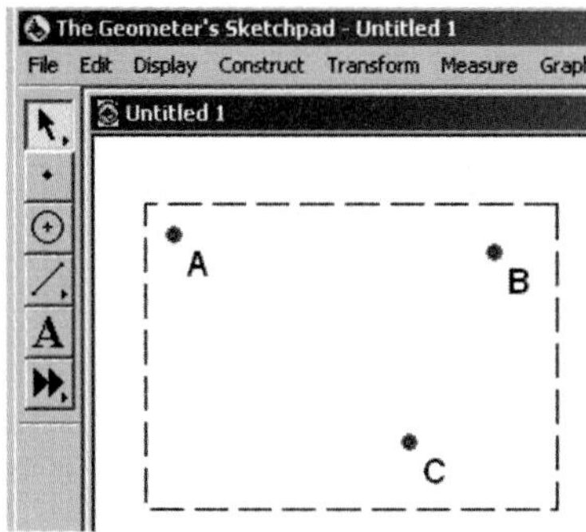


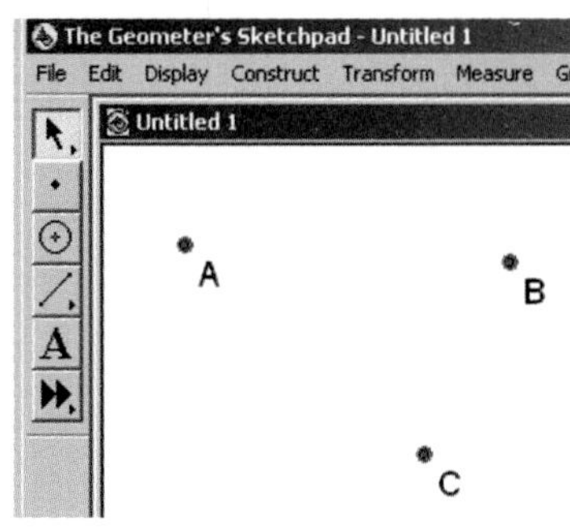


c) From the **Construct** pull-down menu, choose **Segments.** The three selected points should now form a triangle.

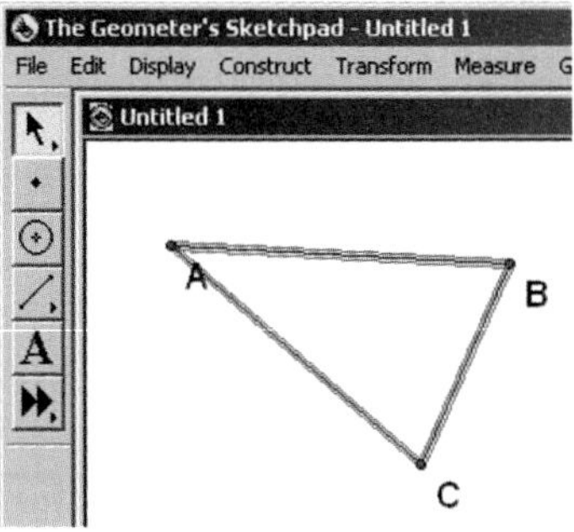


4. The outlines appearing on the line segments show that they are now selected. "Deselect" the segments by clicking on any blank area of the workspace. The outlines will disappear, leaving just the line segments. You can click and drag any of the three points to change the shape of the triangle. This will be important later.

## Part C: Measuring Sides and Angles

5. To measure the length of AB, follow these steps.
   a) Select (click on) the line segment AB.
   b) From the **Measure** pull-down menu, choose **Length.** The length of AB, in centimetres, should appear in the top left corner of the screen.

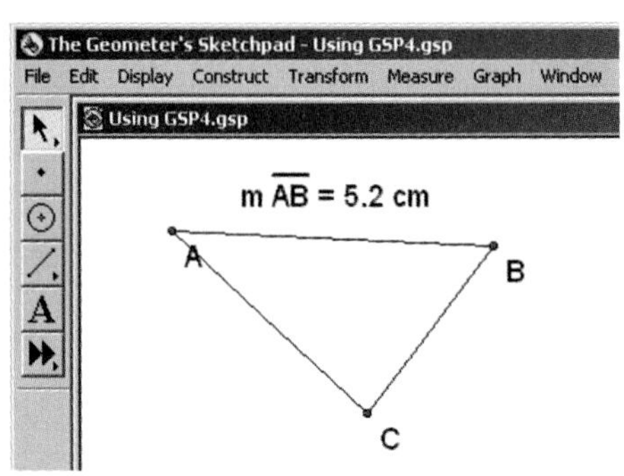


   c) Click and drag this measure to place it where you like.
   d) Deselect this measure, as in step 4.

6. To measure an angle, you must select, in order, the three points that identify the angle. Measure ∠B as follows.
   a) Select points A, B, and C, in that order.
   b) From the **Measure** pull-down menu, choose **Angle**. The measure of ∠ABC, in degrees, will be displayed.
   c) Click and drag this measure to place it anywhere you like.
   d) Deselect the angle measure.

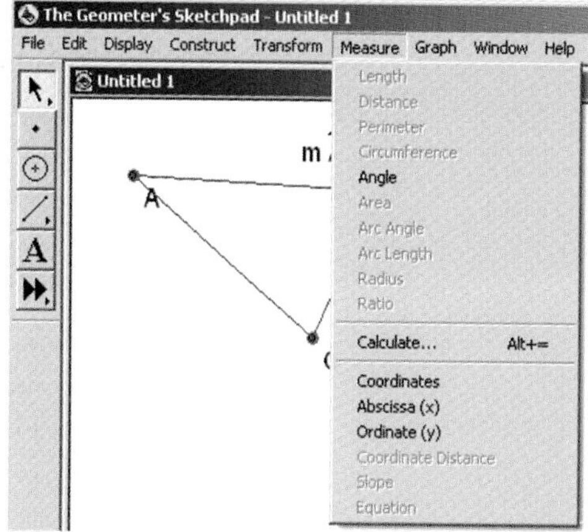


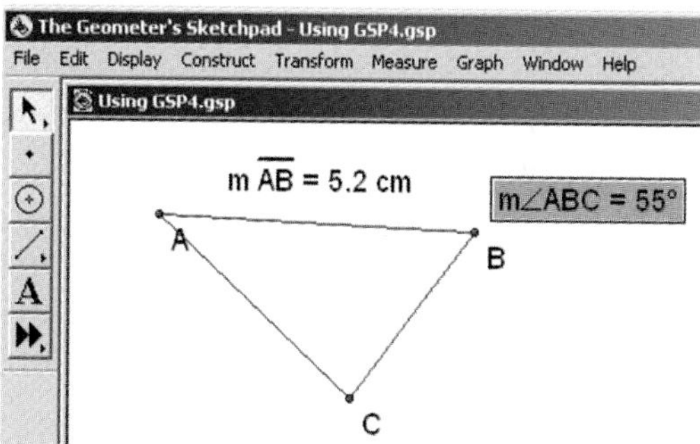


7. Repeat step 6 to measure the other two angles in the triangle.

## Part D: Applying the Custom Tool

In this part of the investigation, you will construct a square on each side of the triangle. The square's area will be equal to the square of the corresponding side length.

8. Click on the **Custom Tool** and choose **4/Square (By Edge)**. Click on points A and B, in order. A square will appear, as shown. If your square overlaps the triangle, go to the **Edit** pull-down menu and choose **Undo**. Then, repeat step 8, selecting the points in *opposite* order.

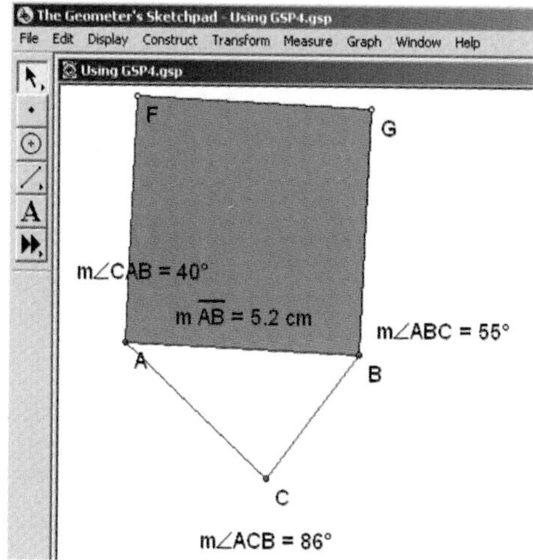


**Did You Know?**

The **Undo** feature can often be used for correcting errors. There is also a **Redo** command for "redoing" a step that has been accidentally "undone".

9. Now, measure the area of the square.
   a) Click on the **Selector Tool** and make sure that nothing is selected.
   b) Select the square by clicking somewhere in the middle of it. The "mesh" shading indicates that the square has been selected.
   c) From the **Measure** pull-down menu, choose **Area**. The area measure will be displayed.

10. Deselect the square. Repeat steps 8 and 9 to create two more squares on the other sides of the triangle and measure their areas.
    Your sketch will now look something like this:

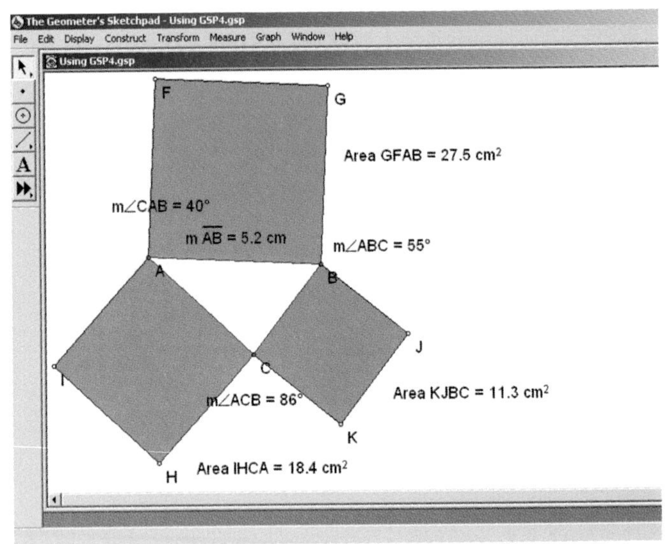


## Part E: Confirming the Pythagorean Theorem

11. a) For what types of triangles does the Pythagorean theorem apply?
    b) Write down the Pythagorean theorem.

12. Follow these steps to show a dynamic sum of the areas of the two smaller squares. (The term dynamic means that the measurement changes automatically, whenever you change the sketch.)
    a) Make sure that no objects are selected. From the **Measure** pull-down menu, choose **Calculate**. A calculator window will appear.
       You can click and drag the calculator around the workspace if you wish.
    b) Click on the area measure of one of the smaller squares.

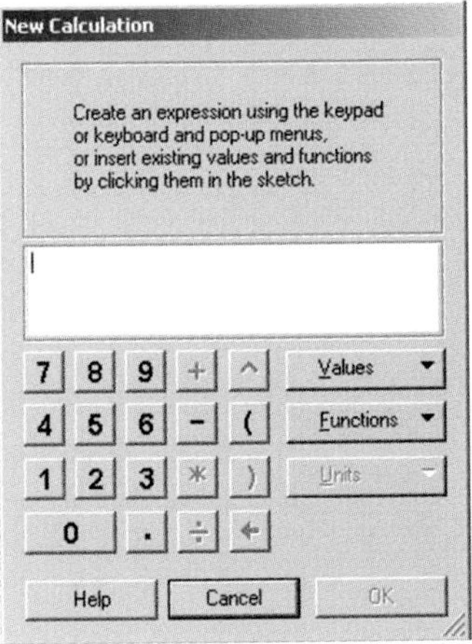

c) Click on the "+" sign on the calculator.

d) Click on the area measure of the other smaller square. The calculator screen will look like this:

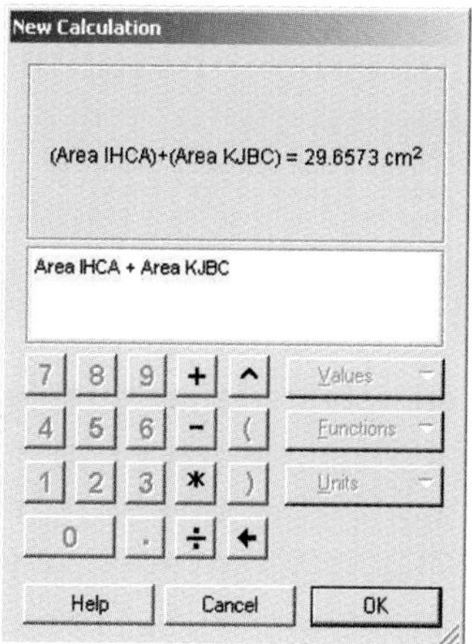


e) Click OK. The dynamic sum of the areas of the two smaller squares will appear in the workspace.

**13. a)** Compare the sum from step 12 to the area measure of the larger square. Are they equal?

**b)** Predict how you can make these measures equal.

**14.** Click and drag point C around to change the shape of the triangle. As you do this, carefully observe

a) the area of the large (AB) square

b) the sum of the areas of the two smaller squares

c) the measure of $\angle C$

**15.** When are the values in 14a) and b) equal?

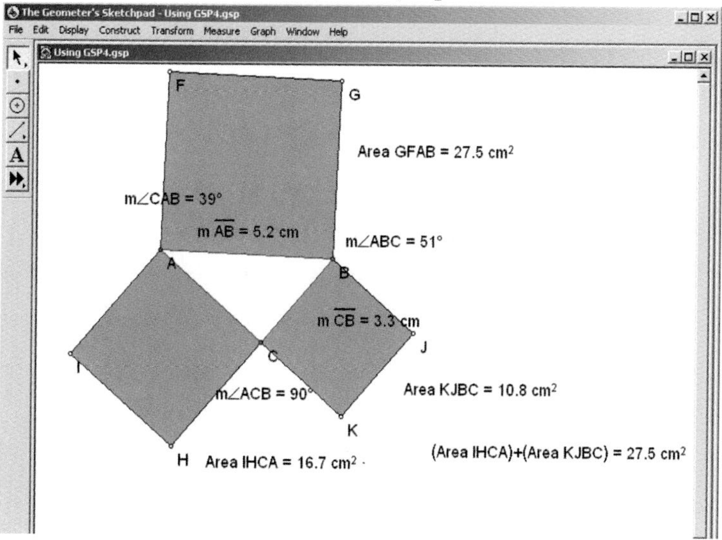


**16.** In a few sentences, explain how your work supports the Pythagorean theorem. Use diagrams, equations, and/or measures to support your explanation.

# 2.4 Perimeter and Area of Composite Figures

You can apply the formulas at the very back of the book to calculate the area and perimeter of simple shapes. Even with everyday tasks like house painting, more complex shapes are usually involved. In this section, you will extend your skills to combinations of the shapes you have already studied.

## DISCOVER

**Chapter Problem**

### Finding the Area of a Composite Figure

Chantal wants to paint the front of her house, including the top triangular region, but not including the door and windows. Paint costs $29.95 per can, plus 8% PST and 7% GST. Each can will cover about 40 m$^2$. Chantal plans to apply two coats of paint. How much will this paint job cost?

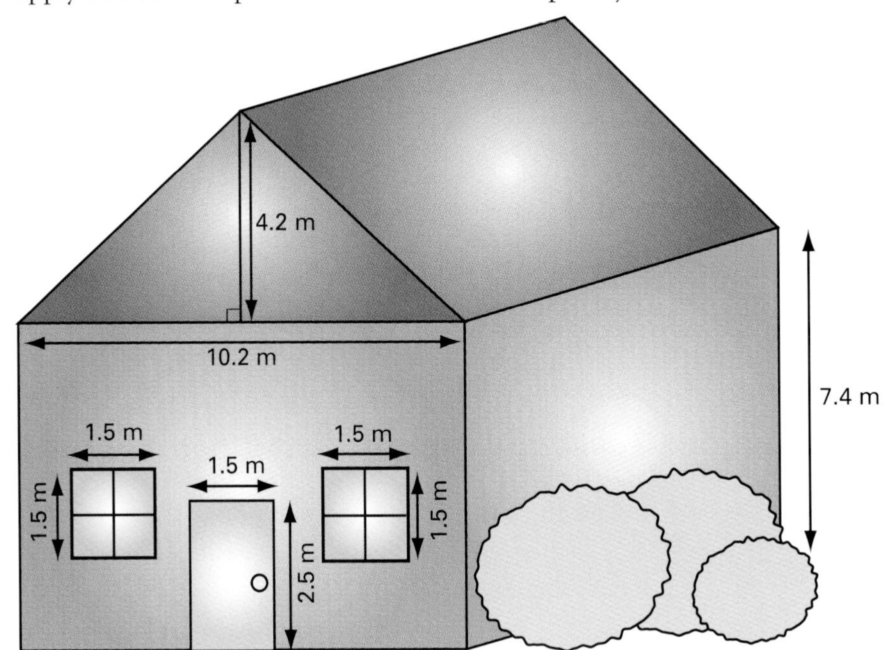

1. Before making any calculations, estimate the cost of the paint.

2. Ignore the door and windows for now.
   a) What two simple shapes combine to make up the front of Chantal's house?
   b) Describe how you can calculate the total area of these two shapes.
   c) Calculate this total area.

3. Now look at the door and windows.
   a) Calculate the area of the door.
   b) Calculate the area of one window.

4. The actual area to be painted will not include the door and the two windows.
   a) Describe how you can calculate the area to be painted.
   b) Calculate the area to be painted.

5. Each can of paint covers about 40 $m^2$. Chantal wants to apply two coats of paint.
   a) Describe how you can calculate the number of cans of paint Chantal needs.
   b) Find the number of cans needed.
   c) Discuss whether you should round *up* or *down* to the nearest can. Would you always round up? Why or why not?

6. Each can of paint costs $29.95 plus 8% PST and 7% GST.
   a) Determine the total cost of the paint. (Hint: 8% + 7% = 15%.)
   b) Compare this answer to your original estimate. How close were you?

A **composite figure** is formed by combining simple shapes. You can calculate the total area of a composite figure by adding or subtracting areas.

**EXAMPLE 1**

## Total Area of a Composite Figure

**a)** Identify the shapes that make up this window.

**b)** Describe how you can find the total area of the window.

**c)** Calculate this total area.

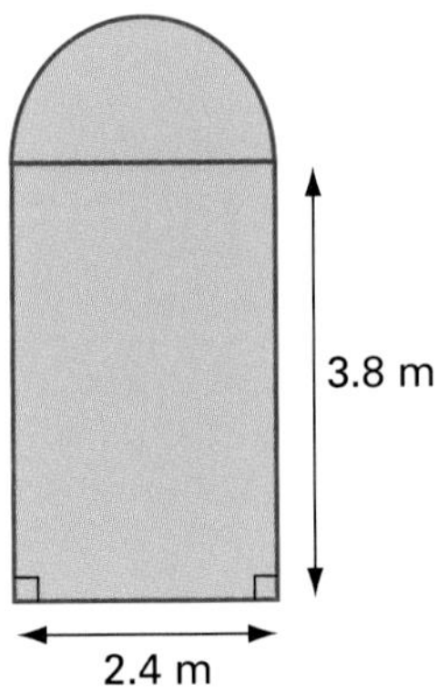


## Solution

**a)** The window is made up of a rectangle and a semicircle.

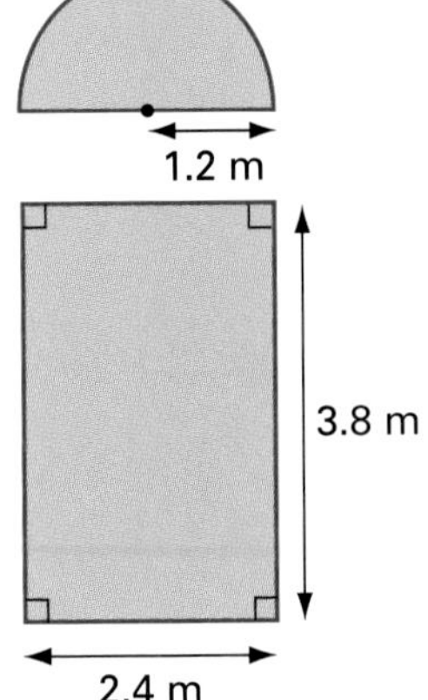


**b)** To find the total area of the window, add the area of the rectangle and the area of the semicircle. The area of the semicircle is half the area of the whole circle.

total area = area of rectangle + $\frac{1}{2}$ of area of circle

**c)** Call the area of the rectangle $A_{rectangle}$.

$$\begin{aligned} A_{rectangle} &= lw \\ &= 2.4 \times 3.8 \\ &= 9.12 \end{aligned}$$

Call the area of the circle $A_{circle}$.

$$\begin{aligned} A_{circle} &= \pi r^2 \\ &= \pi(1.2)^2 \\ &\doteq 4.524 \end{aligned}$$

*r = d ÷ 2*

C π × 1.2 × 1.2 =

Call the total area $A_{total}$.

$$\begin{aligned} A_{total} &= A_{rectangle} + \frac{1}{2} \text{ of } A_{circle} \\ &= 9.12 + \frac{1}{2} \times 4.524 \\ &= 9.12 + \frac{4.524}{2} \\ &\doteq 11 \end{aligned}$$

The total area of the window is 11 $m^2$, to two digits of accuracy.

Sometimes you can find the area of a composite figure by subtracting areas.

## Example 2

### Area of a Composite Figure, by Subtraction

A hang glider sail has the shape and dimensions shown.

**a)** Describe how you can determine the area of the sail.

**b)** Calculate this area.

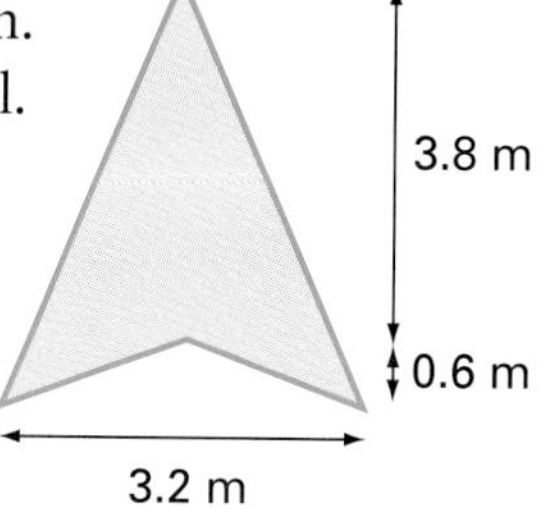


### Solution

**a)** Join the two bottom points as shown.
The sail area is the area of the large triangle, minus the area of the small triangle.

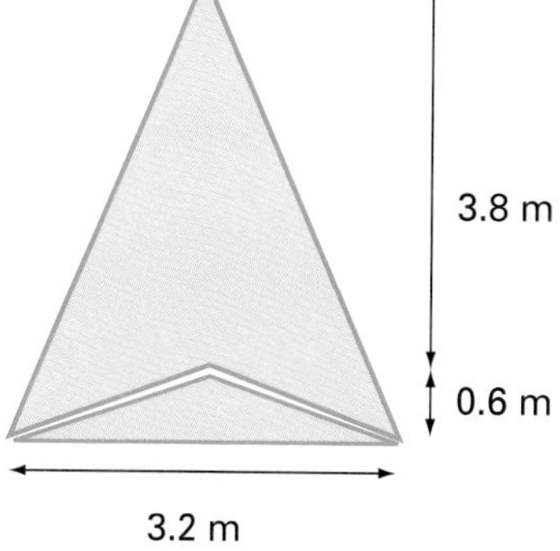


**b)**
$$\begin{aligned} A_{\text{large triangle}} &= \frac{1}{2}bh \\ &= \frac{1}{2} \times 3.2 \times 3.8 \\ &= 6.08 \end{aligned}$$

**Estimate:** $\frac{3 \times 4}{2} = 6$

$$\begin{aligned} A_{\text{small triangle}} &= \frac{1}{2}bh \\ &= \frac{1}{2} \times 3.2 \times 0.6 \\ &= 0.96 \end{aligned}$$

**Estimate:** $\frac{3 \times 0.6}{2} = 1$

$$\begin{aligned} A_{\text{sail}} &= A_{\text{large triangle}} - A_{\text{small triangle}} \\ &= 6.08 - 0.96 \\ &\doteq 5.1 \end{aligned}$$

**Estimate:** $6 - 1 = 5$

The area of the sail is 5.1 $m^2$, to two digits of accuracy.

## EXAMPLE 3

### Perimeter of a Composite Figure

This window needs trim around the outside.

**a)** Describe how to find the perimeter of the window.

**b)** Calculate the perimeter.

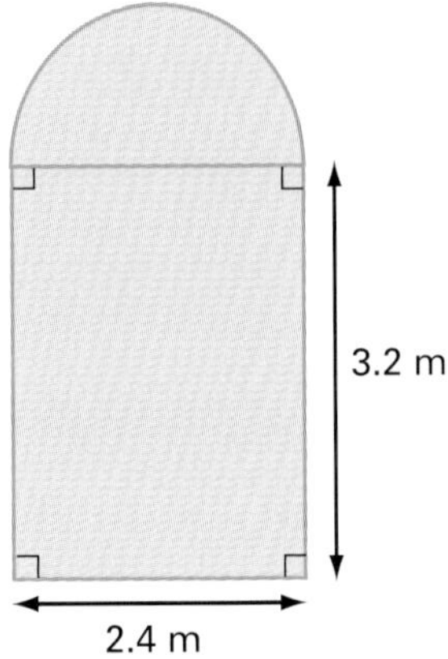


### Solution

**a)** The perimeter is the total distance *around the outside* of an object. The outside edge includes three sides of the rectangle and the curved part of the semicircle. The fourth side goes *through* the object, and should not be included.

**b)** perimeter $= \frac{1}{2}$ of circumference of circle + three sides of rectangle

For the semicircle:

$$
\begin{aligned}
L_{\text{semicircle}} &= \frac{1}{2} \text{ of } \pi d \\
&= \frac{1}{2} \times \pi \times 2.4 \\
&= \pi \times 1.2 \\
&\doteq 3.8
\end{aligned}
$$

$$
\begin{aligned}
P_{\text{window}} &= L_{\text{semicircle}} + \text{three sides of rectangle} \\
&= 3.8 + (3.2 + 2.4 + 3.2) \\
&= 12.6
\end{aligned}
$$

**To include the correct measures, pick a starting point and trace around the outside of the shape.**

The length of trim needed is 12.6 m, to the nearest tenth.

- A composite figure is made up of more than one simple shape.
- To determine the total area of a composite figure, add and/or subtract areas.
- To determine the perimeter of a composite figure, add the distances around the outside of the figure.

## Discuss the Concepts

1. In the solution to Example 2, a smaller triangle was subtracted from a larger triangle. Describe another way to solve this problem.
2. Look at this floor plan of a room.

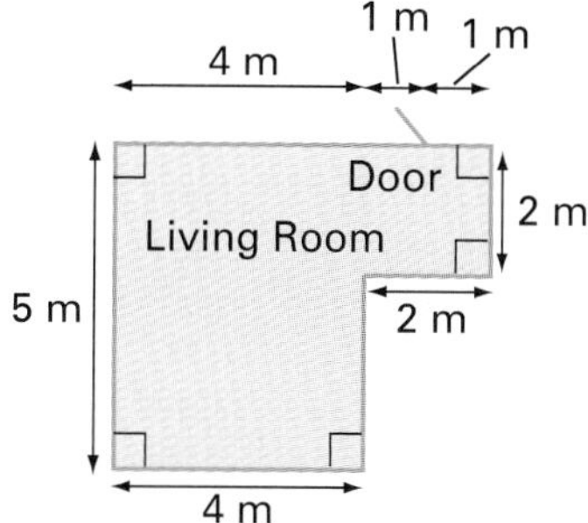


   a) One dimension has been left out. Describe how you can find it.
   b) Describe how you can determine the area by adding areas of simpler shapes.
   c) Describe how you can determine the area by subtracting areas.
   d) Suppose you need to replace the baseboards around the edge of the room. Explain why you cannot simply add perimeters of rectangles.
   e) What measure must you subtract from the perimeter to get the correct length of baseboard? Why?

## PRACTISE

**A** *Include proper units with your answers. Round your answers appropriately.*

*For help with question 1, refer to Example 3.*

1. For each composite figure shown,
   - solve for the missing lengths
   - determine the perimeter

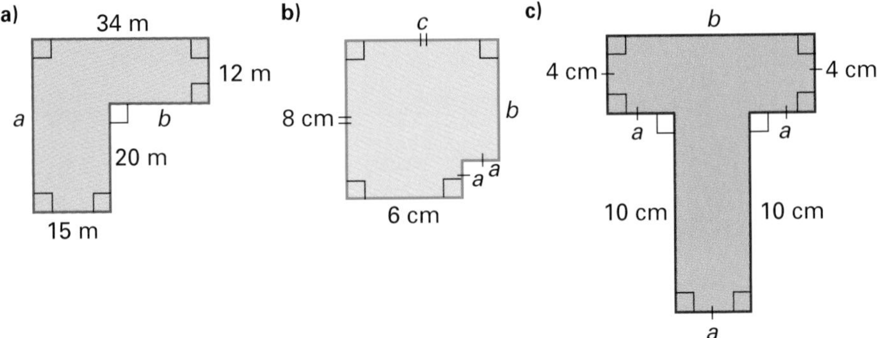

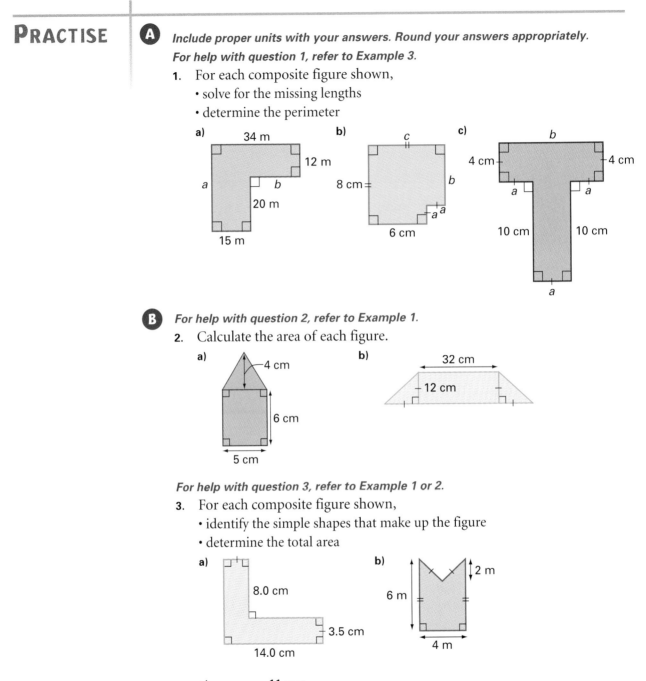

**B** *For help with question 2, refer to Example 1.*

2. Calculate the area of each figure.

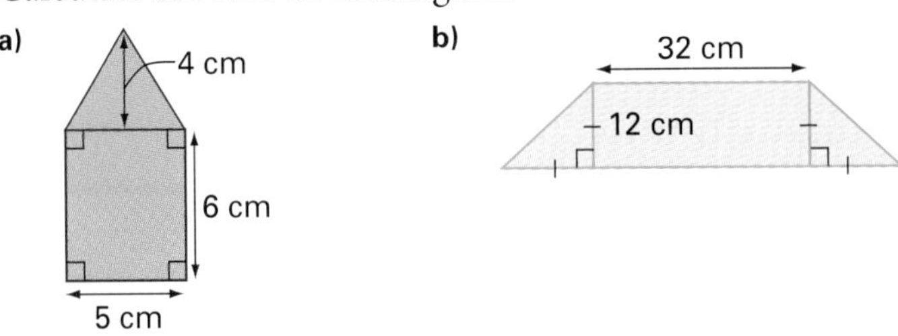


*For help with question 3, refer to Example 1 or 2.*

3. For each composite figure shown,
   - identify the simple shapes that make up the figure
   - determine the total area

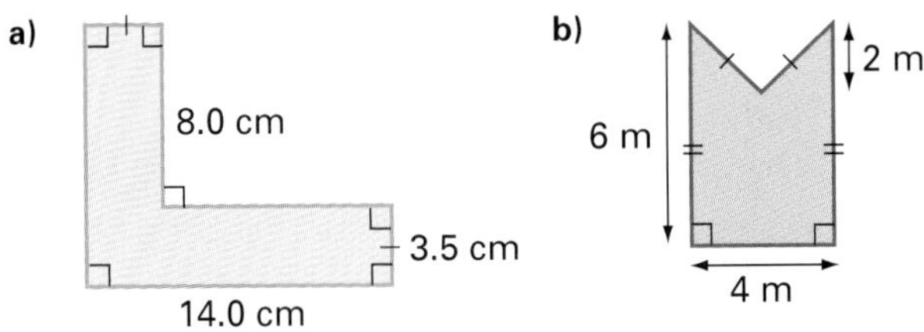


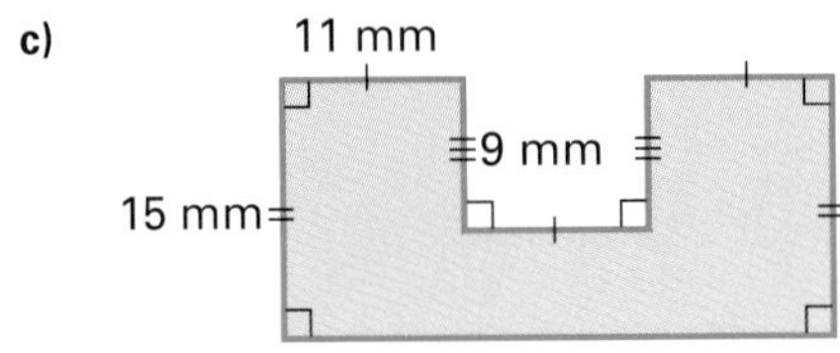

*For help with question 4, refer to Example 3.*

4. Calculate the perimeter of each figure.

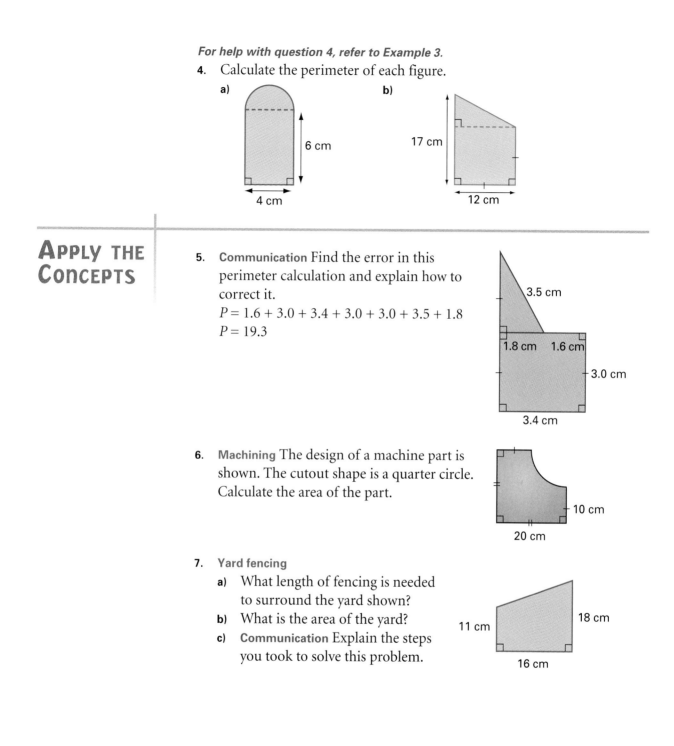

   a)

   6 cm

   4 cm

   b)

   17 cm

   12 cm

## Apply the Concepts

5. **Communication** Find the error in this perimeter calculation and explain how to correct it.

   $P = 1.6 + 3.0 + 3.4 + 3.0 + 3.0 + 3.5 + 1.8$

   $P = 19.3$

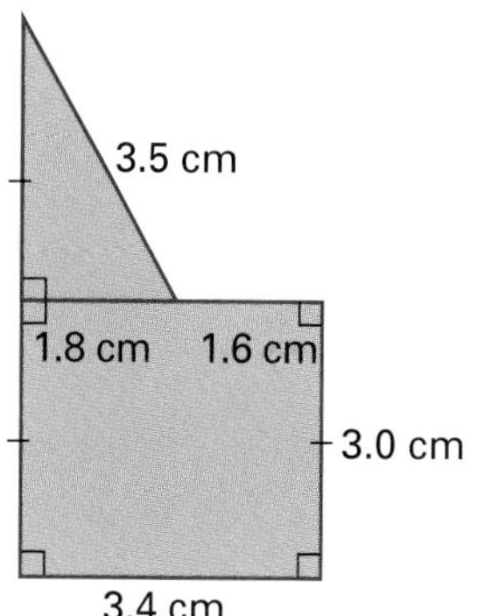


6. **Machining** The design of a machine part is shown. The cutout shape is a quarter circle. Calculate the area of the part.

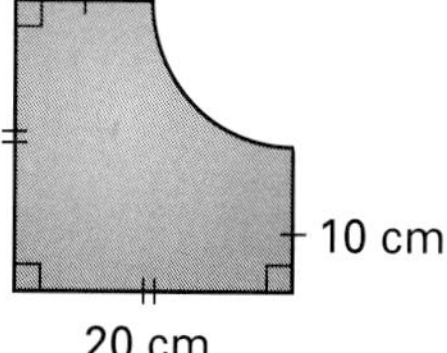


7. **Yard fencing**

   a) What length of fencing is needed to surround the yard shown?

   b) What is the area of the yard?

   c) **Communication** Explain the steps you took to solve this problem.

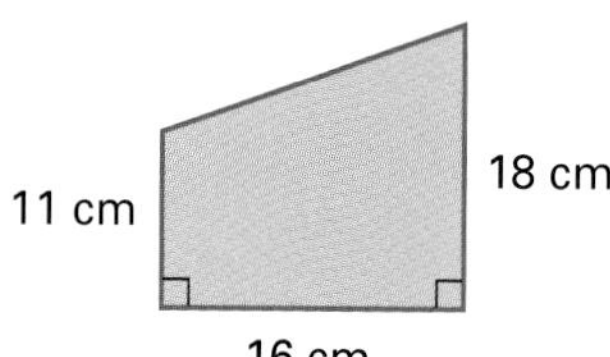

## Did You Know?

In track races of 200 m, 400 m, and 800 m, the competitors start in a staggered formation. In the 800 m event, the runners start in lanes, but are allowed to move to the inside of the track after the first bend. Why do you think track contests have these rules?

8. **Application** The diagram shows a running track at a high school. It consists of two parallel line segments, with a semicircle at each end. The track is 10 m wide.

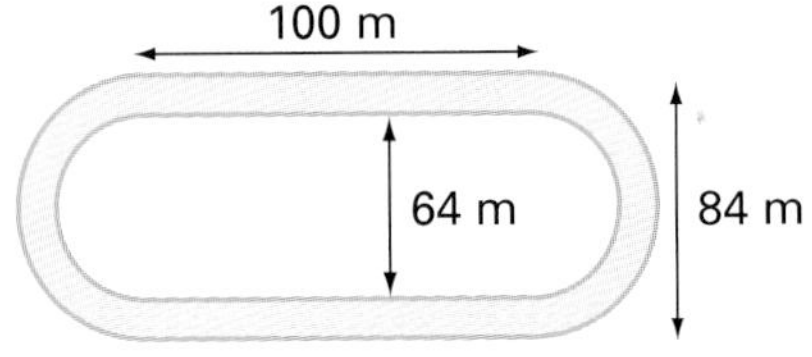


   a) Rhiann runs on the inside edge of the track. How far does she run in one lap?
   b) Dina runs on the outer edge. How far does she run in one lap?
   c) Find the difference between the distances run by Rhiann and Dina.

9. **Thinking/Inquiry/Problem Solving** Enrico is planning a garage sale. To direct customers to his house, he is painting six arrow signs.

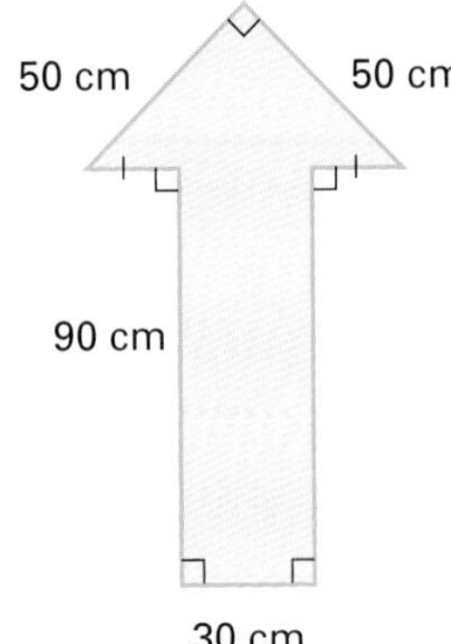


   a) Calculate the area of one sign.
   b) Each can of paint can cover 1 $m^2$. How many cans of paint should Enrico buy for all six signs? Explain your answer.
   c) Paint costs $9.95 per can plus 8% PST and 7% GST. How much will it cost for Enrico to buy paint for the six signs?

10. **Application**
   a) Design a logo of your first or last initial, made of two or more simple geometric shapes. Use shaded regions to give a "3-D" effect.
   b) Make the appropriate measurements and calculate the total area of the shaded regions of your logo.

11. ***The Geometer's Sketchpad®***
   a) Draw your design for question 10, using *The Geometer's Sketchpad®*.
   b) Use the measurement features of *The Geometer's Sketchpad®* to measure the area of the shaded regions of your logo.

***For question 12, use either pencil, paper, and calculator, or The Geometer's Sketchpad®.***

**12.** The diagram shows a property in the shape of a trapezoid. The house, driveway, and patio are each rectangular. The rest of the property is lawn that needs grass seed.

**a)** What is the area of the lawn?

**b)** Alex reads that 0.02 kg of fertilizer covers 1 $m^2$ of lawn. How much fertilizer does he need to buy?

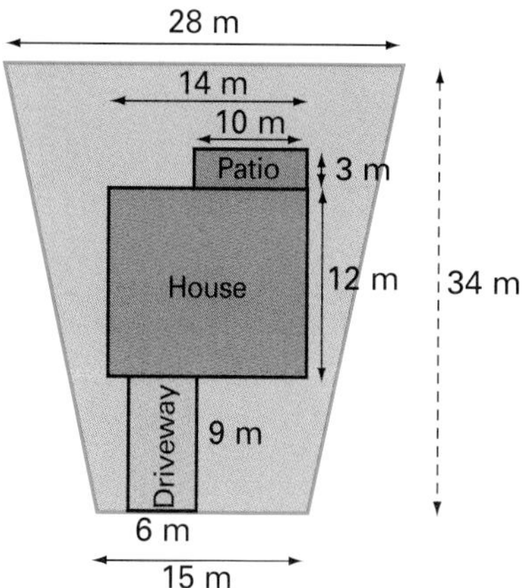


**13.** This Chinese symbol is called Yin-Yang. It is sometimes used to represent four yearly celestial events: summer solstice, autumnal (fall) equinox, winter solstice, and vernal (spring) equinox.

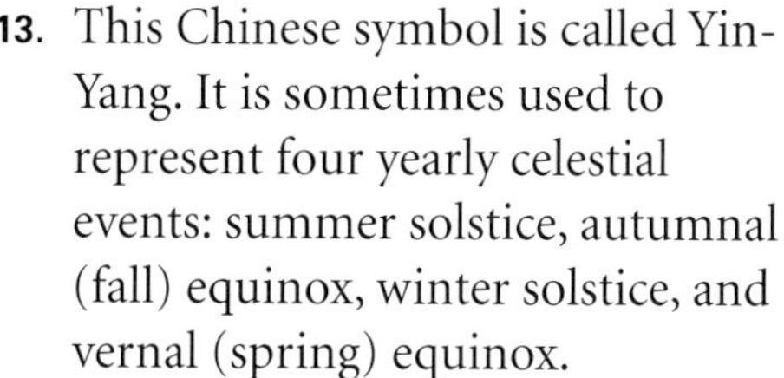

In the Yin-Yang symbol, the white area stands for more sunlight, and is called Yang (Sun). The black area has less sunlight (more moonlight) and is called Yin (Moon). Yin is born (begins) at summer solstice and Yang is born (begins) at winter solstice. Therefore, one little Yin circle is marked on the summer solstice position. A little Yang circle is marked on the winter solstice position. To find out more about Yin and Yang, go to *www.mcgrawhill.ca/links/MATC9* and follow the links.

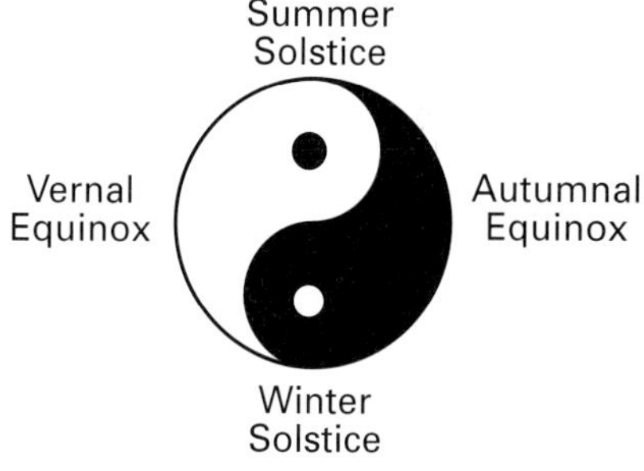

**a)** Measure the radius of each circular part of the Yin-Yang symbol shown above.

**b)** Calculate the area of the large circle.

**c)** Calculate the area of the small white circle.

**d)** Calculate the area of each semicircle that makes up part of the shaded swirl-like figure.

**e)** How would you combine these calculations to find the area of the black (Yin) region on the right?

**f)** What is the area of the Yin region on the right?

# 2.5 Maximizing the Area of a Rectangle

Think about planning a garden layout, designing a parking lot, fencing off a cornfield, or enclosing a swimming area in a lake. All of these situations involve maximizing the area of a rectangle.

Imagine you are helping to organize an outdoor concert. You need to use a number of movable barriers to design an enclosed region for the crowd. For the comfort and safety of the fans, the enclosure must provide as much area as possible. Which barrier set up is best? Some possible designs are shown.

wide and shallow

square-like

narrow and deep

## DISCOVER 1A

- toothpicks

### Maximizing Area of a Rectangle (Fencing Four Sides)

***Using Manipulatives***

You will use toothpicks to design a rectangular enclosure of maximum area. Each toothpick represents a 3 m-long barrier. All barriers must be connected. One barrier can swing open to form an entrance.

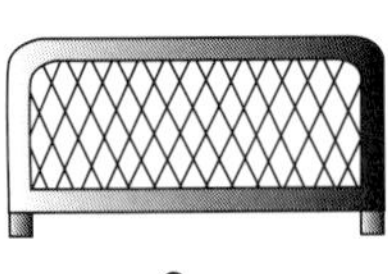


1. To begin with, design a rectangular enclosure consisting of 20 barriers. Count out 20 toothpicks. What will be the perimeter of your enclosure?

2. There are many different choices for the rectangle. Will they all have the same area? What type of shape do you think will provide the greatest area?

3. a) Use all the toothpicks to form a large rectangle.
   b) Multiply the number of toothpicks along the length by 3 and record the length.
   c) Repeat b) to determine the width.
   d) Calculate the area of the rectangle. Record your results in a table.

| Rectangle (sketch) | Length (m) | Width (m) | Perimeter (m) | Area ($m^2$) $A = l \times w$ |
|---|---|---|---|---|
| 9 × 1 | 27 | 3 | 60 | 81 |
| 8 × 2 | 24 | 6 | 60 | 144 |
| | | | | |

4. a) Form a new rectangle using all 20 toothpicks. Record its measures in your table.
   b) Repeat until you have results for six rectangles.

5. a) Examine the area of each rectangle. Are the areas all the same?
   b) What are the dimensions of the rectangle with the greatest area?
   c) Compare this result to your prediction from step 2. Should you change your prediction?

**Did You Know?**

The largest air-supported domed stadium in the world is B.C. Place stadium in Vancouver. Its perimeter is 760 m, and it can hold 60 000 fans.

6. Suppose that you are to design a similar enclosure for a much larger concert venue. For this venue, you have 40 barriers to work with.
   a) Predict the dimensions of the rectangle with the maximum area.
   b) Count out additional toothpicks and test your hypothesis. Do you need to change your hypothesis?

7. a) How could you predict the dimensions of a maximum-area rectangle, if you are given the perimeter?
   b) Predict the dimensions of a maximum-area rectangle made of 100 barriers.
   c) Repeat part b) when you have 30 barriers to work with. Describe any problems in applying your method in this case.

## DISCOVER 1B

## Maximizing Area of a Rectangle (Fencing Four Sides)

***Using The Geometer's Sketchpad®***

You will use *The Geometer's Sketchpad®* to design a rectangular enclosure of maximum area, using 20 barriers of length 3 m. All barriers must be connected. One barrier can swing open to form an entrance.

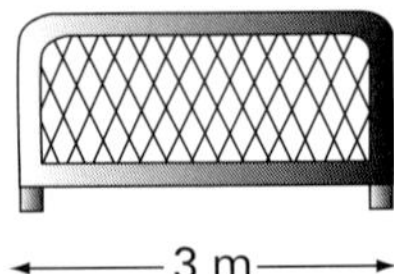


1. From the **Edit** menu, choose **Preferences**.
   a) Set **Distance Units** to "**cm.**"
   b) Set **Distance Units Precision** to "**tenths.**"
   c) Set **Slope and Calculation Precision** to "**tenths.**"
   d) Click on the Text tab. Ensure that **For All New Points** and **As Objects Are Measured** are checked.
   e) Click on "**OK.**"

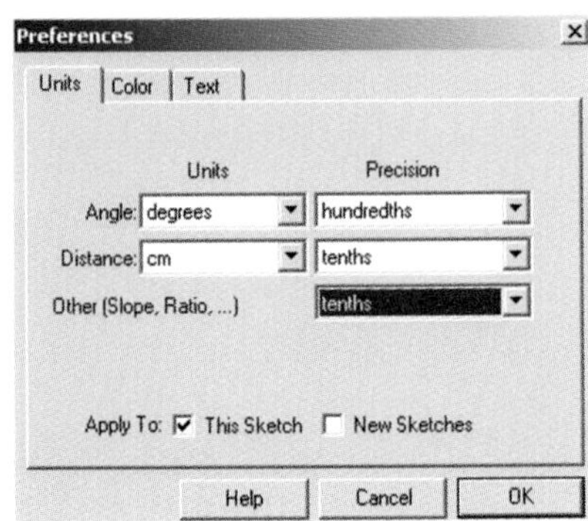


2. From the **Graph** menu, choose **Show Grid**. A grid will appear with two axes. Then, pull down the **Graph Menu** again and choose **Snap Points**.

3. Use the grid feature of the program to try various rectangular designs. Follow these steps to establish a grid that you can use easily.
   a) You do not need the axes for this investigation. Click on the vertical axis and then go to the **Display** menu and choose **Hide Axis**. Repeat for the horizontal axis.
   b) You can change the scale of the grid by dragging point **B**. Set the grid so that the dots are all 1 cm apart, as follows:
      - Select points **A** and **B**.
      - From the **Measure** menu, choose **Distance**.
      - Click and drag point **B** so that the distance between **A** and **B** is exactly 1 cm.

4. For this part of the investigation, you will design a rectangular enclosure consisting of 20 barriers, each 3 m long. What will the perimeter of your enclosure be?

5. There are many different choices for your rectangle. Will they all have the same area? What type do you think will provide the greatest area?

6. Let 1 cm on your grid represent one barrier length (3 m). Begin with a 9 cm by 1 cm rectangle, and then consider other possible rectangles. Use the **Straightedge Tool** to construct a 9 cm by 1 cm rectangle, by joining four line segments, as shown.

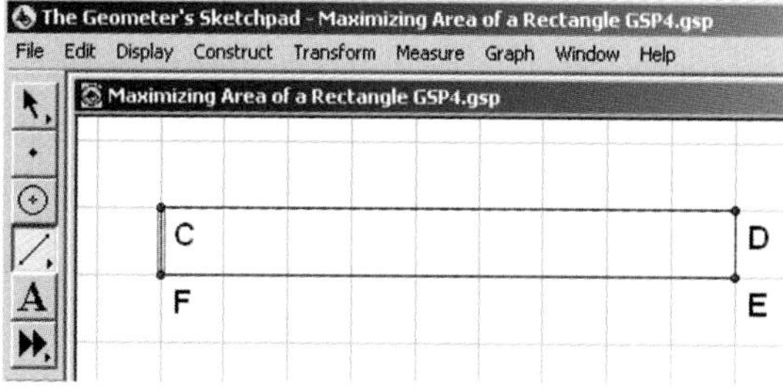


7. Measure the perimeter and area of your rectangle, as follows.
   a) Deselect the last segment you created.
   b) Select the four points that form the rectangle, in either clockwise or counterclockwise order (do not jump across the diagonal).
   c) From the **Construct** menu, choose **Quadrilateral Interior.**
   d) From the **Measure** menu, choose **Perimeter**. Then, deselect this measure.
   e) From the **Measure** menu, choose **Area.** Deselect this measure.

8. Record the measurements in a table. Remember that 1 cm on the screen actually represents a 3 m length. Therefore, 1 $cm^2$ on the screen represents an area of 9 $m^2$.

| Length (m) | Width (m) | Perimeter (m) | Area ($m^2$) |
|---|---|---|---|
| 27 | 3 | 60 | 81 |
| 24 | 6 | | |
| | | | |

9. Change the dimensions by dragging the vertices of the rectangle. Form an 8 cm by 2 cm rectangle and record the perimeter and area, converted into metres as in step 8.

10. Repeat step 8 for as many different rectangles as possible. Remember they all have to have a perimeter of 60 m (20 cm on the screen).

11. a) Examine the area of each rectangle. Are they the same?
    b) What are the dimensions of the rectangle with the greatest area?
    c) Compare this result to your prediction in step 5. Should you change your prediction?

12. Suppose that you are to design a similar enclosure for a larger concert venue. For this venue, you have 40 barriers to work with.
    a) Predict the dimensions of the rectangle with the maximum area.
    b) Use *The Geometer's Sketchpad®* to test your hypothesis. Do you need to change your hypothesis?

13. a) How could you predict the dimensions of a maximum-area rectangle, if you are given the perimeter?
    b) Predict the dimensions of a maximum-area rectangle made of 100 barriers.
    c) Repeat part b) when you have 30 barriers to work with. Describe, and investigate, any problems in applying your method in this case.

## DISCOVER 2

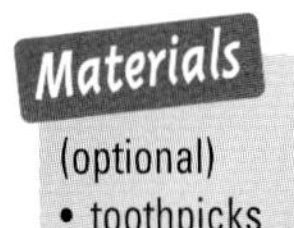


(optional)
- toothpicks

## Maximizing Area of a Rectangle (Fencing Three Sides)

***Using The Geometer's Sketchpad® or Manipulatives***

To improve security for the band, the park has installed a long, permanent fence separating the stage from the crowd. With this new set up, you need only use the barriers to fence in three sides of the rectangle.

1. Suppose you have 20 barriers to work with.
    a) Will you be able to enclose more, less, or the same amount of area now that the permanent fence has been added?
    b) Do you think that a square will have the maximum area?
    c) What dimensions do you predict will have the maximum area?

2. Carry out an investigation to determine the dimensions of the rectangle that has the maximum area. Record your results in a table.

| Rectangle (sketch) | Length (m) | Width (m) | Barrier Length (m) | Area ($m^2$) |
|---|---|---|---|---|
| 18 × 1 | 54 | 3 | 60 | 162 |
| ... | | | 60 | |

3. Notice that the heading for the fourth column is "Barrier Length," not "Perimeter."
    a) Is the perimeter of each rectangle 60 m? Why or why not?
    b) Is the perimeter of each rectangle the same? Why or why not?

4. a) What are the dimensions of the rectangle that provides the maximum area?
   b) Compare this result with your prediction in step 1c). Should you change your prediction?
   c) Compare the maximum area found in this Discover to the maximum area in Discover 1A or Discover 1B. Has the permanent fence allowed you to enclose more, less, or the same amount of area as before?

5. Examine the length and width of the maximum-area rectangle that you found. Explain any relationship that you notice.

6. Suppose you now have 40 barriers to work with.
   a) Predict the dimensions of the rectangle with the maximum area.
   b) Test your hypothesis. Do you need to change your hypothesis?

## Key Concepts

- Different rectangles with equal perimeters can enclose different amounts of area. It is often useful to determine the dimensions of the rectangle that has maximum area.
- The dimensions of a rectangle that has maximum area depend on the number of sides to be fenced. "Natural fencing," such as rivers, can increase the amount of enclosed area.

## Discuss the Concepts

1. A farmer wants to construct a fenced rectangular yard. Suggest two pieces of advice to maximize the enclosed area.
2. a) When does a square-shaped rectangle maximize the enclosed area?
   b) When does a square-shaped rectangle *not* maximize the enclosed area?
3. You need to fence only three sides of a rectangle. How are the maximum-area length and width related in this case?

## PRACTISE

**A** *Include proper units with your answers. Round your answers appropriately.*

1. What dimensions will provide the maximum area for a rectangle with each perimeter?
   a) 16 m   b) 28 cm   c) 48 km   d) 1000 m

## APPLY THE CONCEPTS

2. What is the maximum area of a rectangular garden, surrounded by a perimeter of 24 m of stones?

**B**

3. **Fencing** Suppose you are building a wooden fence to surround a rectangular yard. Each piece of fencing is 4.2 m long. What is the maximum area that you can enclose if you have
   a) 24 pieces?   b) 40 pieces?

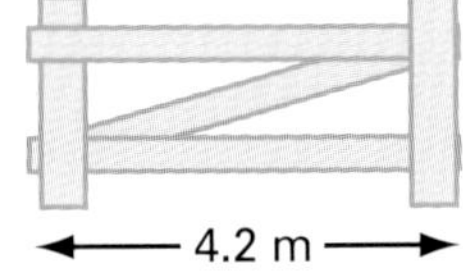


4. **Application** Suppose that you are building a fence using the materials in question 3, but now you have a straight-edged part of a large pond enclosing one side. Draw a diagram and label the dimensions of the maximum-area yard using
   a) 24 pieces   b) 40 pieces
   For the fencing supply in each of parts a) and b), how much additional area does using a natural border provide?

5. **Thinking/Inquiry/Problem Solving** Use *The Geometer's Sketchpad*® or toothpicks to investigate this problem.
   A farmer is using a river and a long tree line as natural borders for a rectangular field. The river and tree line are at right angles. The farmer has 20 pieces of 5-m fencing to complete the field.

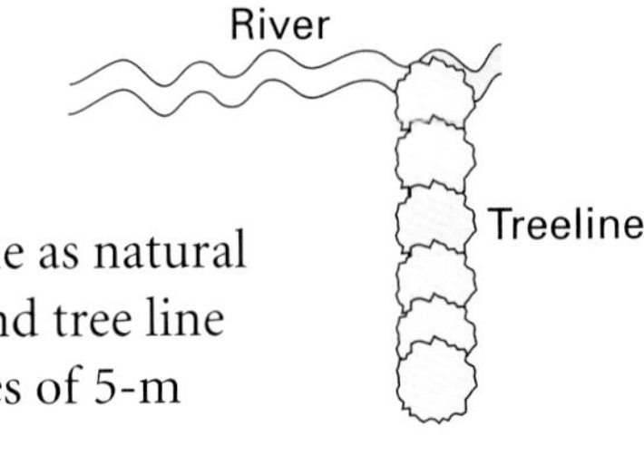


   a) Predict the shape of rectangle that will enclose the maximum area.
   b) Investigate several possible rectangles. Calculate the area for each one.
   c) Draw a diagram of the maximum-area rectangle, label the dimensions, and state the maximum area. Compare this shape to your prediction.
   d) Compare the maximum area the farmer can enclose with these two borders, to the maximum area with no natural borders.
   e) Compare the maximum area the farmer can enclose with these two borders, to the maximum area with one natural border.

6. **Communication** Suppose that you want to create a rectangular enclosure using 90 m of rope.
   a) What are the dimensions of the rectangle of maximum area?
   b) When you use 30 barriers (each 3 m long), you cannot get the same area. Why not?
   c) How much *more* area can you enclose if you use rope instead of barriers? Explain.

7. **Thinking/Inquiry/Problem Solving** The top view of a school is shown. Design a playground enclosure for the back of the school that maximizes area. You have 24 m of fencing to work with.

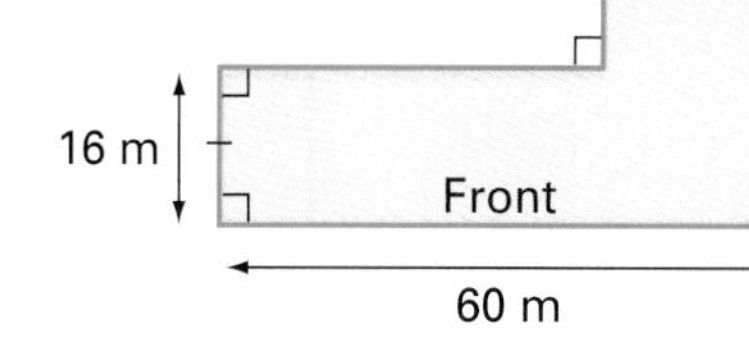


   a) Draw a diagram of the school and your playground.
   b) Find the area of your playground.
   c) Compare your results with your classmates'. Does your design enclose the maximum possible area?

**Chapter Problem**

8. Chantal wants to add a rectangular skylight to her roof. She wants the window to have as much area as possible, but to avoid structural damage the perimeter cannot exceed 10.0 m.

   a) Determine the dimensions of the window that give maximum area.
   b) Determine the area of this window.
   c) Suggest to Chantal how she could cut a window of greater area than the "maximum rectangle" without changing the perimeter. (Hint: Chantal might not need to make the skylight four-sided.)

C 9. **Thinking/Inquiry/Problem Solving, Communication** What happens to area when you change the shape of an enclosure?
   a) Use 36 toothpicks. Try to build enclosures that maximize area, using the following shapes:
      • triangle • rectangle • hexagon • circle
   b) Suppose each toothpick represents a 1-m length of fence. Find the area of each enclosure in part a). (Hint: The hexagon is a composite figure.)
   c) Does the shape of the enclosure affect its area? Write a brief report on your findings.

# Review

***Include proper units with your answers. Round to match the measures given.***

## 2.1 The Pythagorean Theorem, pages 36–41

**1.** For each triangle, determine the missing side length.

**a)**

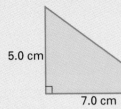

5.0 cm

7.0 cm

**b)**

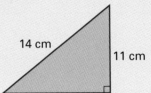

14 cm

11 cm

**2.** A hydro power-line worker is securing a pole with a guy wire. The wire is anchored on the ground, 6 m from the base. It is attached to the pole at a height of 15 m. What length of wire will she need?

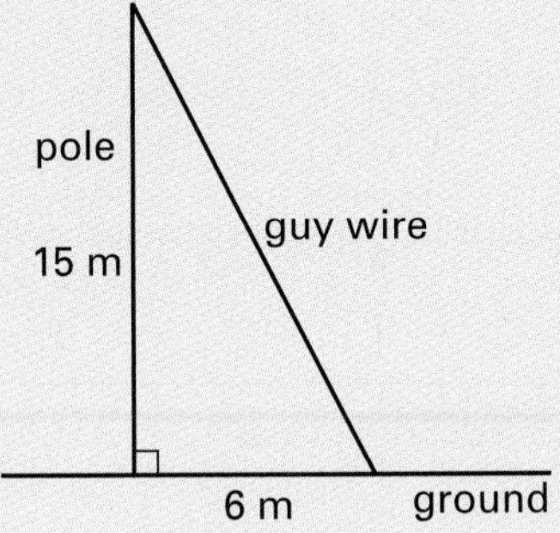


**3.** Jacques travels 2.4 km in his motorboat to visit Kirsten, who lives across the river at Pickerel Road. If Jacques' cottage is 1.5 km from Pickerel Road, find the width of the river.

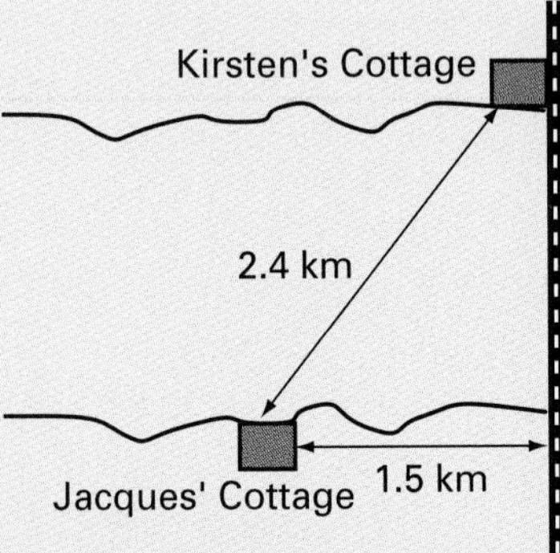


## 2.2 Perimeter and Area of Right Triangles, pages 42–47

**4.** Runners are travelling along the path shown. Determine the length of one lap on this path.

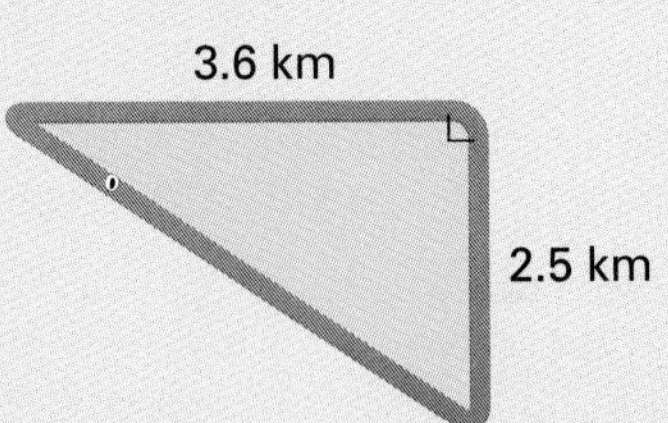

5. Find the area of the yard shown.

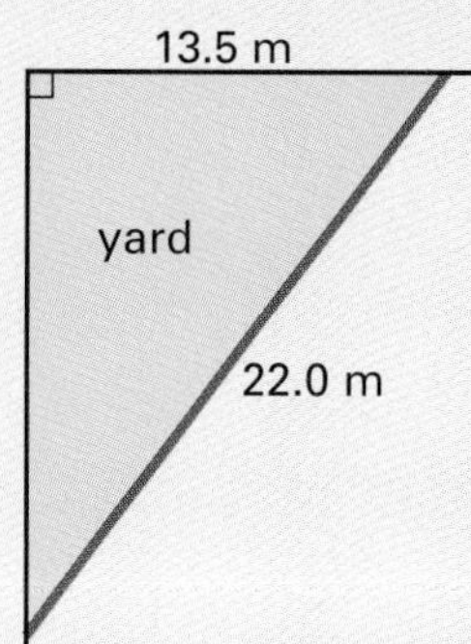

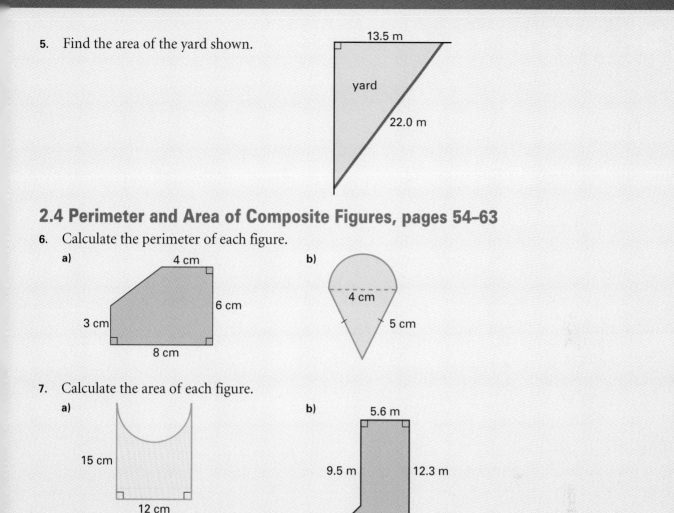

## 2.4 Perimeter and Area of Composite Figures, pages 54–63

6. Calculate the perimeter of each figure.

a)

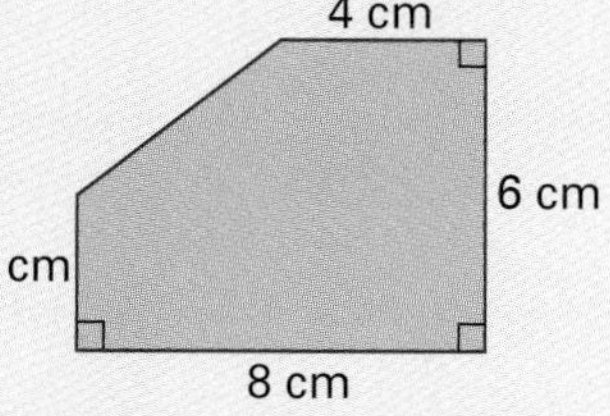


b)

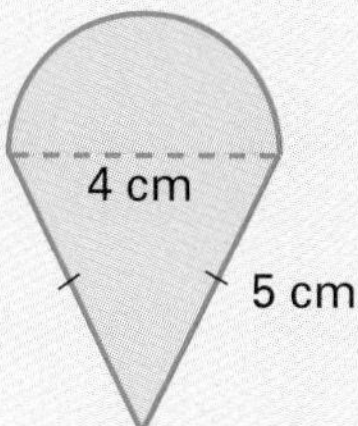


7. Calculate the area of each figure.

a)

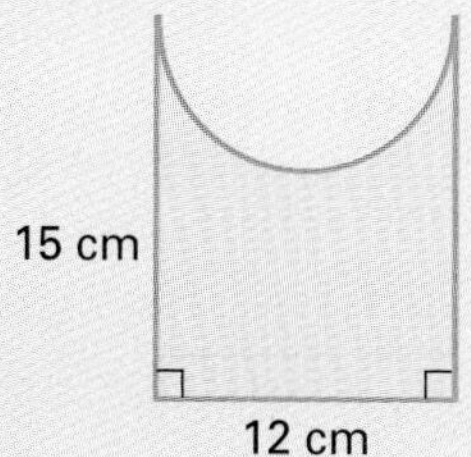


b)

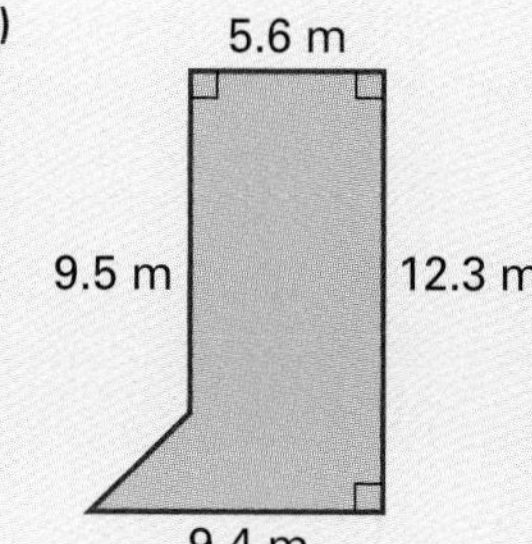


8. Consider painting your classroom.
   a) Estimate the area of the walls of your classroom. Be sure to subtract any areas not to be painted, such as doors and windows.
   b) Describe your method.

## 2.5 Maximizing the Area of a Rectangle, pages 64–71

9. a) Find the dimensions of a rectangular yard of maximum area that can be enclosed with 68 m of fencing.
   b) Repeat for a yard that backs onto a river, so that only three sides need to be fenced.
   c) How much more area can be enclosed by using the river as natural fencing?

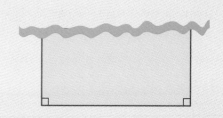

# Practice Test

## Multiple Choice

***For questions 1 to 5, select the best answer. Some answers have been rounded.***

1. Which statement is not true?
   - **A** You can solve for the unknown side in any triangle, if you know the lengths of any two sides, using the Pythagorean theorem.
   - **B** The hypotenuse is the longest side in a right triangle.
   - **C** The hypotenuse is always opposite the 90° angle in a right triangle.
   - **D** The Pythagorean theorem states that in a right triangle, the square of the length of the hypotenuse equals the sum of the squares of the two shorter side lengths.

2. The length of side $q$ is:

   - **A** 16.4 m
   - **B** 19.3 m
   - **C** 25.5 m
   - **D** 300 m

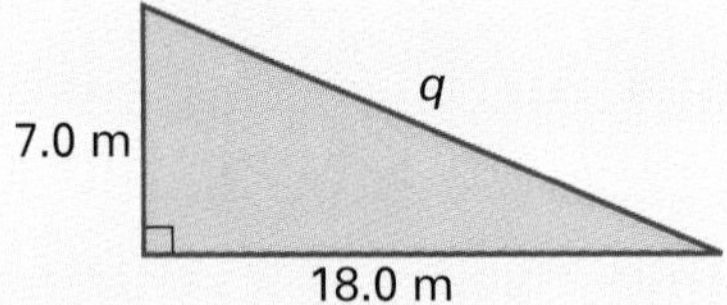


3. The length of side $w$ is:
   - **A** 16 cm
   - **B** 25 cm
   - **C** 29 cm
   - **D** 38 cm

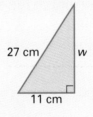

27 cm
w
11 cm

4. The perimeter of the triangle is:
   - **A** 23 m
   - **B** 48 m
   - **C** 55 m
   - **D** 128 m

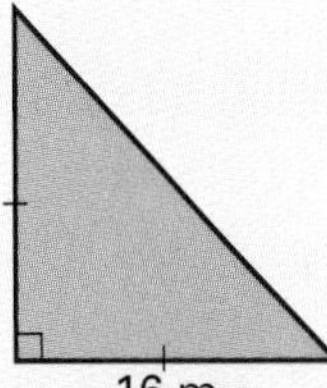


5. The area of the triangle is:
   - **A** 41 $mm^2$
   - **B** 68 $mm^2$
   - **C** 135 $mm^2$
   - **D** 238 $mm^2$

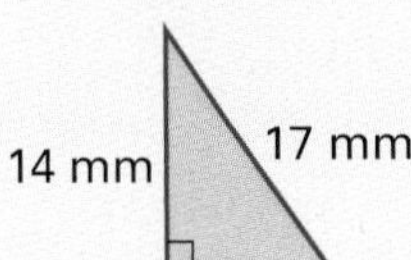

## Short Answer

6. The top of a doughnut is to be covered with maple fudge. Describe how you can make a good estimate of the area to be covered.

***Refer to the composite window design for questions 7 and 8.***

7. a) Describe how you can determine the total area of the window.
   b) Determine the area.

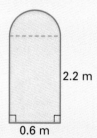

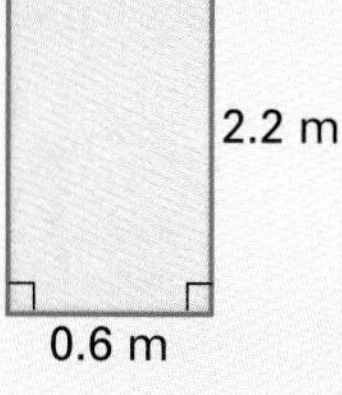


8. Suppose a classmate described the following method for calculating the window's perimeter:
   "First, you find the perimeter of the rectangle. Next, you find the perimeter of the circle. Then, you add these two numbers to get the total perimeter."
   a) State two errors in this student's method, and describe how to fix them.
   b) Determine the perimeter of this shape.

## Extended Response

9. Karen is building a rectangular pen for her goats, using 28 m of fencing. She wants her goats to have as much room to move around as possible.
   a) Design a pen for Karen's goats. Explain why you think it is the best design.
   b) Suppose Karen decides to move her pen close to the house. This way, she can use the house as one side of the pen, and just fence along the other three sides. Explain how Karen should build her pen in this case, and why.

**ACHIEVEMENT CHECK** Knowledge/Understanding Thinking/Inquiry/Problem Solving Communication Application

10. Mario has bought 20 square patio tiles, of side 60 cm. He wants to use them to make a continuous path around a rectangular flower bed, as shown in the diagram.
    a) Use grid paper to draw all the possible paths and flower beds that make use of all 20 tiles.
    b) What do you notice about the perimeters of the flower beds?
    c) What is the area of each flower bed?
    d) What dimensions give the greatest and least areas? Explain and justify your results. Can you think of any ways to make the flower bed larger?

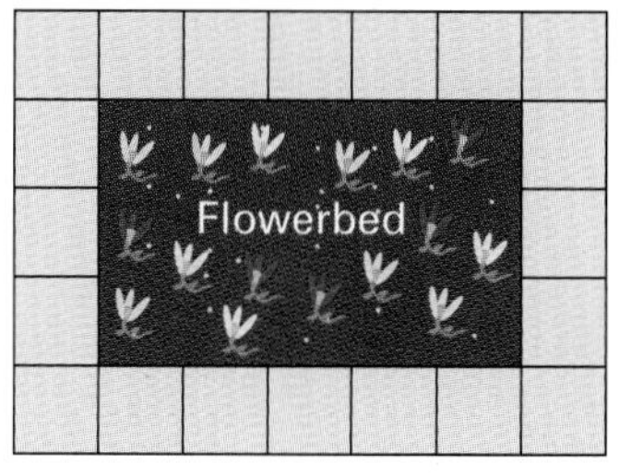

# 3

# Surface Area and Volume Relationships

Surface area and volume are important in the design of many objects, from grocery packages to airplanes. In this chapter, you will

- work with volumes and surface areas of simple solid shapes
- investigate how to save surface area in making packages of given volume

**Chapter Problem**

Cliff is modelling a spacecraft for his design and technology project, including:

- a rocket
- a display platform for the rocket
- moon rocks
- a box for storing and carrying his project

As you work through this chapter, you will calculate dimensions and areas of surfaces to help Cliff with his project.

# Get Ready

## Circumference and Area of Circles

Calculate the circumference and the area of a circle with diameter 3.8 cm.

radius $= \frac{1}{2}$ of diameter

$r = \frac{3.8}{2}$

$r = 1.9$

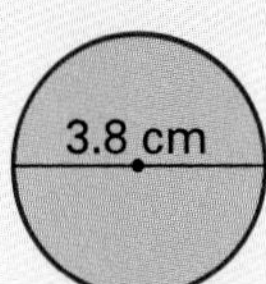


circumference $= 2\pi r$

$C = 2\pi(1.9)$

$C \doteq 12$

area $= \pi r^2$

$A = \pi(1.9)^2$

$A \doteq 11$

The circle has circumference 12 cm and area 11 cm$^2$, to two digits of accuracy.

**1.** Calculate the circumference of each circle.

**a)**

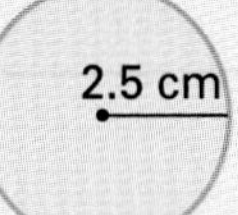


**b)**

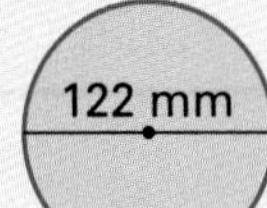


**c)**

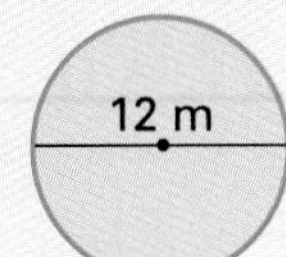


**2.** Calculate the area of each circle in question 1.

## Substituting Into Formulas

Substitute the values $b = 3.1$ and $h = 7.5$ into the formula $V = \frac{1}{3}b^2h$ and evaluate.

$V = \frac{1}{3}b^2h$

$V = \frac{1}{3} \times (3.1)^2 \times 7.5$

$V = \frac{9.61 \times 7.5}{3}$ **Square 3.1, multiply by 7.5, and divide by 3.**

$V \doteq 24$ **Round to two digits of accuracy.**

3. Substitute the given values into each formula and evaluate the expression. Round answers to two digits of accuracy.

| | | |
|---|---|---|
| **a)** | $V = lwh$ | $l = 6.0$, $w = 2.5$, $h = 4.2$ |
| **b)** | $S = 2(ab + bc + ca)$ | $a = 4.0$, $b = 5.6$, $c = 7.1$ |
| **c)** | $S = 6l^2$ | $l = 2.5$ |
| **d)** | $b^2 = c^2 - a^2$ | $c = 8.9$, $a = 4.5$ |
| **e)** | $S = 2\pi r(r + h)$ | $r = 3.6$, $h = 5.3$ |
| **f)** | $V = \frac{4}{3}\pi r^3$ | $r = 3.0$ |

## Pythagorean Theorem

Solve for the unknown side length in the right triangle.

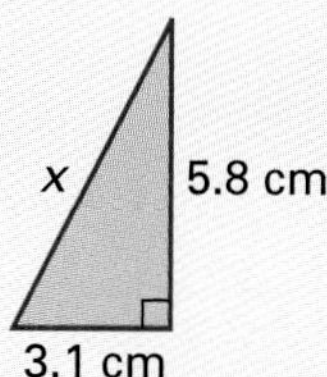


The unknown side is the hypotenuse.

$x^2 = (3.1)^2 + (5.8)^2$

$x^2 = 9.61 + 33.64$

$x^2 = 43.25$

$x = \sqrt{43.25}$

$x \doteq 6.6$

The unknown side measures 6.6 cm, to the nearest tenth.

4. Solve for the unknown side length in each triangle.

**a)**

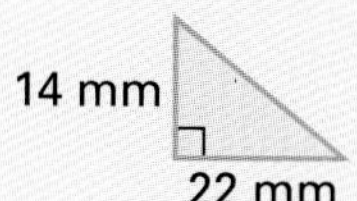

**b)**

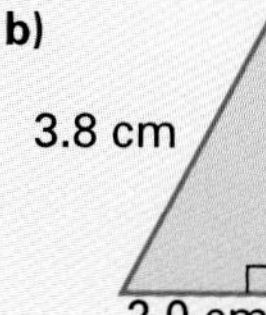


**c)**

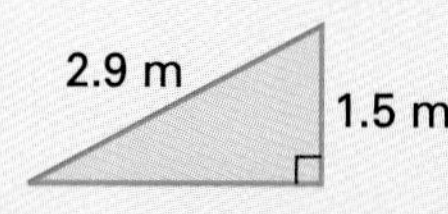

# 3.1 Volume: Prisms and Cylinders

In the design of containers and packages, two of the most important measurements to consider are volume and surface area. The **volume** of a three-dimensional object is a measure of how much space it occupies.

The mathematical name for a box, with right angles at every corner, is **rectangular prism**. The volume of a rectangular prism can be calculated using the formula:

$V = l \times w \times h$

Volume is measured in cubic units, because volume is a three-dimensional measurement. Typical cubic units for volume are cubic centimetres ($cm^3$), cubic metres ($m^3$), and cubic millimetres ($mm^3$).

Another unit that is commonly used is the **litre (L)**, which is defined as the volume of a cube with sides of length 10 cm.

one litre = 10 cm × 10 cm × 10 cm

1 L = 1000 $cm^3$

10 cm

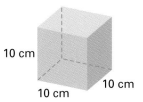

10 cm

10 cm

Litres are generally used when measuring the volume of a liquid. They are often used to describe the capacity of a container. **Capacity** is the greatest volume that a container can hold. For example, your family may have a milk jug with a capacity of 1 L.

## EXAMPLE 1

### Volume of a Rectangular Prism

a) Determine the volume of the package in the photograph, in cubic centimetres.

b) Express the capacity in litres.

### Solution

a) $V = l \times w \times h$

$= 12 \times 5 \times 15$

$= 900$

The volume of this package is 900 $cm^3$.

b) 1 L = 1000 $cm^3$

Therefore,

$V = 900\ cm^3 \times \frac{1\ L}{1000\ cm^3}$ **To convert to litres, divide by 1000.**

$= 0.9$ L

The capacity of the package is 0.9 L.

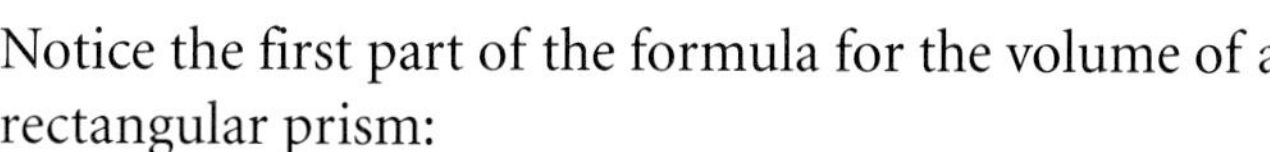

Notice the first part of the formula for the volume of a rectangular prism:

$V = l \times w \times h$

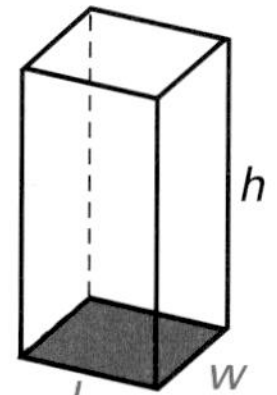


This part, in red type, is the formula for the area of the rectangular base of the prism.

Therefore, the volume is the area of the base times the height:
volume = base area × height

This volume relationship also applies to other types of prisms. Think of a **prism** as a flat shape, such as a rectangle or a triangle, stretched through space to form a three-dimensional solid.

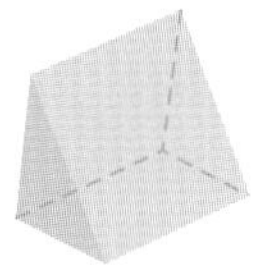

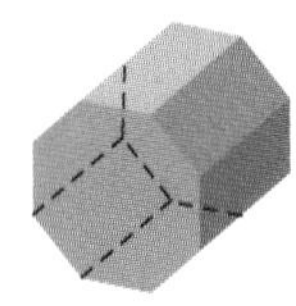

The volume of any prism is the base area times the height (or depth).
volume = base area × height

$$V = A_{base} \times h$$

## EXAMPLE 2

### Volume of a Triangular Prism

Determine the volume of the tent.

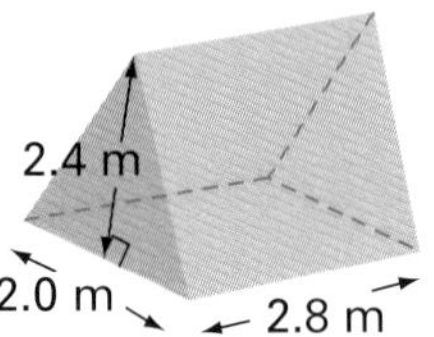


### Solution

First, calculate the area of the triangular end of the prism (the front of the tent).

$$A_{end} = \frac{1}{2}bh_{end}$$ **Apply the formula for the area of a triangle.**

$$= \frac{1}{2} \times 2.0 \times 2.4$$ **Estimate:** $\frac{1}{2} \times 2 \times 2 = 2$

$$= 2.4$$

Then, multiply the base area by the depth of the prism (the length of the tent from front to back).

$$V = A_{end} h_{prism}$$ **Do not confuse the prism's "height" or depth, $h_{prism}$, with the height of the tent end, $h_{end}$.**

$$= 2.4 \times 2.8$$ **Estimate:** $2 \times 3 = 6$

$$= 6.72$$

$$\doteq 6.7$$ **When multiplying, round to match the number of digits of accuracy of the given measures.**

The volume of the tent is 6.7 m$^3$, to two digits of accuracy.

A **cylinder** is like a prism with a circular base. To determine the area of the circular base, you need to know its radius or diameter.

## Example 3

### Volume of a Cylinder

A cylindrical storage tank has a diameter of 12.0 m and a height of 7.0 m. Determine the volume of the tank.

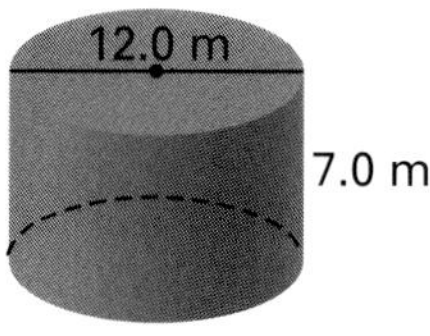


### Solution

For a cylinder,

$A_{base} = \pi r^2$

$= \pi \times (6.0)^2$ — Divide diameter by 2 to get radius 6.0 m.

$\doteq 113.097$ — Do not round to final accuracy until the end.

Now, calculate the volume:

$V = A_{base}h$

$= 113.097 \times 7.0$

$\doteq 790$

The volume of the storage tank is 790 $m^3$, rounded to two digits of accuracy.

The volume of a cylinder is given by the formula:

Volume = (base area) × (height)

$V = \pi r^2 h$

- Volume is a measure of how much space a three-dimensional object occupies. Capacity is the maximum volume a container can hold.
- The units for volume are cubic units (for example: 12.5 $cm^3$, 3 $m^3$).
- The litre (L) is a measure of capacity or volume often used for liquids. 1 L = 1000 $cm^3$.
- For a prism, volume = base area × height.
- A rectangular prism has the shape of a box. A cylinder is like a prism with a circular base.

## Discuss the Concepts

1. a) Discuss the volumes of some everyday objects.
   b) Estimate the volumes of a textbook, an eraser, and a locker.

2. a) Describe how a prism can be formed from a flat shape.
   b) Why is a box called a rectangular prism?

3. Name two everyday objects that are each shape.
   a) rectangular prism b) triangular prism c) cylinder

## Practise

**A** ***Include proper units with your answers. Round your answers appropriately.***

***For help with question 1, refer to Example 1.***

1. Determine the volume of each rectangular-based prism.

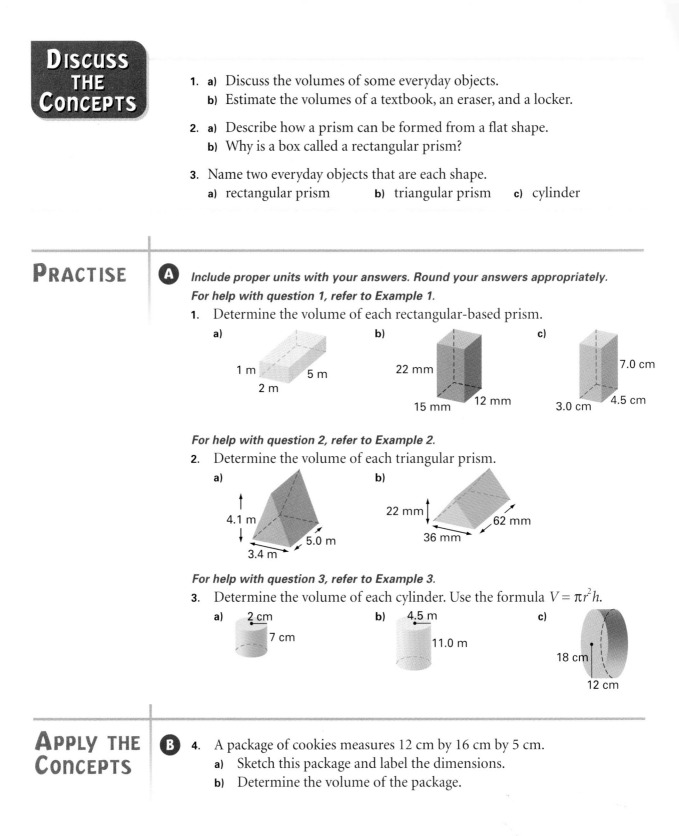

a)

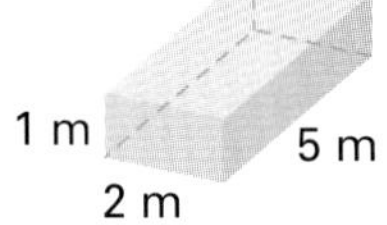


b)

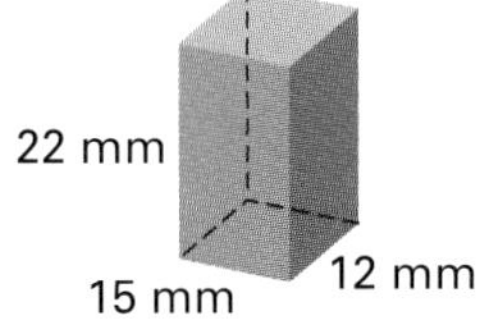


c)

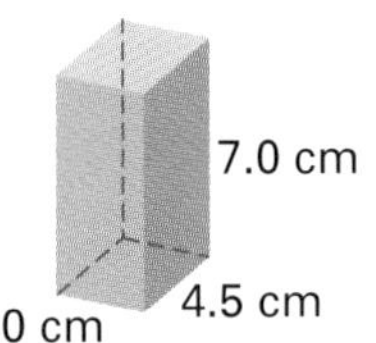


***For help with question 2, refer to Example 2.***

2. Determine the volume of each triangular prism.

a)

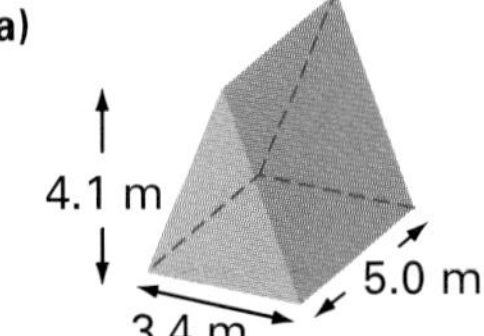


b)

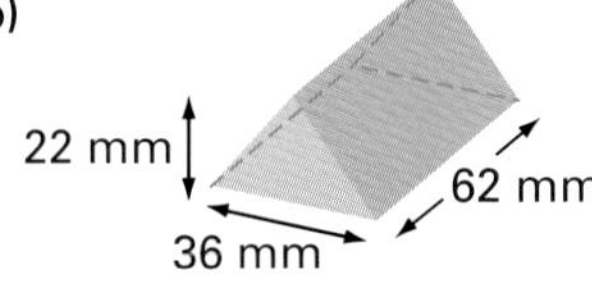


***For help with question 3, refer to Example 3.***

3. Determine the volume of each cylinder. Use the formula $V = \pi r^2 h$.

a)

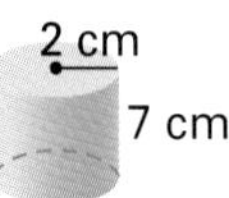


b)

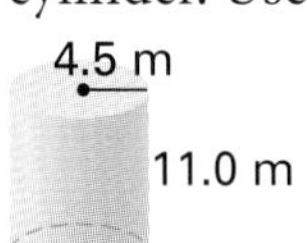


c)

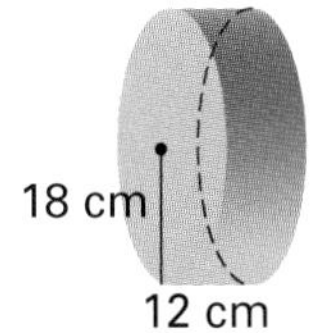


## Apply the Concepts

4. A package of cookies measures 12 cm by 16 cm by 5 cm.
   a) Sketch this package and label the dimensions.
   b) Determine the volume of the package.

5. **Thinking/Inquiry/Problem Solving**

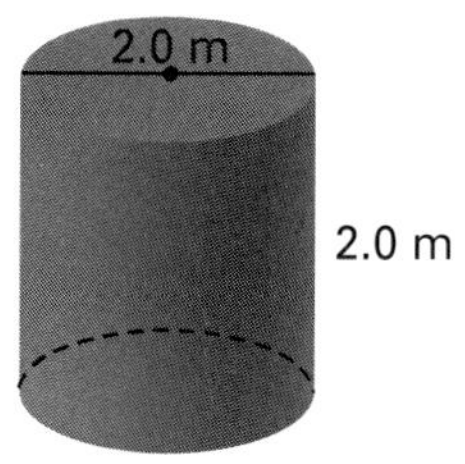


a) Calculate the volume of this tank.
b) Which do you think would provide a greater increase in volume: a tank with double the diameter, or a tank with double the height? Draw each new tank and label the dimensions.
c) Calculate the volume of each new tank drawn in part b).
d) Compare the volume measures to your prediction in part b). Was your prediction correct? Explain.

6. **Milk carton**
a) Take an empty 1-L milk carton. Predict its volume in cubic centimetres.
b) Measure the length, width, and height, in centimetres.
c) Calculate the volume of the carton.
d) Does this result agree with your prediction? Explain why or why not.

**Chapter Problem**

7. Here is Cliff's model spacecraft design. Determine the volume of the living quarters.

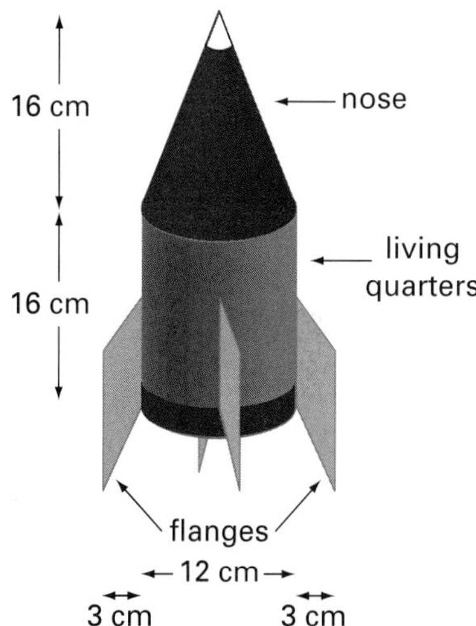


**Did You Know?**

One of the largest cylinders ever made is the first stage of the Saturn V moon rocket. This giant structure, 42 m high and 10 m across, held over 2.1 million litres of fuel and oxidizer.

**C** 8. **Thinking/Inquiry/Problem Solving, Communication**
a) Determine the volume of the container.
b) Explain how you solved this problem.

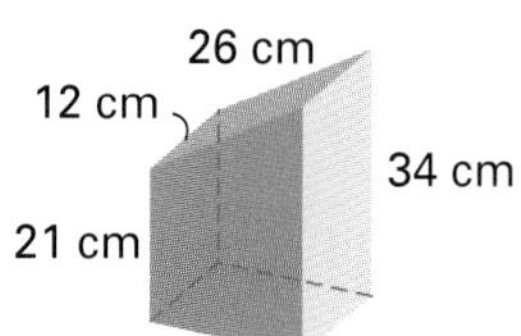

# 3.2 Volume: Cones and Spheres

In the last section, you discovered how to calculate the volume of prisms. In this section, you will extend and apply your understanding to cones and spheres.

## DISCOVER

**Materials**

- paper or card
- scissors
- tape
- ruler
- rice or unpopped popcorn

### Comparing the Volumes of a Cylinder and a Cone

Work with a partner or in a small group.

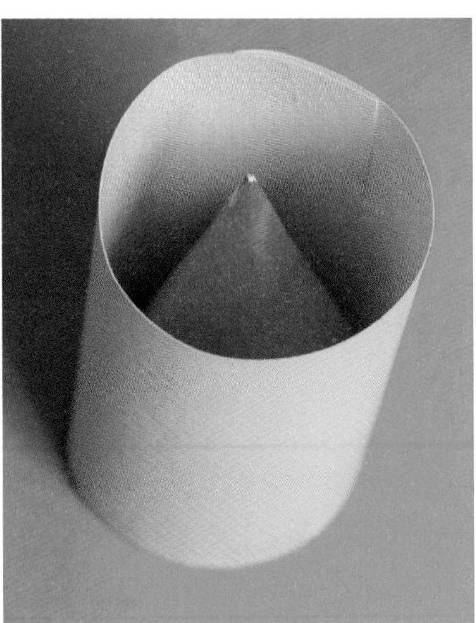

1. Use paper or card to make a cone. (Or, your teacher may supply one.)
2. Measure the diameter and the height of the cone. Make sure you measure the vertical height, not the slant height.
3. Take a new blank sheet. Cut a strip as wide as the cone is high. Wrap it around the cone to make a cylinder with the same diameter and height as your cone. Tape the cylinder carefully, so it stays the correct size. Cover and seal one end.
4. Which container will hold the greater volume? How much more do you think it will hold? Write down your prediction.
5. **a)** Fill the cone with rice. Level the contents so that the top is flat.
   **b)** Pour the rice from the cone to the cylinder. Be careful not to spill any.
   **c)** Fill the cone again. Transfer the contents to the cylinder. Repeat until the cylinder is completely full.
6. **a)** How many times could you pour the contents of the cone into the cylinder?
   **b)** How accurate was your prediction from step 4?
   **c)** Compare your results with your classmates' findings. Does the size of the original cone matter? Explain.

7. a) Write down the formula for the volume of a cylinder with radius $r$ and height $h$.
   b) Based on your findings in this investigation, predict the formula for the volume of a cone with radius $r$ and height $h$.

You should have discovered that a cylinder holds three times the volume of a cone with the same radius and height. The formula for the volume of a cone is:

$$V_{cone} = \frac{1}{3}\pi r^2 h$$

## EXAMPLE 1

### Calculating the Volume of a Cone

A farmer is using a cone-shaped hopper. The hopper has a diameter of 3.5 m and a height of 4.2 m.

a) Draw a diagram of this hopper.
b) Determine the volume of the hopper.

### Solution

a)

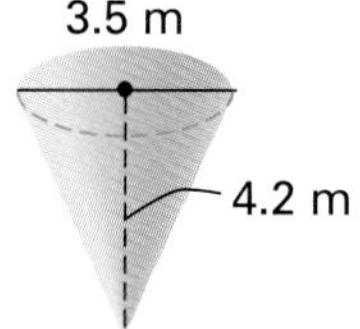


b) The diameter is 3.5 m. Therefore, the radius is 1.75 m.

$$V = \frac{1}{3}\pi r^2 h$$
$$= \frac{\pi \times 1.75^2 \times 4.2}{3}$$
$$\doteq 13$$

C π × 1.75 $x^2$ × 4.2 ÷ 3 =

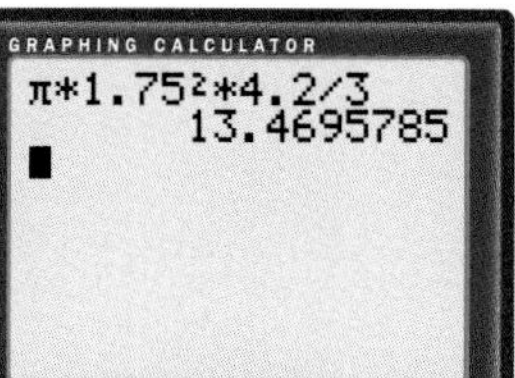

The volume is 13 m$^3$, to two digits of accuracy.

A **sphere** is a ball-shaped object. The volume of a sphere can be calculated, if you know its radius, using the formula:

$$V = \frac{4}{3}\pi r^3$$

In Section 3.1, you used the relationship 1 L = 1000 cm$^3$ to convert cubic centimetres to litres.

Using the relationship 10 cm = 0.1 m, you can also convert cubic metres to litres:

$$1 \text{ L} = 0.1 \text{ m} \times 0.1 \text{ m} \times 0.1 \text{ m}$$
$$1 \text{ L} = 0.001 \text{ m}^3$$

or $1000 \text{ L} = 1 \text{ m}^3$

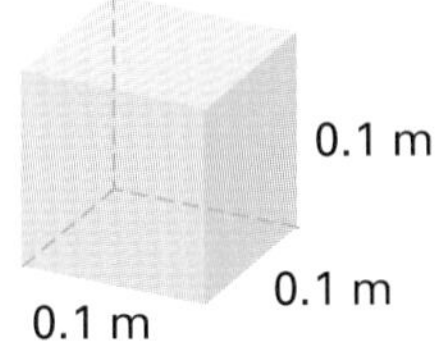


## EXAMPLE 2

### Calculating the Volume of a Sphere

A city water storage tank is in the shape of a sphere. The radius of the sphere is 9.5 m.

**a)** Find the volume of the storage tank in cubic metres.

**b)** Find the capacity of the tank in litres.

### Solution

**a)** Apply the formula for the volume of a sphere.

$$V = \frac{4}{3}\pi r^3$$

**Estimate:** $\frac{4}{3} \times 3 \times 1000 = 4000$ (with the 3s cancelled)

$$= \frac{4 \times \pi \times 9.5^3}{3}$$

C 4 × π × 9.5 × 9.5 × 9.5 ÷ 3 =

$$\doteq 3600$$

The volume of the tank is 3600 m$^3$, to two digits of accuracy.

**b)** To convert to litres, use the relationship 1000 L = 1 m$^3$.

$$V = 3600 \text{ m}^3 \times \frac{1000 \text{ L}}{1 \text{ m}^3}$$

**Multiply the answer by 1000.**

$$= 3\,600\,000 \text{ L}$$

The capacity of the tank is about 3 600 000 L.

## Key Concepts

- The volume of a cone can be calculated using the formula:
  $V = \frac{1}{3}\pi r^2 h$

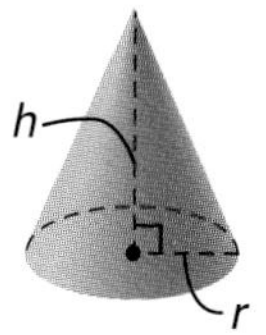


- The volume of a sphere can be calculated using the formula:
  $V = \frac{4}{3}\pi r^3$

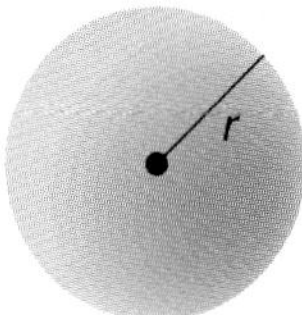


- You can convert cubic metres to litres using the relationship $1\ \text{m}^3 = 1000\ \text{L}$.

## Discuss the Concepts

1. A cylinder and a cone have the same radius and height. Describe the relationship between their volumes.
2. You are to calculate the volume of a sphere with radius 12.5 cm. Describe how the answer should be rounded.

## Practise

**A** ***Include proper units with your answers. Round your answers appropriately.***

***For help with question 1, refer to Example 1.***

1. Find the volume of each cone.

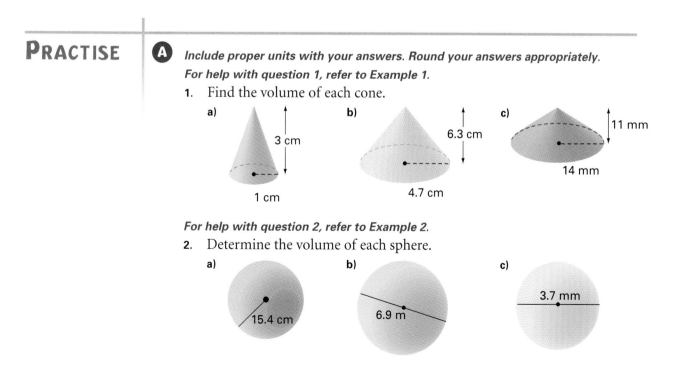

   a) 3 cm; 1 cm

   b) 6.3 cm; 4.7 cm

   c) 11 mm; 14 mm

***For help with question 2, refer to Example 2.***

2. Determine the volume of each sphere.

   a)

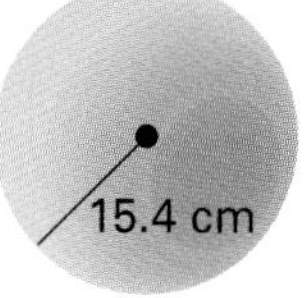


   b)

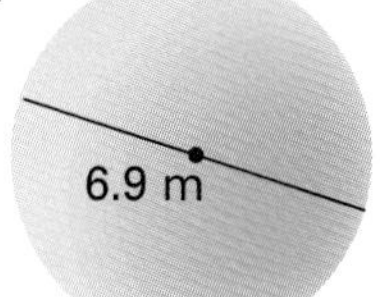


   c)

## Apply the Concepts

3. Calculate the volume formed by the cone-shaped speaker. Round your answer to two digits of accuracy.

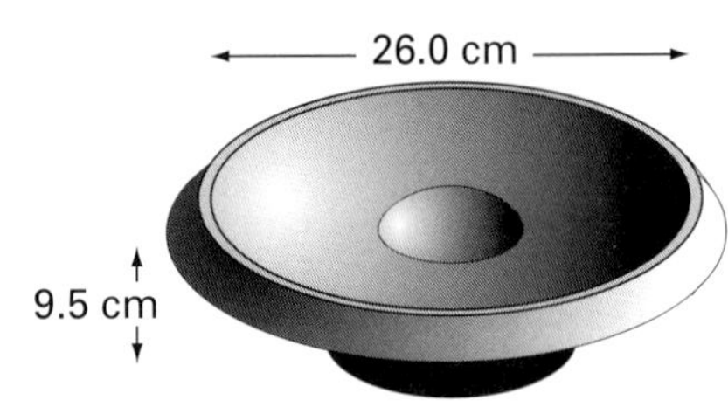


**B**

4. **Candy** A "chocoball" is a solid sphere of chocolate with diameter 1.8 cm.
   a) Determine the volume of one chocoball.
   b) How much chocolate will you consume if you eat a package of 12 chocoballs?

**Did You Know?**

Supermarket displays of oranges are often stacked in a pyramid shape. This is not only attractive as a display, but also the most efficient use of space. The volume wasted between oranges is minimized in this type of stack.

5. **Application** A petting zoo allows visitors to feed animals grain from paper cones.
   a) How much grain, in cubic centimetres, will fit into a cone with a diameter of 6.0 cm and a height of 8.0 cm?
   b) Billy, the goat, usually eats 500 $cm^3$ of grain for lunch. How many times will Hoshi need to fill her cone in order to give Billy his lunch?

6. **Application** Suppose that the zoo in question 5 allows animals to be fed "wonder pellets," which are just as filling as regular grain. Each sphere-shaped pellet has a diameter of 3.0 cm.
   a) Determine the volume of one wonder pellet.
   b) How many wonder pellets will Billy typically eat for lunch?

7. **Packaging fries** Farouk's French Fries come in a cylindrical container for \$3.00, while Charlene's Chips come in a cone-shaped container for \$1.50.
   a) Who offers the better deal?
   b) What assumptions must you make?

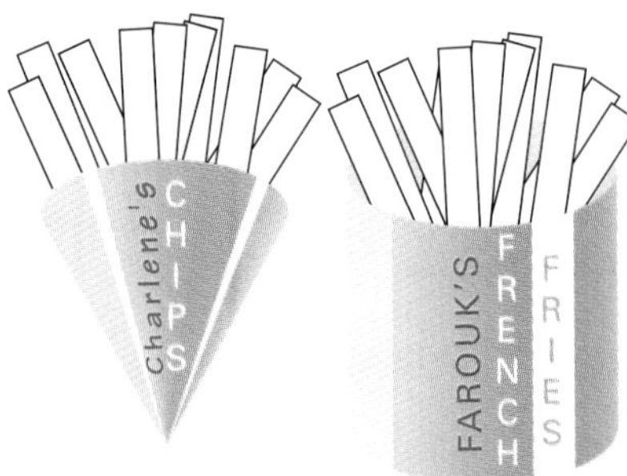

8. **Thinking/Inquiry/Problem Solving**

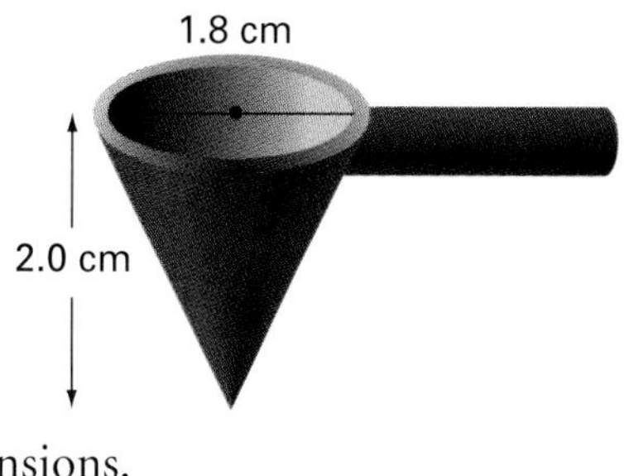


a) Calculate the capacity of this coffee scoop.
b) Which do you think would provide a greater increase in capacity: doubling the radius, or doubling the height? Draw each of these new scoops and label the dimensions.
c) Calculate the capacity of each new scoop drawn in part b).
d) Compare the capacity measures to your prediction in part b). Was your prediction correct? Explain.

9. **Thinking/Inquiry/Problem Solving**
a) A sphere has radius 2.0 cm. Calculate its volume.
b) A second sphere has radius double the radius of the first sphere. Predict how the volumes of the two spheres are related.
c) Calculate the volume of the second sphere. Compare this value to your prediction, and explain what you notice.

10. **Communication**
a) Repeat question 9 with a sphere with a radius of 3.0 cm.
b) Can you see a pattern? Explain how the volume of a sphere changes each time you double its radius.

**Chapter Problem**

11. Cliff is using Plasticine™ to make some spherical moon rocks for his project.
a) What is the volume of a moon rock measuring 3.6 cm in diameter?
b) How many moon rocks of this size can Cliff make with 75 $cm^3$ of Plasticine™?

**Did You Know?**

Earth's diameter is about 20 km greater at the equator than from pole to pole.

12. **Application** The distance straight through Earth from the North Pole to the South Pole is approximately 6400 km. Determine Earth's volume, in cubic kilometres.

C

13. **Thinking/Inquiry/Problem Solving** A jawbreaker gumball is a hollow sphere with outside radius 3.0 cm and inside radius 2.5 cm.
a) What volume of gum is used to make the jawbreaker?
b) Explain how you solved this problem.

14. **Thinking/Inquiry/Problem Solving**
a) Determine the volume of the cone.
b) Explain how you solved this problem.

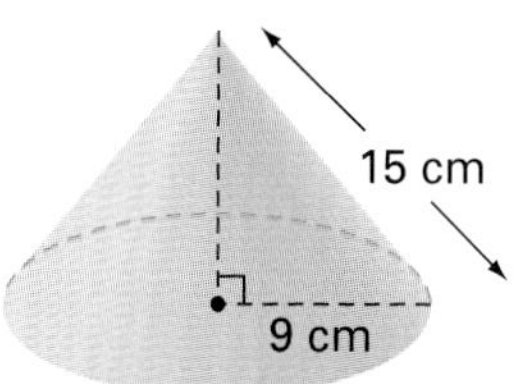

# 3.3 Surface Area: Rectangular Prisms

You have seen how the volume of a container or package can tell you its storage capacity. Another important measure is **surface area**, or how much material is needed to build or paint an object, such as an airplane wing.

When you carefully take a box apart, and lay it flat, you can see the way it is constructed. The flat pattern is called a net.

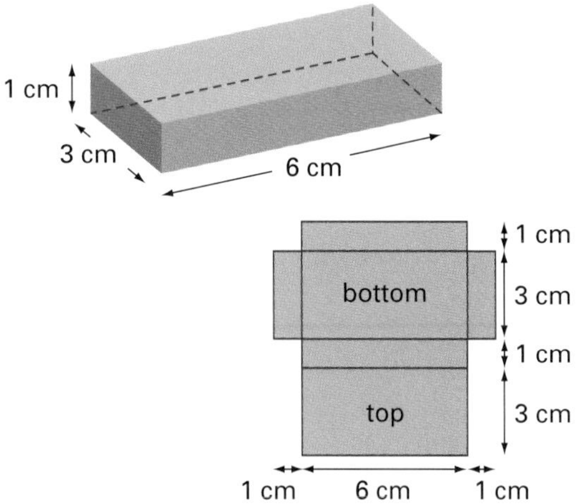


A **net** is a two-dimensional pattern that can be used to construct a three-dimensional object.

## Discover

**Materials**
- centimetre grid paper (equal-size sheets)
- scissors
- tape
- ruler

### Constructing Boxes Using Nets

Work with a partner or in a small group.

1. Construct a square-based box that measures 4 cm by 4 cm by 2 cm, as follows:
   a) On centimetre grid paper, accurately draw the net shown.
   b) Cut out the net. Fold along the interior lines and tape the box together. Save your scraps.

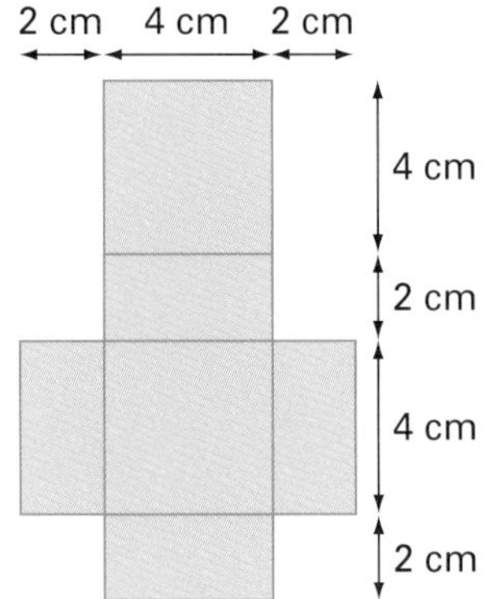

2. Repeat step 1 to construct another box, which measures 2 cm by 2 cm by 8 cm. Use the same size sheet of paper. Save your scraps, separately from the scraps in step 1.

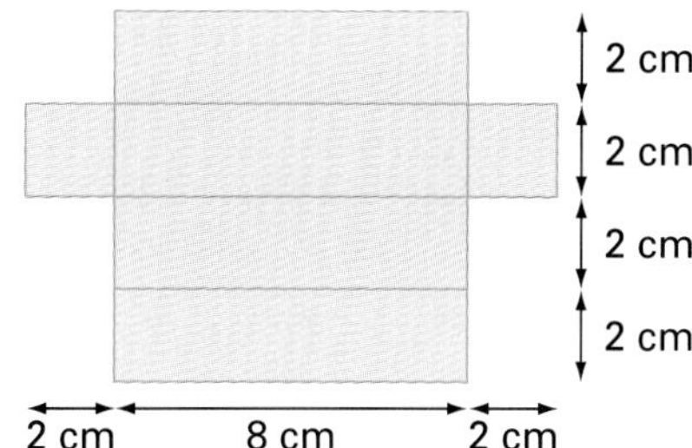


3. a) Examine the two boxes you have constructed. Which do you think has the greater volume? Explain.
   b) Calculate the volume of each box.
   c) Compare your results to your prediction. Were you correct?

4. The surface area of a box is a measure of the amount of material required to construct it. Look at the scraps from your cut-outs. Does it appear that one box required more paper than the other? Explain.

5. To calculate the surface area of the first box, you need to calculate the area of all six rectangular faces of the box.

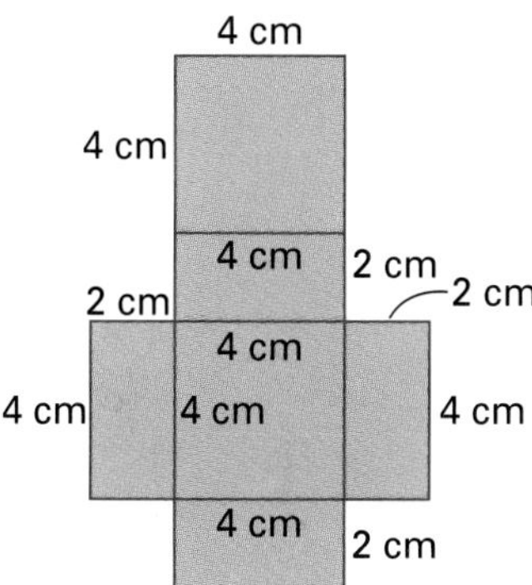

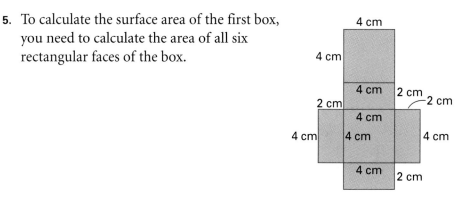

   a) Find the area of each rectangular face. Apply the formula for area of a rectangle. Record your results in a table.

| Rectangular Face | Length (cm) | Width (cm) | Area (cm$^2$) |
|---|---|---|---|
| front face | 4 | 2 | 8 |
| | | | |
| | | | |

   b) Add up the areas of all six faces to get the total surface area.

6. Repeat step 5 for the second box.

7. Compare the total surface areas of the two boxes. Are they the same? Compare your results to your answer in step 4. Explain what you notice.

Two different containers can have the same volume but be constructed from different amounts of material. For this reason, the surface area of a package or container is an important feature of its design.

## Example 1

### Surface Area of a Box

Determine the surface area of the box shown.

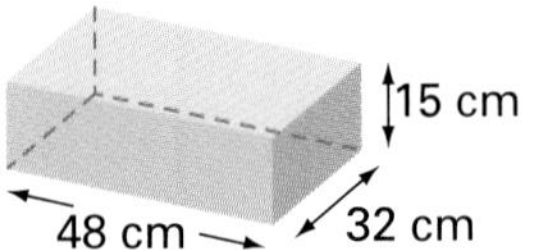


### Solution

To help visualize the six sides of the box, draw a net and label the dimensions.

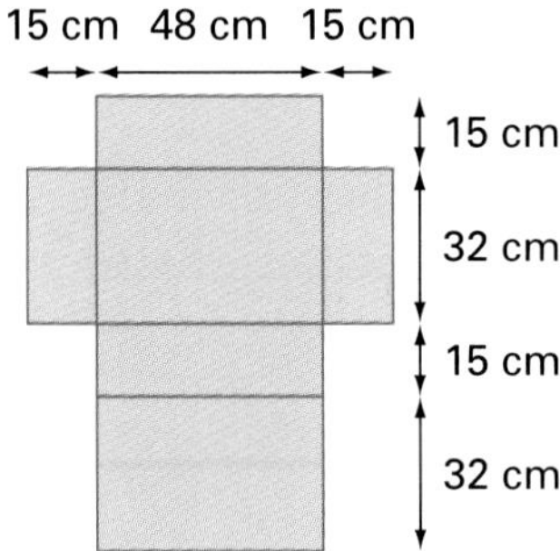


Calculate the area of the top and bottom rectangles.
Each of these areas is given by

$$\begin{aligned} A_{\text{top, bottom}} &= lw \\ &= 48 \times 32 \\ &= 1536 \end{aligned}$$

So, the top and bottom each have area 1536 $cm^2$ (remember that area is measured in square units).

Repeat for the front and back:

$$\begin{aligned} A_{\text{front, back}} &= 15 \times 48 \\ &= 720 \end{aligned}$$

Repeat for the side faces:

$$\begin{aligned} A_{\text{sides}} &= 32 \times 15 \\ &= 480 \end{aligned}$$

To determine the total surface area, add up the areas of all six rectangles. Since there are two of each size, double each of the areas calculated:

$$S = 2 \times A_{\text{top, bottom}} + 2 \times A_{\text{front, back}} + 2 \times A_{\text{sides}}$$
$$= 2 \times 1536 + 2 \times 720 + 2 \times 480$$
$$= 3072 + 1440 + 960$$
$$\doteq 5500$$

**Since the measures of the box are given to two digits of accuracy, round the surface area to two digits of accuracy.**

The surface area is 5500 $cm^2$, to two digits of accuracy.

Note that, even though you are working with a three-dimensional object, surface area is a sum of two-dimensional area measurements. The units for area are square units, in Example 1 square centimetres.

The surface area of the box, or rectangular prism, can be calculated using this formula:

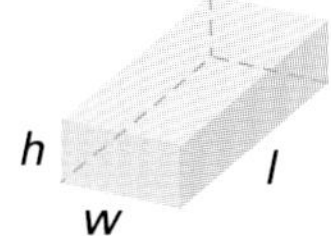


$$S = 2lw + 2wh + 2lh$$
or $S = 2(lw + wh + lh)$

where $l$, $w$, and $h$ are the length, width, and height of the rectangular prism.

## Example 2

### Using the Formula for the Surface Area of a Rectangular Prism

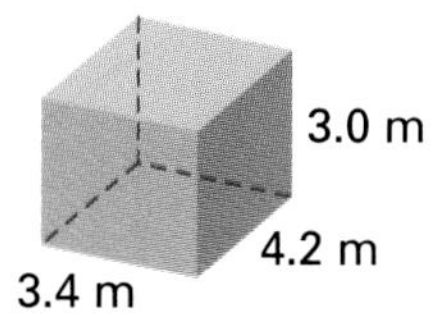


What is the total surface area (walls, floor, and ceiling) of a room that measures 4.2 m by 3.4 m along the floor, and has a ceiling height of 3.0 m?

### Solution

Apply the formula for surface area of a rectangular prism.
Substitute the values $l = 4.2$, $w = 3.4$, and $h = 3.0$.

$$S = 2(lw + wh + lh)$$
$$= 2 \times (4.2 \times 3.4 + 3.4 \times 3.0 + 4.2 \times 3.0)$$
$$= 2 \times (14.28 + 10.2 + 12.6)$$
$$= 2 \times (37.08)$$
$$\doteq 74$$

**Estimate:** $2 \times (4 \times 3 + 3 \times 3 + 4 \times 3)$
$= 2 \times (12 + 9 + 12)$
$= 2 \times 33$
$\doteq 70$

The surface area of the room is 74 $m^2$, to two digits of accuracy.

- Surface area is a measure of how much material is required to cover or construct a three-dimensional object, such as a package or container.
- A net is a two-dimensional pattern that can be used to construct a three-dimensional object.
- The surface area of a rectangular prism can be calculated using the formula:

  $S = 2(lw + wh + lh)$

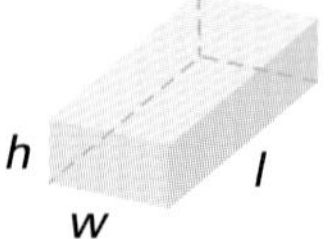

## DISCUSS THE CONCEPTS

1. a) What is the difference between the surface area of a container and its volume?
   b) Give a reason why you might need to know the volume of a storage tank.
   c) Give a reason why you might need to know the surface area of a storage tank.
2. Why is there a "2" in the formula for the surface area of a rectangular prism?

## PRACTISE

***Include proper units with your answers. Round your answers appropriately.***

***For help with questions 1 to 3, refer to Example 1.***

1. Find the surface area of the rectangular prism made by each net.

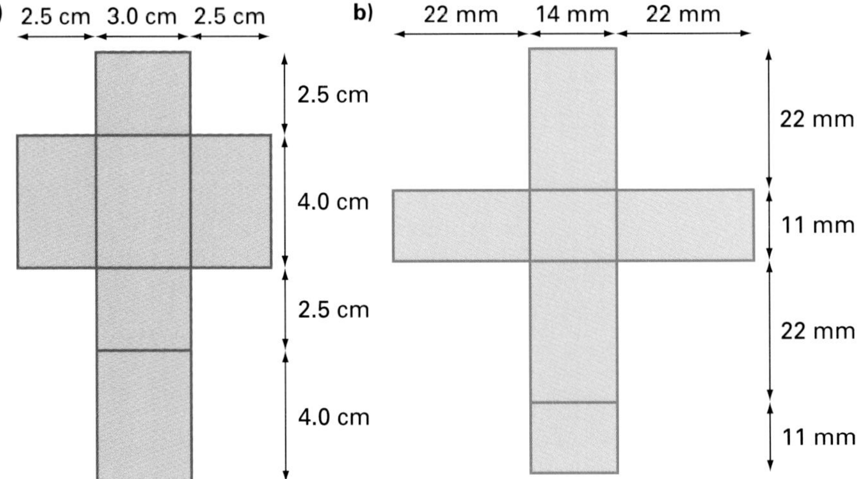

2. Draw a net for each rectangular prism. Label the dimensions.

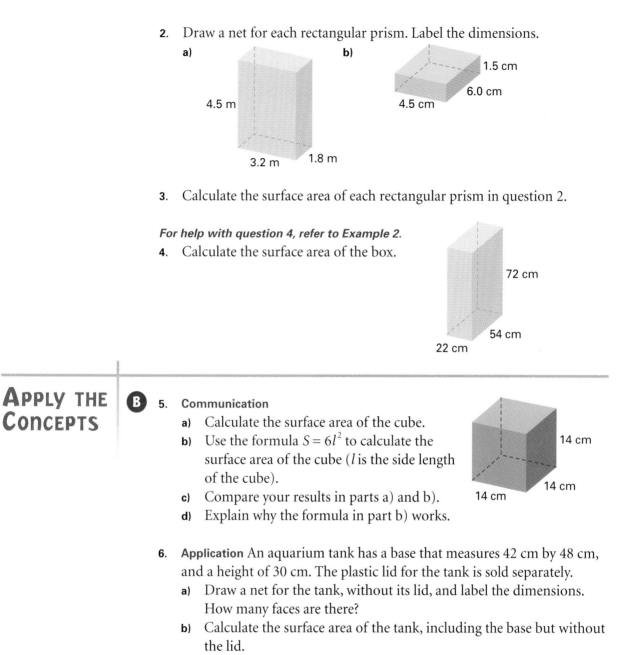

a)

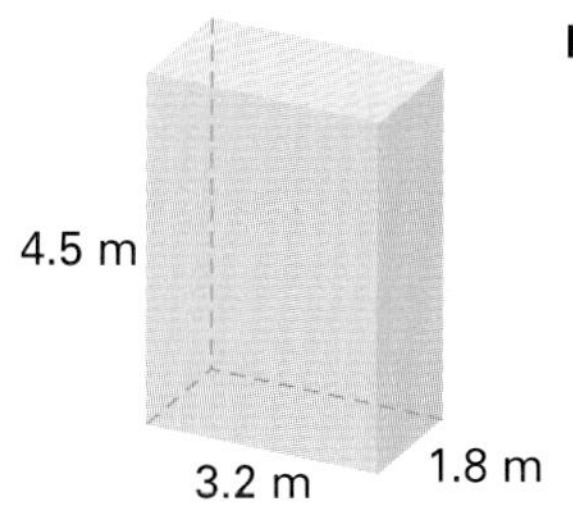


b)

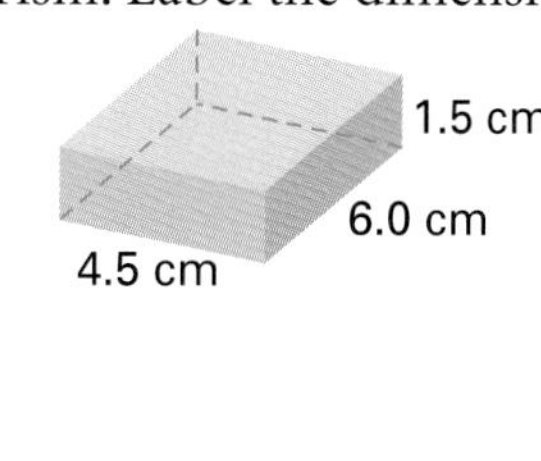


3. Calculate the surface area of each rectangular prism in question 2.

***For help with question 4, refer to Example 2.***

4. Calculate the surface area of the box.

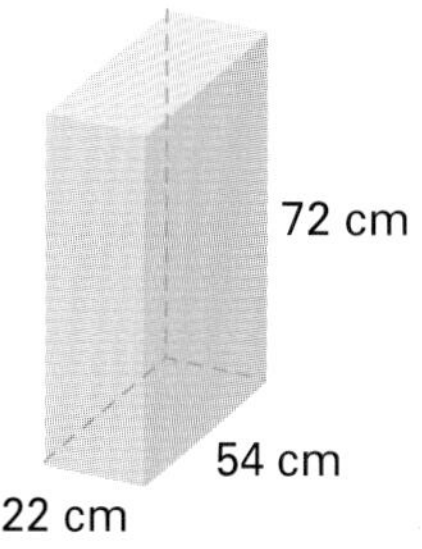


## Apply the Concepts

5. **Communication**
   a) Calculate the surface area of the cube.
   b) Use the formula $S = 6l^2$ to calculate the surface area of the cube ($l$ is the side length of the cube).
   c) Compare your results in parts a) and b).
   d) Explain why the formula in part b) works.

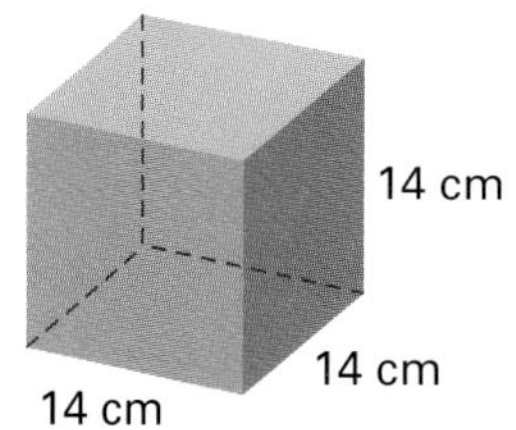


6. **Application** An aquarium tank has a base that measures 42 cm by 48 cm, and a height of 30 cm. The plastic lid for the tank is sold separately.
   a) Draw a net for the tank, without its lid, and label the dimensions. How many faces are there?
   b) Calculate the surface area of the tank, including the base but without the lid.
   c) How much glass is saved by making the lid from plastic?

**Chapter Problem**

7. Cliff designs a box-shaped platform for his spacecraft. He wants the platform to be 15 cm high and have a square base.
   **a)** What should the dimensions of Cliff's platform be? Explain.
   **b)** Draw a diagram of this platform and label the dimensions.
   **c)** Cliff decides to paint the top and all four sides of the platform. Determine the total surface area to be painted.

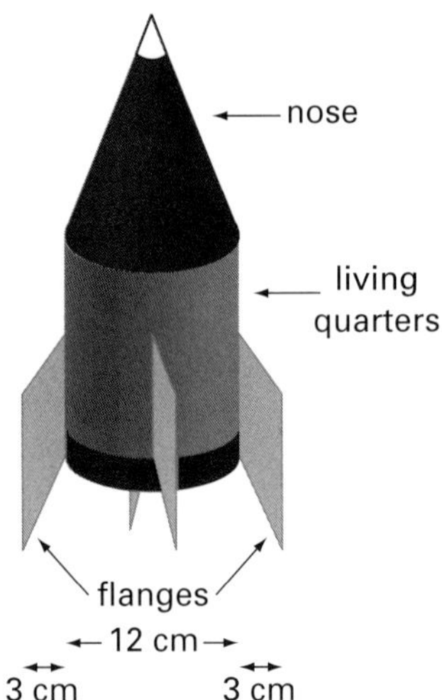


**C** 8. **Thinking/Inquiry/Problem Solving**

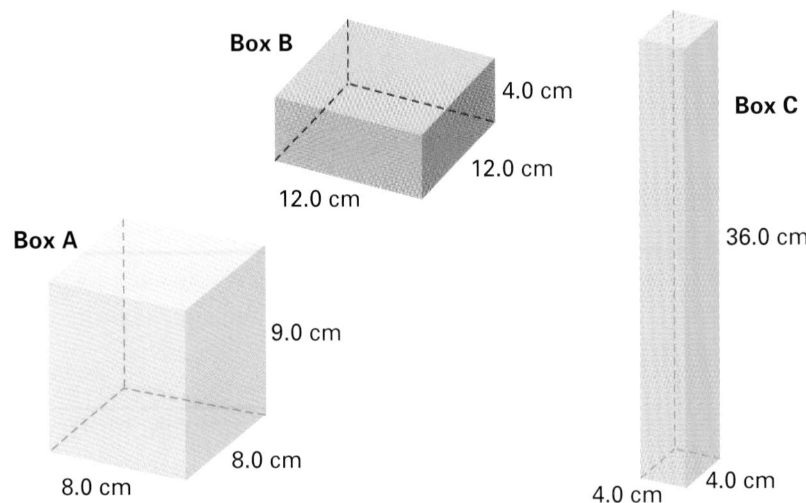


**a)** Predict which box has the least volume. Which has the most?
**b)** Calculate the volume of each box. Compare these results to your predictions.
**c)** Predict which box has the least surface area. Which has the most?
**d)** Calculate the surface area of each box. Compare the results to your predictions.
**e)** A square-based box is to have a volume of 576 $cm^3$. What dimensions do you think will use the least surface area? Use these dimensions to calculate the surface area and compare this result to your answers for part d).

9. **Thinking/Inquiry/Problem Solving, Communication**

   a) Calculate the surface area of a cube that has a side length of 0.5 m.

   b) Predict what will happen to the surface area when you double the side length.

   c) Calculate the surface area for a cube with double the side length. Compare the result with your prediction. Describe what you notice.

   d) Double the side length again, and repeat parts b) and c).

   e) Predict what will happen to the surface area if you triple the side length of the original cube. Test your prediction. Were you correct?

10. **Problem Solving**

   a) Determine the total surface area of this child's building block.

   b) How much paint is required to paint the block's surface, if 1 L of paint covers an area of 10 000 $cm^2$?

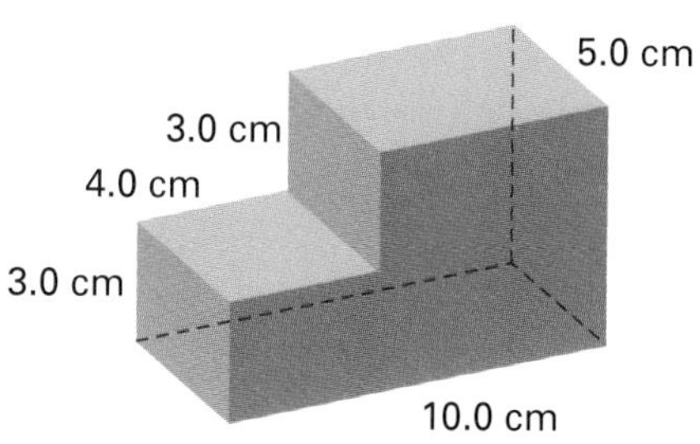

# 3.4 Surface Area: Cylinders and Prisms

The wing of a large passenger airplane has two functions. It holds the fuel for the engines, and provides lift to keep the airplane in the air. So, the airplane's design should take account of both the volume and the surface area of the wing.

Nets are often helpful in recognizing the two-dimensional surfaces of an object, and in finding their dimensions.

## DISCOVER

**Materials**

- soup or juice cans (with labels)
- string
- ruler
- water

### Finding the Surface Area of a Cylinder

Work with a partner or in a small group to analyse the construction of a can.

1. Select a can. Follow these steps to draw a net for the can:
   - **a)** Without tearing, dampen and carefully remove the label of the can. Lay the label flat on a blank piece of paper. What shape does the flattened label make?
   - **b)** Trace the label onto the paper, as shown. Measure and label the length and width of this shape.
   - **c)** Place the bottom of the can above the label trace, so that the circle just touches the top of the rectangle. Trace around the can.

## Did You Know?

Some cylindrical products use a different net. For example, the tube for a roll of paper towels has a slanting seam. It is made from a parallelogram rolled at an angle.

d) Measure the diameter of the circle. Calculate the circumference. How does this compare to the length of the label tracing?

e) Place the can just below the rectangle and repeat part c). Your net should look like this:

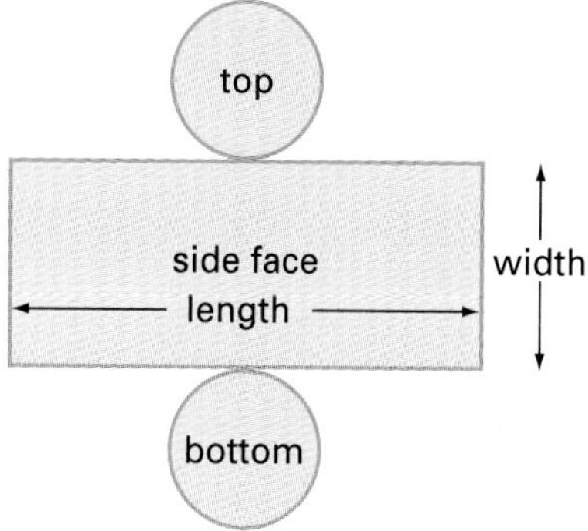


2. Apply the formula for the area of a circle to calculate the area of the top and bottom faces of your cylinder.

3. Apply the formula for the area of a rectangle to calculate the area of the side face.

4. Add the areas of the top, bottom, and side faces to determine the total surface area of the cylinder.

5. a) Compare the measure of the circumference with the length of the side face, and describe what you notice.
   b) Explain why this relationship exists.

When finding the surface area of a cylinder, you need to add the areas of two identical circles and a rectangle.

Therefore, the total surface area can be calculated as:

$$S_{cylinder} = \underset{\text{(top + bottom)}}{2(\pi r^2)} + \underset{\text{(side face)}}{lw}$$

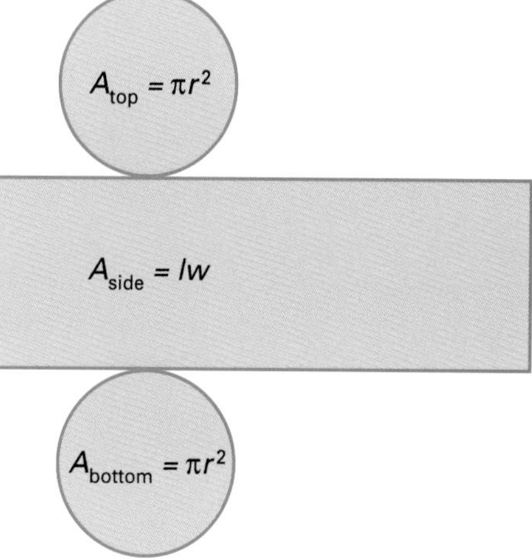

Think of the label wrapping around the side face of the can. The length of the side face is equal to the circumference of either circle. The width of the side face is equal to the height of the can.

$S_{cylinder} = 2\pi r^2 + 2\pi rh$

$C = 2\pi r$

$l = 2\pi r$

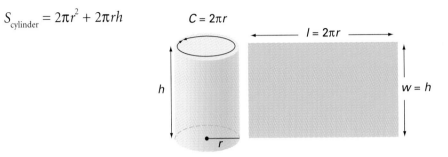

$h$

$w = h$

$r$

Go to *www.mcgrawhill.ca/links/MATC9* for an interactive activity for measuring the surface area of cylinders.

## EXAMPLE 1

### Surface Area of a Cylinder Using a Formula

Find the area of aluminum needed to make a can with height 16.5 cm and diameter 12.8 cm.

### Solution

Draw a diagram and label the dimensions.

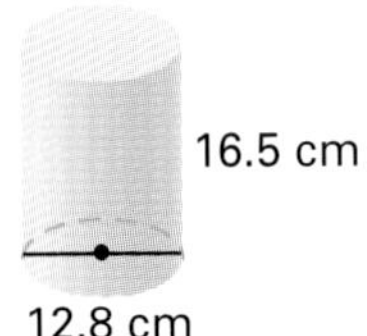


The height is 16.5 cm.
The radius is half of 12.8 cm, or 6.4 cm.

$$\begin{aligned} S_{cylinder} &= 2\pi r^2 + 2\pi rh \\ &= 2 \times \pi \times (6.4)^2 + 2 \times \pi \times 6.4 \times 16.5 \\ &\doteq 921 \end{aligned}$$

The amount of aluminum required is 921 cm$^2$, to three digits of accuracy.

## Example 2

**Did You Know?**

The largest moveable tent in history, Tensile 1, is used to stage exhibitions around the world. Its surface measures 11 000 $m^2$, and is anchored to a double row of poles 25 m high.

### Surface Area of a Triangular Prism

Determine the amount of material needed to make the tent shown.

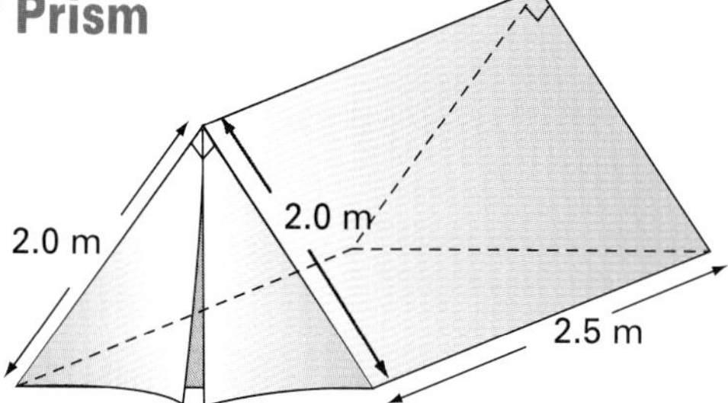


### Solution

Each end is a right triangle.

$$\begin{aligned} A_{end} &= \frac{1}{2}bh \\ &= \frac{1}{2} \times 2.0 \times 2.0 \\ &= 2.0 \end{aligned}$$

**In a right triangle, *b* and *h* are the two shorter sides.**

Apply the formula for the area of a rectangle for one side face.

$$\begin{aligned} A_{side} &= 2.0 \times 2.5 \\ &= 5.0 \end{aligned}$$

To calculate the area of the bottom of the tent, first calculate its width. Since the width is also the hypotenuse of a right triangle, apply the Pythagorean theorem.

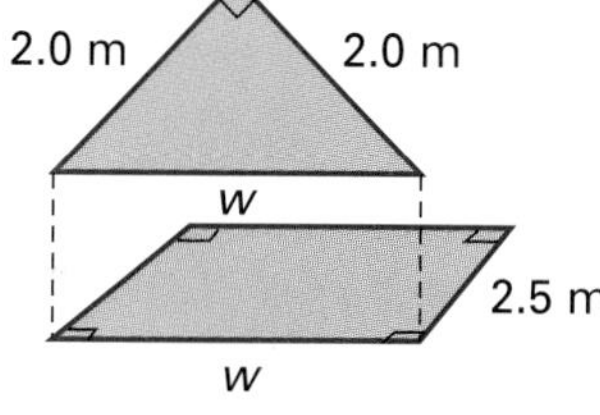


$$\begin{aligned} w^2 &= (2.0)^2 + (2.0)^2 \\ w^2 &= 4.0 + 4.0 \\ w^2 &= 8.0 \\ \sqrt{w^2} &= \sqrt{8.0} \\ w &\doteq 2.83 \end{aligned}$$

**Take the square root of both sides.**

The width of the bottom rectangle is 2.83 m.

Now, apply the formula for the area of a rectangle.

$$\begin{aligned} A_{bottom} &= lw \\ &= 2.5 \times 2.83 \\ &\doteq 7.07 \end{aligned}$$

To determine the total surface area, add up the areas of the five surfaces.

$$\begin{aligned} S &= \underset{\text{(ends)}}{2A_{end}} + \underset{\text{(sides)}}{2A_{side}} + \underset{\text{(bottom)}}{A_{bottom}} \\ &= 2 \times 2.0 + 2 \times 5.0 + 7.07 \\ &\doteq 21 \end{aligned}$$

The tent requires 21 $m^2$ of material, to two digits of accuracy.

## Key Concepts

- The net for a cylinder consists of a rectangle and two identical circles. The length of the rectangle equals the circumference of each circle.
- The surface area of a cylinder can be calculated using the formula:

  $S_{cylinder} = 2\pi r^2 + 2\pi rh$
- The surface area of a solid object can be determined by adding up the areas of all the outer faces of the object.
- Nets can be helpful in recognizing the shapes and dimensions of faces.

## Discuss the Concepts

1. How many surfaces does each three-dimensional shape have? Describe the shapes of the surfaces.

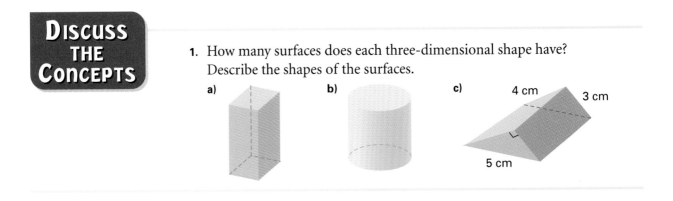

a) 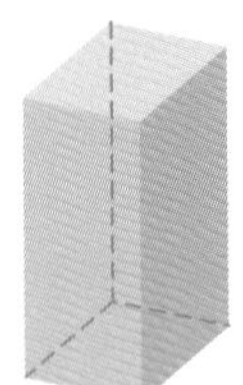

b) 

c) 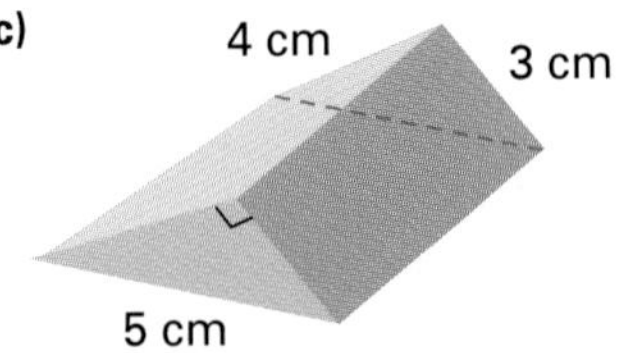


## Practise

**A** *Include proper units with your answers. Round your answers appropriately.*
*For help with questions 1 and 2, refer to Example 1 or 2.*

1. Determine the surface area of each cylinder shown.

a) 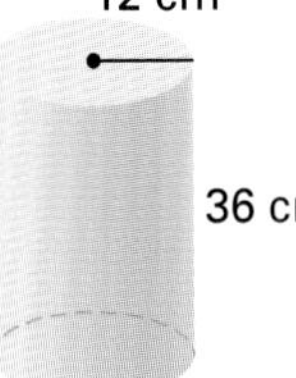


b) 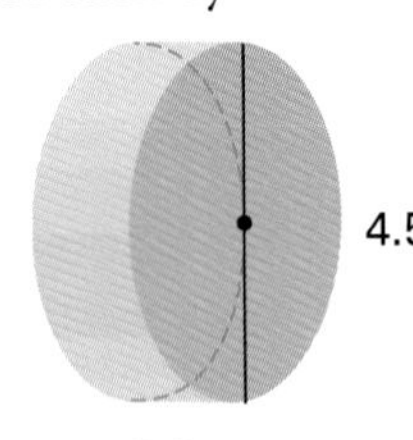


c) 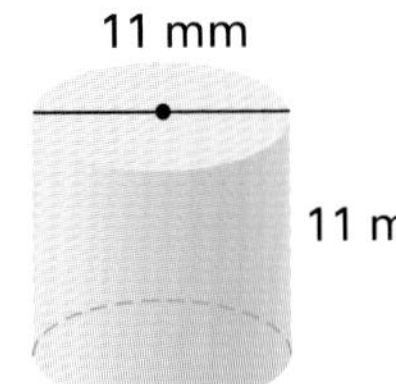


**B** 2. Calculate the surface area of each solid shape.

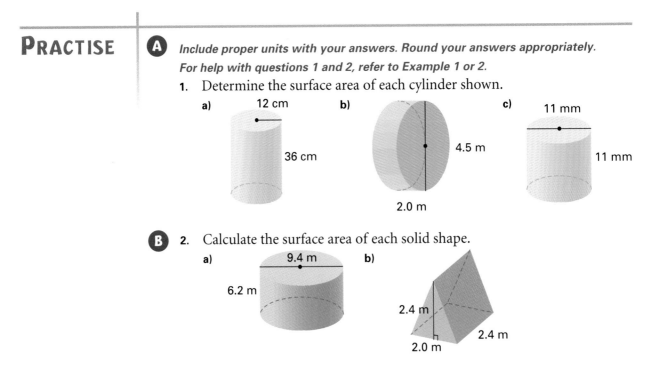

a) 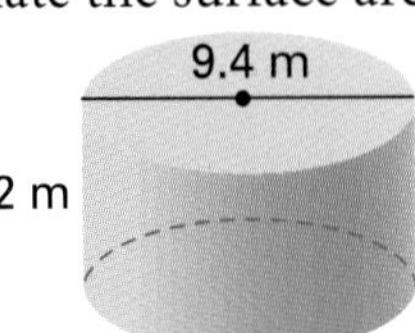


b) 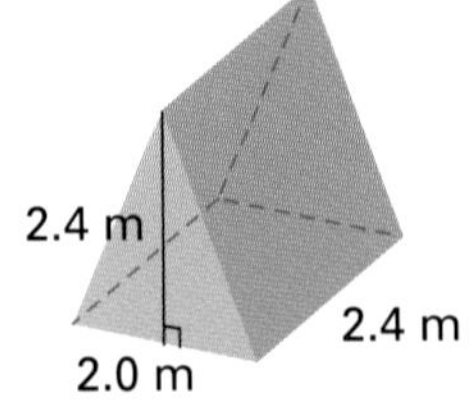

## Apply the Concepts

3. **Application** Determine the outer surface area of a cylindrical pail that has a radius of 16 cm and a height of 34 cm. The pail has a bottom, but no lid.

4. **Thinking/Inquiry/Problem Solving, Communication**
   a) Which do you think will have a greater surface area: Cylinder X, which has a radius of 4 cm and a height of 8 cm, or Cylinder Y, which has a radius of 8 cm and a height of 4 cm?
   b) Calculate the surface area of each cylinder. Compare the results to your prediction and explain what you notice.
   c) Which of these cylinders do you think has the greater volume?
   d) Calculate the volume of each cylinder. Compare the results to your prediction and explain what you notice.

5. Determine the surface area of each triangular prism.
   a) 15 cm, 24 cm, 12 cm
   b) 3.0 m, 4.5 m

6. **Communication** A chocolate bar is in the shape of a triangular prism, as shown.
   a) Draw a net for this prism.
   b) Calculate the surface area.

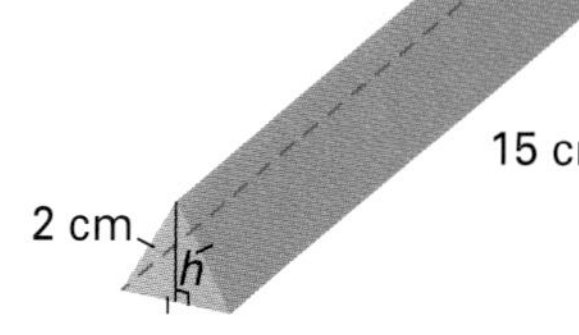


C 8. **Cheese Packaging** A piece of cheese has the shape of a right-angled triangular prism.
   a) Determine the minimum surface area for a wrapper.
   b) Describe the steps in your solution.
   c) In practice, the wrapper is formed from a rectangular piece of waxed paper. Suggest a minimum length and width for the wrapper, and calculate its area. Hint: Draw a net of the surface of the piece of cheese.

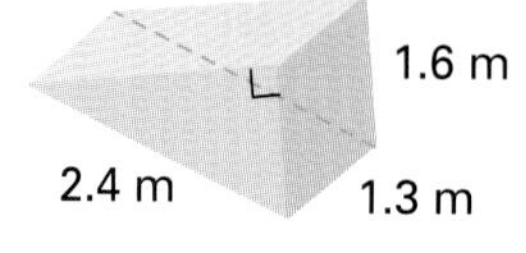

# 3.5 Minimizing Surface Area

The design of a product's package is very important. Merchandisers want their packages to be

- practical
- visually appealing
- cost-efficient

The boxes and cylinders used for packaging come in so many different sizes and shapes. Which ones are the best?

## DISCOVER 1

### Comparing the Volumes and Surface Areas of Different Cylinders

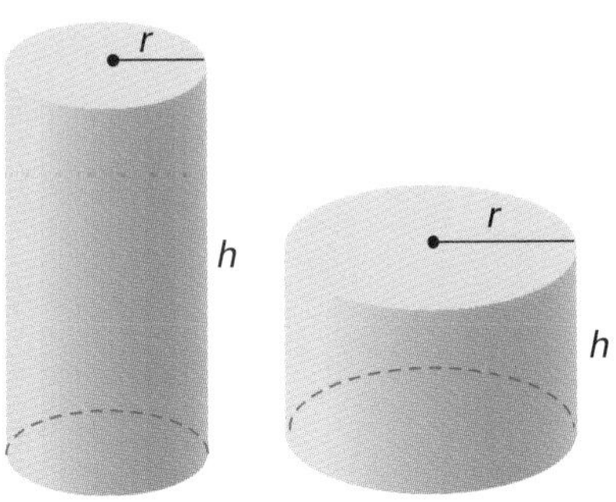


1. Compare the two cylinders shown. Which do you think has the greater volume? Explain why.
2. a) Measure the radius and height of each cylinder and calculate its volume.
   b) Compare the volumes. Was your prediction correct? Explain.
3. Based on your findings, which cylinder do you think has the greater surface area? Do you think they have the same surface area? Explain.
4. a) Calculate the surface area of each cylinder.
   b) Compare the surface areas. Was your prediction correct?

Two drink cans may have different dimensions, but the same volume. Minimizing the surface area of a can reduces material costs and waste.

## DISCOVER 2

**Materials**

- transparent beakers and/or graduated cylinders
- unpopped popcorn, rice, or water
- ruler

### Comparing the Surface Areas of Cylinders With the Same Volume

Work with a partner or in a small group.

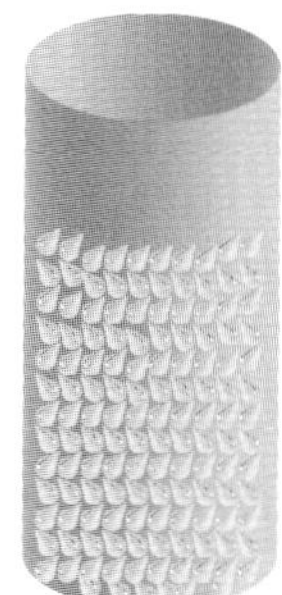

1. Take the narrowest container and fill it three-quarters full with popcorn. Gently shake the container to level the popcorn.

2. a) Measure the radius of this container and the height of the popcorn.
   b) Use these measurements to calculate the volume of popcorn.
   c) Imagine that a lid to this container was placed just high enough to contain the popcorn. Calculate the surface area needed to enclose this volume. Record your results in a table.

| Container | Radius (cm) | Height (cm) | Volume (cm$^3$) | Surface Area (cm$^2$) |
|---|---|---|---|---|
| small beaker | | | | |
| large beaker | | | | |
| | | | | |

3. a) Transfer the popcorn into one of the other cylinders. Be careful not to spill any, to ensure a constant volume.
   b) After levelling the popcorn, record the new radius and height measurements.
   c) Calculate the surface area needed to hold this volume.

4. a) Repeat step 3 for each container.
   b) Which container requires the minimum surface area? What do you think is special about this type of cylinder?
   c) Describe any patterns that you observe.

5. Is there a relationship between the radius and the height of a cylinder that will minimize surface area for a given volume? Explain this relationship.

**DISCOVER 3**

**Materials**
- several sheets of paper
- scissors
- tape
- ruler

## Minimizing Surface Area of a Square-Based Prism

Work with a partner or a small group. You will construct several boxes, to see if there is a way to minimize surface area in package design. Each box is to have a volume of 100 cm$^3$.

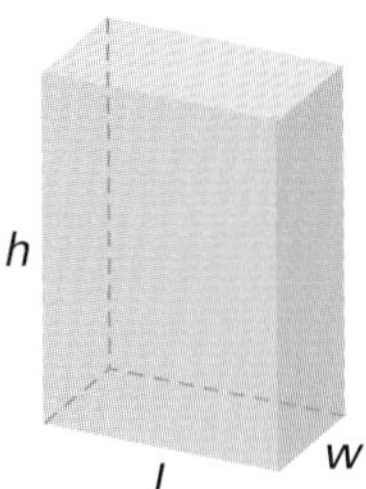


The volume of a box can be found using the formula:
$V = lwh$

When the base is square, $l = w$, and the above formula can be written as:
$V = llh$
$V = l^2h$

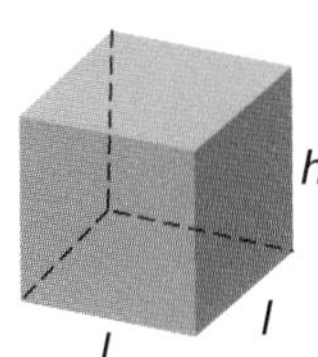


Since all boxes that you will construct are to have a volume of 100 cm$^3$, substitute this value for $V$:
$100 = l^2h$

You will choose several length values.

1. Let Box A have a 3 cm by 3 cm base. Calculate the height.
   $100 = 3^2 \times h$
   $100 = 9 \times h$
   $100 \div 9 = h$ **Divide both sides by 9.**
   $h \doteq 11.1$ **Check: 3 cm × 3 cm × 11.1 cm ≐ 100 cm$^3$**
   Box A will measure 3 cm by 3 cm by 11.1 cm. Draw a net for this box.

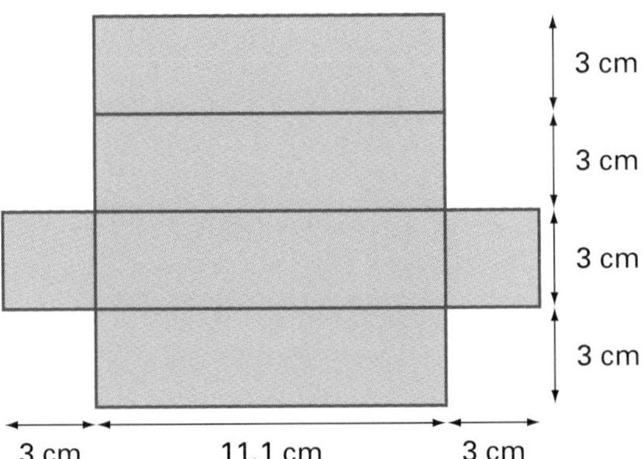


2. Construct Box A using scissors and tape.

3. Determine the surface area of Box A.

4. Repeat steps 1 to 3 for several different square-based boxes. Remember that the volume of every box must be 100 cm$^3$. Organize your results in a table.

| Box | Base, $l \times l$ (cm) | Height, $h$ (cm) | Volume (cm$^3$) | Surface Area (cm$^2$) |
|---|---|---|---|---|
| A | $3 \times 3$ | 11.1 | 100 | |
| B | $4 \times 4$ | | 100 | |
| C | | | 100 | |
| ... | | | | |

5. Examine your results. Try to determine the dimensions that will produce the box with the minimum surface area. Try some decimal values between the dimensions from step 4 that seem best.

6. a) What are the dimensions of the box that has the minimum surface area? Give your result to one decimal place.
   b) What is the value of the minimum surface area?
   c) Describe what you notice about the relationship between the length, width, and height of the minimum surface area box.

## Key Concepts

- Minimizing surface area for a given volume is important when designing packages and containers, in order to save on materials.
- A cylinder will contain the most volume for its surface area, when its height equals its diameter.
- A square-based box will contain the most volume for its surface area, when it is cube-shaped.

## Discuss the Concepts

1. a) Describe a situation when you would need to minimize the surface area for a given volume.
   b) If you look around a supermarket, you will see that
      • large cans are usually about as high as they are wide
      • soup cans are taller than their width
      • cans of salmon or tuna are shorter than their width
      Suggest a reason for each shape.

2. What is the relationship between radius and height of a minimum surface area cylinder?

## PRACTISE

***Include proper units with your answers. Round your answers appropriately.***

1. The cylinders shown below all have the same volume. Rank them in order from least to greatest surface area.

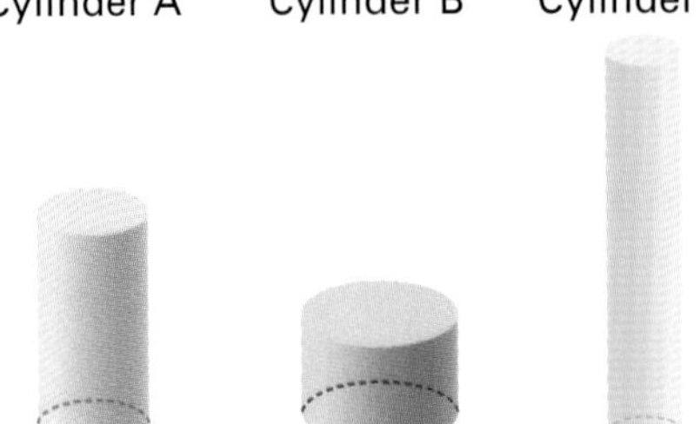


2. The square-based boxes shown below all have the same volume. Rank them in order from least to greatest surface area.

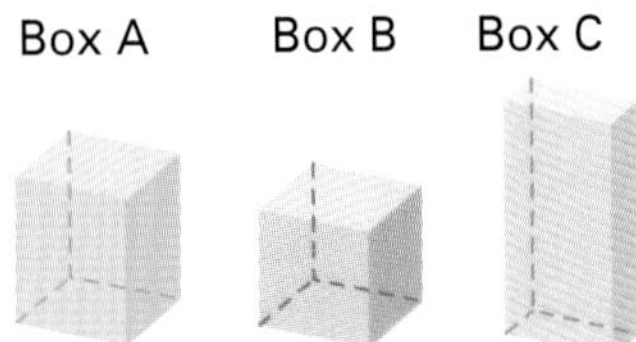


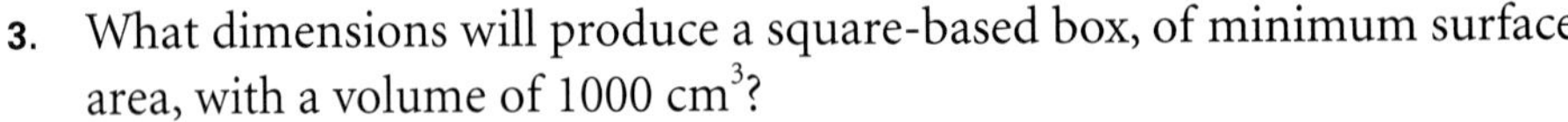

## APPLY THE CONCEPTS

3. What dimensions will produce a square-based box, of minimum surface area, with a volume of 1000 $cm^3$?

4. **Communication**
   a) What dimensions will produce a square-based box, of minimum surface area, that will contain 2 L of detergent? 1 L = 1000 $cm^3$
   b) Explain how you solved this problem.

5. **Application** Design a cylindrical plastic container, of minimum surface area, that will hold 500 $cm^3$ of flour. Hint: Consider possible values for the radius, and use your values to calculate the height. Remember, you need the height to be twice the radius.

6. **Application, Communication**
   a) Design a cylindrical can that will hold 400 mL of soda.
   b) Explain the steps to your solution.

**Chapter Problem**

7. Cliff decides to build a wooden case to carry and transport his entire design and technology project. The box is to hold the spacecraft, moon rocks, platform, and all reports and pictures. Cliff estimates that the box's volume must be 100 000 $cm^3$. Cliff builds a square-based box with a lid that requires as little wood as possible.

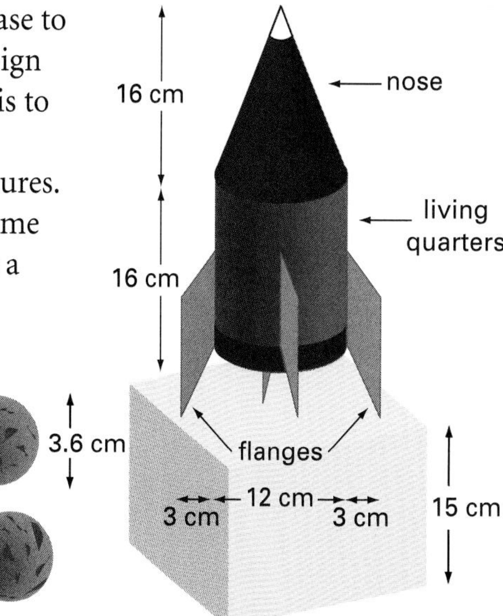


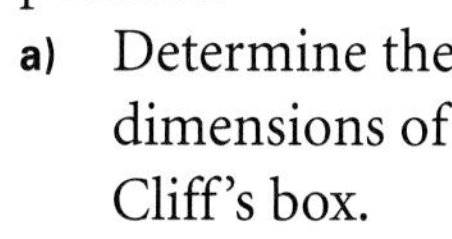


   a) Determine the dimensions of Cliff's box.
   b) Determine the total surface area of the box.
   c) Could Cliff use a smaller box? Suggest, with reasons, the dimensions you would use.

8. **Inquiry/Problem Solving** How can you minimize the surface area of a box with no lid? Suppose you need to design a square-based, lidless box that has a volume of 100 $cm^3$.
   a) Carry out an investigation to determine the dimensions of the minimum surface area box.
   b) Compare your results to those in **Discover 3** on page 108. Are the dimensions the same or different?
   c) Does the lidless box require more, less, or the same amount of material to construct, compared to a six-sided box?

C 9. **Inquiry/Problem Solving** How can you minimize the surface area of a pail? Suppose you need to design a cylindrical pail, with no lid, that can hold a volume of 10 L.

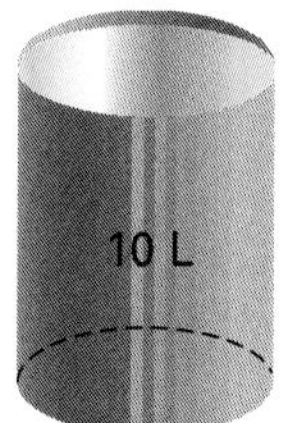


   a) Carry out an investigation to determine the dimensions of the minimum surface area pail.
   b) Describe any relationship that you notice between the height and the radius or diameter of the minimum surface area pail.

# Review

## 3.1 Volume: Prisms and Cylinders, pages 80–85

1. Find the volume of each shape.

   a) 2.8 cm, 3.5 cm, 3.1 cm

   b) 5.0 mm

2. Calculate the volume of this tent.

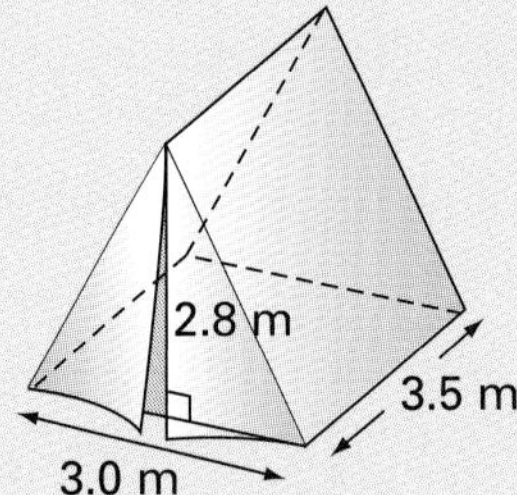


3. A cylindrical farm silo has a diameter of 3.8 m and a height of 5.2 m.
   a) Draw the silo and label its dimensions.
   b) Find the volume of the silo.

## 3.2 Volume: Cones and Spheres, pages 86–91

4. A marble has a radius of 12.5 mm. Calculate its volume.

5. After practice, a hockey team gathers the pucks and carries them off in an inverted pylon.

   a) Calculate the volume of the pylon.
   b) Find the volume of one puck.
   c) Approximately how many pucks equal one pylon in volume? Is this a reasonable estimate of the number of pucks a pylon can hold? Explain why or why not.

6. Cliff has determined that the volume of the living quarters for his spacecraft model is about 1800 $cm^3$.
   a) Predict how many times greater the volume of the living quarters is than the volume of the nose of the spacecraft. Explain your prediction.
   b) Calculate the volume of the nose.
   c) Compare this value to the volume of the living quarters. Was your prediction correct?

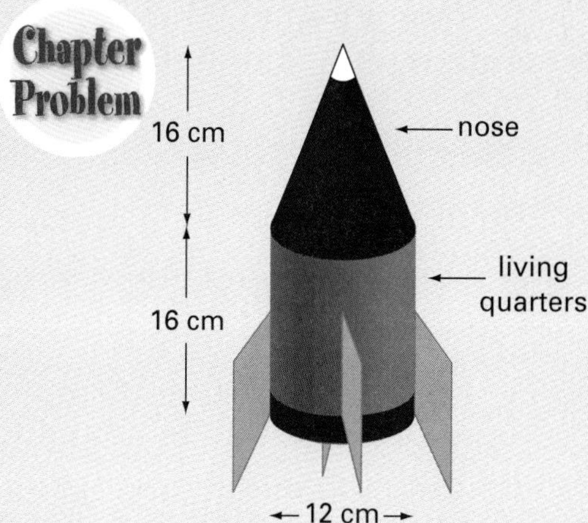


## 3.3 Surface Area: Rectangular Prisms, pages 92–99

7. a) Draw a net for the box shown, and label the dimensions.
   b) Determine the surface area.

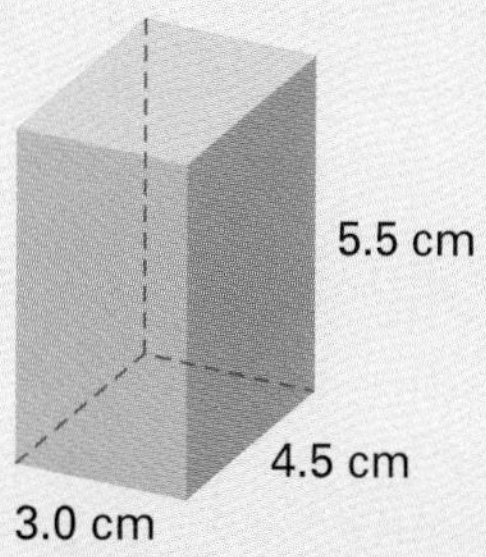


8. Determine the surface area of a square-based prism that has a base side length of 5.4 cm and a height of 8.2 cm.

## 3.4 Surface Area: Cylinders and Prisms, pages 100–105

9. Determine the surface area of a cylindrical storage tank with radius 5.7 m and height 5.7 m.

## 3.5 Minimizing Surface Area, pages 106–111

10. You are to design a jewellery box with a square base and a volume of 250 $cm^3$.
    a) Use trial and error to determine the dimensions of the box that has minimum surface area.
    b) Determine the surface area of this box.

11. A cylindrical storage tank is to have a capacity of 50 000 L.
    a) Use trial and error to determine the dimensions of the cylinder that has minimum surface area.
    b) Determine the surface area of this tank.

# Practice Test

## Multiple Choice

***For questions 1 to 7, select the best answer. Some answers have been rounded.***

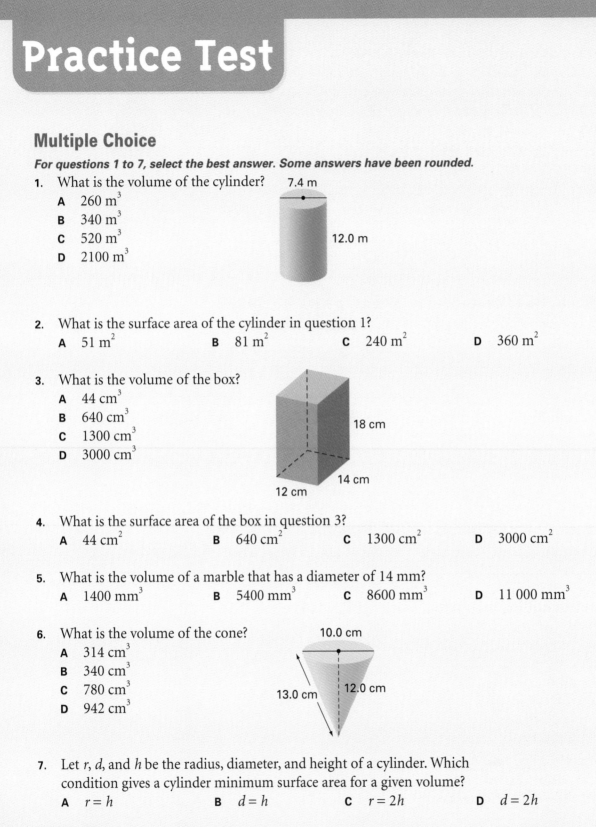

1. What is the volume of the cylinder?

   A $260\text{ m}^3$
   B $340\text{ m}^3$
   C $520\text{ m}^3$
   D $2100\text{ m}^3$

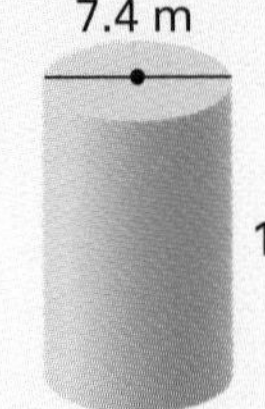


2. What is the surface area of the cylinder in question 1?

   A $51\text{ m}^2$  B $81\text{ m}^2$  C $240\text{ m}^2$  D $360\text{ m}^2$

3. What is the volume of the box?

   A $44\text{ cm}^3$
   B $640\text{ cm}^3$
   C $1300\text{ cm}^3$
   D $3000\text{ cm}^3$

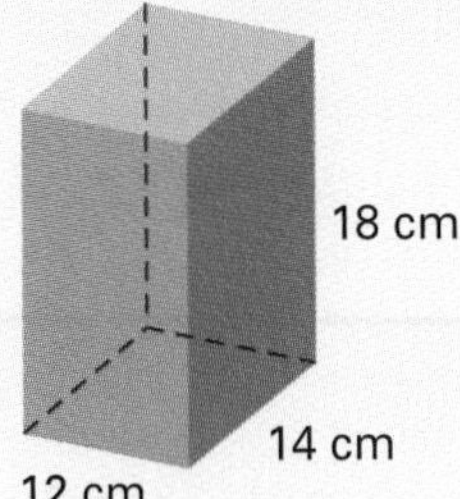


4. What is the surface area of the box in question 3?

   A $44\text{ cm}^2$  B $640\text{ cm}^2$  C $1300\text{ cm}^2$  D $3000\text{ cm}^2$

5. What is the volume of a marble that has a diameter of 14 mm?

   A $1400\text{ mm}^3$  B $5400\text{ mm}^3$  C $8600\text{ mm}^3$  D $11\,000\text{ mm}^3$

6. What is the volume of the cone?

   A $314\text{ cm}^3$
   B $340\text{ cm}^3$
   C $780\text{ cm}^3$
   D $942\text{ cm}^3$

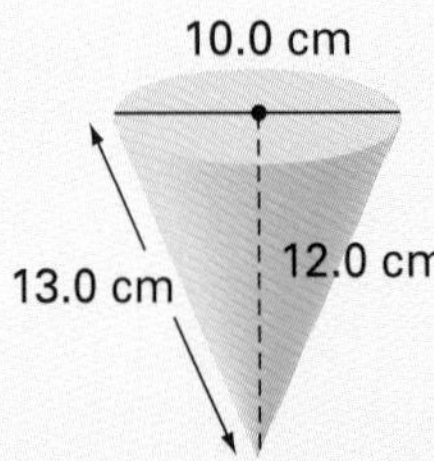


7. Let $r$, $d$, and $h$ be the radius, diameter, and height of a cylinder. Which condition gives a cylinder minimum surface area for a given volume?

   A $r = h$  B $d = h$  C $r = 2h$  D $d = 2h$

## Short Answer

**8.** Container A is a cube with a side length of 30 cm. Container B is a cylindrical can with radius 15 cm and height 30 cm.

**a)** Sketch each container and clearly indicate its measurements.

**b)** Determine which container has a greater volume, and by how much.

**9.** Olav is painting and decorating his tree house, built in the shape of a triangular prism. Unfortunately, while taking measurements, Olav drops his tape measure into the bushes below, and cannot find it. Determine the surface area and volume of Olav's tree house, based on the measurements he has already taken.

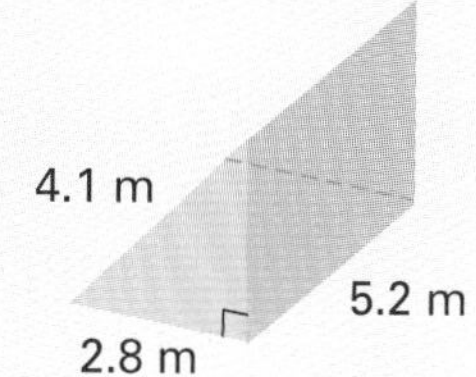


**10.** A square-based box is to have a volume of 729 cm$^3$. Determine the dimensions that will give the box a minimum surface area.

## Extended Response

**11.** Claudia is designing a cylindrical can that will hold 525 mL of soup. She builds a cylinder whose radius equals its height, and claims that this is the best design because it minimizes the surface area. Mathematics tells you that Claudia's design is not the best. Explain to Claudia what she should do instead, and why.

**ACHIEVEMENT CHECK** Knowledge/Understanding Thinking/Inquiry/Problem Solving Communication Application

**12.** Yevgeny and Luisa are planning to sell flavoured popcorn at a craft show. They would like to package their popcorn in identical boxes. Then, they plan to wrap the boxes with brightly coloured wrapping paper. They have found four possible square-based boxes, as shown.

**a)** Which of the boxes has a very different volume from the others? Show your work.

**b)** Of the boxes with approximately equal volumes, which has the smallest surface area, and will cost the least to wrap?

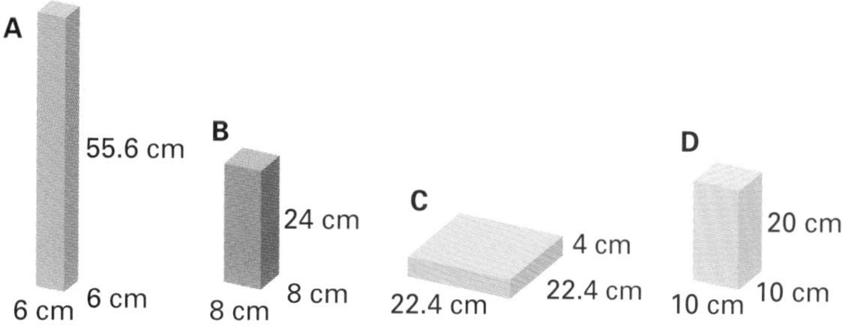


**c)** Is there another square-based box with this same volume that has an even smaller surface area? Explain.

# Cumulative Review

## Chapters 1 to 3

1. Find the perimeter of each shape.

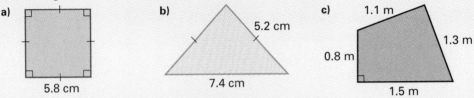

   a) 5.8 cm

   b) 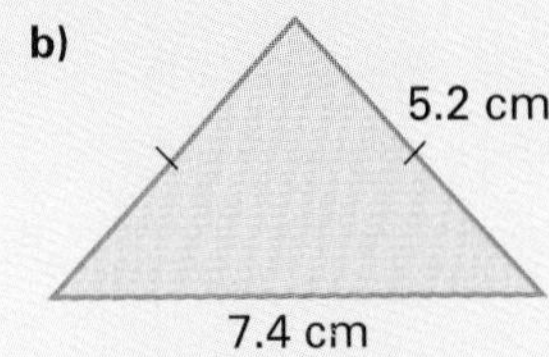


   c) 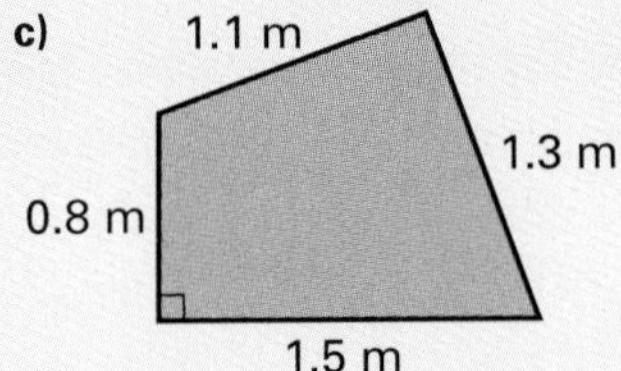


2. Estimate and then calculate the area of each circle.

   a) 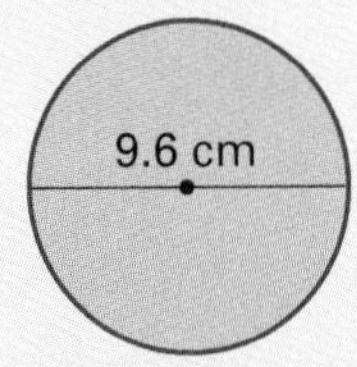


   b) 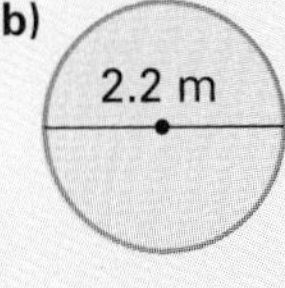


3. Evaluate each expression.

   a) $5^2 - 3 \times 4$ b) $120 \div 6 + 6$ c) $\sqrt{5^2 + 4 \times 6}$

4. **Application** The surface area of a cube can be found using the formula $S = 6l^2$, where $l$ is the length of one edge. Find the surface area of a cube with each edge length.

   a) 2 cm b) 30 cm c) 1.5 m

5. Solve for the missing side length in each triangle.

   a) 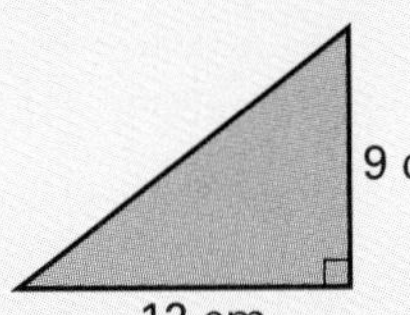


   b) 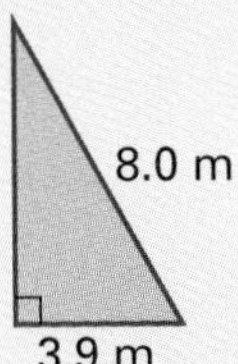


   c) 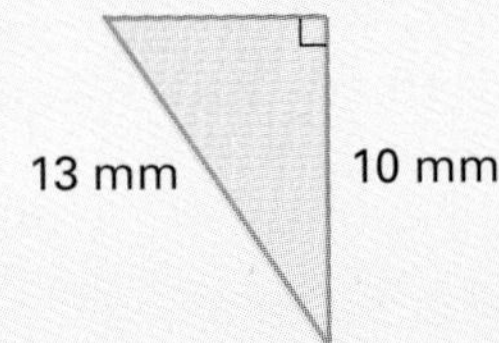


6. **Application** The Kim family are planning to redecorate their kitchen/dining room.

   a) What is the perimeter of the room?

   b) There are two doors in the room, each 0.9 m wide. What is the total length of baseboard to be painted?

   c) What area of carpet do the Kims need to buy? Explain your answer.

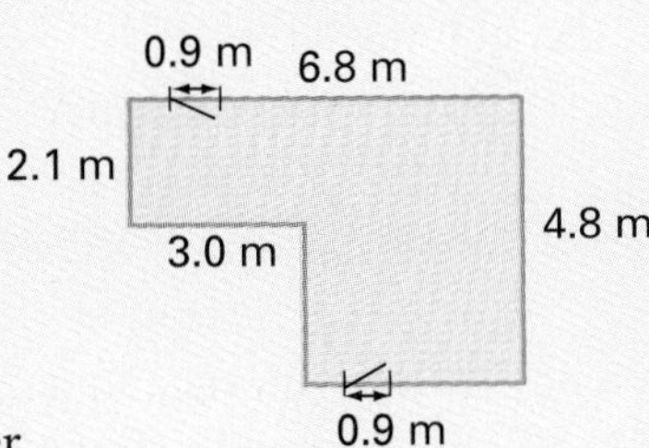

7. **Thinking/Inquiry/Problem Solving** The organisers of a fair decide to create a temporary parking lot in a field.
   - There are enough stakes and rope for 270 m of fencing.
   - An entrance and an exit are required, each 5 m wide.
   - The edge of the field is to be used for one side of the parking lot.

   Design a plan for the parking lot, creating as much area for cars as possible.

8. **Application** A cylindrical tank has a diameter of 2.60 m and a height of 1.65 m.
   a) Sketch the tank and label the measurements.
   b) Determine the volume of the tank.
   c) Express the storage capacity in litres.

9. **Sports balls** Hi-Bounce sports balls are made from a special elastic compound. The compound is poured into moulds in liquid form. If each ball is to be 3.2 cm in diameter, how many balls can be made from 12 L of the compound? (1 L = 1000 $cm^3$.)

10. **Communication** A box is to be 14 cm wide by 20 cm long by 11 cm high.
    a) Draw the box, and add labels for the dimensions.
    b) Draw a net for the box.
    c) Calculate the surface area of the box.
    d) Describe the method you used in part c).

11. **Application** A cylindrical storage tank is to be painted. The tank is 15.6 m high and has a diameter of 10.3 m.
    a) Calculate the surface area of the tank, including the top and the bottom.
    b) An area of 5.0 $m^2$ is covered by 1 L of paint. How much paint is needed to cover the tank?

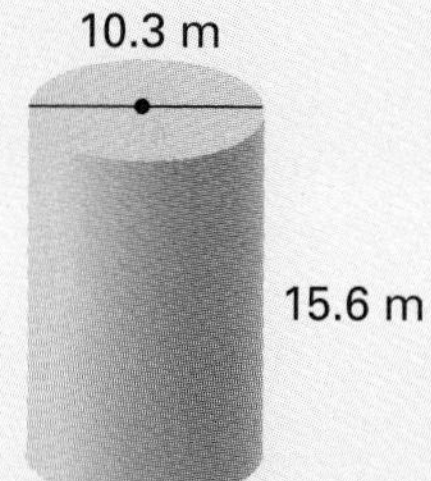


12. a) What is the relationship between diameter and height, for a minimum surface area cylinder?
    b) A soup can is to have a volume of 350 $cm^3$, and a radius of 3.8 cm. What is the height of the can? What is the can's diameter?
    c) Use trial and error to find the dimensions of a 350 $cm^3$-can that use the least material.

# Tasks

## CD Collection

Gregor has a collection of music CDs.

**a)** CDs have a diameter of exactly 12 cm. The unrecorded area in the centre of one CD has a diameter of 3.5 cm. How much area on this CD is available for storing recorded information?

**b)** Gregor wants to organize his CD collection in a container. Each plastic CD case measures 12.4 cm by 14.3 cm by 1.0 cm thick. He has found a wooden, lidless box that has inside dimensions 12.5 cm by 17.3 cm by 12.5 cm. How many CDs can Gregor fit in this box?

1.0 cm

14.3 cm

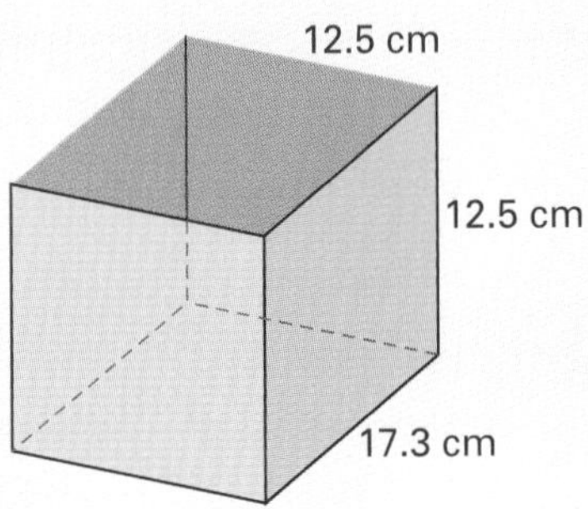

**c)** There are 143 CDs in Gregor's collection. What size of storage box would you recommend for the whole collection?

## Plastic Greenhouses

Hoa's Garden Centre sells two sizes of plastic greenhouses in the shape of rectangular prisms.

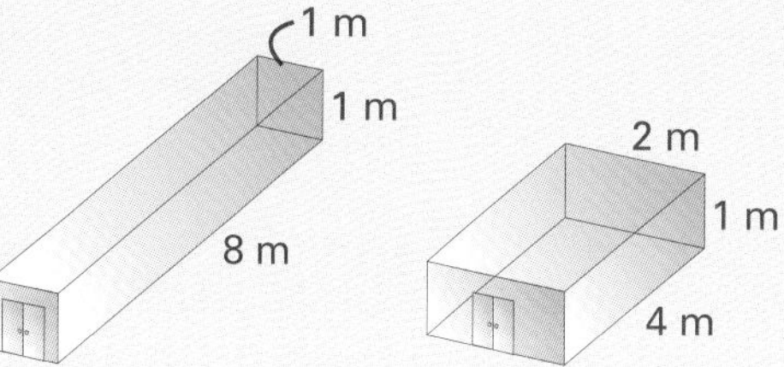


a) Calculate the volume of each greenhouse

b) Calculate the total area of plastic needed to construct each greenhouse. Hint: The floor is also made of plastic.

c) How many times more plastic does the first greenhouse require than the second one?

d) The greenhouses have metal frames that hold the plastic in place. The framing defines all the edges of the greenhouse and costs \$5/m. In addition, there are brackets, costing \$3.75 each, that connect the framing at each corner. Calculate the total cost of framing for each greenhouse.

e) Which greenhouse has more volume per square metre of plastic used? Explain your reasoning. Is it possible to design a more efficient greenhouse?

## Salt Pile

A conveyor belt unloading salt from a ship makes a conical pile 15 m high with a base diameter of 30 m.

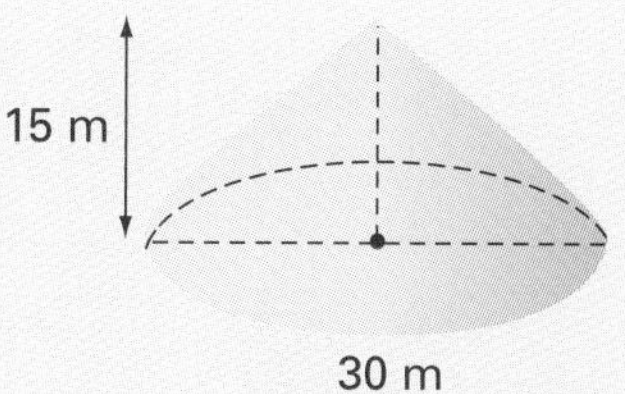


volume of a cone $= \frac{1}{3}\pi r^2 h$

surface area of a cone $= \pi rs$, where $s$ = slant height

a) What is the volume of the salt in the pile?

b) How much plastic sheeting would it take to cover the pile of salt?

c) The salt is transported in trailers 7.0 m long by 2.5 m wide and 2.0 m high. If each trailer can safely carry only three quarters of its volume, how many trailer loads of salt are in the pile?

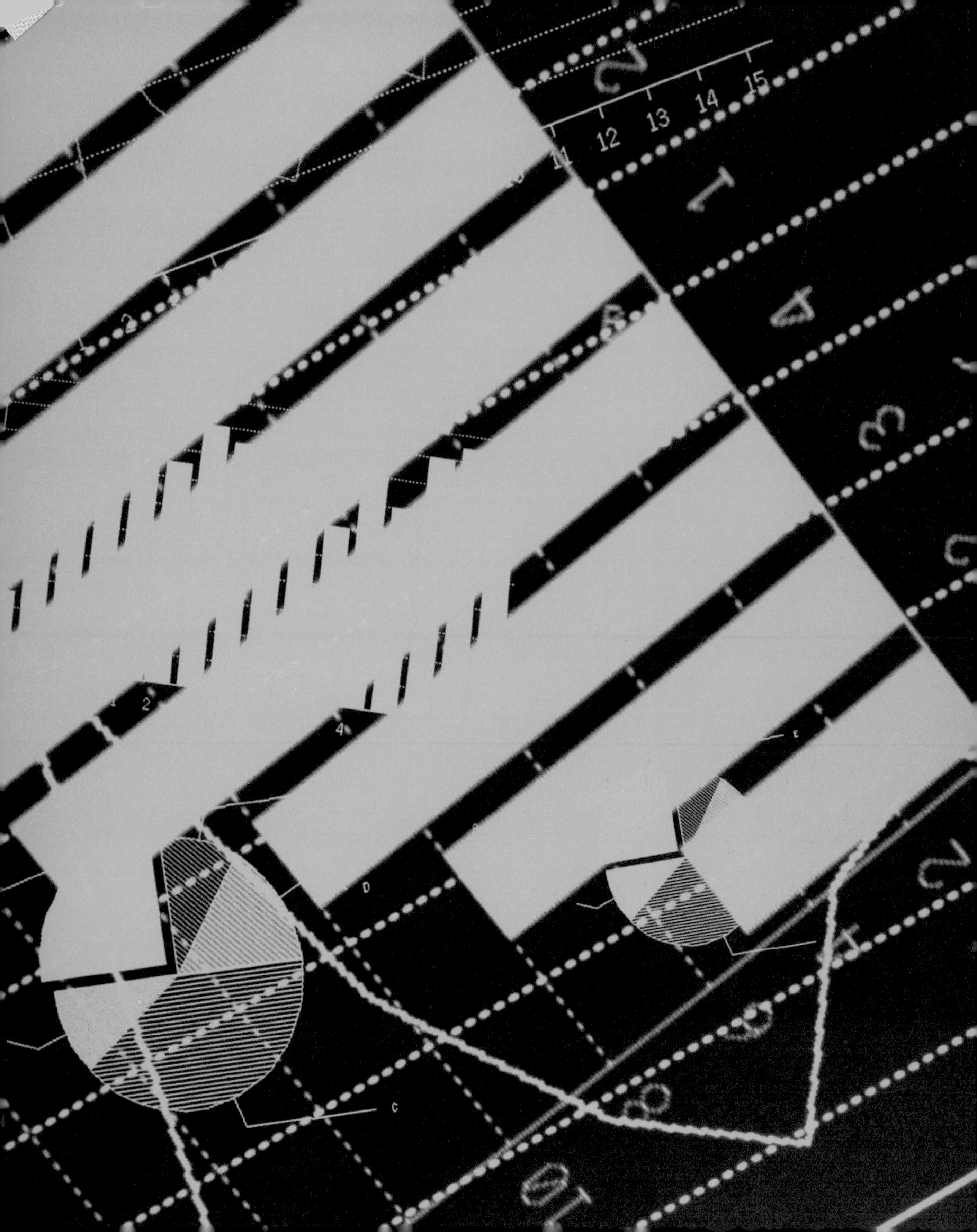

11
12
13
14
15
C
D
E

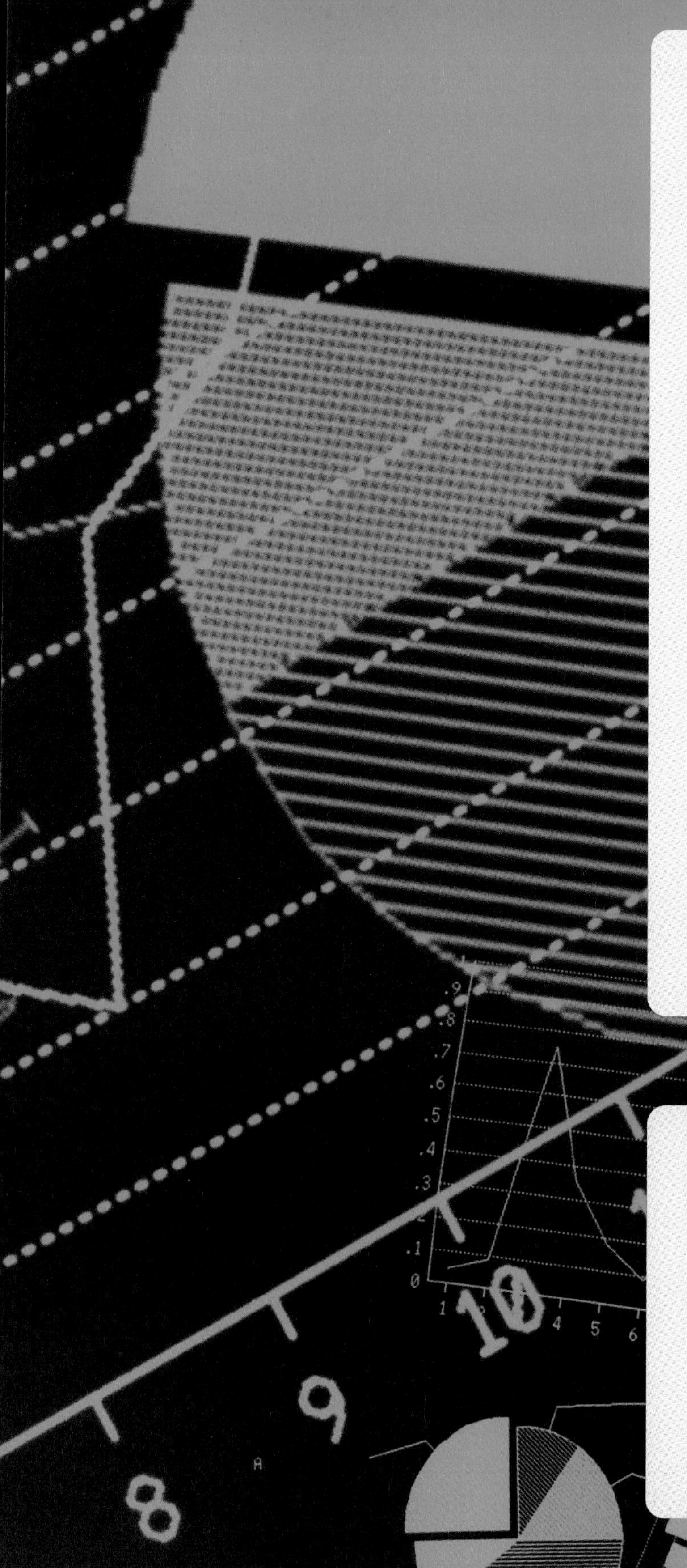

# CHAPTER 4

# Analysing Relationships With Data

You meet data relationships every day in many places. Some examples are:

- newspapers and magazines
- television
- sports
- the Internet
- school

In the chapter, you will learn to interpret and analyse data and to make conclusions based on data.

**Chapter Problem**

Develop a study of a topic relevant to you or to people your age. Look for a relationship between two data sets of numbers in your study. State a hypothesis for the topic you selected. Develop survey questions. Perform your survey to collect data. Organize, graph, and analyse your results. Make conclusions based on your results. Determine any related issues that you might study as a follow up.

# Get Ready

## Percent of a Number

Percent means "out of 100". For example, 12% means 12 out of 100.
A percent can be written in decimal or fraction form.

For example, 56% means 0.56 or, in fraction form, $\frac{56}{100}$ or $\frac{14}{25}$.

To find the percent of a number, write the percent as a decimal and then multiply by the number.

$$\begin{aligned} 15\% \text{ of } 60 &= 0.15 \times 60 \\ &= 9 \end{aligned}$$

1. Express each percent as a decimal, then as a fraction in lowest terms.

   **a)** 88% **b)** 16% **c)** 36% **d)** 75%
   **e)** 66% **f)** 15% **g)** 12.5% **h)** 8.75%

2. Use a calculator to express each fraction as a percent. Round to two decimal places.

   **a)** $\frac{68}{75}$ **b)** $\frac{39}{42}$ **c)** $\frac{5}{12}$ **d)** $\frac{2}{3}$

3. Find each amount.

   **a)** 12% of 40 **b)** 18% of $36.00 **c)** 5% of 320 m
   **d)** 21.5% of 2500 **e)** 4.5% of 20 kg **f)** 7.5% of 360°

## Interpreting Graphs

The graphs show the results of a survey of viewers' ratings of a new television program. E means Excellent, VG means Very Good, G means Good, F means Fair, P means Poor, and VP means Very Poor.

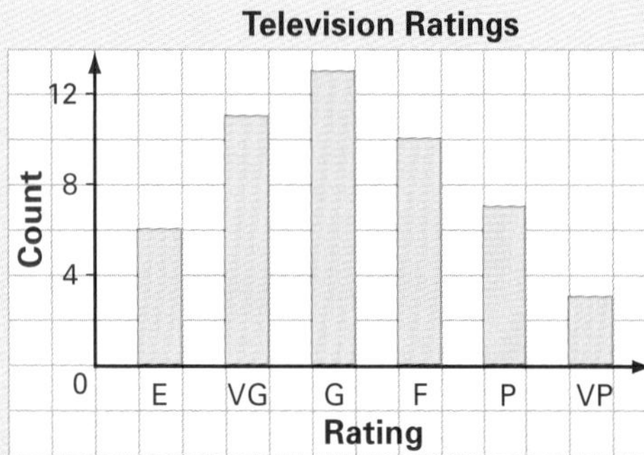


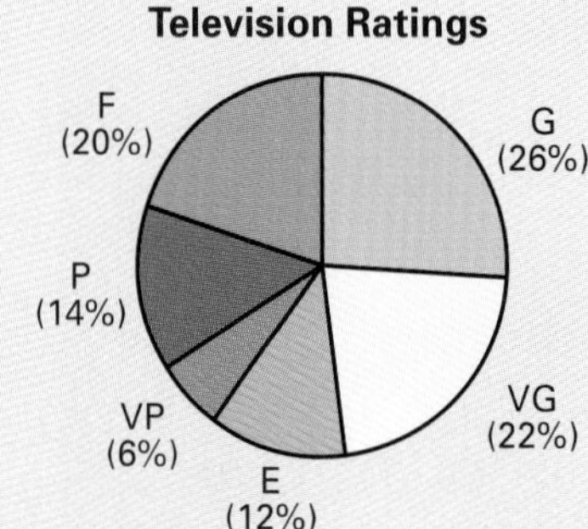

The total number of viewers surveyed is 50.
The most frequent response was Good, with 13 viewers giving this response.
The least frequent response was Very Poor, with 3 viewers giving this response.
The difference between the number of viewers responding Excellent, Very Good, or Good, and the number responding Fair, Poor, or Very Poor, is:

$$
\begin{aligned}
&(\text{Excellent} + \text{Very Good} + \text{Good}) - (\text{Fair} + \text{Poor} + \text{Very Poor}) \\
&= (6 + 11 + 13) - (10 + 7 + 3) \\
&= 30 - 20 \\
&= 10
\end{aligned}
$$

The results show that the new television program was reasonably well liked.

**4.** The graph shows the average daily attendance at a movie theatre.
- **a)** What type of graph is this?
- **b)** Which day had the greatest daily attendance?
- **c)** Which day had the lowest daily attendance?
- **d)** Why might daily attendance vary?
- **e)** How might the theatre manager use these data?

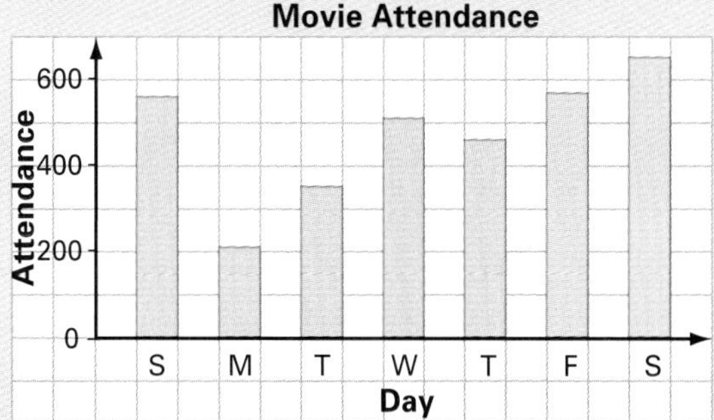


**5.** The graph shows the percent breakdown of favourite activities by members of a fitness club.
- **a)** What type of graph is this?
- **b)** Which activity is the favourite of the most members?
- **c)** Which activity is the least favourite?
- **d)** 200 members were surveyed. Calculate the number of members who selected each activity as their favourite.

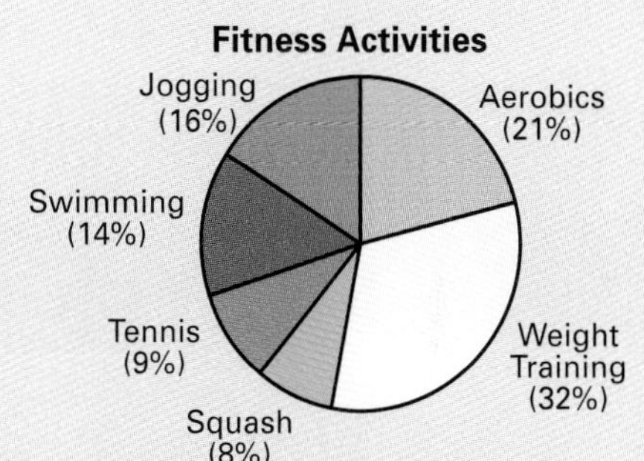


## Graphing Skills

The points A(1, 2), B(3, 6), C(7, 3), D(5, 0), E(0, 8) can be plotted on a coordinate grid, as shown.

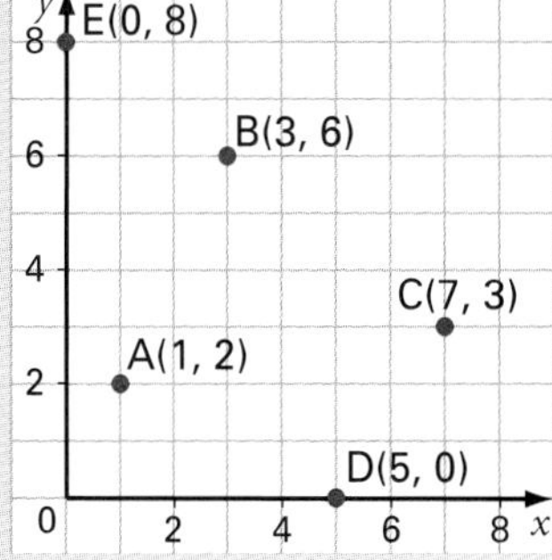


**6.** Plot these points on a coordinate grid.

| | | | |
|---|---|---|---|
| **a)** B(3, 5) | **b)** F(0, 4) | **c)** A(3, 0) | **d)** C(1, 5) |
| **e)** D(2, 2) | **f)** G(0, 0) | **g)** J(5, 1) | **h)** H(4, 3) |

**7.** **a)** Plot a graph of the following ordered pairs.
A(2, 6), B(4, 2), C(6, 4), D(8, 2), E(10, 6)
- **b)** Join the points with line segments in order from A to E. What letter is formed?

# 4.1 Formulating Hypotheses and Gathering Data

How often have you or a friend made a claim such as:

- Boys watch TV more than girls.
- It seems to rain more on weekends.

Each of these claims is known as a **hypothesis** and can be tested by taking a survey or collecting data.

## Making Hypotheses

Answer questions 1 and 2 in groups of two or three students.

1. Provide your best estimate as an answer to each question.
   a) Which is the favourite type of music the students in grade 9 at your school listen to?
   b) Which sport is played most by Canadians?
   c) What percent of the teachers in your school teach mathematics?

2. Discuss how you would go about finding the data to answer each question accurately.

3. As a class, compare answers to questions 1 and 2. Discuss alternative ways of finding appropriate data.

When creating possible answers to questions, such as those in question 1 of the Discover, you are **formulating a hypothesis**. A **hypothesis** is a possible answer to a question.

To test a hypothesis, you need to collect data. **Data** are answers to surveys or results of experiments or other tests. Data are collected by the person conducting the study.

In question 2 of the **Discover**, you may have suggested surveying some or all of the students in part 1a) or teachers in part 1c). These are **primary sources**. For part 1b), you might have suggested checking data on the Internet or in a sports record book. These are **secondary sources**. When you gather your own data to test a hypothesis, you are using **primary data-gathering methods**. When you use someone else's data to test a hypothesis, you are using **secondary data-gathering methods**.

## EXAMPLE 1

### Using Secondary Data to Check a Hypothesis

Gina stated that boys tend to watch TV more than girls. She checked E-STAT at the Statistics Canada web site on the Internet for data. She found the data shown.

**a)** What was Gina's hypothesis?

**b)** Identify Gina's data-gathering method.

**c)** Make a bar graph of the data.

**d)** Do the data support Gina's hypothesis?

**Percent of Boys and Girls Watching TV per Day**

| | Males Age 13 | Females Age 13 |
|---|---|---|
| Not at all | 1 | 2 |
| Less than $\frac{1}{2}$ h | 4 | 5 |
| $\frac{1}{2}$ h to 1 h | 22 | 27 |
| 2 h to 3 h | 44 | 43 |
| 4 h | 13 | 11 |
| More than 4 h | 16 | 12 |

### Solution

**a)** Gina's hypothesis was that boys watch more TV than girls.

**b)** Because she found the data on the Internet, Gina used a secondary data-gathering method.

**c)**

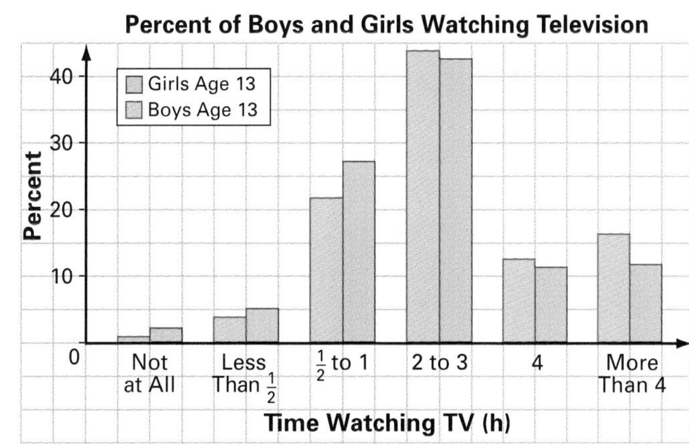


**d)** The data do support Gina's hypothesis because, as the time spent watching TV increases, the boys' percents become greater than the girls'.

You can access E-STAT by going to *www.mcgrawhill.ca/links/MATC9* and using the link.

## Example 2

### Using Primary Data to Test a Hypothesis

For a geography assignment, students were asked to determine the two most frequent countries of birth of shoppers at a shopping mall. Ismail's group thought the countries would be Canada and China. They took a survey of 40 shoppers one Saturday. The following data were collected:

| | | | | |
|---|---|---|---|---|
| Canada | Great Britain | Germany | Sri Lanka | Canada |
| Canada | India | Jamaica | Great Britain | Canada |
| India | Canada | Canada | Pakistan | Canada |
| China | Canada | China | Canada | Jamaica |
| China | Canada | Canada | China | Canada |
| Canada | France | New Zealand | Uganda | Canada |
| France | Canada | Great Britain | Great Britain | India |
| Canada | China | China | Canada | Canada |

**a)** State Ismail's group's hypothesis.

**b)** Put the data into a frequency table.

**c)** Rank the data by frequency.

**d)** Identify the group's data-gathering method.

**e)** Do the data support the group's hypothesis?

### Solution

**a)** Canada and China are the two most frequent countries of origin of the shoppers.

**b)** and **c)**

| Country | Tally | Frequency | Rank |
|---|---|---|---|
| Canada | 卌 卌 卌 \|\|\| | 18 | 1 |
| Great Britain | \|\|\|\| | 4 | 3 |
| Germany | \| | 1 | 6 |
| Sri Lanka | \| | 1 | 6 |
| India | \|\|\| | 3 | 4 |
| Jamaica | \|\| | 2 | 5 |
| Pakistan | \| | 1 | 6 |
| China | 卌 \| | 6 | 2 |
| France | \|\| | 2 | 5 |
| New Zealand | \| | 1 | 6 |
| Uganda | \| | 1 | 6 |

**d)** Because they surveyed the shoppers themselves, the group used a primary data-gathering method.

**e)** Canada and China were ranked first and second. The data support the group's hypothesis.

- A hypothesis is a possible answer to a question.
- Data are answers to surveys or results of experiments or tests that are conducted to test a hypothesis.
- A primary source is one that you survey yourself in order to collect data. You are using a primary data-gathering method.
- A secondary source is one in which you use data collected by someone else. You are using a secondary data-gathering method.

## DISCUSS THE CONCEPTS

1. Keith surveyed all the customers visiting his store one Saturday. Is he using a primary or a secondary source of data?
2. Explain why it is important to gather data on an issue after you have formulated a hypothesis.

## PRACTISE

***For help with questions 1 and 2, refer to Examples 1 and 2.***

1. Is each of the following a primary or a secondary source of data?
   - **a)** an article in a magazine
   - **b)** counting the number of cars travelling on local streets
   - **c)** an encyclopedia
   - **d)** using a scientific experiment to test the effectiveness of a new fertilizer
   - **e)** generating 100 random numbers, from 1 to 6, on a calculator, to simulate the rolling of a die

2. Would you use a primary or a secondary data-gathering technique for each of the following? Explain why.
   - **a)** The city council needs to find out the opinions of local residents on whether there is enough parkland in the community.
   - **b)** A marketing student wants to know the average attendance at first-run movies in theatres across Canada.
   - **c)** You want to find out MuchMusic's top ten all-time music videos.
   - **d)** The Students' Council wants to determine the students' preferences for the date of a school dance.
   - **e)** A company needs to know if its product is satisfactory to its customers.

## Apply the Concepts

**B**

3. The owners of a small company hear that their employees want vending machines in their lunchroom. They ask each employee what types of machines they want. The employees' responses are:

   *First shift*: pop, sandwiches, pop, coffee, snacks, juice, snacks, sandwiches, coffee, pop, pop, coffee, snacks

   *Second shift*: pop, pop, snacks, snacks, pop, pop, juice, sandwiches, pop, sandwiches, coffee, juice, coffee, sandwiches

   *Third shift*: coffee, snacks, coffee, sandwiches, sandwiches, coffee, pop, sandwiches, coffee, snacks, pop, pop, sandwiches

   a) State a hypothesis for employee preference.
   b) Put the data into a frequency table.
   c) Rank the data by frequency.
   d) Identify the owners' data-gathering method.
   e) Do the data support the owners' hypothesis?
   f) If the owners were to install two vending machines, which two should be installed? Explain your answer.

4. In a discussion with her friends, Kendra argued that the Internet was used mostly for e-mail, rather than for general browsing or entertainment. She discovered this table showing the percent of households that used the Internet for each activity in 2000.

| Activity | Percent |
|---|---|
| Chat groups | 11.0 |
| Electronic banking | 14.7 |
| E-mail | 37.4 |
| Financial information | 18.5 |
| Find sports related information | 17.3 |
| Formal education/training | 19.0 |
| General browsing | 36.2 |
| Government information | 18.9 |
| Listening to the radio | 9.3 |
| Medical or health information | 22.9 |
| Obtain and save music | 17.8 |
| Other Internet services | 17.7 |
| Playing games | 18.2 |
| Purchasing goods and services | 9.6 |
| Travel information/arrangements | 21.9 |
| View the news | 20.4 |

   a) State Kendra's hypothesis.
   b) Identify Kendra's data-gathering method.
   c) Make a bar graph of the data.
   d) Do the data support Kendra's hypothesis?
   e) Would it be relevant to combine the "entertainment" categories and add the percents? Explain.

5. Formulate a hypothesis for each question.
   a) Which group exercises more—girls or boys?
   b) What is the favourite sport among girls? among boys?
   c) Rank the lunch habits of the students in your school: cafeteria food, bring your own lunch, purchase lunch elsewhere, go home for lunch.
   d) Which letter of the alphabet is used most frequently in the first names of the students in your math class?
   e) Which digit occurs most often in telephone numbers (not counting the exchange and area code)?

6. For each hypothesis you formulated in question 5, survey the students in your class or in another class to see how your hypothesis holds up.

7. Work in groups of three or four students. Over the next few sections of this chapter, you will examine a topic your group finds interesting. You will use a primary data-collection technique to gather your data. Select one of the following topic questions or use one of your own. Note that each topic question looks for a relationship between two numeric values. Formulate a hypothesis about the topic you selected.
   a) What is the relationship (if any) between the cost of CDs and the number of CDs students buy?
   b) What is the relationship (if any) between the time spent playing computer games and marks?
   c) What is the relationship (if any) between the distance students live from school and arrival time?
   d) What is the relationship (if any) between the time spent watching videos or DVDs and playing computer games?
   e) What is the relationship (if any) between a person's age and the amount of exercise the person gets per week?

# 4.2 Surveys and Sampling Principles

Some radio stations play their listeners' Top 100 Songs of All Time. How does the radio station arrive at the results? Do they ask listeners to call in? Do they interview people at a shopping mall? Do they randomly select people to interview?

A **population** is the entire group that is being studied, such as the student body of your school. A survey of only part of a population is known as a **sample**. An example of a sample would be a selection of students in each grade at your school. The views of the sample are used to represent those of the entire population of the school.

## DISCOVER

**Did You Know?**

A survey of an entire population is known as a **census**.

### Populations and Samples

Answer questions 1 and 2 in groups of two or three students.

1. For each of the following questions, decide whether you need to survey the entire population of the group in question, or only a sample. Explain your answer.
   a) What is the average mark in this class?
   b) What are the most popular radio stations among students in your school?
   c) What percent of Canadian families own a computer?

2. For each of the following survey issues, discuss how you would go about sampling the population being studied.
   a) *Issue*: Should the computer lab be kept open after school?
   *Population*: Student body of your school
   b) *Issue*: There is not enough free parking in the downtown area of your community.
   *Population*: Taxpayers in your community
   c) *Issue*: The owner of the 200-store chain of Big O Doughnuts needs to know if customer service is good.
   *Population*: All the customers of Big O Doughnuts
   d) *Issue*: Should Canadian students take a Phys. Ed. course each year?
   *Population*: All residents of Canada
   e) *Issue*: Which extra-curricular sports should be offered to the students in your school?
   *Population*: Student body of your school

**Did You Know?**

There are more doughnut shops per capita in Canada than in any other country. There is a doughnut shop in Canada for every 9700 people.

In your answers to question 1 of the **Discover**, you said to survey the entire population or only part of the population.

### Random Sampling

When surveying a sample of a population, it is important that the participants be selected **randomly** (by chance). This will reduce **sampling error**, which is the difference between the results of the survey and the truth. There are many ways of randomly selecting a sample to be studied. Three of them are described here.

#### Simple Random Sampling

A specific number of people are selected from the population. Each person has the same chance of being selected. For example, 30 names are placed into a hat and 5 names are selected at random.

#### Systematic Random Sampling

Participants are selected at pre-determined intervals. For example, beginning with the 4th person, every 10th person on the school's roll is selected to be interviewed.

#### Stratified Random Sampling

The population is divided into groups, and samples are randomly selected from within each group. For example, participants are randomly selected from each grade level, proportional to the number of students in each grade.

### Non-Random Sampling

Participants may volunteer or be selected by convenience. Callers to radio phone-in shows are volunteers. Participants in on-the-street interviews by reporters are selected by convenience. This type of sampling may have a high degree of sampling error.

## EXAMPLE 1

### Random Sampling

The Dance Committee at a school wants to know the types of music to play at an upcoming dance. A sample of 100 students are to be interviewed from the total population of 1000 students. The total population includes 300 grade 9s, 286 grade 10s, 210 grade 11s, and 204 grade 12s.

**a)** Describe how a simple random sampling procedure could be used.
**b)** Describe how a systematic random sampling procedure could be used.
**c)** Describe how a stratified random sampling procedure could be used.

### Solution

**a)** Obtain an alphabetical list of all students.
Using a random number generator on a calculator or computer, generate 100 different numbers between 1 and 1000.
Count down the list to the person represented by each number.

**b)** Obtain an alphabetical list of all students.
Divide 1000 by 100 to get 10.
Using a random number generator, select a number between 1 and 10.
Count down to that person on the list.
Count every 10th person after that.

**c)** Obtain alphabetical lists of the students in each grade.
To find the number of participants from each grade, divide the total number of students from each grade number by the total population and multiply by the total sample size. Round to the nearest unit.

Grade 9: $\frac{300}{1000} \times 100 = 30$ students

Grade 10: $\frac{286}{1000} \times 100 \doteq 29$ students

Grade 11: $\frac{210}{1000} \times 100 = 21$ students

Grade 12: $\frac{204}{1000} \times 100 \doteq 20$ students

Randomly select the indicated number of students in each grade to be interviewed.

## EXAMPLE 2

### Identifying a Population

Identify the population for each of the following questions. Suggest a sampling technique that would be most appropriate.

a) Do boys and girls in your school have different tastes when buying music?
b) Are Canadian voters supportive of the Prime Minister?
c) Who are the favourite players of the fans at a hockey game?

### Solution

a) The population is the students in your school. A stratified sampling technique is best. Obtain a list of students for each gender. Randomly select a proportional number of students from each list.

b) The population is the voting-age population of Canada. A systematic technique is best. Select people at equal intervals on the voters' list.

c) The population is the fans at the hockey game. A simple random sampling technique is best. Draw ticket stubs from a container or randomly select seat numbers.

## KEY CONCEPTS

- A population is the entire group that is being studied.
- A survey of only part of a population is known as a sample.
- In random sampling, each participant has the same chance of being selected.
- There are many types of random sampling, including simple random sampling, systematic random sampling, and stratified random sampling.
- Non-random sampling occurs when participants are not randomly selected.

## DISCUSS THE CONCEPTS

1. A sports shoe company will test 1 out of every 100 shoes for defects. Explain why they do not test every shoe.
2. Why are different sampling techniques used? Why not always use a simple random sample?

## PRACTISE

*For help with question 1, refer to Example 1.*

1. Classify the sampling technique used in each survey as
   - simple random sampling
   - systematic random sampling
   - stratified random sampling
   - non-random sampling

   **a)** A market research company arranges to interview every 20th person on a company's customer database.

   **b)** A radio show host invites listeners to call in to vote for their favourite song.

   **c)** The government interviews recent immigrants, randomly selecting them in proportion to the number of immigrants from each country.

   **d)** A teacher pulls three names out of a hat to determine the order of student presentations.

   **e)** The Students' Council selects people in the cafeteria to interview about the quality of the cafeteria food.

   **f)** The Parents' Council randomly selects one person from each home form to complete a survey on school safety.

*For help with question 2, refer to Example 2.*

2. Identify the population suggested in each statement.

   **a)** 36% of people use the Internet for e-mail.

   **b)** Half the readers of the Toronto Star disagreed with yesterday's editorial.

   **c)** Today's teenagers are more aware of fashion trends than teenagers in the past.

   **d)** Two thirds of Canadians eat at a restaurant at least once a week.

   **e)** The new drug was effective in 95% of the test cases.

   **f)** Most campers at provincial parks use tents.

## APPLY THE CONCEPTS

3. **Communication** Describe a suitable stratified random grouping for surveying the student body of your school about changing the school hours. Explain why this would be suitable.

4. **Application** Describe a simple random sampling technique that could be used by the Canadian Figure Skating Association to determine how often figure skaters practise each week.

5. **Application** Describe a systematic random sampling technique that the police could use to determine the average speed of cars on a local highway.

6. **Application** Describe a stratified random sampling technique that could be used by the Town Council to determine the residents' use of the local library.

**Chapter Problem**

7. In Section 4.1, question 7, you selected a topic and formulated a hypothesis. You will continue to develop your study in this section.
   a) Develop two questions you will ask in a survey. Make sure the questions are non-biased, that is, they do not lead to, or encourage, a particular answer. Have the questions approved by your teacher.
   b) What lists of data will you gather using your survey questions?
   c) What is the population of your study?
   d) What random sampling technique will you use? Describe how you will identify your participants. Have your plans approved by your teacher.
   e) Prepare your survey sheet and make enough copies for 50 participants.
   f) Perform your survey.

**C**

8. **Thinking/Inquiry/Problem Solving** Identify each population. Suggest a sampling technique that could be used to study each issue. Describe how this would be accomplished.
   a) A computer-chip manufacturer needs to test one of every 1000 chips.
   b) The federal government wants to determine the average tax bill per taxpayer.
   c) A radio station wants to know the age profile of its listeners.
   d) A door-to-door survey is done to find out residents' opinions on crime in the community.
   e) A bank manager wishes to determine if waiting times at the branch's automatic banking machines are too long.

# 4.3 Organizing Data Using the TI-83 Graphing Calculator

Most statistics that you have worked with in school have involved counting the number of occurrences of each measure in a data set. A bar graph is used to display the frequency of these measurements. Usually you graphed the data using paper and pencil. Graphing calculators make this task very easy and can help you analyse the data much faster.

In data relationships, a **variable** is a particular type of measurement that is taken repeatedly. A variable could be age, or hair colour, or even letters chosen at random from a sentence. The number of times a measure occurs in the data set is called the **frequency**. If five people have red hair, the frequency would be 5.

## Discover 1

Refer to the Technology Appendix for details on how to use the TI-83 graphing calculator.

### Lists and Bar Graphs on a TI-83 Graphing Calculator

In this activity, you will learn how to use a TI-83 graphing calculator to enter data into a table and to produce a **bar graph**.

The following list of numbers represents the birth month of the 25 students in a particular grade 9 class. January is represented by 1, February by 2, and so on.

3, 7, 12, 11, 5, 5, 9, 8, 9, 1, 2, 12, 10, 12, 6, 12, 4, 5, 3, 11, 8, 9, 12, 2, 7

1. First, clear the lists (or tables) on the calculator. To clear list **L1**, press STAT **4:ClrList** 2nd [L1] ENTER.

2. To begin entering data, press STAT **1:Edit.**

3. List **L1** will represent the birth months of the students. Enter the birth month data into the column under **L1**. Press ENTER after each number you type.

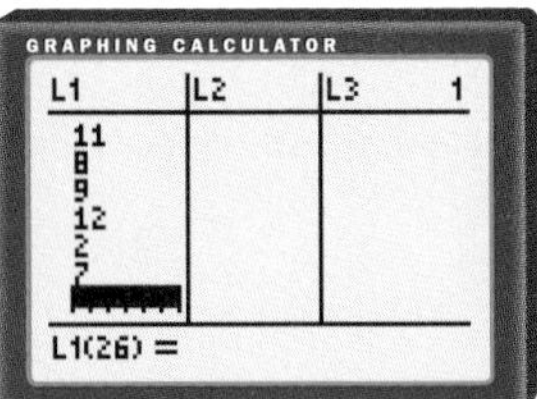

4. Clear any existing equations in the Y= editor by pressing Y= and then CLEAR for each equation.

5. To set up the graph, press 2nd **[STATPLOT]**. Use the arrow keys, if necessary, to highlight **1:Plot1** and press ENTER.
Using the arrow ◀ ▶ keys and the ENTER key:
   - Turn the graph on by setting the **On-Off** to **On.**
   - Set the **Type** to a **Bar Graph** (third picture on top row).
   - Set the **Xlist** to **L1.**
   - Set the **Freq** to **1.**

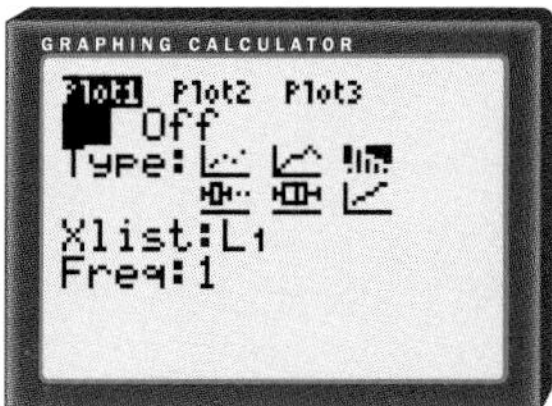


6. To set the viewing window for your graph, press ZOOM and use the arrow keys to highlight **9:ZoomStat**. To set up the scale on your **L1** (horizontal) axis, press WINDOW and set **Xscl=1**. Press ENTER.

7. To view the final graph of the data, press GRAPH.

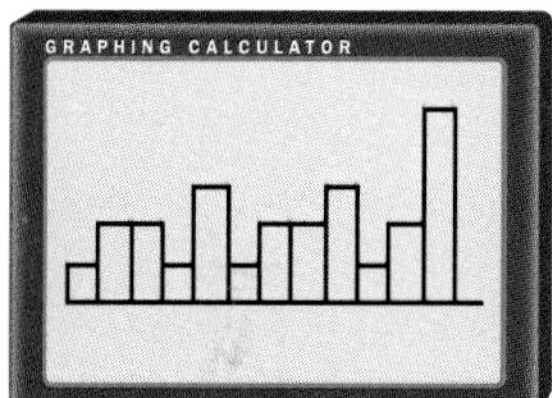


8. You now have a bar graph of this data set.
   a) What is the variable?
   b) What does each bar represent?
   c) Describe what the scale represents on the vertical axis.
   d) What is the most frequent measure? What is its frequency?
   e) What is the least frequent measure? What is its frequency?

9. Copy the graph into your notebook. Label the graph fully. Include the following labels:
   - scales of the horizontal and vertical axes
   - names of the horizontal and vertical axes
   - title of the graph

In **Discover 1**, you made a bar graph. Bar graphs are made from a set of **single-variable data**. The data are called single-variable because there is only one data list. The measurements are placed along the horizontal axis. The frequencies are placed along the vertical axis.

Often, a set of data is made up of two or more lists, with each entry in one list related to entries in one or more other lists. You can graph **two-variable data** as well. One way to graph two-variable data, especially when time is one of the variables, is to make a **broken-line graph**. It is called a broken-line graph because it is made up of several connected line segments. A broken-line graph could be used to plot height versus age of a child, or speed versus time of a car.

## DISCOVER 2

Refer to the Technology Appendix for help with **Entering Data Into Lists**.

### Broken-Line Graphs on a TI-83 Graphing Calculator

In this activity, you will learn how to work with two-variable data to make a broken-line graph, and identify values on the graph.

The data show the maximum daily temperature for the city of Thunder Bay during the first two weeks of September one year.

| September Date | Maximum Temperature, °C |
|---|---|
| 1 | 23 |
| 2 | 25 |
| 3 | 21 |
| 4 | 18 |
| 5 | 15 |
| 6 | 19 |
| 7 | 21 |
| 8 | 21 |
| 9 | 17 |
| 10 | 14 |
| 11 | 15 |
| 12 | 12 |
| 13 | 16 |
| 14 | 18 |

1. First, clear lists **L1** and **L2** by pressing STAT **4:ClrList** 2nd [L1] , 2nd [L2] ENTER.

2. Enter the data into the calculator. **L1** will represent the date and **L2** will represent the temperature. Enter the dates from the above table in list **L1** and the temperatures in list **L2**. Use the method for entering data as described in **Discover 1** on page 136.

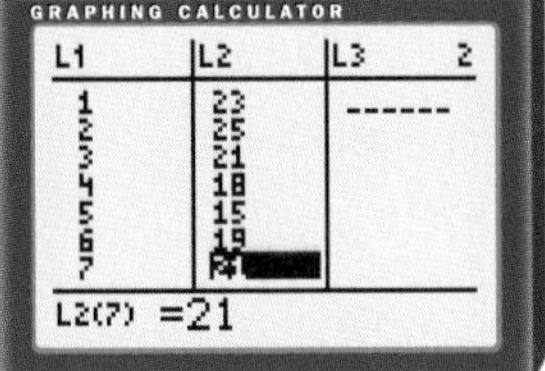

3. Plot the data using a broken-line graph. To set up the graph, press 2nd [**STATPLOT**]. Use the arrow keys, if necessary, to highlight **1:Plot1** and press ENTER.
Using the arrow ◄ ► keys and the ENTER key:
   - Turn the graph on by setting **On-Off** to **On.**
   - Set the **Type** to a **Line Graph** (second picture on top row).
   - Set the **Xlist** to **L1.**
   - Set the **Ylist** to **L2.**
   - Set the **Mark,** or shape, you wish to use when plotting the data.

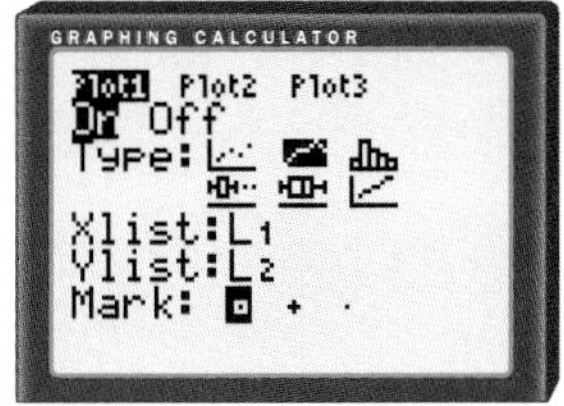


4. Press Y= and make sure **Plot2** and **Plot3** are set to **Off** (not darkened) and clear any existing equations from the Y = editor.

5. To set the viewing window for your graph, press ZOOM and use the arrow keys to highlight **9:ZoomStat**. Press ENTER. To set up the scale on your **L1** (horizontal) axis, press WINDOW and set **Xscl=1**.

6. To view the final graph of the data, press GRAPH.

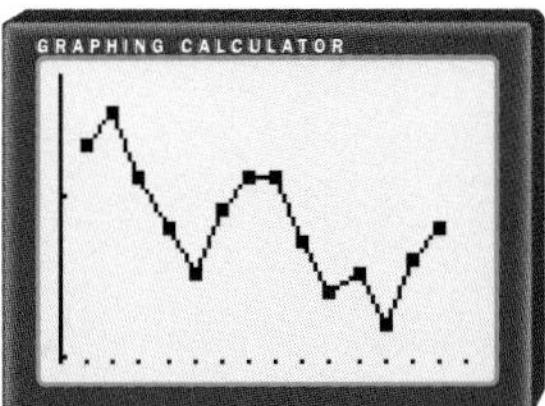


Refer to the Technology Appendix for help with **Tracing a Graph**.

7. Use the **Trace** feature to view the coordinate values of each point. Press TRACE. By pressing the ◄ and ► keys, you will be able to see the **L1** (X=) and **L2** (Y=) values for each point.

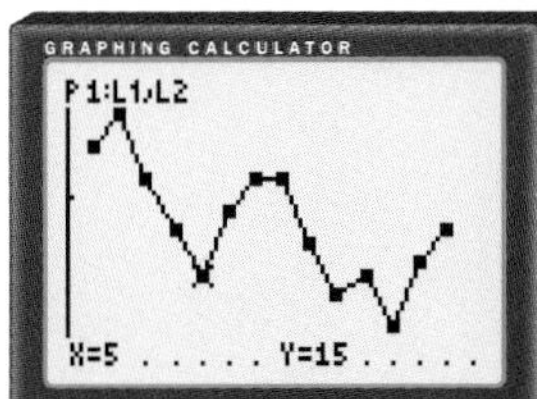


8. a) What are the variables?
   b) Which axis represents each variable?
   c) Describe what happened to the temperature during the two weeks.

9. Copy the graph into your notebook. Label the graph fully. Include the following labels:
   - scale of the horizontal and vertical axes
   - names of the horizontal and vertical axes
   - title of the graph

## Key Concepts

- A variable is a measurement that is taken repeatedly, and that can have different values.
- A single-variable data set has only one list of data.
- The frequency of each measure in the data set is the number of times the measure occurs.
- A bar graph is made from a set of single-variable data. The measurements are placed along the horizontal axis. The frequencies are placed along the vertical axis.
- A two-variable data set has two sets of measurements.
- A broken-line graph is made up of connected line segments and is used to graph two-variable data sets, especially those involving time.

## Discuss the Concepts

1. Explain why bar graphs are not used to graph two-variable data sets.
2. a) What are two advantages of using a graphing calculator to graph data?
   b) What are two disadvantages of using a graphing calculator to graph data?
3. For each data set, identify the variable(s) and discuss whether it would be more appropriate to graph the data using a bar graph or a broken-line graph.
   a) The number of times each model of automobile is passed on the highway.
   b) The price of gasoline at a particular gas station at 8:00 a.m. each day during a one-month period.

## Practise

1. Identify each variable.
   a) The time it takes for each student in your class to get to school.
   b) The frequency that each digit occurs in people's street addresses.
   c) The average high temperature during each month of the year.
   d) The number of times your favourite hockey player scored 1, 2, 3, and so on, goals in a game.

2. State whether each data set in question 1 would be graphed using a bar graph or a broken-line graph.

**Did You Know?**

An average heart rate is about 72 beats per minute. In one year, the heart beats almost 38 million times. By the time a person is 70 years old, on average, the heart has beaten 2.5 billion times.

3. **Communication** The broken-line graph shows Kadijah's heart rate each day at the end of Phys. Ed. class.

   a) On which day was her heart rate the highest?

   b) On which day was her heart rate the lowest?

   c) Why was a broken line graph used instead of a bar graph?

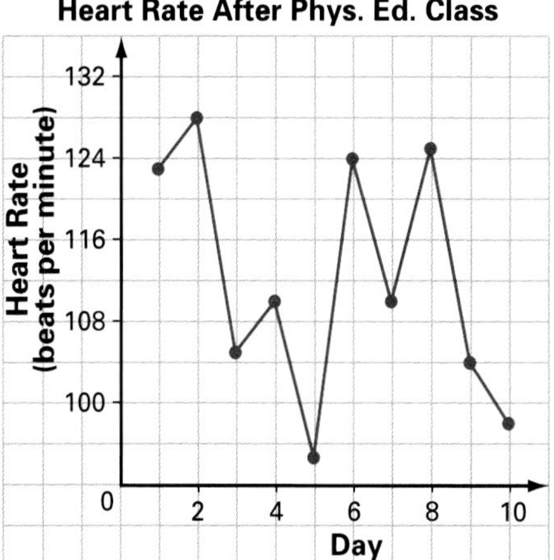


## APPLY THE CONCEPTS

4. The data represent the number of CDs purchased in the past month by 20 different students.

   2, 0, 2, 5, 3, 2, 1, 6, 2, 3, 0, 5, 2, 3, 8, 2, 4, 10, 1, 2

   a) Enter the data into list **L3** of a graphing calculator.

   b) Make a bar graph of the data.

   c) Copy the graph into your notebook. Label the axes, along with their scales. Provide a title.

   d) Describe the graph and what it shows.

Refer to the Technology Appendix for help with **Entering Data Into Lists**.

5. The data show how the average heart rate changes as you age.

| **Age (years)** | Birth | 1 | 2 | 3 | 4 | 5 | 6 |
|---|---|---|---|---|---|---|---|
| **Average Heart Rate (beats per minute)** | 130 | 120 | 115 | 100 | 100 | 100 | 100 |
| **Age (years)** | 7 | 8 | 9 | 10 | 11 | 12 | |
| **Average Heart Rate (beats per minute)** | 95 | 90 | 90 | 90 | 90 | 85 | |

   a) Enter Age into list **L4** and Heart Rate into list **L5** of a graphing calculator.

   b) Make a broken-line graph of the data.

   c) Copy the graph into your notebook. Label the axes, along with their scales. Provide a title.

   d) Describe the graph and what it shows.

6. **Application** The following table shows the number of days with precipitation (rain or snow) in the city of Belleville each month during one year.

| Month Number | 1 | 2 | 3 | 4 | 5 | 6 | 7 | 8 | 9 | 10 | 11 | 12 |
|---|---|---|---|---|---|---|---|---|---|---|---|---|
| Number of Days With Precipitation | 12 | 8 | 10 | 12 | 9 | 8 | 4 | 7 | 8 | 10 | 9 | 12 |

   a) Use a graphing calculator to make a bar graph showing the frequency of each Number of Days With Precipitation. Copy the graph into your notebook. Label it properly.
   b) Use a graphing calculator to make a broken-line graph showing the number of days with precipitation each month over the year. Copy the graph into your notebook. Label it properly.
   c) **Communication** Explain the difference between the two graphs and how each graph is used.

7. In Section 4.1, question 7, you selected a topic and formulated a hypothesis. In Section 4.2, question 7, you performed a survey to gather data. You will continue to develop more of your study in this section.
   a) Compile your survey results into a table or chart.
   b) Make a bar graph of the data from each survey question.

Refer to the Technology Appendix for help with **Entering Data Into Lists**.

8. To make a bar graph using **L1** as your measurement and **L2** as your frequency on a TI-83 graphing calculator, set up the graph by pressing 2nd [STATPLOT] **1:Plot1**. Then, assign **L2** as the **frequency**.

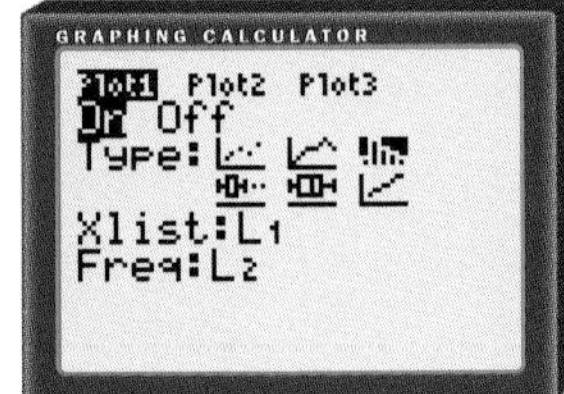


   a) Two dice were rolled 50 times. The frequencies of the sum of the two die were recorded in the following chart. Enter the data into **L1** and **L2** appropriately and make a bar graph.

| Sum | 2 | 3 | 4 | 5 | 6 | 7 | 8 | 9 | 10 | 11 | 12 |
|---|---|---|---|---|---|---|---|---|---|---|---|
| Frequency | 3 | 5 | 6 | 7 | 6 | 9 | 6 | 5 | 6 | 3 | 4 |

   b) Copy the graph into your notebook. Label the axes, along with their scales. Provide a title.
   c) Describe the graph and what it shows.

# 4.4 Measures of Central Tendency

It is said that the average family has 2.3 children. Does this mean that a typical family really has 2.3 children (which is impossible, of course), or does it mean something else?

## DISCOVER

### What is Meant by the Word "Average"?

1. Explain what is meant by each use of the word "average".
   a) Karen's report card average is 74%.
   b) The average table has 3.7 legs.
   c) The average table has 4 legs.
   d) The average family has 2.3 children.
   e) Chang's batting average is .194.
   f) The average cat has 2 ears, 2 eyes, 4 legs, and 1 tail.
   g) Thuan is of average height.

2. Explain how the word "average" can have confusing meanings.

As seen in the **Discover**, the word "average" can be very misleading. In statistics, this word is generally not used. It is replaced by:

- **Mean**, which is the sum of the measurements divided by the number of measurements. The mean is most affected by changes in the data because each piece of data helps determine it.
- **Median**, which is the middle measurement when the data are placed in order from smallest to greatest. When there is an even number of data, the median is half way between the two middle values. The median is useful when there are unusual pieces of data that affect the mean.
- **Mode**, which is the most frequent measurement. The mode measures popularity within the data set. Sometimes, a data set will have more than one mode. This type of set is known as a multi-modal set.

These are all called **measures of central tendency**. They describe how the data are *centred* around these so-called averages.

Many sets of data have **outliers**, which are data that do not fit the obvious pattern. They may be perfectly natural occurrences, or they may occur because of poor surveying techniques, not being truthful on a survey, or experimental error. Outliers will affect the mean, but generally do not affect the median or the mode. Often, they are excluded from the analysis.

## EXAMPLE 1

### Mean, Median, and Mode, With an Outlier

The following scores, in points, were given to 15 competitors by the judges in a dance competition.

13, 12, 9, 13, 13, 11, 12, 13, 14, 10, 15, 14, 4, 10, 13

**a)** Determine the mean score, to one decimal place.
**b)** Determine the median score.
**c)** Determine the mode score.
**d)** Are there any outliers? If so, how do they affect the measures of central tendency?
**e)** What might have caused the outlier(s)?

### Solution 1: Paper and Pencil

**a)** $$\text{mean} = \frac{13+12+9+13+13+11+12+13+14+10+15+14+4+10+13}{15}$$
$$= \frac{176}{15}$$
$$\doteq 11.7$$

The mean score is about 11.7 points.

**b)** Place the data in order.
4, 9, 10, 10, 11, 12, 12, 13, 13, 13, 13, 13, 14, 14, 15
There are 15 measurements. Add 1 to 15, then divide by 2.
$16 \div 2 = 8$
The median, or middle value, is the eighth measurement, which is 13.
There are seven scores smaller than 13 and seven scores greater than 13.
The median score is 13 points.

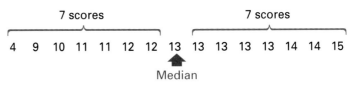

7 scores 7 scores
4 9 10 11 11 12 12 13 13 13 13 13 14 14 15
Median

**c)** The most frequent score is 13. So, the mode is 13 points.

**d)** The score of 4 is an outlier, because it is not close in value to the other scores. The outlier does not affect the median because the middle measurement remains the same if the outlier has a greater value. The outlier does not affect the mode, because the most frequent score is still 13. The outlier does affect the mean, because changing the value of the outlier changes the sum in the numerator.

**e)** The outlier might have been caused by a competitor not being ready for the competition, or there might have been an error in recording the score.

## Solution 2: Graphing Calculator

Refer to the Technology Appendix for help with **Entering Data Into Lists** and **1-Variable Statistics**.

Enter the data into list **L1**.
Press the STAT key.
From the **CALC** menu, select **1:1-Var Stats**. Press ENTER ENTER.

**a)** You will see several mathematical symbols and numbers, most of which you will learn about in future grades. The symbol for the mean is $\bar{x}$. You can see from the screen that the mean is 11.73333333, or approximately 11.7 points.

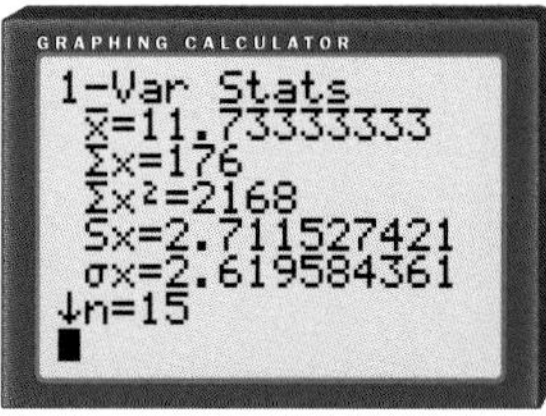


**b)** Scroll down to see the rest of the list. The median is shown as Med = 13. The median is 13 points.

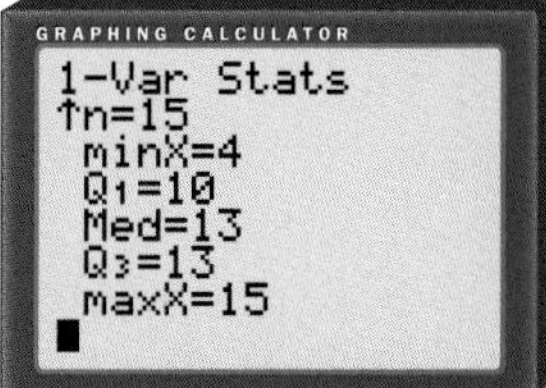


**c)** The mode cannot be found using a graphing calculator, so you will have to find this yourself. The most frequent score is 13. The mode is 13 points.

**d)** and **e)** See Solution 1.

## Example 2

### Medians With an Even Number of Data

The following is a list of ages (in years) of 18 students, recorded in a random survey. The ages have been ranked from smallest to greatest.

13, 14, 14, 15, 15, 15, 16, 16, 16, 17, 17, 17, 17, 18, 18, 19, 19, 19

**a)** Determine the median age.
**b)** Describe the meaning of the median.

### Solution

**a)** There are 18 students. Add 1 to 18 and divide by 2.
$19 \div 2 = 9.5$
Take the midpoint of the 9th and 10th measurements so that there are nine measures less than the median and nine measures greater than the median.
$(16 + 17) \div 2 = 16.5$
The median age is 16.5 years.

9 measures | 9 measures

13 14 14 15 15 15 16 16 16 17 17 17 17 18 18 19 19 19

16.5
Median

**b)** Half the student ages are less than 16.5 years and half are above 16.5 years.

- The mean is the sum of the measurements in a data set divided by the number of measurements.
- The median is the middle measurement when the data are placed in order from smallest to greatest. When there is an even number of data, the median is the midpoint of the two middle values.
- The mode is the most frequent measurement.
- An outlier is a measurement that is very different from the other measurements.
- An outlier will affect the mean, but, generally, not the median or mode.

## Discuss the Concepts

1. Explain why the word "average" is not an ideal word to use to describe measures of central tendency.

2. Many report cards show the class median instead of the mean. Why would it be done this way?

## Practise

**A**

***For help with question 1, refer to Example 1.***

1. Determine the mean, median, and mode of each set of numbers of CDs in students' collections. Identify any outliers in each set.
   a) 20, 34, 20, 5, 3, 20, 6, 10, 13, 16, 10, 20, 6
   b) 10, 18, 14, 29, 0, 56, 17, 21, 24, 23, 48, 2, 13, 19, 26, 13, 15

***For help with questions 2 and 3, refer to Examples 1 and 2.***

2. Determine the mean, median, and mode of each set of marks, out of 100.
   a) 88, 56, 71, 44, 84, 65, 65, 64, 71, 90, 71, 60, 76
   b) 56, 72, 88, 76, 88, 45, 64, 90, 88, 61, 75, 72, 54, 70

3. Determine the mean, median, and mode of each set of children's heights, in centimetres.
   a) 62, 81, 77, 50, 69, 53, 41, 66, 83, 102, 53
   b) 83, 59, 112, 58, 70, 51, 70, 82, 108, 97

## Apply the Concepts

**B**

4. **Communication** Identify the measure of central tendency that best describes each of the following. Explain why you chose that measure of central tendency.
   a) the number of pages in a typical textbook
   b) the most requested song at a school dance
   c) the middle-ranked person on a basketball team, in terms of height
   d) the typical distance run around the track by a student in a Phys. Ed. class
   e) the most frequent number of successful serves by the members of a volleyball team during a serving practice

5. **Application** The following data were used in **Discover 2** on page 138 of Section 4.3. The data show the maximum daily temperature for the city of Thunder Bay during the first two weeks of September of one year.

a) Calculate the mean, median, and mode of the maximum temperatures.

b) Would it be accurate to use any of these measures as a suitable "average" maximum temperature for these two weeks in September? If so, which one? Explain.

| September Date | Maximum Temperature, °C |
|---|---|
| 1 | 23 |
| 2 | 25 |
| 3 | 21 |
| 4 | 18 |
| 5 | 15 |
| 6 | 19 |
| 7 | 21 |
| 8 | 21 |
| 9 | 17 |
| 10 | 14 |
| 11 | 15 |
| 12 | 12 |
| 13 | 16 |
| 14 | 18 |

6. In Section 4.1, question 7, you selected a topic and formulated a hypothesis. In Section 4.2, question 7, you performed a survey to gather data. You compiled the results and made bar graphs in Section 4.3, question 7. You will continue to develop more of your study in this section. Calculate the appropriate measures of central tendency for each of your numeric variables.

C 7. **Thinking/Inquiry/Problem Solving** A car dealership has 20 previously owned cars for sale. The odometer readings of the cars, in thousands of kilometres, are listed below.

| | | | | | | | | | |
|---|---|---|---|---|---|---|---|---|---|
| 125 | 131 | 98 | 102 | 105 | 178 | 164 | 125 | 44 | 182 |
| 173 | 125 | 165 | 110 | 159 | 200 | 192 | 95 | 144 | 130 |

a) Calculate the mean, median, and mode.

b) Identify any outliers.

c) Recalculate the mean, median, and mode, excluding the outliers.

d) Describe how the outliers have affected the measures of central tendency.

e) Which measure of central tendency should the dealership use in its advertising? Explain your answer.

f) From a consumer's standpoint, which measure is fairest? Justify your answer.

8. **Thinking/Inquiry/Problem Solving** Jason has a mean mark of 76% on his first five tests. What mark does he need to get on his next test in order to raise his mean mark to 80%?

# 4.5 Data Analysis: Trends and Relationships

When two sets of numeric data are provided, a trend or relationship between them can sometimes be seen. Is there a relationship between a person's height and his or her marks? What about time watching TV and marks? You will investigate statistical relationships in this section.

## Discover

### Interpreting Climate Graphs

Work in pairs. The graphs show the precipitation (rain or snow) and temperature of four Canadian cities. These cities are St. John's, Saskatoon, Sudbury, and Victoria. Discuss the graphs with your partner and decide which graph should be matched with each city. Justify your answers.

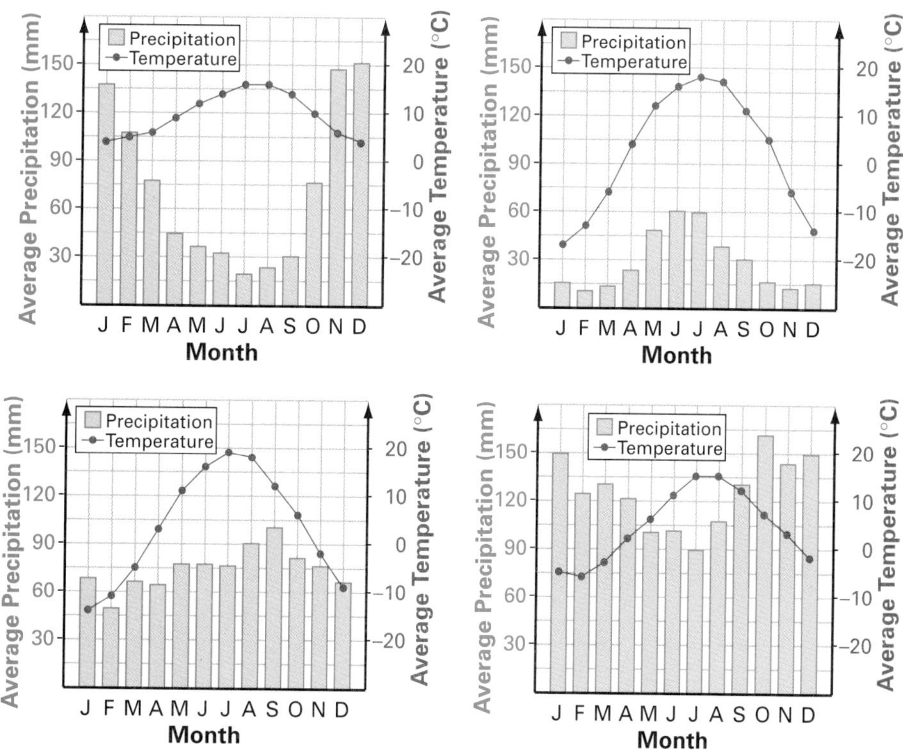

The graphs that you analysed in the **Discover** were double graphs. They showed the relationship between the month and two components of the weather—temperature and precipitation. You probably also considered another variable—location of each city, which would have helped you match all or some of the graphs to the correct cities.

A **scatter plot** is another type of graph that is used for two-variable data. A scatter plot graphs ordered pairs of numeric data, and is used to see relationships between the two variables. Place the **independent variable** (the variable you need to know first) on the horizontal axis and the **dependent variable** (the variable that is affected by the other) on the vertical axis.

A **relationship** between two data sets is the obvious pattern that the data sets follow, when outliers (if any) are excluded.

## Example 1

**Did You Know?**

Earth's 365-day orbit is at a distance of 150 million kilometres from the Sun. So, we are all moving through space at an orbital speed of over 100 000 km/h!

### Creating a Scatter Plot

The data in the table show the average distance of each planet from the Sun and its orbiting speed.

| Planet | Distance From Sun (million km) | Orbiting Speed (thousand km/h) |
|---|---|---|
| Mercury | 58 | 173 |
| Venus | 108 | 126 |
| Earth | 150 | 107 |
| Mars | 228 | 87 |
| Jupiter | 778 | 47 |
| Saturn | 1427 | 35 |
| Uranus | 2871 | 25 |
| Neptune | 4498 | 20 |
| Pluto | 5906 | 17 |

a) Make a scatter plot of the data, with the distance from the Sun as the independent variable.

b) Use the scatter plot to determine the relationship (if any) between the distance of a planet from the Sun and its orbiting speed.

### Solution

a) **Method 1: Paper and Pencil**

Make a scatter plot by graphing ordered pairs with Distance along the horizontal axis and Speed along the vertical axis.

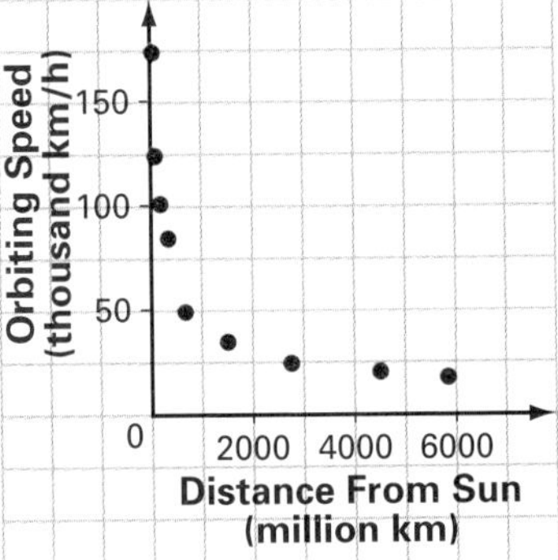

Refer to the Technology Appendix for help with **Creating a Scatter Plot**.

**Method 2: Graphing Calculator**

Enter the data into lists **L1** (distance) and **L2** (speed). To set up the graph, press (2nd) **[STATPLOT]**. Highlight **1:Plot1** and press (ENTER).

Using the (◀)(▶) keys and the (ENTER) key:

- Turn the graph on by setting the **On-Off** to **On.**
- Set the **Type** to a **Scatter Plot.** (first picture on top row)
- Set the **Xlist** to **L1 and the Ylist** to **L2.**

Press (ZOOM) and select **9: ZoomStat** to set the axes and see the graph.

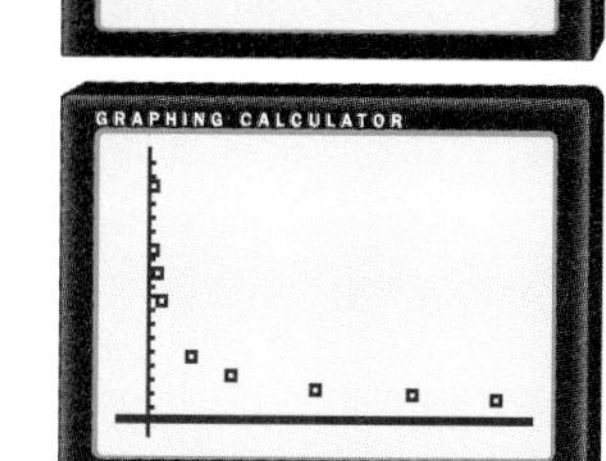

**b)** The graph shows that, as the distance from the Sun increases, the orbiting speed decreases. The speed decreases by smaller amounts at greater distances.

# EXAMPLE 2

## Outliers

The data show the daily average times, in hours, of watching TV and the mathematics marks for 10 students.

| Time (h) | 1 | 6 | 3 | 2 | 9 | 0 | 2 | 5 | 2 | 12 |
|---|---|---|---|---|---|---|---|---|---|---|
| Mark (%) | 85 | 56 | 73 | 75 | 90 | 81 | 69 | 53 | 70 | 40 |

**a)** Make a scatter plot of the data, with time as the independent variable.

**b)** Use the scatter plot to describe the relationship between daily average time watching TV and mathematics marks.

**c)** Identify the outlier. Describe how the outlier does not follow the trend.

## Solution

**a)**

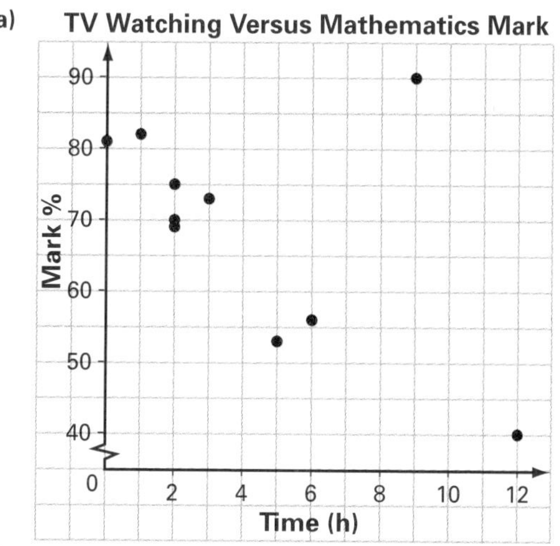


**b)** As the time watching TV increases, student math marks tend to decrease, approximately following a straight line.

**c)** The outlier is a mark of 90%, with 9 h of watching TVdaily. This mark is much greater than the trend shows.

## Key Concepts

- A scatter plot is a type of graph in which ordered pairs are plotted from the two sets of data (variables). The scatter plot is used to see relationships between the two variables.
- The independent variable (the variable you need to know first) is placed on the horizontal axis. The dependent variable (the variable that is affected by the other) is placed on the vertical axis.
- A relationship between two data sets is the obvious pattern that the data follow.
- Outliers are data points that do not fit into the obvious relationship and are usually not included in the analysis.

## Discuss the Concepts

1. Explain why it is usually easier to identify trends and relationships with a scatter plot than with the original data.
2. Describe the steps involved in making a scatter plot
   a) by paper and pencil  b) using a graphing calculator

## Practise

**A**

*For help with question 1, refer to Example 1.*

1. Use the scatter plot to answer each question.
   a) Identify the independent and dependent variables.
   b) Which of the labelled points represents a height of 175 cm and a mark of 60%? a height of 170 cm and a mark of 93%? a height of 195 cm and a mark of 77%?

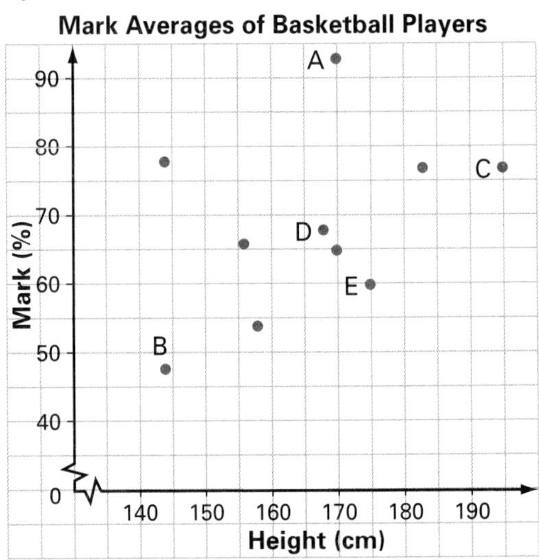


   c) Describe what is represented by the two labelled points not mentioned in part b).
   d) Use the scatter plot to describe the relationship (if any) between basketball players' heights and their mark averages.

*For help with questions 2 and 3, refer to Example 2.*

2. **Communication** For each scatter plot, state whether there is a relationship between variable 1 and variable 2. Describe that relationship.

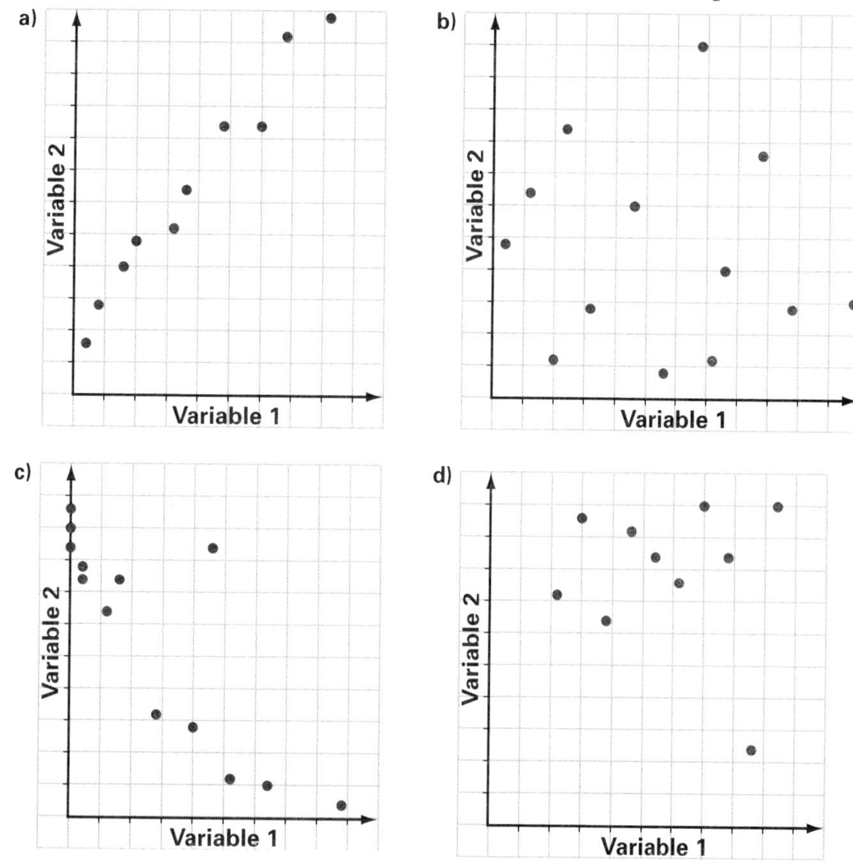


3. For each part of question 2, state whether there are any outliers. If there are outliers, describe how they are different from the rest of the data.

## Apply the Concepts

4. **Thinking/Inquiry/Problem Solving** The chart shows the number of days absent for each student in a class and the corresponding mark.

| Number of Days Absent | Mark (%) |
|---|---|
| 12 | 65 |
| 4 | 78 |
| 0 | 67 |
| 10 | 52 |
| 15 | 43 |
| 21 | 36 |
| 8 | 58 |
| 1 | 85 |
| 3 | 92 |
| 8 | 74 |
| 9 | 62 |
| 7 | 64 |
| 11 | 57 |
| 6 | 70 |
| 10 | 61 |
| 2 | 80 |

**a)** Which is the independent variable? Why?

**b)** Make a scatter plot of the data.

**c)** Use the scatter plot to determine the relationship (if any) between a student's marks and the number of days absent from class. Consider trends with and without outliers.

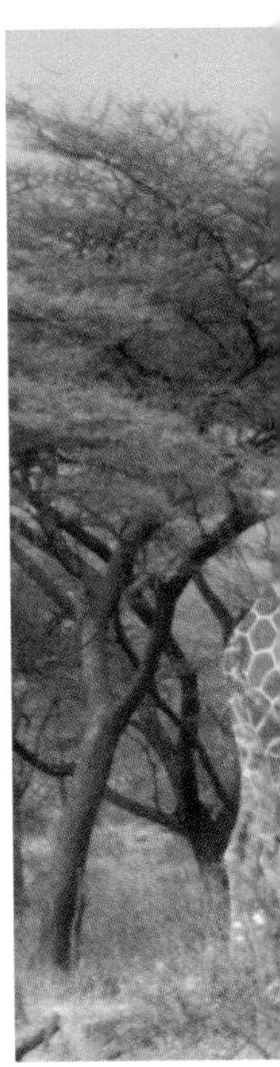

5. The table shows the average masses of selected animals and their average life spans in the wild.
   a) Which is the independent variable? Why?
   b) Make a scatter plot of the data.
   c) Use the scatter plot to determine the relationship (if any) between an animal's average mass and its average life span. Consider trends with and without outliers.

| Animal | Average Mass (kg) | Average Life Span (years) |
|---|---|---|
| African Elephant | 5400 | 60 |
| Arctic Wolf | 80 | 16 |
| Beaver | 23 | 19 |
| Beluga Whale | 1000 | 30 |
| Bobcat | 9 | 14 |
| Chimpanzee | 55 | 40 |
| Deer Mouse | 0.02 | 3 |
| Dromedary Camel | 550 | 40 |
| Eastern Box Turtle | 5 | 100 |
| Giraffe | 1800 | 12 |
| Grey Squirrel | 0.6 | 6 |
| Grizzly Bear | 375 | 25 |
| Kangaroo | 35 | 7 |
| Lion | 140 | 18 |
| Opossum | 3.5 | 1 |
| Red Fox | 7 | 7 |

6. In Section 4.1, question 7, you selected a topic and formulated a hypothesis. In Section 4.2, question 7, you performed a survey to gather data. You compiled the results and made bar graphs in Section 4.3, question 7. In Section 4.4, question 6, you calculated measures of central tendency.
   a) Draw a scatter plot to investigate the relationship between your two variables.
   b) Answer the topic question by making inferences about any trends or relationships. Explain your answers.
   c) State two related issues that could be studied as a follow up.

# 4.6 Experiments

In their jobs, many people perform experiments in order to study relationships between two or more variables. A taxi owner might investigate the relationship between the distance driven and the cost to run the cab. A fire safety officer investigates the relationship between a ladder's angle with the ground and how safe it will be. A sprinter investigates the relationship between stride length and speed.

In the following **Discovers**, you will investigate a few relationships.

## DISCOVER 1

- metre stick

### Estimation Skills

*Objective:* To test how closely people can estimate a distance of 2 m.

*Hypothesis:* State your hypothesis.

*Procedure:*

**a)** In an area free of distance markings, such as a hallway, ask a participant to estimate a distance of 2 m. Do not allow other participants to watch, to prevent influencing the results.

**b)** Measure the distance, accurate to the nearest tenth of a metre.

**c)** Enter the data in a table using the following heading.

**Length of Estimate (m)**

**d)** Repeat the procedure for a total of 15 participants.

**e)** Calculate the mean, median, and mode estimates.

**f)** Make a bar graph of the data.

*Observations:* Make notes about how well the participants estimate a distance of 2 m.

*Conclusion:* Make a conclusion on how closely people can estimate a distance of 2 m.

*Evaluation:* Discuss the validity of your hypothesis.

## DISCOVER 2

### Materials

- string with mass attached
- thumbtacks or tape
- stopwatch or watch with a second hand

### Period of a Pendulum

*Objective:* To investigate the relationship between the length of a pendulum and its period (the time it takes to complete one back-and-forth swing).

*Hypothesis:* State your hypothesis.

*Procedure:*

**a)** Make a chart using the following headings. Provide enough rows for ten trials.

| Length of Pendulum | Time (s) |
|---|---|

**b)** Attach a pendulum to the doorway with tape or thumbtacks.

**c)** Measure the length of the pendulum.

**d)** Swing the pendulum.

**e)** Measure the time, in seconds, it takes to swing a total of five swings.

**f)** Enter the data into your chart.

**g)** Repeat the procedure a total of ten times, each with a different length of the pendulum.

**h)** Enter the data into a scatter plot.

*Observations:* Describe the relationship or trend.

*Conclusion:* Make a conclusion about the relationship between pendulum length and the time taken for one full swing.

*Evaluation:* Discuss the validity of your hypothesis.

## DISCOVER 3

### Materials

- 8 styrofoam coffee cups
- pen
- masking tape
- pitcher of water
- stopwatch or watch with a second hand

### Draining Times

*Objective:* To investigate the relationship between the number of holes in a container and the time it takes to drain.

*Hypothesis:* State your hypothesis.

*Procedure:*

**a)** Prepare a chart with the following headings. Make enough rows for eight trials.

| Number of Holes | Draining Time (s) |
|---|---|

**b)** Use a pen to punch one hole in the base of the first coffee cup. Use the same pen to punch two holes in the base of the second coffee cup. Continue up to eight holes in the base of the eighth cup. Make sure all holes are the same size.

**c)** Draw a line at the same level in each cup.

d) On the outside of the cup, seal the holes with masking tape. Pour water into the cup up to the line you drew.
e) Hold the cup over the pitcher. Quickly peal off the tape and allow the water to drain into the pitcher. Measure the time, in seconds, it takes to drain.
f) Enter the data in your chart.
g) Make a scatter plot of the data.

*Observations:* Describe the relationship or trend.

*Conclusion:* Make a conclusion about the relationship between the number of holes and the draining time.

*Evaluation:* Discuss the validity of your hypothesis.

## DISCOVER 4

- 2 measuring tapes

### Jump Height

*Objective:* To investigate the relationship between a person's height and his or her vertical jumping ability.

*Hypothesis:* State your hypothesis.

*Procedure:*

a) Measure a participant's height, in centimetres.
b) Have the participant jump, from a standing start, and touch as high up the wall as possible.
c) Measure the height of the spot where the participant touched the wall, in centimetres.
d) Subtract the participant's height from the jump height.
e) Enter the data into a table with the following headings.

| Participant's Height (cm) | Jump Height (cm) | Jump Height – Participant's Height (cm) |
|---|---|---|

f) Repeat the procedure for a total of ten participants.
g) Make three scatter plots, each with data from two columns at a time.

*Observations:* Describe the relationship or trend.

*Conclusion:* Make a conclusion about the relationship between each pair of variables.

*Evaluation:* Discuss the validity of your hypothesis.

## Key Concepts

- A statistical experiment is conducted to investigate a relationship between variables.
- An experiment consists of the following components:
  - hypothesis
  - materials
  - procedure
  - observations
  - conclusion
  - evaluation

## Discuss the Concepts

1. Explain why it is important to evaluate your hypothesis at the end of an experiment.
2. Would four to six individual results be enough to formulate a conclusion at the end of an experiment? Explain.

## Apply the Concepts

**B** **Thinking/Inquiry/Problem Solving** For situations 1 to 7, design and carry out all components of an experiment.

1. *Objective*: To investigate the physical flexibility of your classmates.
2. *Objective*: To investigate the relationship between the distance a person stands from a light source and the length of the person's shadow.
3. *Objective*: To investigate the relationship between the circumference of a person's neck and of the same person's wrist.
4. *Objective:* To investigate the relationship between the slope of a ramp and the time a ball takes to roll down the ramp.
5. *Objective:* To investigate the relationship between types of canned soup and the time the can takes to roll down a ramp.
6. *Objective:* To investigate the relationship between the initial temperature of some water and the time it takes for the water to cool to room temperature.
7. *Objective:* To investigate the relationship between the number of times the back wheel turns for one turn of the pedals on a bicycle, as the gears are stepped through.

# Review

## 4.1 Formulating Hypotheses and Gathering Data, pages 124–129

1. State whether each of the following is a primary or a secondary source of data.
   a) reading a chart of automobile prices in a magazine
   b) accessing a list of song titles on the Internet
   c) going door-to-door to take an opinion survey
   d) measuring the actual volume of juice in 100 bottles

2. Would you use a primary or a secondary source of data for each of the following? Justify your answer.
   a) You need to find data on the longest rivers in Canada.
   b) A company wishes to determine the needs of its customers.
   c) A school administration needs to find out the neighbours' opinions on students parking on local streets.
   d) You have a science assignment to determine the average masses of various animals.

3. State a hypothesis for each question. Explain why you made that hypothesis.
   a) What is happening to the prices of CDs?
   b) Who watch TV more — adults or teenagers?
   c) What are the three most multicultural cities in Canada?
   d) How are school marks related to the amount of time spent playing video games?

## 4.2 Surveys and Sampling Principles, pages 130–135

4. **Communication** Describe a simple random sampling technique that could be used by the Board of Education to determine the effectiveness of parent-teacher interviews.

5. **Communication** Describe a stratified random sampling technique that could be used by the Students' Council to determine students' opinions on school safety.

6. **Communication** Describe a systematic random sampling technique that could be used by a clothing store to determine the needs of its customers.

## 4.3 Organizing Data Using the TI-83 Graphing Calculator, pages 136–142

**7.** Identify each variable.

**a)** The number of students at each age between 13 and 21.

**b)** The average number of days of sunlight each month of the year.

**c)** The price of taking the bus to school on January 15 of each year for 5 years.

**d)** The frequency that each letter, A, B, C, and D, is used for the correct answer in a multiple-choice test.

**8.** For each part in question 7, state whether the data set would be graphed using a bar graph or a broken-line graph.

**9.** **Application** The following data represent the number of centimetres of snow that fell each day in a two-week period in January.

| 1.3 | 0 | 2.2 | 2.8 | 0.3 | 0 | 0 | 1.1 | 0 | 3.4 | 0.5 | 0.8 | 0 | 5.6 |
|---|---|---|---|---|---|---|---|---|---|---|---|---|---|

**a)** Enter the data into list L3 of a graphing calculator.

**b)** Make a bar graph of the data.

**c)** Copy the graph into your notebook. Label the axes, along with their scales. Provide a title.

**d)** Describe the graph and what it shows.

**e)** Explain why a bar graph was used instead of a broken-line graph.

## 4.4 Measures of Central Tendency, pages 143–148

**10. a)** The data show the number of baby teeth lost by the children in a kindergarten class. Determine the mean, median, and mode.

**b)** Which measure of central tendency best describes these numbers of teeth? Explain.

| 2 | 5 | 1 | 3 | 1 | 3 | 4 | 3 | 3 | 6 | 2 |
|---|---|---|---|---|---|---|---|---|---|---|
| 3 | 1 | 1 | 3 | 2 | 5 | 3 | 8 | 3 | 1 | 4 |

**11. a)** The data show the masses of full-grown pet cats, in kilograms, that visited a veterinarian. Determine the mean, median, and mode.

**b)** Which measure of central tendency best describes these cats? Explain.

| 3 | 3.6 | 3.5 | 5.5 | 4.4 | 3.1 | 2.9 |
|---|---|---|---|---|---|---|
| 3.7 | 3.6 | 4.5 | 3.5 | 5.1 | 4.8 | 3.6 |
| 3.2 | 3.6 | 4.0 | 2.8 | 3.9 | 3.0 | 3.6 |

## 4.5 Data Analysis: Trends and Relationships, pages 149–155

**12. Communication** For each of the following scatter plots, state whether there is a relationship between variable 1 and variable 2. Describe that relationship.

**a)**

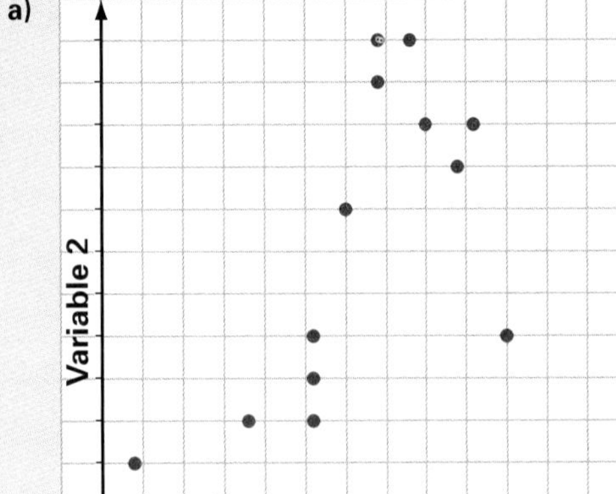


**b)**

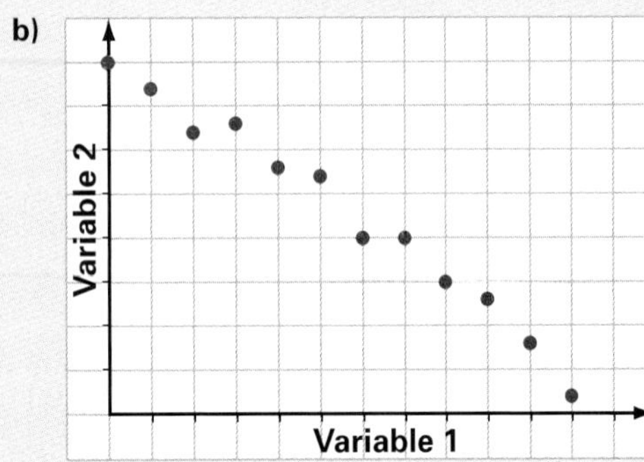


**c)**

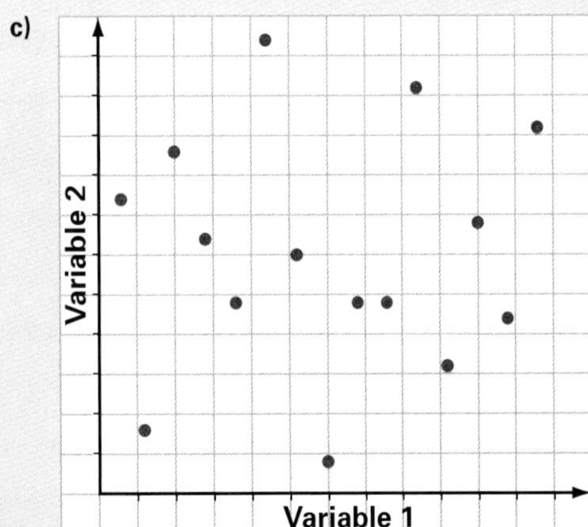

**13.** For each scatter plot in question 12, state whether there are any outliers. If so, describe how the outliers are different from the rest of the data.

**14.** **Application** The following data show the flight distance, for Air North's flights from Toronto to various Canadian cities, as well as the flight time to that city.

| City | Distance (km) | Flight Time (h) |
|---|---|---|
| Montréal, PQ | 554 | 1.2 |
| Ottawa, ON | 399 | 1.0 |
| Halifax, NS | 1929 | 2.1 |
| Winnipeg, MB | 2084 | 2.7 |
| Saskatoon, SK | 2874 | 3.3 |
| Edmonton, AB | 3390 | 4.5 |
| Vancouver, BC | 4537 | 5.0 |
| Charlottetown, PE | 1738 | 2.0 |
| St. John's, NF | 3141 | 3.0 |
| Fredericton, NB | 1373 | 1.9 |

**a)** Which is the independent variable? Why?

**b)** Make a scatter plot of the data.

**c)** Use the scatter plot to determine the relationship (if any) between the flight distance and the time of flight. Consider trends with and without outliers.

## 4.6 Experiments, pages 156–159

**15.** **Thinking/Inquiry/Problem Solving** Perform the following experiment to investigate the relationship between the volume of water in a cylindrical container and its mass.

*Materials*

- large, graduated cylindrical container
- water
- beam balance or kitchen balance

*Hypothesis:* State your hypothesis.

*Procedure:*

**a)** Use the following column headings in a chart to record the results of your experiment.

**Volume of Water (L)** **Mass (kg)**

**b)** Fill the container with 0.2 L of water.

**c)** Using the beam balance, determine the mass, in kilograms, of the container and water. Record the results in your chart.

**d)** Repeat part c) for volumes of 0.4 L, 0.6 L, 0.8 L, 1.0 L, 1.5 L, and 2.0 L.

**e)** Make a scatter plot of the data in your chart.

*Observations:* Describe the relationship or trend.

*Conclusion:* Make a conclusion about the relationship between the volume of water in a cylindrical container and its mass.

*Evaluation:* Evaluate your hypothesis.

# Practice Test

## Multiple Choice

***For each question, select the best answer.***

**1.** Identify the variable for the following question:

How many hours of homework does a grade 9 student in your school have each week?

**A)** number of grade 9 students in your school **B)** number of hours of homework per week
**C)** number of students in your class **D)** number of hours of class time per week

**2.** Determine the median of the data set 18, 21, 16, 25, 18, 28, 32, 34.

**A)** 18 **B)** 24 **C)** 25 **D)** 23

**3.** Identify the outlier in the data set 6, 50, 18, 13, 15, 11, 22, 6.

**A)** 6 **B)** 22 **C)** 50 **D)** 15

## Short Answer

**4.** State whether each of the following is a primary or a secondary source of data.

**a)** asking grade 10 students their opinions of the literacy test
**b)** a table of river lengths found in an encyclopedia
**c)** finding sports statistics on the Internet
**d)** conducting an experiment to find a relationship between age and height

**5.** Classify the sampling technique used in each survey, as simple random, systematic random, stratified random, or non-random sampling.

**a)** A TV host asks for opinions by selecting people and interviewing them on the street corner.
**b)** A computer is programmed to randomly select 100 names from a club's membership list.
**c)** Students are selected at random, with the number of students in each age group selected proportional to the size of the age group.
**d)** To select 100 people who can buy concert tickets, the ticket agent randomly selects one wristband number and then every tenth number after that.

**6.** The list gives the amounts of weekly allowances, in dollars, received by 20 high school students.

**a)** Determine the mean, median, and mode allowances.
**b)** Which measure of central tendency best represents this group of students? Explain.

| | | | | |
|---|---|---|---|---|
| 20 | 25 | 20 | 0 | 15 |
| 20 | 0 | 0 | 40 | 10 |
| 30 | 0 | 25 | 100 | 0 |
| 10 | 30 | 50 | 15 | 20 |

## Extended Response

**15. Thinking/Inquiry/Problem Solving** Carry out the following experiment.

**Materials**
- grid paper

*Objective:* To investigate the relationship between the side length of a square and its area.

*Hypothesis:* State your hypothesis.

*Procedure:*

**a)** Make a chart with the following headings, with enough rows for eight trials.

**Side Length** **Area**

**b)** On grid paper, draw eight squares of different sizes.

**c)** Measure the side lengths. Enter the data in the first column of your chart.

**d)** Count the grid squares inside each square you drew. Enter the data in the second column of your chart.

**e)** Make a scatter plot of the data.

*Observations:* Describe the pattern or trend.

*Conclusion:* Make a conclusion on the relationship between side length of a square and its area.

*Evaluation:* Discuss the validity of your hypothesis.

**ACHIEVEMENT CHECK** Knowledge/Understanding Thinking/Inquiry/Problem Solving Communication Application

**8.** Lee wanted to find out if grade nine girls spend more on clothes and shoes than do grade nine boys. She randomly selected ten male and ten female students that she met in the school cafeteria and got the following data.

| **Male Student** | Al | Bob | Vin | Ian | Dan | Tad | Cal | Ed | Mat | Jon |
|---|---|---|---|---|---|---|---|---|---|---|
| **Monthly Spending** | $15 | $18 | $19 | $20 | $23 | $23 | $27 | $29 | $31 | $32 |
| **Female Student** | Ann | Dee | Jan | Zee | Hana | Lyn | Nan | Bea | Lou | Ena |
| **Monthly Spending** | $13 | $18 | $19 | $20 | $22 | $22 | $25 | $26 | $29 | $37 |

**a)** Suggest what Lee's hypothesis could be.

**b)** Using a graphing calculator, or otherwise, draw broken-line graphs of the data.

**c)** Find the mean, median, and mode for each set of data.

**d)** What trends do you recognize in the data? Justify your answer.

**e)** If you were making this investigation, how would you set up the samples, collect the data, and analyse it?

# CHAPTER 5

# Exploring Integers and Rational Numbers

In this chapter, you will combine skills with integers, fractions, and decimals.

You will

- add, subtract, multiply, and divide integers and rational numbers
- extend your knowledge of locating integers on a number line to plotting points on the Cartesian plane
- apply skills of proportional reasoning to ratio and rates

## Chapter Problem

Maria is 22 and has been working for almost two years. She is considering investing some money in the stock market. She wants to make a wise investment. Before investing, she decides to research the behaviour of the stock(s) she is considering.

As you work through this chapter, you will use your skills with integers and rational numbers to study changes in the stock market.

# Get Ready

## Using Integer Tiles

Integers include positive whole numbers, negative whole numbers, and zero. Tiles can be used to model integers.

One red tile represents +1.

One white tile represents −1.

One red tile and one white tile together represent zero.

The diagrams show three ways of representing the integer +3.

The diagrams show three ways of representing the integer −2.

1. Write the integer shown in each diagram.
   a) 
   b) 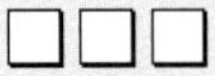
   c) 
   d)

2. Use integer tiles or diagrams to show two ways of representing each integer.
   a) +2
   b) −5
   c) 0
   d) +4
   e) −1
   f) −4

## Integers on a Number Line

Integers can be shown on a horizontal number line.
The integer 0 is neither positive nor negative.
Positive integers are located to the right of 0.
Negative integers are located to the left of 0.

To mark +3 on a number line, start at 0 and move 3 units to the right.
To mark –5 on a number line, start at 0 and move 5 units to the left.

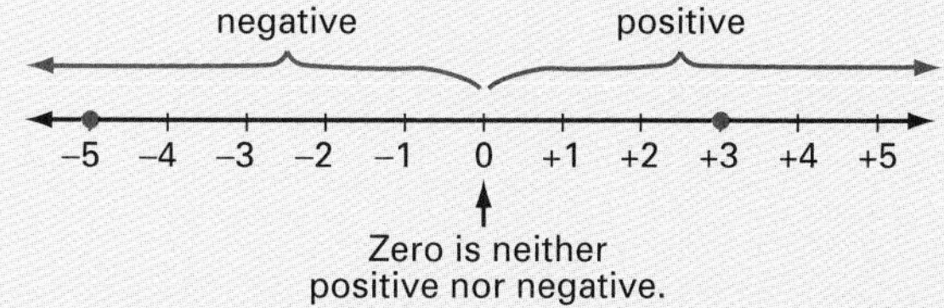


**3.** In your notebook, draw a horizontal number line and mark the following points.

**a)** $-3, 12, 0, 6, -1$ **b)** $3, -2, 1, -11, 4$

**4.** A thermometer is an example of a vertical number line. In your notebook, draw a thermometer and mark the following temperatures (in degrees Celsius) on it: 5°, –6°, 0°, –4°, 8°.

## Order of Operations

To remember the order of operations, use BEDMAS.

- Do all calculations inside the brackets first. **B**
- Simplify numbers with exponents. **E**
- Divide and multiply in order from left to right. **DM**
- Add and subtract in order from left to right. **AS**

$$\begin{aligned} 2(5+3)^2 - 18 \div 2 &= 2(8)^2 - 18 \div 2 && \textbf{B} \\ &= 2(64) - 18 \div 2 && \textbf{E} \\ &= 128 - 9 && \textbf{DM} \\ &= 119 && \textbf{AS} \end{aligned}$$

**5.** Evaluate.

**a)** $8 \times 5 - 6$ **b)** $2^2 + 4 \times 3$ **c)** $3(6 - 2) + 3^2$

**d)** $(15 - 3) \div 4$ **e)** $9 + 8 \div 2$ **f)** $3 + 4 \times 3 \div 6$

**g)** $4^2 + (14 - 2) \div 2$ **h)** $(3 + 2)^2 + 10 \div 2$ **i)** $4(5 - 2) + 5(3 + 1)$

## Improper Fractions and Mixed Numbers

What part of the figure is shaded? Write this as a mixed number and as an improper fraction.

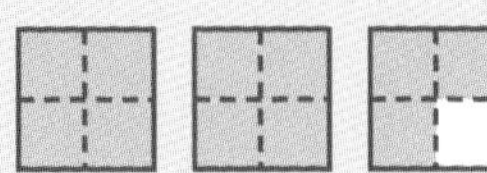

Two whole squares and three quarters are shaded.

As a mixed number, the shaded part is $2\frac{3}{4}$.

To change to an improper fraction: $2\frac{3}{4} = \frac{2 \times 4 + 3}{4}$

$= \frac{11}{4}$

As an improper fraction, the shaded part is $\frac{11}{4}$.

**Check: In the figure, 11 quarter-squares are shaded.**

**6.** Write a fraction to represent the shaded part of each figure. For parts b) and c), express your answer as an improper fraction and as a mixed number.

**a)** 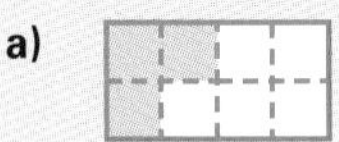

**b)** 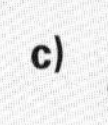

**c)** 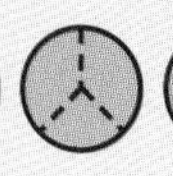  

**7.** Draw regular shapes and shade them to show each fraction. Write the fraction, using the form $\frac{\text{numerator}}{\text{denominator}}$, below each drawing.

**a)** one quarter **b)** three fifths

**c)** one half **d)** seven tenths

**8.** Draw a diagram and shade it to show each mixed number. Write the number, as both a mixed number and an improper fraction, below each drawing.

**a)** $2\frac{1}{2}$ **b)** $1\frac{2}{3}$ **c)** $5\frac{3}{4}$ **d)** $3\frac{1}{5}$

## Lowest Common Multiple (LCM)

Find the lowest common multiple of 2 and 3.

The multiples of 2 are 2, 4, 6, 8, 10, …

The multiples of 3 are 3, 6, 9, 12, 15, …

The lowest common multiple of 2 and 3 is 6.

**9.** Find the lowest common multiple of each pair.

**a)** 2 and 5 **b)** 3 and 4 **c)** 4 and 10 **d)** 6 and 4

## Adding and Subtracting Fractions

Find the sum $\frac{1}{2} + \frac{2}{3}$.

To add, fractions need to be expressed with a common denominator.
The LCM of 2 and 3 is 6, so use the common denominator 6.
Express each fraction in sixths.

$$\frac{1}{2} + \frac{2}{3} = \frac{3}{6} + \frac{4}{6}$$
$$= \frac{7}{6} \text{ or } 1\frac{1}{6}$$

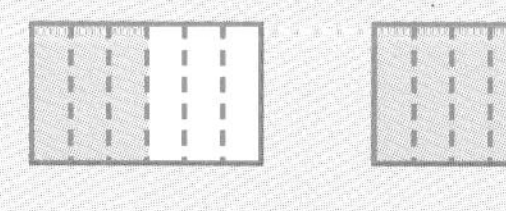

The same process is needed to subtract fractions with different denominators.

**10.** Find the lowest common denominator for the fractions in each pair. Express the two fractions with that denominator. Then, find their sum or difference.

**a)** $\frac{1}{2} + \frac{4}{5}$ **b)** $\frac{1}{3} + \frac{3}{4}$ **c)** $\frac{1}{4} + \frac{3}{10}$ **d)** $\frac{5}{6} + \frac{3}{4}$

**e)** $\frac{2}{5} + \frac{1}{3}$ **f)** $\frac{1}{2} + \frac{3}{8}$ **g)** $\frac{3}{4} - \frac{2}{3}$ **h)** $\frac{5}{6} - \frac{1}{4}$

## Decimal Fractions

A decimal can be expressed in fraction form using place value.
The fraction form can be reduced to lowest terms by dividing the numerator and the denominator by common factors.

Express 0.25 as a fraction in lowest terms.
0.25 means 25 hundredths

$$0.25 = \frac{25}{100}$$
$$= \frac{1}{4} \quad \begin{matrix} \leftarrow 25 \div 25 = 1 \\ \leftarrow 100 \div 25 = 4 \end{matrix}$$

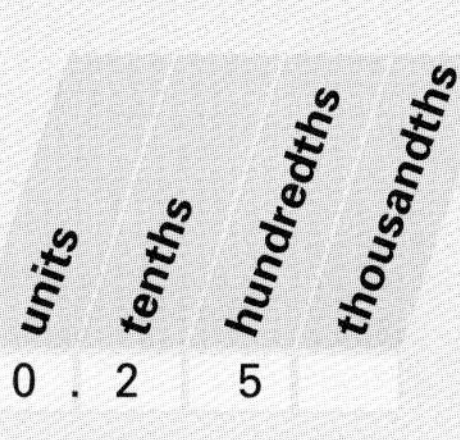


**11.** Express each decimal as a fraction in lowest terms.

**a)** 0.5 **b)** 0.8 **c)** 0.3 **d)** 0.45 **e)** 0.32

**f)** 0.75 **g)** 0.28 **h)** 0.95 **i)** 0.325 **j)** 0.675

# 5.1 Adding and Subtracting Integers

One fall morning, the temperature was –2°C. During the day, the temperature rose by 11°C. What was the high temperature that day?

The Celsius temperature scale is a common application of integers. To solve this problem, you add integers.

You can use a number line to add integers.
Follow these steps when drawing a number line.

- Use a pencil and a straightedge.
- Use evenly spaced tick marks to show the numbers on the line.
- Include arrows at both ends of the line to show that the line continues indefinitely.
- Mark the numbers below the number line. This row of numbers is called the scale.
- Mark positive numbers to the right of zero.
- Mark negative numbers to the left of zero.

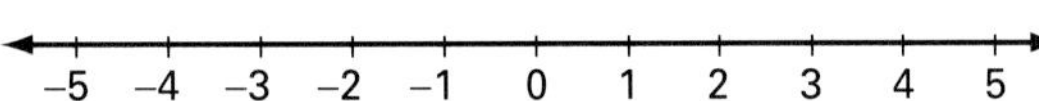

## Example 1

### Modelling Addition

Draw a number line to model each sum.

**a)** $-2 + 11$ **b)** $+5 + (-4)$ **c)** $-1 + (-6)$

### Solution

**a)** Draw a number line. Start at –2 and move 11 units to the right. The number you reach is 9.

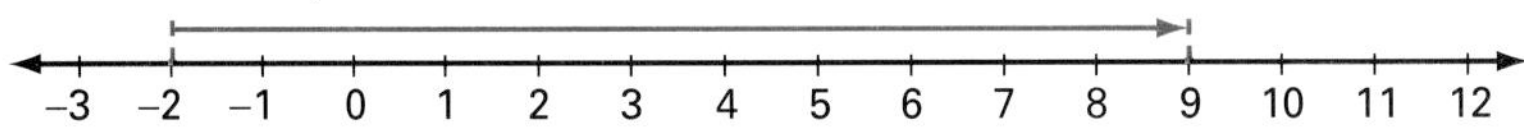

**Parentheses are used in the expression +5 + (–4) so that the sign of the number is not confused with a subtraction sign.**

**b)** Draw a number line. Start at +5 and move 4 units to the left. The number you reach is +1.

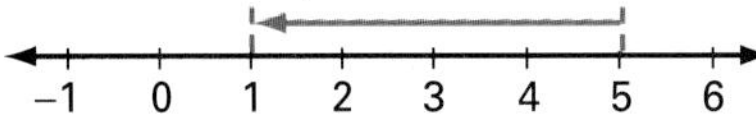

**c)** Draw a number line. Start at –1 and move 6 units to the left. The number you reach is –7.

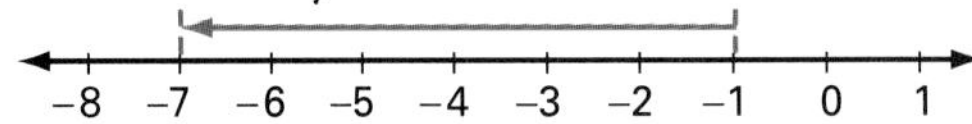

## EXAMPLE 2

### Temperatures

In one day, the temperature started at 3°C, increased 5°C, and dropped 15°C by midnight. What was the temperature at midnight?

### Solution

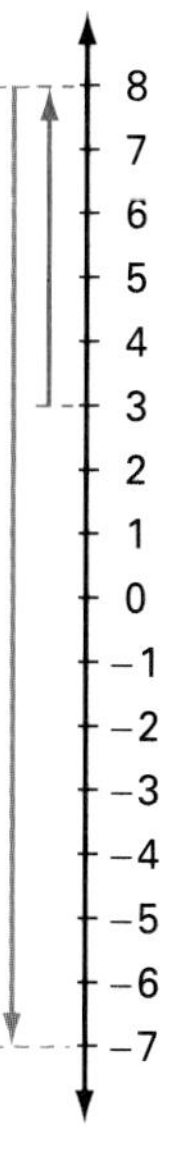


Model the addition on a thermometer.
Draw a thermometer scale.
Start at 3°C and add an increase of 5°C by moving 5 units up.
Add a decrease of 15°C by moving 15 units down.
The arrow ends at −7.

The temperature at midnight was −7°C.

For every positive integer, there is a negative integer located the same distance from zero on the opposite side of the number line. These pairs of integers are called **opposites**.

For example, the opposite of +3 is −3 and the opposite of −7 is +7.

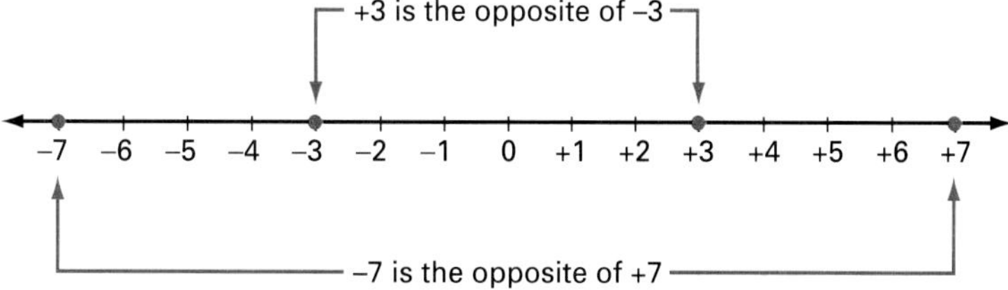


You already know how to add integers.
To subtract integers, you can change the subtraction to an addition by

- changing the subtraction sign to an addition sign, and
- changing the integer being subtracted to its opposite.

To subtract an integer, add its opposite.

## EXAMPLE 3

### Subtracting Integers

Simplify.

**a)** $-5 - 3$ **b)** $4 - (-2)$ **c)** $-6 - (-3)$

### Solution

Rewrite each subtraction sentence as an addition.

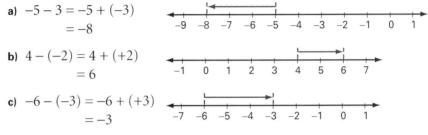

**a)** $-5 - 3 = -5 + (-3)$
$= -8$

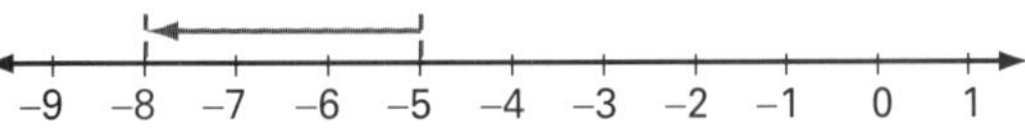

**b)** $4 - (-2) = 4 + (+2)$
$= 6$

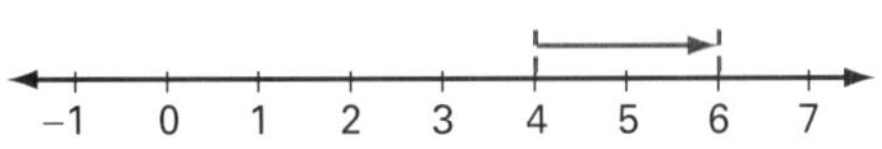

**c)** $-6 - (-3) = -6 + (+3)$
$= -3$

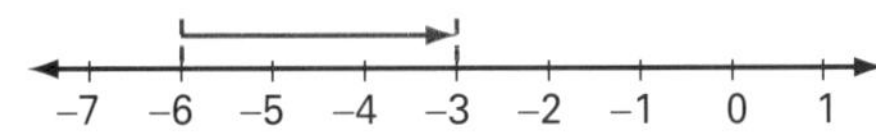

## DISCOVER

Refer to the Technology Appendix for an introduction to the TI-83 graphing calculator.

### Adding and Subtracting Integers Using a Calculator

When working with large numbers, it is easier to use a calculator. You might use a TI-83 graphing calculator or a scientific calculator. For each calculator, the keystrokes involved in performing a particular function may vary.

1. On most scientific calculators and graphing calculators, you will find two "minus" keys. On most calculators, these keys appear as (−) and ((-)) or as (−) and (+/−). Experiment with your calculator to determine which key is the subtraction symbol and which key is the negative sign.

2. To represent −53, on some calculators, you must press the (+/−) key or the ((-)) key followed by 53. On other calculators, you have to input the number 53, followed by the (+/−) or ((-)) key. Record the correct key sequence for your calculator in your notebook.

3. What happens on your calculator if you use the negative sign key instead of the subtraction key? Test this by entering the expression $-1 + 4$ both ways.

4. Use your calculator to confirm these results.
   **a)** $-53 - 73 = -126$ **b)** $-418 + 726 = 308$ **c)** $-37 - (-27) = -10$

5. Use your calculator to find each result.
   **a)** $-458 + 213$ **b)** $93 - 925$ **c)** $-79 + 381$
   **d)** $312 - (-110)$ **e)** $129 - (-250)$ **f)** $-45 - (-89)$

## Key Concepts

- To add integers using a number line, start at the location of the first integer and move the number of spaces (positive to the right, negative to the left) indicated by the next integer in the expression.
- To subtract an integer, add the opposite.
- When using a calculator, use the (−) key for subtraction and use the (-) or (+/−) key for a negative sign.

## Discuss the Concepts

1. When an integer is written without a sign in front, how is this integer marked on the number line?
2. Describe how you would evaluate $-8 - (-9)$ without a calculator.
3. Using a TI-83 graphing calculator, Randy entered the following key sequence: 45 (-) 10 (ENTER). Randy got the message ERR:SYNTAX. Explain what Randy did wrong.

## Practise

***For help with questions 1 to 3, refer to Example 1.***

1. Match each expression with the correct number line.

a) $-5 + 2$

b) $+12 + 7$

c) $+8 + (-5)$

d) $-9 + (-6)$

A
−1 0 1 2 3 4 5 6 7 8 9

B
11 12 13 14 15 16 17 18 19 20

C
−16 −15 −14 −13 −12 −11 −10 −9 −8

D
−6 −5 −4 −3 −2 −1 0 1

2. Draw a number line to show each sum.

a) $+10 + 5$ b) $-2 + 5$ c) $-7 + 3$

d) $3 + (-5)$ e) $5 + (-2)$ f) $-4 + (-6)$

3. Draw a number line to show each sum.

a) $+5 + 1 + 4$ b) $-11 + 4 + 5$ c) $0 + (-2) + 7$

d) $-3 + 4 + 1$ e) $-2 + 2 + 5$ f) $-5 + (-3) + 3$

*For help with question 4, refer to Example 2.*

4. Draw a thermometer scale to show each temperature change.
   a) 4°C + (−3°C) + 5°C
   b) 12°C + (−4°C) + (−8°C)
   c) −2°C +(−4°C) + (−5°C)
   d) 7°C + 10°C + (−11°C)

5. The diagrams show how you can use integer tiles to find the sum 5 + (−2).

| Start with 5 red tiles. | Add 2 white tiles. | Combine and remove zero combinations. | There are 3 red tiles left. |
|---|---|---|---|
|  | 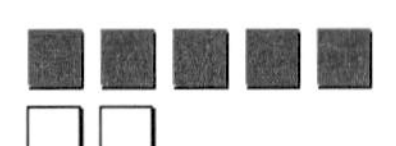 | 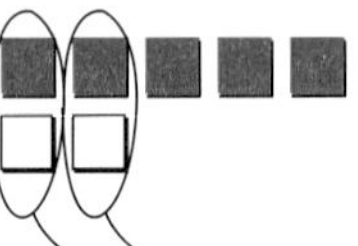 | 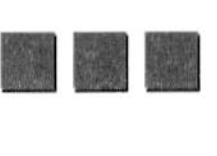 |

   So, 5 + (−2) = 3.

   Use integer tiles or draw diagrams to show each sum.
   a) 8 + (−3)  b) −5 + (−6)  c) 7 + (−9)
   d) −3 + 7  e) −12 + 8  f) 5 + (−5)

*For help with questions 6 and 7, refer to Example 3.*

6. Write the opposite of each integer.
   a) +4  b) −6  c) −12  d) +15

7. Find each difference using a number line.
   a) 11 − 4  b) 7 − 9  c) −3 − 5  d) −2 − (−8)

8. Evaluate.
   a) 7 + 9  b) −9 − 6  c) −12 + 4
   d) −22 − 4  e) −4 + 7  f) 3 − (−9)
   g) 1 + 3 + (−6)  h) −2 − 6 + 4  i) 14 + (−3) − (−5)
   j) −1 − 2 − 3  k) −3 + 5 − 9  l) 7 − (−3) + 3

9. Evaluate using a calculator.
   a) 19 − 36  b) −59 + 28  c) 141 − 263  d) −17 − 12
   e) −7 + 28  f) −64 − 158  g) 17 − (−5)  h) 84 − (−17)

## APPLY THE CONCEPTS

**10.** **Communication** Allison drew the following number line to show the sum of $12 + 6$.



a) Does the number line have to start at 0? Explain why or why not.
b) Does the number line extend far enough to show the answer? Explain.
c) Draw a more efficient number line.
d) Could the number line start at $+10$ and go up by 2s? If so, draw what the number line would look like. If not, explain why not.

To calculate the average, find the sum of all the values and divide by the total number of values.

**11.** **Average temperature** For a science project, one day Rennish recorded the temperature in four Ontario locations from a weather web site on the Internet.

Haliburton: −14°C
Ottawa: −22°C
Niagara Falls: −8°C
Brockville: −10°C

What was the average temperature for these four locations?

**12.** **Stock market** On Monday, Fly-By-Night Airlines' stock went up 25¢, on Tuesday it went down 53¢, on Wednesday it went down 24¢, on Thursday it went up 36¢, and on Friday it went down 48¢. By the end of the day on Friday, was the price of Fly-By-Night Airlines' stock higher or lower than it was when the stock market first opened that Monday? By how much?

**13.** **Profit and loss** Sonilla sells antiques at a flea market every Saturday. In three consecutive weeks, she had a profit of \$125, a profit of \$112, and a loss of \$320. How much was her net profit or loss over the three weeks?

**14.** **Bank account** Eric kept a record of the following deposits and withdrawals to his bank account for one month. How much money was in Eric's bank account at the end of the month?

| | |
|---|---:|
| Starting balance: | \$275 |
| Deposit: | \$74 |
| Deposit: | \$48 |
| Withdrawal: | \$100 |
| Withdrawal: | \$60 |
| Deposit: | \$125 |
| Withdrawal: | \$150 |
| Withdrawal: | \$80 |

15. **Time zones** A time-zone map of Canada is shown.

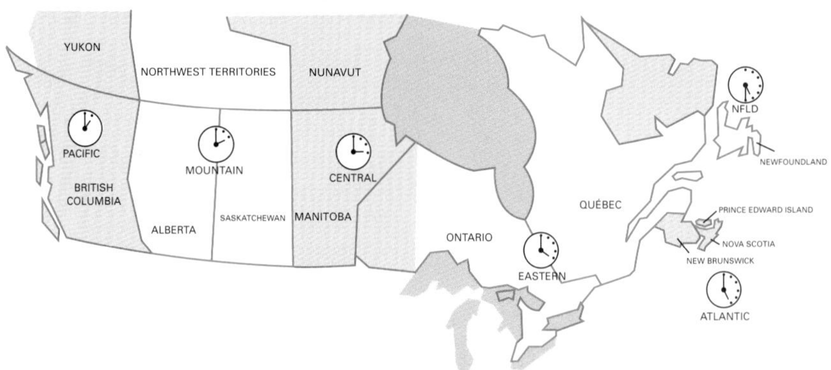


a) If it is 7:00 p.m. in Ontario, what time is it in Yukon?

b) While travelling through Prince Edward Island, you want to phone a relative in Saskatchewan. How many hours ahead of Saskatchewan is Prince Edward Island?

c) If the time in Nova Scotia is 10:00 a.m., determine the time in British Columbia. Show your work.

C 16. **Time zones** Calling overseas involves checking the time-zone charts. Several countries and the time difference (TD) to Ontario are shown. Calculate the time in Ontario, if the time in each country is 3 p.m. (15:00). Use a 24-hour clock to simplify the calculations.

| Country | TD |
|---|---|
| China | +13 |
| Israel | +7 |
| Morocco | +5 |
| New Zealand | +17 |

## MATH TIP

### Adding Integers

You can use playing cards to model addition of integers. Consider black cards positive and red cards negative.
The cards shown represent +6 and –8.
To add 6 + (–8), let 6 diamonds cover 6 spades—they are equal and opposite so they sum to 0.
The remaining two spades show the answer of –2.

# 5.2 Multiplying and Dividing Integers

Ryan would like to purchase five CD-Rs for his new computer system. At the store, he is faced with the following choices:

Single CD-R: \$2 each 10-pack: \$15

How can Ryan determine which choice is the better buy?

To help solve problems like this, you need to recall your skills for multiplying and dividing.

Multiplication by a positive integer can be written as repeated addition.

$3 \times 5 = 5 + 5 + 5$
$= 15$

$3 \times (-5) = (-5) + (-5) + (-5)$
$= -15$

The product of two positive integers is a positive integer.
The product of a positive integer and a negative integer is a negative integer.

However, the product of a negative integer and a positive integer, or the product of a negative integer and a negative integer cannot be easily represented as repeated addition.

## Patterns in Multiplication

1. Compare these tables.
   a) From the first table, what is the sign of the product of a positive integer and a negative integer?
   b) From the second table, what is the sign of the product of a negative integer and a positive integer?

| |
|---|
| $4 \times 3 = 12$ |
| $4 \times 2 = 8$ |
| $4 \times 1 = 4$ |
| $4 \times 0 = 0$ |
| $4 \times (-1) = -4$ |
| $4 \times (-2) = -8$ |
| $4 \times (-3) = -12$ |

| |
|---|
| $3 \times 4 = 12$ |
| $2 \times 4 = 8$ |
| $1 \times 4 = 4$ |
| $0 \times 4 = 0$ |
| $(-1) \times 4 = -4$ |
| $(-2) \times 4 = -8$ |
| $(-3) \times 4 = -12$ |

2. Compare these tables.
   a) Describe the pattern in the answers to the first four rows in each table.
   b) In your notebook, copy each table and complete the last three rows.
   c) What is the sign of the answer when you multiply two negative integers?

| |
|---|
| $(-5) \times 3 = -15$ |
| $(-5) \times 2 = -10$ |
| $(-5) \times 1 = -5$ |
| $(-5) \times 0 = 0$ |
| $(-5) \times (-1) =$ ? |
| $(-5) \times (-2) =$ ? |
| $(-5) \times (-3) =$ ? |

| |
|---|
| $3 \times (-5) = -15$ |
| $2 \times (-5) = -10$ |
| $1 \times (-5) = -5$ |
| $0 \times (-5) = 0$ |
| $(-1) \times (-5) =$ ? |
| $(-2) \times (-5) =$ ? |
| $(-3) \times (-5) =$ ? |

## Example 1

### Multiplying Integers

Multiply.

**a)** $8 \times 3$ **b)** $9 \times (-3)$ **c)** $(-5) \times 4$ **d)** $(-4) \times (-3)$

### Solution

**a)** $8 \times 3 = 24$ positive × positive = positive

**b)** $9 \times (-3) = -27$ positive × negative = negative

**c)** $(-5) \times 4 = -20$ negative × positive = negative

**d)** $(-4) \times (-3) = 12$ negative × negative = positive

Multiplication and division are inverse operations. For each multiplication statement, there are two related division statements. The pattern in the signs for division of integers is similar to the pattern for multiplication of integers.

$3 \times 6 = 18$, so $18 \div 6 = 3$ and $18 \div 3 = 6$.

$2 \times (-7) = -14$, so $-14 \div (-7) = 2$ and $-14 \div 2 = -7$.

$-4 \times 2 = -8$, so $-8 \div 2 = -4$ and $-8 \div (-4) = 2$.

$-5 \times (-6) = 30$, so $30 \div (-6) = -5$ and $30 \div (-5) = -6$.

## Example 2

### Dividing Integers

Divide.

**a)** $16 \div 8$ **b)** $21 \div (-3)$ **c)** $-36 \div 4$ **d)** $-24 \div (-2)$

### Solution

**a)** $16 \div 8 = 2$ positive ÷ positive = positive

**b)** $21 \div (-3) = -7$ positive ÷ negative = negative

**c)** $-36 \div 4 = -9$ negative ÷ positive = negative

**d)** $-24 \div (-2) = 12$ negative ÷ negative = positive

# EXAMPLE 3

## Multiplying and Dividing Integers Using a Calculator

Calculate.

a) $-15 \times 12$  b) $(-32)(-14)$  c) $\frac{105}{-7}$

## Solution

Remember to use the (–) or (+/–) key for the negative sign and not the (−) key.

The appearance of the keys and the order in which the keys are pressed may vary on other scientific calculators.

a) On a scientific calculator, press

C 15 +/– × 12 =

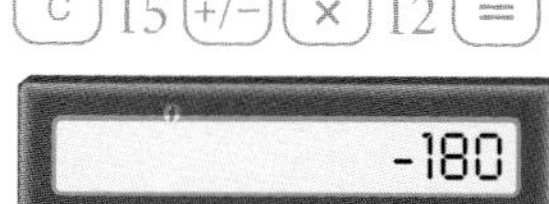


On a graphing calculator, press

(–) 15 × 12 ENTER

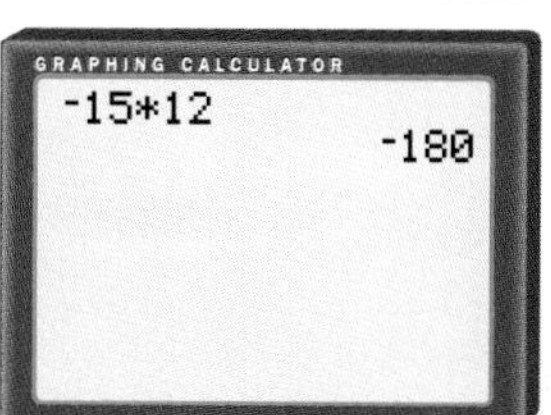


b) On a scientific calculator, press

C 32 +/– × 14 +/– =

On a graphing calculator, press

(–) 32 × (–) 14 ENTER

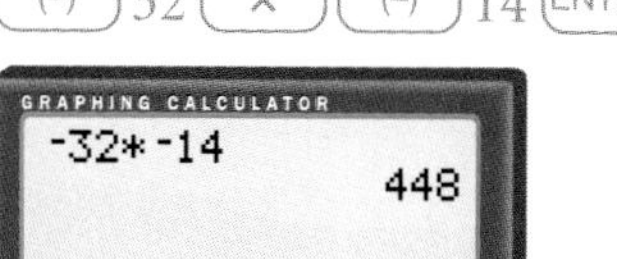

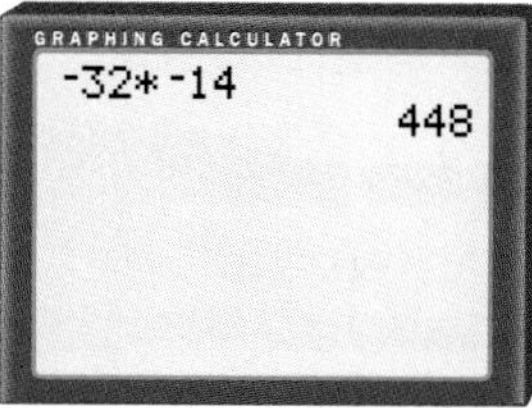


c) On a scientific calculator, press

C 105 ÷ 7 +/– =

On a graphing calculator, press

105 ÷ (–) 7 ENTER

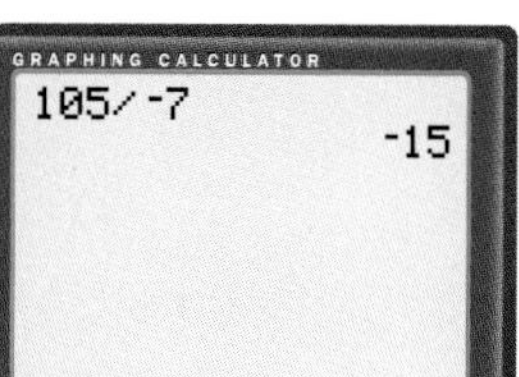

## Key Concepts

- Multiplication by a positive integer can be expressed in terms of repeated addition.
- Since multiplication and division are inverse operations, the rules for multiplying and dividing two integers are the same.

| Multiplication | Division |
|---|---|
| positive × positive = positive | positive ÷ positive = positive |
| positive × negative = negative | positive ÷ negative = negative |
| negative × positive = negative | negative ÷ positive = negative |
| negative × negative = positive | negative ÷ negative = positive |

## Discuss the Concepts

1. Use an example to explain when multiplication can be expressed in terms of addition.
2. Brackets are used to enclose a negative integer if it is the second or later term in an expression. Discuss the usefulness of enclosing a negative integer in brackets if it is the first term in an expression.

## Practise

***For help with question 1, refer to Examples 1 and 2.***

1. Predict the sign of each answer. Explain why.

   a) $15(-10)$ b) $-7 \times 7$ c) $(-10)(-9)$
   d) $-32 \div 16$ e) $14 \div (-2)$ f) $-169 \div (-13)$

***For help with questions 2 and 3, refer to Examples 1 and 3.***

2. Write each expression as a repeated addition. Then, evaluate.

   a) $3 \times 6$ b) $4 \times (-8)$ c) $5 \times 3$ d) $6(-4)$

3. Calculate.

   a) $7 \times (-4)$ b) $-5 \times (-8)$ c) $45(-2)$ d) $-12 \times (-3)$
   e) $(42)(3)$ f) $11 \times 5$ g) $(-8)(10)$ h) $(-4)(-12)$

***For help with questions 4 and 5, refer to Examples 2 and 3.***

4. For each equation, write two related division statements.

   a) $-7 \times 3 = -21$ b) $2(-9) = -18$ c) $(-5)(-7) = 35$

5. Calculate.

   a) $-16 \div (-8)$ b) $48 \div 3$ c) $125 \div (-5)$
   d) $\frac{80}{-4}$ e) $\frac{-50}{2}$ f) $\frac{-24}{-8}$

6. Follow the order of operations (BEDMAS) to simplify each expression.

 a) $-2(5 + 8) - 1$
 b) $4(-3) + 2(-2)$
 c) $17(2) + 8(2)$
 d) $36 \div 2 - (4 \times 5)$
 e) $6(-2) + 4(-4) - 21 \div 7$
 f) $-2(45 \div 9) - 3(72 \div 8)$

## Apply the Concepts

7. **Communication** Explain why a negative integer divided by a positive integer gives a negative answer. Use an example to support your explanation.

8. **Owing and earning money** Owing money can be expressed as a negative number. Earning money can be expressed as a positive number. Write a multiplication expression to model each situation. For example, suppose you cut three lawns and were paid $10 for each lawn. This can be expressed mathematically as $3 \times 10$.

 a) On three different days, you borrowed $2 from your friend.
 b) For three nights a week you walked the neighbour's dog. You were paid $5 each time you walked the dog.

9. Evaluate the expressions you wrote for question 8.

10. **Owing and earning money** Write a division expression to model each situation.

 a) You owe your parents $60 and have agreed to pay back your loan in three payments.
 b) You earned $125 for doing yard work for your neighbours and budget your money so that you spend equal amounts over five weeks.

11. Evaluate the expressions you wrote for question 10.

12. **Theatre seating** A theatre has 25 seats in each of its 30 rows.

 a) Write an expression for the total seating capacity of the theatre.
 b) The cost for a theatre ticket is $10. Write an expression for the revenue for one showing, assuming all the seats are filled.

13. **Stock market** Maria decided on Monday that she wanted to buy 50 shares of Fly-By-Night Airlines stock. The price of the stock on Monday was $13 per share. Then, she remembered that payday was not until Friday and she would not have enough money until then. On Friday, the price of the stock had dropped to $12 per share.

 a) How much money did she save on her purchase of 50 shares by waiting until Friday?
 b) How many more shares could she buy on Friday if she received a bonus that day of $360?

# 5.3 Plotting Points on the Cartesian Plane

The Global Positioning System (GPS) is commonly used to determine a location. A GPS unit is available as a hand-held unit that can be taken hiking, boating, or flying. Some high-end vehicles also have GPS units built in. When activated, the GPS unit receives signals from satellites orbiting Earth. The position is referenced according to the lines of latitude and longitude, and can be written as position (latitude, longitude). Once your location is determined, the GPS can provide other information such as displaying your position on a map or indicating how far you are from your destination.

With a GPS, all units are positive because measures of latitude are measured from 0° to 90° and longitude is measured from 0° to 180°.

Similarly, mathematics uses a coordinate system for locating points.

## Locating Points on a Plane

Work with a partner.

1. On a new sheet of plain paper, mark a dot anywhere on the page. Do not show your partner.
2. Describe to your partner where your point is on the page so that your partner can mark your point on a sheet of plain paper.
3. Exchange roles and repeat.
4. Discuss techniques you and your classmate used to describe the position of your point on the page.
5. Did you have difficulty communicating the location of your point on a plain piece of paper? Explain why.

Did You Know?

René Descartes, a 17th century French mathematician, developed a system for graphing ordered pairs on a grid. The system is called the Cartesian coordinate system.

The Cartesian coordinate system has the following characteristics:

- The $x$-axis is a horizontal number line.
- The $y$-axis is a vertical number line.
- The horizontal and vertical axes intersect at zero to form the Cartesian coordinate system. This system is often referred to as the Cartesian plane or the $xy$-plane.

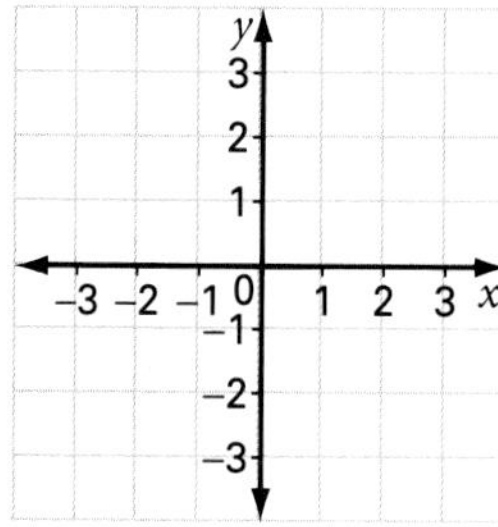

The values along the $x$-axis are called **$x$-coordinates.**
The values along the $y$-axis are called **$y$-coordinates.**
A **point** is made up of an $x$-coordinate and a $y$-coordinate.
A point is called an **ordered pair**, because the $x$-coordinate is always listed before the $y$-coordinate, $(x, y)$.
The point at which the $x$-axis and the $y$-axis cross is called the **origin**, (0, 0).

## Example 1

### Plotting Points on the Cartesian Plane

Plot the following points on the Cartesian plane.
A(2, 3), B(5, −2), C(−4, 5), D(−3, −3), E(−2, 0)

### Solution

*Step 1*: Determine the scale. The smallest $x$-coordinate is −4, and the largest is 5. If you draw an $x$-axis from −6 to 6 along the $x$-axis, with increments of 1, you will be able to incorporate all the $x$-coordinates.

*Step 2*: Repeat step 1 to determine the scale for the $y$-coordinates. The smallest $y$-coordinate is −3 and the largest is 5. A $y$-axis from −6 to 6 will work here.

*Step 3*: On grid paper, draw and label the $x$-axis and the $y$-axis. Mark the origin on the grid.

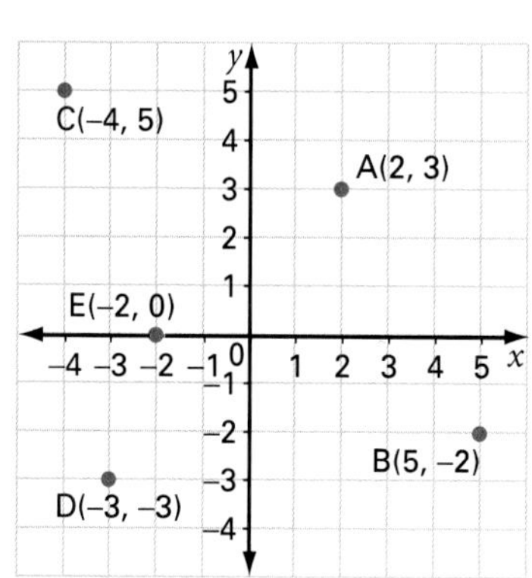


*Step 4*: Plot the points. For example,

- To plot A(2, 3), put your pencil at (0, 0). Move 2 units to the right and then up 3 units. Mark a dot and label the coordinates.
- To plot B(5, −2), put your pencil at (0, 0). Move 5 units to the right and then down 2 units. Mark a dot and label the coordinates.

The Cartesian plane is divided into four **quadrants.** The quadrants are labelled in a counterclockwise fashion, as shown. The axes themselves, and any points lying on the axes, do not belong to any of the quadrants.

Second Quadrant | First Quadrant
Third Quadrant | Fourth Quadrant

## EXAMPLE 2

### Characteristics of Points in Each Quadrant

Describe the similarities of the points shown in each quadrant.

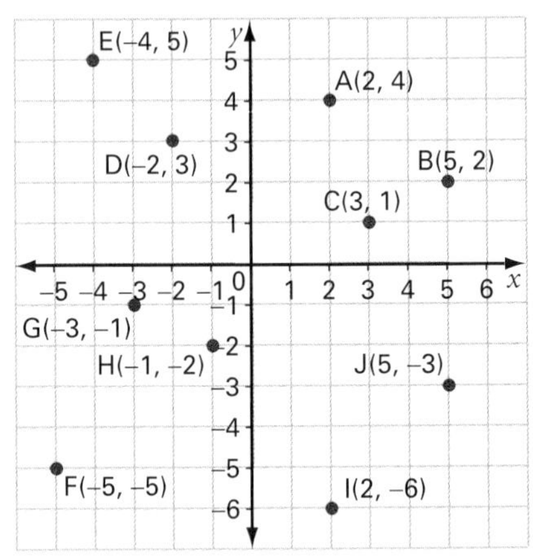


### Solution

First Quadrant: Both the $x$- and $y$-coordinates are positive.
Second Quadrant: The $x$-coordinate is negative and the $y$-coordinate is positive.
Third Quadrant: Both the $x$- and $y$-coordinates are negative.
Fourth Quadrant: The $x$-coordinate is positive and the $y$-coordinate is negative.

A graphing calculator can be used to plot points on a coordinate grid.

## EXAMPLE 3

### Plotting Points Using a Graphing Calculator

Using a TI-83 graphing calculator, plot these points.
(2, 3), (−4, 3), (−4, −5), (2, −5)

### Solution

Refer to the Technology Appendix for details on how to use the TI-83 graphing calculator.

*Step 1:* **Set window variables**
Set your window size and scale as shown.

```
GRAPHING CALCULATOR
WINDOW
 Xmin=-6
 Xmax=6
 Xscl=1
 Ymin=-6
 Ymax=6
 Yscl=1
 Xres=1
```

← Remember to use the (−) key to enter a negative number.

*Step 2:* **Turn grid on**
Press 2nd [FORMAT] to display the **FORMAT** menu. Highlight **GridOn** and press ENTER to turn the grid on.

*Step 3:* **Plot points**

To plot the point (2, 3), use the **DRAW** menu. Press 2nd [DRAW].
Move the cursor right to **POINTS**. Select **1:Pt-On(**.
The default symbol for a point is a small dot. You can change this symbol to a box by entering **Pt-On(2, 3, 2)**. The third number refers to the shape of the point using the following coding system:

1 = • (dot)   2 = □ (box)   3 = + (cross)

Complete the prompt by pressing 2 , 3 , 2 ) ENTER. Your point will be displayed as a square. If you omit the third number, a small dot is used to plot the point and it will not show with the **GridOn**.

To exit, or QUIT, from the graph, press 2nd [QUIT].

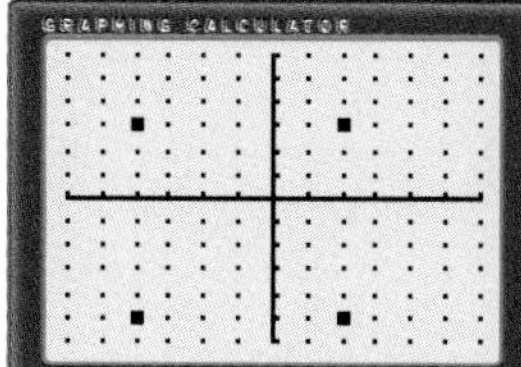

*Step 4:* Repeat step 3 to enter the points (–4, 3), (–4, –5), (2, –5).

# EXAMPLE 4

## Area of a Triangle

Calculate the area of a triangle with vertices at A(–5, –3), B(3, –3), and C(3, 8).

## Solution

Plot the points. Connect the points to form a triangle.

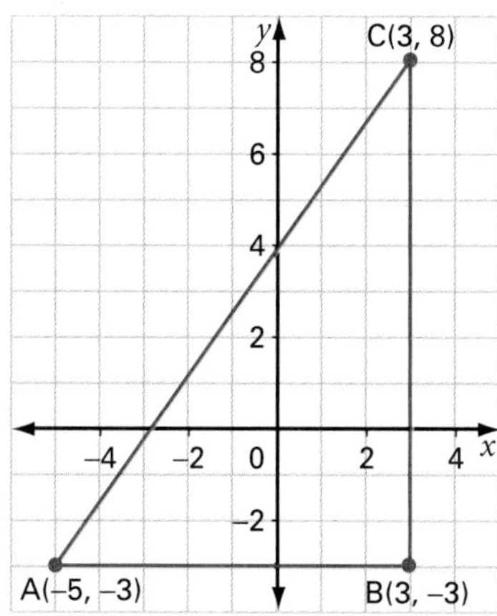


The formula for the area of a triangle is $A = \frac{1}{2}bh$, where $b$ is the length of the base and $h$ is the height of the triangle.

Find the length of the base.

$b = 3 - (-5)$

$b = 8$

Calculate the height.

$h = 8 - (-3)$

$h = 11$

Substitute into the area formula.

$A = \frac{1}{2}bh$

$A = \frac{1}{2} \times 8 \times 11$

$A = 44$

The area of the triangle is 44 square units.

## Key Concepts

- To plot points on the Cartesian plane:
  **a)** Draw and label axes to fit the points.
  **b)** Start at the origin (0, 0).
  **c)** Locate the $x$-coordinate first by moving along the $x$-axis the required number of units. Then, locate the $y$-coordinate by moving up or down the required number of units.
  **d)** Mark a dot on your grid at your final location. Label the point with its ordered pair.

- The Cartesian plane is divided into four quadrants as shown.

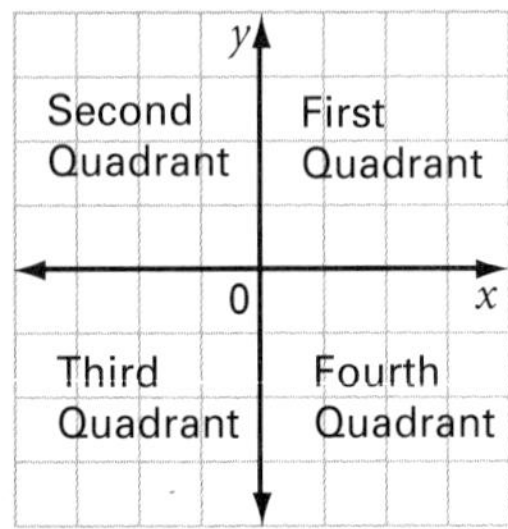


## Discuss the Concepts

1. How do you know whether to move left or right when plotting points?
2. How you know whether to move horizontally or vertically when plotting points?
3. Give two examples of points that lie on the $x$-axis and two examples that lie on the $y$-axis. Describe the steps you would follow to plot these points.

## Practise

1. Match each term with its definition. Copy the terms, followed by the correct definitions, into your notebook.

| Term | Definition |
|---|---|
| **a)** Cartesian | **A** A position or location along an axis. |
| **b)** Ordered Pair | **B** A term named after René Descartes to describe the Cartesian plane. |
| **c)** Coordinate | **C** The point (0, 0) on the Cartesian plane where the $x$-axis and the $y$-axis meet. |
| **d)** Axis | **D** A line used to represent a horizontal or vertical plane. |
| **e)** Origin | **E** The region of the Cartesian plane containing points with similar characteristics. |
| **f)** Quadrant | **F** Divisions used to indicate equally spaced positions along an axis. |
| **g)** Scale | **G** A position on the Cartesian plane indicated by an $x$-coordinate followed by a $y$-coordinate. |

*For help with question 2, refer to Example 1.*

2. Plot the following points. Use a new Cartesian plane for each part of the question.
   a) (4, 3), (3, 5), (−2, 6), (12, 3), (−7, 4)
   b) (−1, 0), (−3, 10), (−3, −5), (−6, −3)
   c) (9, −3), (−3, −1), (6, −1), (5, −5)
   d) (−3, 8), (−1, 0), (2, 2), (−5, 3)

*For help with question 3, refer to Example 2.*

3. For each part of question 2, state the quadrant in which most of the points lie.

*For help with question 4, refer to Example 1.*

4. The points on the Cartesian plane shown are labelled A, B, C, D, E, and F . State the coordinates of each point.

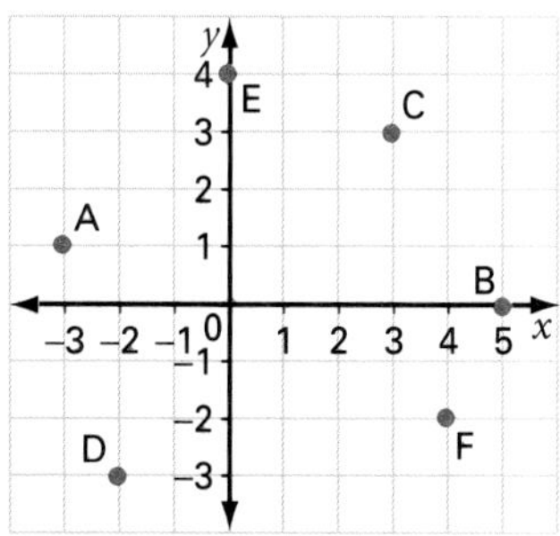


## Apply the Concepts

**B**

5. **Communication** Describe the advantages of labelling each point you plot.

6. **Application** Plot each set of points on a separate Cartesian plane. Connect the points to create a figure. Identify each figure. Calculate the area of each figure.
   a) (2, 2), (2, 7), (5, 2)
   b) (−5, 3), (−6, −2), (−3, −2)
   c) (3, 3), (3, −3), (8, −3), (8, 3)
   d) (−3, −4), (−2, 1), (5, −4), (6, 1)
   e) (2, −2), (6, −2), (6, 1), (4, 3), (2, 1)

*For help with question 7, refer to Example 3.*

7. a) Using a graphing calculator to plot the points (−8, 4), (3, 2), and (−4, −1) using a symbol other than a dot.
   b) Explain why entering a point in the form of Pt-On(5, 3, 1) might be confusing.

**8.** On a Cartesian plane, it is acceptable to label every second point along the axes. Identify the coordinates of each point on this Cartesian plane.

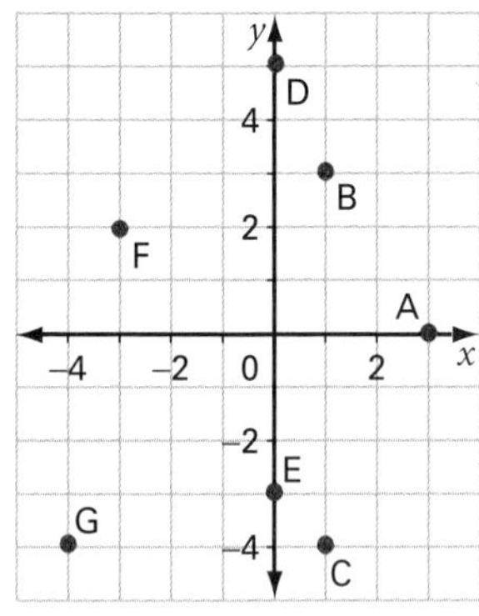


**9.** The points on this Cartesian plane are a little more challenging to read. Identify the coordinates of each point. You may have to estimate a coordinate if it does not fall directly on a grid line.

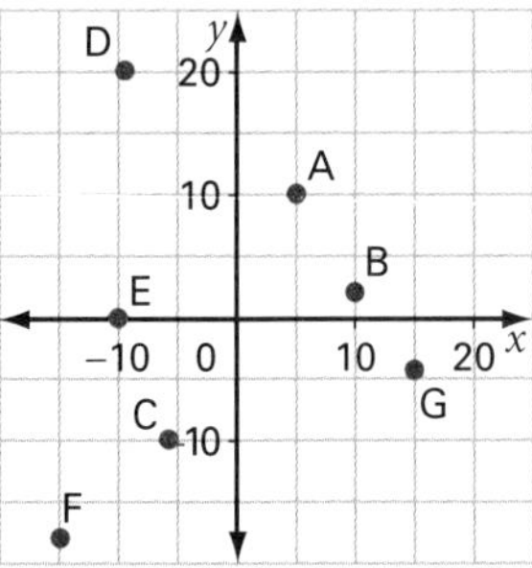


C **10. Thinking/Inquiry/Problem Solving** How do the scales on the axes make it more difficult to identify the coordinates of the points shown on this Cartesian plane?

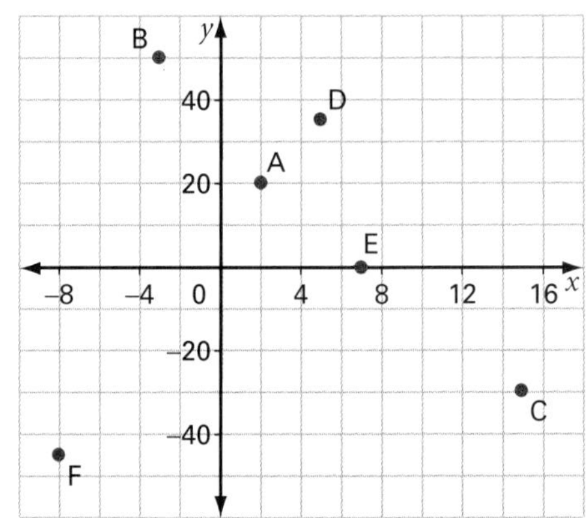


**11.** Carolin used the window settings shown to create a graph on her graphing calculator. Draw a diagram on a piece of grid paper to show these *x*- and *y*- scales on the Cartesian plane.

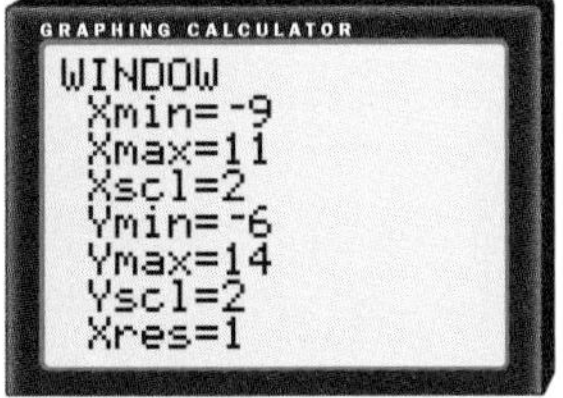


**12.** Draw a simple picture on a piece of grid paper. Identify all the important points in your picture. Locate these points on the Cartesian plane. Label the points in order with A, B, C, and so on, to create a connect-the-dots activity for a grade one math book.

# 5.4 Exploring Rational Numbers

This photo is a digitally-enhanced image of an iceberg. The visible part is approximately $\frac{1}{8}$ of the whole iceberg. The visible part can also be written as 0.125. The numbers $\frac{1}{8}$ and 0.125 are **equivalent rational numbers**. Both numbers, the fraction form and the decimal form, represent the same part of the whole. **Rational numbers** are all numbers that can be written as the quotient of two integers, where the divisor is not zero. Rational numbers include decimals, integers, and positive and negative fractions.

For example: $\frac{3}{8}$, 0.5, 3, $-\frac{2}{5}$, $-4\frac{3}{4}$, 0, −12.25.

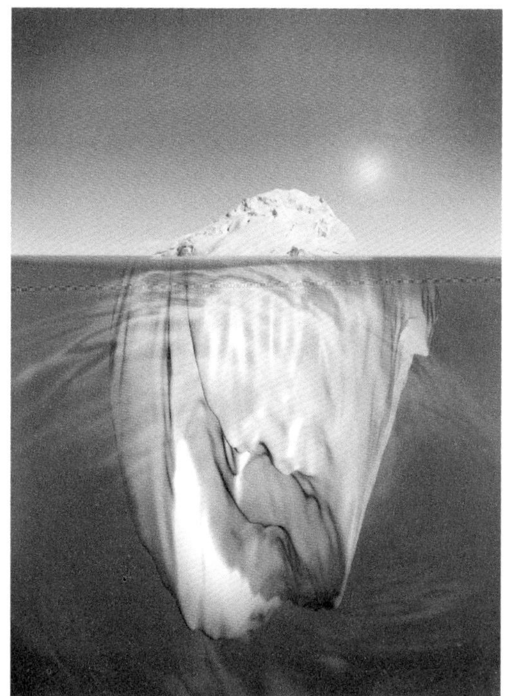

## DISCOVER 1

### Rational Numbers on a Number Line

1. Create your own rational number ruler as follows.
   a) Cut a strip of paper 20 cm long and 5 cm wide.
   b) Fold the strip in half to make a crease at the middle.
   c) Along the lower edge, draw marks at each centimetre.
   d) Label the centre 0, the left end −1, and the right end +1.
   e) Label each mark to the right of the centre in tenths: 0.1, 0.2, 0.3, …. Then label each mark to the left of the centre −0.1, −0.2, −0.3, ….

   

   f) Now fold the strip at the centre, fold in half again, and then in half again.
   g) Open the strip and label the fold marks on the upper edge: $-\frac{3}{4}, -\frac{1}{2}, -\frac{1}{4}, 0, \frac{1}{4}, \frac{1}{2}, \frac{3}{4}$.

2. Use your rational number ruler to compare each pair of rational numbers using >, <, or =.
   a) $0.2$ ? $\frac{1}{4}$
   b) $-0.5$ ? $-\frac{1}{2}$
   c) $-0.8$ ? $-\frac{3}{4}$

It is easier to compare rational numbers if they are written in the same form, either as decimals or as fractions. Calculators may help with some of the work.

## Example 1

### Converting From Fraction to Decimal Form

Convert $-1\frac{3}{5}$ to decimal form.

### Solution

$$\begin{aligned}-1\frac{3}{5} &= -\frac{8}{5} \\ &= -1.6\end{aligned}$$

**For the numerator think: 1 × 5 + 3.**

$$5\overline{)8.0}\quad 1.6$$

## Example 2

### Converting From Decimal to Fraction Form

Convert −0.125 to fraction form. Express the fraction in lowest terms.

### Solution

The last digit of the number −0.125 is in the thousandths place.

$$\begin{aligned}-0.125 &= -\frac{125}{1000} \\ &= -\frac{125 \div 125}{1000 \div 125} \\ &= -\frac{1}{8}\end{aligned}$$

**To express the fraction in lowest terms, divide the numerator and the denominator by 125. Alternatively, you could divide by 25, and then by 5.**

## Example 3

### Comparing Rational Numbers

Compare $-1\frac{3}{4}$ ? −1.5 by replacing ? with <, > or =.

### Solution

*Method 1:* Sketch a number line and mark the numbers approximately.

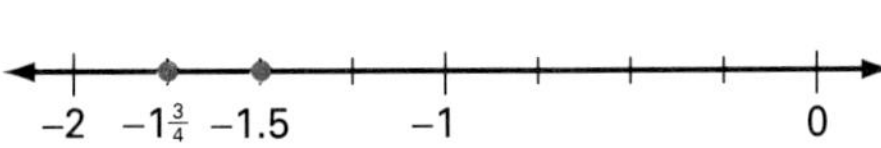


Since $-1\frac{3}{4}$ is to the left of −1.5, $-1\frac{3}{4}$ is less than −1.5.

*Method 2:* Express both numbers in decimal form, so they can be compared.

$-1\frac{3}{4} = -1.75$ and $-1.75 < -1.5$

Using either method, $-1\frac{3}{4} < -1.5$.

## DISCOVER 2

### Fractions Using a Scientific Calculator

Most scientific calculators have a fraction key that lets you enter and work with fractions. The position, labels, and keystrokes needed vary with different models of calculator. Experiment to find the right sequence for your calculator.

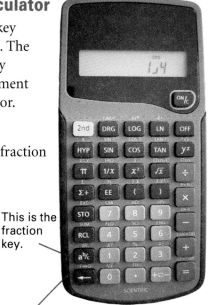

1. a) What fraction is equivalent to 0.25?
   b) A key sequence for changing 0.25 to fraction form is as follows.
   (C) 0.25 (2nd) [F↔D]
   Experiment to find the correct key sequence on your calculator. Note how the fraction is shown in the display.
   c) Record the key sequence that you need to use in your notebook.

This is the fraction key.

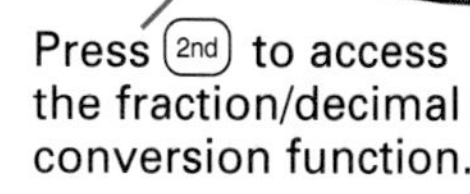

Press (2nd) to access the fraction/decimal conversion function.

2. From Example 2, you know that $-0.125 = -\frac{1}{8}$. A key sequence for changing −0.125 into fraction form is shown.
   (C) 0.125 (+/−) (2nd) [F↔D] -1⌟8
   a) Experiment to find the correct key sequence on your calculator.
   b) Record the key sequence in your notebook.

3. Use your calculator to find the fraction form of each decimal.
   a) 0.8 b) 1.325 c) −0.15 d) −2.75

4. The sequence below shows how a calculator can be used to enter $-1\frac{3}{5}$, in fraction form, and then change it to decimal form. Write the key sequence needed to do these two steps using your calculator.
   *Step 1*: Use the fraction key (a b/c) to enter the rational number.
   (C) 1 (a b/c) 3 (a b/c) 5 (+/−) -1_3⌟5
   *Step 2*: Change to decimal form.
   (2nd) [F↔D] -1.6

5. Enter each number into your calculator in fraction form. Then, change it to decimal form.
   a) $\frac{2}{5}$ b) $2\frac{5}{8}$ c) $-\frac{7}{20}$ d) $-3\frac{3}{4}$

## DISCOVER 3

### Fractions Using a Graphing Calculator

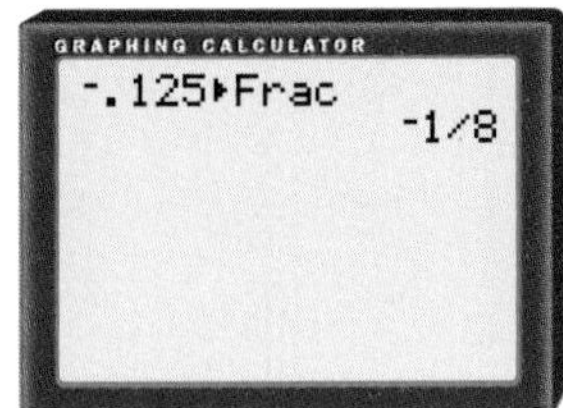


1. Use the following steps to change −0.125 to fraction form:
   - Enter (−) 0.125.
   - Press MATH, choose **1:▸Frac.**
   - Press ENTER.

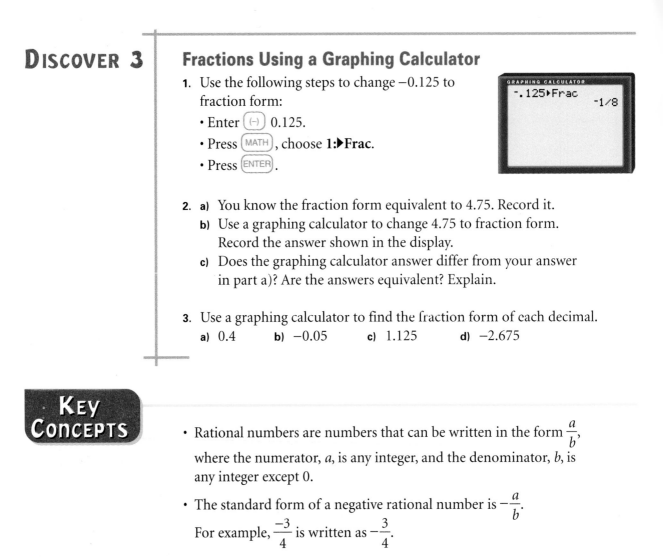

2. **a)** You know the fraction form equivalent to 4.75. Record it.
   **b)** Use a graphing calculator to change 4.75 to fraction form. Record the answer shown in the display.
   **c)** Does the graphing calculator answer differ from your answer in part a)? Are the answers equivalent? Explain.

3. Use a graphing calculator to find the fraction form of each decimal.
   **a)** 0.4 **b)** −0.05 **c)** 1.125 **d)** −2.675

## KEY CONCEPTS

- Rational numbers are numbers that can be written in the form $\frac{a}{b}$, where the numerator, $a$, is any integer, and the denominator, $b$, is any integer except 0.
- The standard form of a negative rational number is $-\frac{a}{b}$. For example, $\frac{-3}{4}$ is written as $-\frac{3}{4}$.
- Rational numbers can be expressed in fraction form or decimal form. For example,

| Fraction Form | Decimal Form |
|---|---|
| $\frac{3}{4}$ | 0.75 |
| $-\frac{7}{10}$ | −0.7 |
| $-2\frac{1}{2}$ | −2.5 |

## Discuss the Concepts

1. Describe how you would decide which is greater, $-0.6$ or $-\frac{2}{3}$.
2. Which one of these rational numbers is not equivalent to the others? Give your reasoning.

   **A** $-0.3$ **B** $-\frac{3}{10}$ **C** $\frac{-3}{-10}$ **D** $\frac{3}{-10}$

3. Which of these numbers is not equivalent to the others? Give your reasoning.

   **A** $-2\frac{3}{4}$ **B** $-\frac{11}{4}$ **C** $-\frac{5}{4}$ **D** $\frac{-11}{4}$

## Practise

**A**

***For help with questions 1 and 2, refer to Example 1.***

1. Match each rational number with its equivalent decimal form.

   **a)** $-\frac{1}{4}$ **b)** $-1\frac{1}{4}$ **c)** $-3\frac{1}{2}$ **d)** $\frac{1}{4}$ **e)** $-2\frac{1}{4}$

   **A** $-1.25$ **B** $0.25$ **C** $-0.25$ **D** $-2.25$ **E** $-3.5$

2. Express each rational number in decimal form.

   **a)** $\frac{3}{10}$ **b)** $3\frac{1}{4}$ **c)** $-1\frac{3}{10}$

   **d)** $-4\frac{2}{5}$ **e)** $2\frac{3}{8}$ **f)** $-5\frac{4}{5}$

***For help with question 3, refer to Example 2.***

3. Express each rational number in fraction form, in lowest terms.

   **a)** 0.4 **b)** $-1.5$ **c)** 0.25

   **d)** $-0.75$ **e)** $-0.625$ **f)** 2.8

4. Write each mixed number as an improper fraction.

   **a)** $2\frac{3}{4}$ **b)** $-3\frac{1}{3}$ **c)** $1\frac{5}{8}$

   **d)** $-2\frac{4}{5}$ **e)** $-5\frac{2}{3}$ **f)** $4\frac{3}{5}$

**B** **5.** Draw and label an integer number line from –5 to 5. Mark the following rational numbers on your number line.

**a)** 3.25 **b)** $-0.8$ **c)** $\frac{4}{5}$ **d)** $2\frac{3}{4}$ **e)** $-1.6$

*For help with question 6, refer to Example 3.*

**6.** Copy and compare by replacing ? with >, <, or =.

**a)** $-3\frac{2}{3}$ ? $-3\frac{1}{4}$ **b)** $-0.56$ ? $-0.65$

**c)** $2\frac{3}{5}$ ? $2.35$ **d)** $-0.375$ ? $-\frac{3}{8}$

**7.** Some fractions are equivalent to repeating decimals. For example, $\frac{5}{6} = 0.8\dot{3}$. The dot over the digit 3 means that digit keeps repeating: $0.8\dot{3} = 0.833\,333\ldots$. Write the decimal equivalent for each of the following, using a dot over the repeating digit.

**a)** $\frac{1}{3}$ **b)** $\frac{1}{6}$ **c)** $-\frac{2}{3}$

**d)** $-3\frac{5}{6}$ **e)** $-\frac{5}{12}$

## Apply the Concepts

**8.** **Communication** Give two examples of everyday measures that are typically expressed using

**a)** rational numbers in fraction form

**b)** rational numbers in decimal form

**9.** **Tools** Calipers look similar to a wrench. Calipers are used to measure the diameter of a pipe or a bolt. The scale on many calipers is in inches. Both decimal and fraction forms are marked.

| $\frac{1}{8}$ | $\frac{3}{16}$ | | |
|---|---|---|---|
| 0.125 | 0.1875 | 0.25 | 0.3125 |

**a)** Convert the last two decimals to fractions to find the missing entries in the table.

**b)** Describe where and when a construction person might use fractional/decimal calipers.

**Chapter Problem**

10. **Stock market** Changes in the price of stocks are reported using rational numbers. Arrange the following stocks in order, from the one that has gained the most to the one that has lost the most.

| | |
|---|---|
| Stock A | +3.25 |
| Stock B | −5.18 |
| Stock C | +0.98 |
| Stock D | −1.25 |
| Stock E | −0.48 |

**Did You Know?**

We put salt on icy roads because it lowers the melting point of the ice. A 10% salt solution melts at −6.5°C.

11. **Science** Water melts at 0°C, mercury at −38.8°C, bromine at −7.2°C, krypton at −156.6°C, and potassium at 63.3°C. List the five substances in order from the one with the highest melting point to the one with the lowest melting point.

12. **Exploring multiplication** The number line model shows that $3 \times \left(-\frac{1}{2}\right) = -\frac{3}{2}$ or $1\frac{1}{2}$.

Write the multiplication statement that is shown by each diagram.

a) 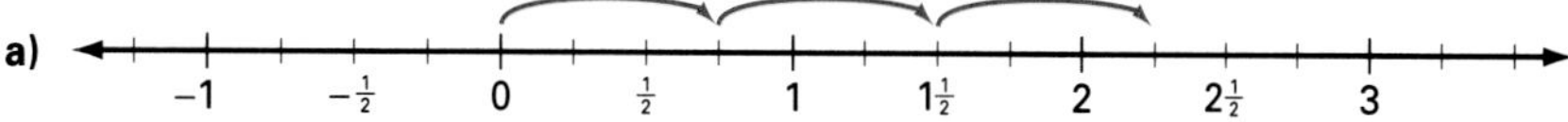


b) 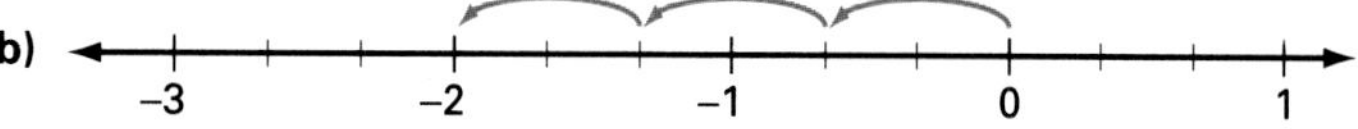


c) 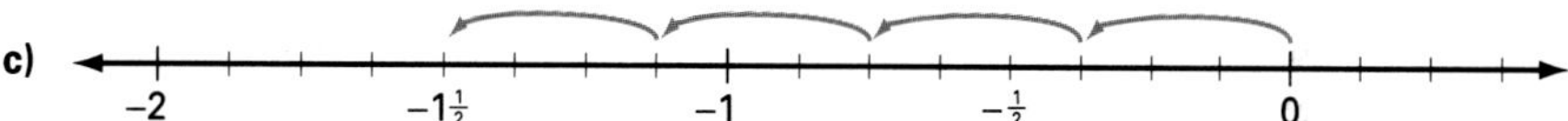


13. **Exploring addition** The number line model shows that $-1\frac{1}{2} + 2\frac{3}{4} = 1\frac{1}{4}$.

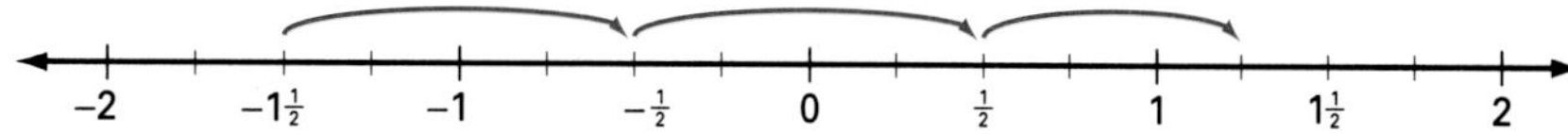


Use a number line to find each sum.

a) $-2 + 1\frac{1}{2}$

b) $-\frac{3}{4} + \left(-1\frac{1}{4}\right)$

c) $3\frac{1}{2} + \left(-2\frac{1}{4}\right)$

**C** 14. a) Mark the four points on a coordinate grid. Then, join them in order.
P(−2.5, 5.75) Q(4.5, 5.75) R(4.5, −1.25) S(−2.5, −1.25)

b) What type of shape is PQRS?

c) Find the area of PQRS in square units.

# 5.5 Operations With Rational Numbers

One evening the temperature fell from 0°C to −10.5°C in 3 h.

The average temperature change per hour is found by dividing −10.5 by 3. This is a negative divided by a positive, so the answer is negative.

$$\frac{-10.5}{3} = -3.5$$

The average temperature change was −3.5°C/h.

To work with rational numbers in decimal form, you combine skills with decimals and integers. To work with rational numbers in fraction form, you need to combine your skills with integers and fractions.

Recall that to multiply fractions, you multiply the numerators and you multiply the denominators. For example,

$$\frac{1}{2} \times \frac{3}{5} = \frac{3}{10}$$

## DISCOVER

### Multiplying Positive and Negative Fractions

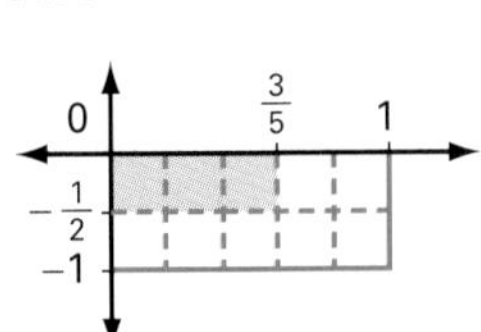

1. a) Explain how the diagram models $-\frac{1}{2} \times \frac{3}{5}$.
   b) What sign, positive or negative, do you expect for the answer?
   c) Copy and complete the steps for the multiplication.

$$-\frac{1}{2} \times \frac{3}{5} = \frac{-1 \times \blacksquare}{2 \times 5}$$
$$= \frac{\blacksquare}{\blacksquare}$$
$$= -\frac{\blacksquare}{\blacksquare}$$

2. a) Explain how the diagram models $-\frac{2}{3} \times \left(-\frac{1}{4}\right)$.

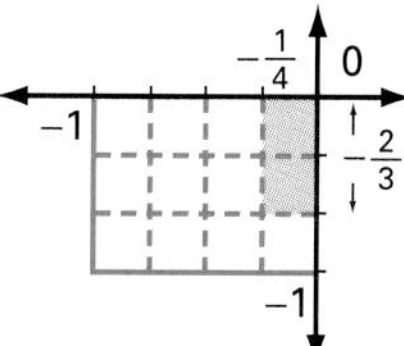

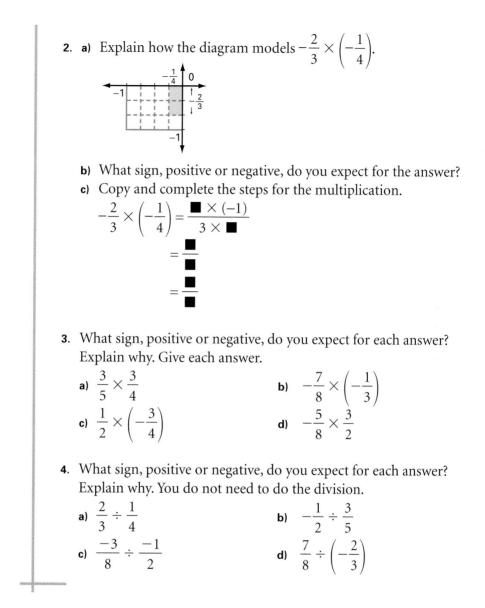

b) What sign, positive or negative, do you expect for the answer?

c) Copy and complete the steps for the multiplication.

$$-\frac{2}{3} \times \left(-\frac{1}{4}\right) = \frac{\blacksquare \times (-1)}{3 \times \blacksquare}$$
$$= \frac{\blacksquare}{\blacksquare}$$
$$= \frac{\blacksquare}{\blacksquare}$$

3. What sign, positive or negative, do you expect for each answer? Explain why. Give each answer.

a) $\frac{3}{5} \times \frac{3}{4}$

b) $-\frac{7}{8} \times \left(-\frac{1}{3}\right)$

c) $\frac{1}{2} \times \left(-\frac{3}{4}\right)$

d) $-\frac{5}{8} \times \frac{3}{2}$

4. What sign, positive or negative, do you expect for each answer? Explain why. You do not need to do the division.

a) $\frac{2}{3} \div \frac{1}{4}$

b) $-\frac{1}{2} \div \frac{3}{5}$

c) $\frac{-3}{8} \div \frac{-1}{2}$

d) $\frac{7}{8} \div \left(-\frac{2}{3}\right)$

## Example 1

### Multiplying and Dividing Rational Numbers

Simplify. Check your work using a scientific calculator or a graphing calculator.

**a)** $\frac{1}{2} \times \left(-\frac{3}{4}\right)$ **b)** $-\frac{5}{6} \times 1\frac{1}{2}$ **c)** $-3\frac{3}{4} \div 1\frac{1}{2}$

### Solution

**a)**
$$\frac{1}{2} \times \left(-\frac{3}{4}\right) = \frac{1}{2} \times \frac{-3}{4}$$
$$= \frac{1 \times (-3)}{2 \times 4}$$
$$= \frac{-3}{8}$$
$$= -\frac{3}{8}$$

Check:

*Using a scientific calculator:*

C 1 a b/c 2 × 3 +/− a b/c 4 = -3⌟8

*Using a graphing calculator:*

Enter the rational numbers as shown.

Press MATH.

Choose **1: ▶Frac**.

Press ENTER twice.

**b)**
$$-\frac{5}{6} \times 1\frac{1}{2} = -\frac{5}{6} \times \frac{3}{2}$$
Change the mixed number to an improper fraction.
$$= \frac{-5 \times \overset{1}{\cancel{3}}}{\underset{2}{\cancel{6}} \times 2}$$
Divide both numerator and denominator by 3.
$$= \frac{-5}{4}$$
$$= -\frac{5}{4} \text{ or } -1\frac{1}{4}$$

Check:

*Using a scientific calculator:*

C 5 a b/c 6 +/− × 1 a b/c 1 a b/c 2 = -1⌞1⌟4

*Using a graphing calculator:*

First change any mixed numbers to improper fractions.

c) $-3\frac{3}{4} \div 1\frac{1}{2} = \frac{-15}{4} \div \frac{3}{2}$

$= \frac{-15}{4} \times \frac{2}{3}$ To divide by a fraction, multiply by the reciprocal (invert and multiply).

$= \frac{\overset{-5}{\cancel{-15}}}{\underset{2}{\cancel{4}}} \times \frac{\overset{1}{\cancel{2}}}{\underset{1}{\cancel{3}}}$ Divide numerator and denominator by common factors.

$= \frac{-5}{2}$

$= -\frac{5}{2}$ or $-2\frac{1}{2}$

Check:

*Using a graphing calculator:*

*Using a scientific calculator:*

C 3 a b/c 3 a b/c 4 +/− ÷
1 a b/c 1 a b/c 2 = -2 ⌟1 ⌟2

Adding and subtracting rational numbers can require more steps. If the rational numbers have different denominators, you need to find a common denominator first. If one or both of the rational numbers are negative, then you also need to use your skills with integers.

## Example 2

## Adding and Subtracting Rational Numbers

Find each sum or difference.

a) $-\frac{2}{3} + \frac{1}{2}$

b) $\frac{3}{8} - \frac{3}{4}$

### Solution

a) $-\frac{2}{3} + \frac{1}{2} = -\frac{4}{6} + \frac{3}{6}$ Write equivalent fractions using the lowest common denominator.

$= \frac{-4 + 3}{6}$

$= \frac{-1}{6}$

$= -\frac{1}{6}$

b) $\frac{3}{8} - \frac{3}{4} = \frac{3}{8} - \frac{6}{8}$

$= \frac{3 - 6}{8}$

$= \frac{-3}{8}$

$= -\frac{3}{8}$

You can check these answers with a scientific or a graphing calculator, using the same steps as in **Example 1**.

## Key Concepts

- To multiply rational numbers in fraction form, by hand:
  - Change any mixed numbers to improper fractions.
  - Divide the numerators and denominators by any common factors.
  - Multiply the numerators and multiply the denominators. Use the sign rules for multiplying integers.
- To divide rational numbers in fraction form, by hand:
  - Change any mixed numbers to improper fractions.
  - Change to multiplying by the reciprocal of the second fraction.
  - Continue using the steps for multiplying.
- To add or subtract rational numbers, by hand:
  - If the denominators are the same, add or subtract the numerators.
  - If the denominators are not the same, first find the lowest common denominator.
- You can perform operations with rational numbers using a scientific calculator. The keystrokes may vary.
- You can perform operations with rational numbers using a graphing calculator. Enter the numbers as improper fractions. Press MATH and choose **1:▶Frac** to obtain the answer in fraction form.

## Discuss the Concepts

1. Nicla and Ditar both got the correct answer, but they did the work differently. Describe the steps used by each person.

Nicla:

$$1\frac{1}{2} \times -\frac{2}{3} = \frac{3}{2} \times \frac{-2}{3}$$
$$= \frac{-6}{6}$$
$$= -1$$

Ditar:

$$1\frac{1}{2} \times -\frac{2}{3} = \frac{\overset{1}{\cancel{3}}}{\underset{1}{\cancel{2}}} \times \frac{\overset{-1}{\cancel{-2}}}{\underset{1}{\cancel{3}}}$$
$$= \frac{1 \times (-1)}{1}$$
$$= -1$$

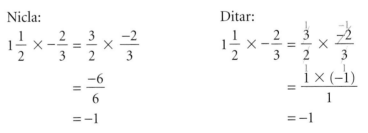

2. You can add or subtract each of the following directly. Explain why. Give each answer.

   **a)** $\frac{4}{5} - \frac{1}{5}$ **b)** $-\frac{5}{7} + \frac{3}{7}$ **c)** $\frac{3}{10} - \frac{7}{10}$

3. Why can you not add $-\frac{2}{3} + \frac{1}{4}$ directly? What is the first step needed?

## PRACTISE

**A**

***Express answers in lowest terms.***

***For help with questions 1 and 2, refer to Example 1.***

1. Multiply.
   - a) $\frac{2}{5} \times \frac{3}{4}$
   - b) $-\frac{2}{3} \times \frac{3}{4}$
   - c) $-\frac{7}{8} \times 2\frac{4}{5}$
   - d) $-2\frac{1}{2} \times \left(-\frac{9}{10}\right)$

2. Divide.
   - a) $\frac{4}{9} \div \frac{1}{3}$
   - b) $\frac{2}{5} \div \left(-\frac{1}{2}\right)$
   - c) $-\frac{5}{6} \div 3\frac{3}{4}$
   - d) $-\frac{3}{8} \div \left(-1\frac{3}{5}\right)$

***For help with questions 3 to 5, refer to Example 2.***

3. Find each sum or difference.
   - a) $\frac{3}{5} + \frac{1}{5}$
   - b) $\frac{4}{9} - \frac{1}{9}$
   - c) $\frac{3}{8} - \frac{1}{8}$
   - d) $\frac{1}{4} - \frac{3}{4}$
   - e) $\frac{-1}{6} + \frac{-1}{6}$
   - f) $\frac{-5}{12} + \frac{7}{12}$

4. Find each sum.
   - a) $\frac{3}{4} + \frac{5}{12}$
   - b) $\frac{-2}{3} + \frac{1}{2}$
   - c) $\frac{3}{5} + \frac{-1}{4}$
   - d) $\frac{-7}{8} + \frac{3}{4}$
   - e) $\frac{-4}{5} + \frac{-1}{3}$
   - f) $\frac{-5}{6} + \frac{3}{4}$

5. Find each difference.
   - a) $\frac{3}{4} - \frac{1}{2}$
   - b) $\frac{1}{3} - \frac{2}{5}$
   - c) $\frac{-1}{2} - \frac{1}{4}$
   - d) $\frac{-5}{8} - \frac{3}{4}$
   - e) $-\frac{2}{3} - \frac{1}{6}$
   - f) $\frac{11}{12} - \left(-\frac{3}{4}\right)$

6. Calculate.
   - a) $4.2 \times (-1.5)$
   - b) $-3 \times 2.4$
   - c) $-3.6 \div 1.2$
   - d) $50.4 \div (-0.6)$
   - e) $-0.5 \div (-0.25)$
   - f) $-2.5 \times (-0.2)$
   - g) $0.8 \times (-0.5)$
   - h) $-1.2 \div 0.4$
   - i) $1.5 \times (-2.4)$

## Apply the Concepts

7. A ratchet set has sockets labelled $\frac{3}{16}, \frac{1}{4}, \frac{5}{16}$.

   a) By what fraction are the sockets increasing?

   b) Calculate the size of the fourth socket in this set.

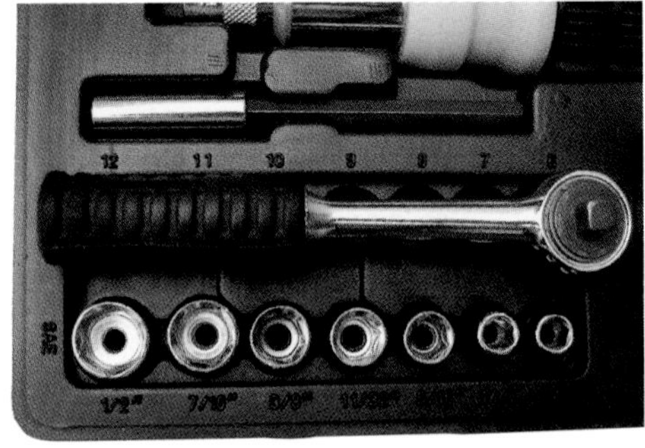

8. Study each example and describe where the errors are. Provide a correct solution for each.

   a) $\frac{4}{9} \div \frac{3}{4} = \frac{\overset{1}{\cancel{4}}}{\underset{3}{\cancel{9}}} \div \frac{\overset{1}{\cancel{3}}}{\underset{1}{\cancel{4}}}$
   $= \frac{1}{3}$

   b) $\frac{2}{5} \times \frac{3}{7} = \frac{5}{35}$

9. Each of the following has an error in its solution. Describe what mistake has been made. Provide a correct solution for each.

   a) $\frac{4}{5} + \frac{5}{7} = \frac{4}{\underset{1}{\cancel{5}}} + \frac{\overset{1}{\cancel{5}}}{7}$
   $= \frac{4}{7}$

   b) $\frac{2}{9} - \frac{1}{6} = \frac{2}{18} - \frac{1}{18}$
   $= \frac{1}{18}$

10. **Communication** One of the rational numbers below is the correct answer for $-3\frac{1}{3} \div \frac{5}{4}$. Without actually working it out, tell why three of the numbers must be wrong.

    **A** $-2\frac{2}{3}$ **B** $6\frac{1}{4}$ **C** $2$ **D** $2\frac{2}{3}$

11. **Catalogue shopping** In a mail-order catalogue, a roll-away cot is described as 75 inches long and $31\frac{1}{8}$ inches wide. The mattress for this bed is $\frac{3}{8}$ inch shorter than the cot on each end and at each side. Find the length and the width of the mattress.

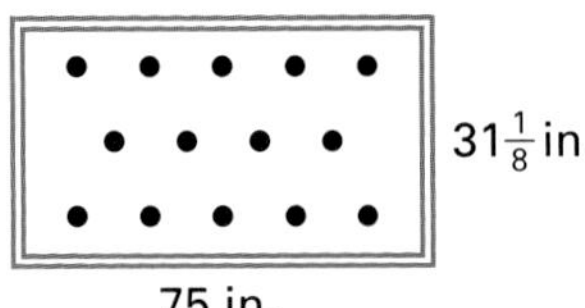

12. **Recipes** Fran has only 1 cup of brown sugar. To use the recipe for caramel corn she needs to cut all the quantities in half. Rewrite the recipe using half of each ingredient.

16 cups of popped corn
1 cup of peanuts (optional)
2 cups brown sugar
1 cup of butter
$\frac{1}{2}$ cup light corn syrup
1 tsp. salt
$\frac{1}{2}$ tsp. soda

13. The waiters at a restaurant have agreed to give one third of their tips to the kitchen staff. If a waiter collects $32.75 in tips, how much does he end up keeping?

14. **Stock market** Maria's friend, Kurt, has 325 shares of X-Tar stock. One day the stock reported a change of –$0.12 per share. What was the change in Kurt's X-Tar stock value that day?

15. One day, the temperature fell from 2°C to –5°C in 3 h. What was the temperature change per hour?

16. **Communication** Bethany claims that she can find the answer for $-3 + \left(-1\frac{2}{5}\right)$ in her head. She says it is $-4\frac{2}{5}$. Do you agree? Give your reasoning.

17. **Communication** What would you do if a fraction has a negative in the denominator, such as $\frac{1}{-2} + \frac{3}{4}$? Test your method using a calculator.

C 18. **Electricity** The resistance, $R$, in ohms, through a parallel circuit is determined by $\frac{1}{R} = \frac{1}{R_A} + \frac{1}{R_B}$.

$R_B$
$R_A$
current

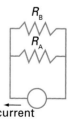

a) If the resistance of resistor A is 5 ohms and that of resistor B is 3 ohms, find the resistance of the circuit.

b) The resistance through a parallel circuit is 6 ohms. The resistance of resistor A is 10 ohms. Find the resistance of resistor B.

# 5.6 Ratio and Rate

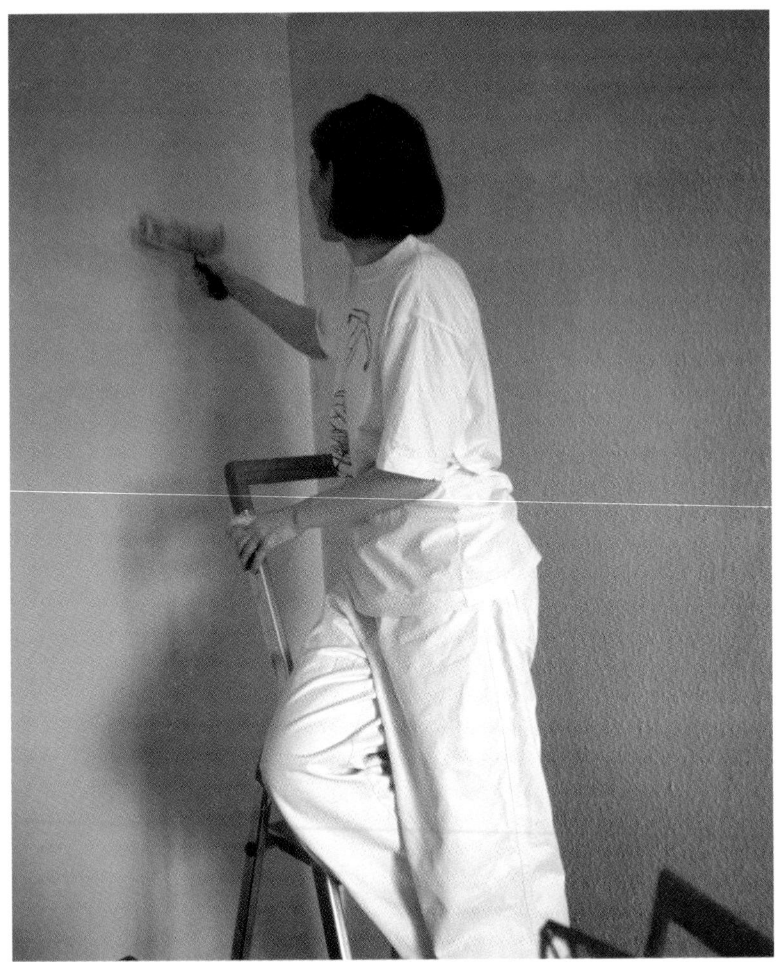

When Nina redecorated her room, she used four cans of green paint and one can of white paint. The ratio of green paint to white paint is 4:1. A **ratio** compares quantities of items that are measured in the same units.

The label on the paint can says that 1 L covers 10 $m^2$. The rate of coverage by this paint is 1 L/10 $m^2$. A **rate** compares quantities that are measured using different units.

## DISCOVER

### Comparing Fractions and Ratios

1. Jared's dog had seven puppies, 3 females and 4 males.
   a) Write the ratio of male to female puppies.
   b) What fraction of the litter was female?

2. To make orange juice, mix 1 can of concentrate with 3 cans of water.
   a) Write the ratio of concentrate to water.
   b) What fraction of the mixture is water?

3. Ellie has 33 rock CDs, 10 classical CDs, and 2 jazz CDs.
   a) What does the ratio 33:10 compare in this example?
   b) What does the fraction $\frac{33}{45}$ represent?

Like fractions, ratios can be expressed in lowest terms. You find **equivalent ratios** by multiplying or dividing all the terms of the ratio by the same factor. Ratios are in **simplest form** when the terms have no common factor other than 1 and they do not involve any decimals or fractions. For example, 10:2 and 5:1 are equivalent ratios, 5:1 is in simplest form.

## EXAMPLE 1

### Writing a Ratio in Simplest Form

Erin is making a bird bath. The recipe for the mixture to be poured into the mold is

12 cups sand
3 cups cement
6 cups water

**a)** Write the ratio of sand:cement:water in lowest terms.

**b)** For her next project, Erin needs 35 cups of the mixture. How much of each ingredient should she use?

### Solution

**a)** sand:cement:water = 12:3:6 **All three terms can be divided by 3.**
= 4:1:2

The ratio of sand:cement:water, in simplest form, is 4:1:2.

**b)** The mixture in simplest form has a total of 7 cups. **4 + 1 + 2 = 7**
To obtain 35 cups, the recipe must be multiplied by 5. **$7 \times 5 = 35$**

sand $5 \times 4 = 20$
cement $5 \times 1 = 5$
water $5 \times 2 = 10$

For the next project, Erin needs 20 cups of sand, 5 cups of cement, and 10 cups of water.

Rates can also be expressed in simplest form. If you earn $30 for 3 h of work, then your rate of pay is $10/h, or $10 for 1 h of work. A **unit rate** is one in which the second term is 1.

## Example 2

### Finding Unit Rates

Find the equivalent unit rate in each case.

**a)** 180 km in 2 h **b)** \$3.60 for 6 muffins **c)** 100 m in 1.6 s

### Solution

**a)** $\frac{180\text{ km}}{2\text{ h}} = \frac{90\text{ km}}{1\text{ h}}$ **Divide the numerator and the denominator by 2.**

The unit rate is 90 km/h.

**b)** $\frac{\$3.60}{6} = \frac{\$0.60}{1}$

The unit rate is \$0.60 per muffin.

**c)** $\frac{100\text{ m}}{1.6\text{ s}} = \frac{1000\text{ m}}{16\text{ s}} = \frac{62.5\text{ m}}{1\text{ s}}$

The unit rate is 62.5 m/s.

## Example 3

**Chapter Problem**

### Applying Rates

Torntel stock reported a change of –\$120 over a 10-week period.

**a)** What was the average weekly change? Interpret what this value means.

**b)** If this rate of change continues, how much will the stock fall in 15 weeks?

### Solution

**a)** $\frac{-\$120}{10\text{ weeks}} = \frac{-\$12}{1\text{ week}}$ **Divide numerator and denominator by 10.**

The average weekly change was –\$12. This means the value of the stock fell by an average of \$12 per week.

**b)** $\frac{-\$12}{1\text{ week}} = \frac{\blacksquare}{15\text{ weeks}}$ (× 15)

$\frac{-\$12}{1\text{ week}} = \frac{15 \times (-\$12)}{15\text{ weeks}}$ **The denominator has been multiplied by 15, so multiply the numerator by 15 also.**

$\frac{-\$12}{1\text{ week}} = \frac{-\$180}{15\text{ weeks}}$

If this rate of change continues, the stock will fall \$180 in 15 weeks.

## Key Concepts

- A ratio is a comparison of quantities with the same units. For example, in a deck of playing cards, the ratio of aces to face cards (kings, queens, and jacks) is 4:12.
- A ratio is in simplest form when the terms have no common factor except 1. In simplest form, the ratio of aces to face cards is 1:3.
- A rate is a comparison of two quantities expressed in different units. For example, $5.95 for 0.5 kg of salmon.
- A unit rate is a rate in which the second term is 1. The unit price of the salmon is $11.90 for 1 kg, or $11.90/kg.
- You can write equivalent ratios and rates by multiplying, or dividing, all terms by the same number.

## Discuss the Concepts

1. Which one of the following ratios is in simplest form? Explain why the other two are not. Express them in simplest form.
   **A** 10:4 **B** 5:26:3 **C** 3.5:5
2. Which of the following ratios are equivalent? Explain why.
   **A** 24:18 **B** 4:3 **C** 6:2 **D** 20:15
3. Meena paid $15.75 for 3 m of fabric. How can you find the equivalent unit rate?

## Practise

*For help with questions 1 to 4, refer to Example 1.*

1. Write each ratio in simplest form.
   a) number of vowels compared to all letters in the word ONTARIO
   b) value, in cents, of a nickel compared to a quarter
   c) number of days in a week compared to number of days in June

2. For the rectangle shown, write ratios in simplest form to compare the following measures.
   a) length to width
   b) width to length to diagonal
   c) perimeter to diagonal

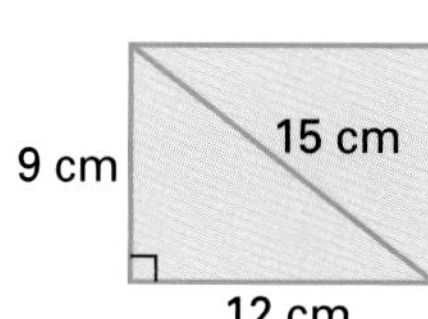

3. Express each ratio in simplest form.

a) 5:55 b) 18:22 c) 45:54 d) 26:13

e) 56:4 f) 27:81 g) 4:8:20 h) 300:125:275

4. Find the missing term in each equivalent ratio.

a) 10:3 = 20:[?] b) 5:[?] = 30:72 c) [?]:18 = 4:3

d) 45:20 = [?]:4 e) 16:4 = 8:[?] f) 12:5:2 = 36:[?]:6

## Apply the Concepts

*For help with questions 5 to 9, refer to Examples 2 and 3.*

5. Find the unit rate in each situation.

a) Gary drives 240 km in 3 h.

b) Hajid pays $110 for 5 h of guitar lessons.

c) A gas station had 15 customers in half an hour.

d) Sudbury received 20 cm of snow in 4 h.

e) Shuna pays $24.99 for one dozen long-stemmed roses.

f) In Timmins, the temperature changed by −16° C in 5 h.

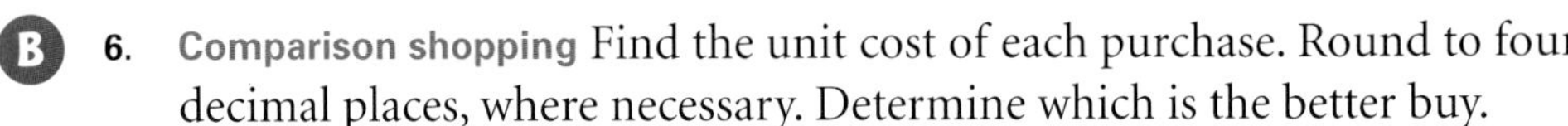

**B** 6. **Comparison shopping** Find the unit cost of each purchase. Round to four decimal places, where necessary. Determine which is the better buy.

a) hotdog buns: $2.75 for 12, or $1.69 for 8

b) oranges: 4 for $1.00 or $3.15 per dozen

c) milk: $1.09 for 500 mL, or $4.19 for 4 L

7. **Problem Solving** Bulk buying stores sell all kinds of products by quantity. They are not always cheaper than a similar packaged product at the grocery store. Determine which is the better buy for each product.

| | Product | Bulk Store Price | Grocery Store Price |
|---|---|---|---|
| a) | flour | $1.15/kg | $5.79 for a 5-kg bag |
| b) | linguini | $0.004/g | $1.39 for a 500-g box |
| c) | dog kibble | $2.09/kg | $14.95 for a 8-kg bag |

8. **Recipe** A recipe for the topping for apple crisp calls for the following.

$\frac{1}{2}$ cup white flour

$\frac{1}{4}$ cup of rolled oats

$\frac{1}{2}$ cup brown sugar

100 g butter

a) Write the ratio flour:sugar:oats in simplest form.

b) Why can you not include butter in the ratio?

c) If you need to make four times the amount of this topping, how much of each ingredient should you use?

9. **Trail mix** Karl's trail mix recipe is

1 cup almonds $2\frac{1}{2}$ cups peanuts

$\frac{1}{2}$ cup raisins $\frac{1}{2}$ cup dried apple

a) Write the ratio almonds:peanuts:raisins:dried apple in simplest form.

b) For a fundraising event, Karl plans to make a total of 45 cups of the mixture. How much of each ingredient does he need?

10. For a two-stroke motor, regular gasoline must be mixed with two-cycle motor oil. The recommended mixture for Jean's lawn mower is 250 mL of oil for every 10 L of gasoline.

a) Express the ratio oil:gasoline in simplest form.

b) If Jean has 8-L of gasoline in a container, how much two-cycle motor oil should be mixed with it before it is poured into the mower's tank?

c) Two-stroke motors have fewer moving parts and last longer than four-stroke engines; however, they have been banned in some countries. Why do you think this type of motor is banned? Research to check.

11. **Application** The gas consumption of cars is reported in litres per 100 km (L/100 km).

a) Car A has an average consumption of 18.1 L/100 km. Car B has an average consumption of 15.2 L/100 km. Which car is more energy efficient?

b) Copy and complete the table. Round each answer to the nearest tenth of a litre per 100 km.

| Car | Distance Driven (km) | Gas Used (L) | Gas Consumption (L/100 km) |
|---|---|---|---|
| X | 720 | 42 | |
| Y | 1200 | 84 | |
| Z | 575 | 29.5 | |

c) Rank the cars X, Y, and Z, from greatest to least gas consumption.

d) Research the fuel consumption rates of some vehicles that you like.

**C** 12. **Scale ratio** The floor plan of a small shopping mall is shown. The length of one side of the square building is actually 80 m.

a) Write a ratio, in lowest terms, for the scale used to draw the plan.

b) Approximately how far is it from the entrance on the north side to the ladies washroom?

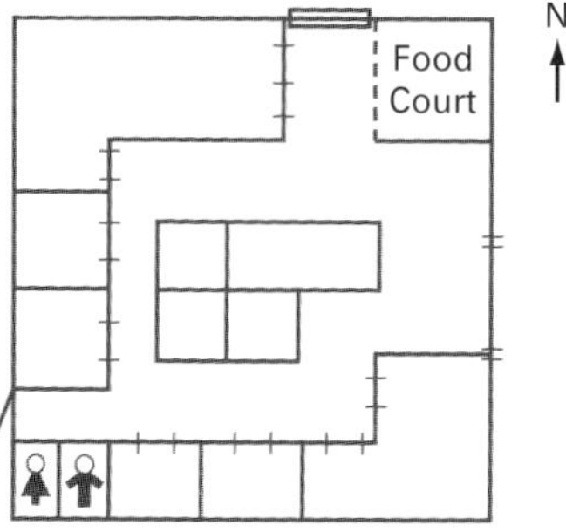

# Review

## 5.1 Adding and Subtracting Integers, pages 172–178

1. Draw a number line to model each situation.
   a) An elevator starts 2 floors below ground level, goes up 14 floors, and then goes down 5 floors.
   b) The temperature started at −7°C one morning, increased 4°C by noon, and increased another 2°C that afternoon.

2. Evaluate, without using a calculator.
   a) $9 - 4$ b) $-11 - (-2)$ c) $4 - (-7)$ d) $-8 - 12$

3. **Communication** Describe how to evaluate $-76 - (-37)$ using your calculator.

4. **Application** The elevation of Mt. Everest is 8850 m. The elevation of the Dead Sea is −400 m. What is the difference between the two elevations?

**Did You Know?**

For many years, the elevation of Mt. Everest was believed to be 8848 m. In 1999, scientists set up GPS equipment at the summit of Mt. Everest and discovered the elevation to be 8850 m.

## 5.2 Multiplying and Dividing Integers, pages 179–183

5. Evaluate.
   a) $7 \times (-2)$ b) $(-3) \times (-6)$ c) $(-8) \times 4$
   d) $5(-9)$ e) $(-42) \div (-6)$ f) $(-32) \div 4$
   g) $(-12)(3)$ h) $\frac{-25}{-5}$ i) $\frac{-48}{6}$

6. **Average temperature** The following outside temperatures were recorded at school at 10:00 a.m. for one week. Calculate the average outside temperature.

   Monday: +2°C
   Tuesday: +3°C
   Wednesday: −2°C
   Thursday: −6°C
   Friday: −7°C

7. **Application** Mountain climbers in the Canadian Rockies must prepare for cold temperatures as they approach the top of a mountain. The temperature drops approximately 6°C for every 1000 m they climb. The height of Mt. Logan is 5960 m. If the temperature at the bottom of Mt. Logan is 14°C, write an expression to determine the temperature at the top of the mountain.

## 5.3 Plotting Points on the Cartesian Plane, pages 184–190

8. a) Give the coordinates of each point.
   b) For each point, state the quadrant in which the point lies, if possible.
   c) Are there any points that do not lie in any of the four quadrants? Explain.

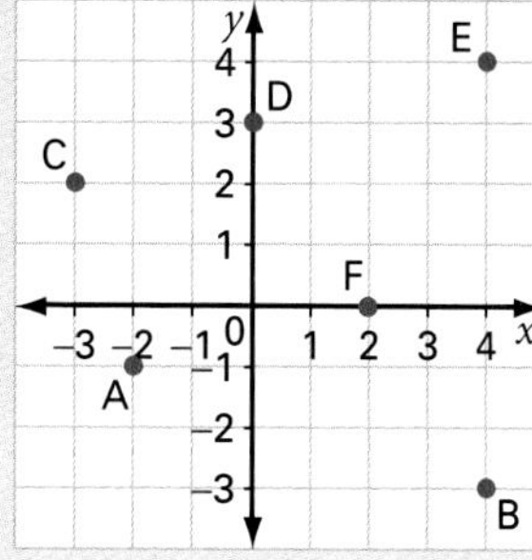


9. **Application**
   a) Plot the points (0, 3), (2, 3), (0, –1), (5, –1) on the Cartesian plane.
   b) Join the points to form a composite figure.
   c) Calculate the area of the figure.

## 5.4 Exploring Rational Numbers, pages 191–197

10. Draw and label a number line from –5 to +5. Show the approximate position of each point.

    a) 0.3 b) $3\frac{1}{8}$ c) $-4\frac{1}{4}$ d) –1.25 e) $1\frac{3}{4}$

11. A measuring jug has a scale marked on one side to show quarter-cup steps, and on the other side a scale shows 50-mL steps. One cup is approximately equal to 250 mL. Make a drawing of the jug, showing the two scales. The capacity of the jug is 1 L.

## 5.5 Operations With Rational Numbers, pages 198–205

12. Evaluate each expression. Use a calculator to confirm your answers.

    a) $7 \times \frac{3}{4}$ b) $1\frac{1}{2} \div \frac{5}{8}$ c) $\frac{1}{3} - \frac{2}{3}$ d) $-\frac{5}{6} + \frac{7}{18}$

13. A bear cub gains 2.3 kg each week. How much does the cub gain in $4\frac{1}{2}$ weeks?

## 5.6 Ratio and Rate, pages 206–211

14. A hot tub fills at the rate of 50 L/min. How long does it take to fill a hot tub that holds 10 000 L?

15. The temperature to which antifreeze will protect the cooling system of a car from freezing depends on the ratio of antifreeze (ethylene glycol) to water. To protect to –40°C, a ratio of 11:9 is needed. How much antifreeze should be put into an empty cooling system with capacity 4.5 L, before filling it with water?

# Practice Test

## Multiple Choice

***For questions 1 to 7, select the correct answer.***

**1.** Evaluate –6 + 13.

**A** 19 **B** −19 **C** 7 **D** −7

**2.** Which expression is shown using the number line?

**A** −7 + 4 **B** 4 − 7

**C** 7 − 4 **D** −4 − 7

**3.** What is the value of 17 – 12 – (–5)?

**A** 10 **B** 0 **C** 34 **D** 24

**4.** Evaluate (−12 ) × 4.

**A** −16 **B** −48 **C** 48 **D** −3

**5.** On a horizontal number line, which number is furthest to the right?

**A** 0.5 **B** $1\frac{3}{4}$ **C** $-1\frac{1}{2}$ **D** 1.5

**6.** Which of the following is *not* equivalent to 2:3?

**A** 6:9 **B** 10:15 **C** 4:5 **D** 1.0:1.5

**7.** A motor requires a mixture of oil and gas in the ratio 1:50. If 10 L of gas is purchased, how much oil is needed?

**A** 5 L **B** 20 mL **C** 0.2 L **D** 50 mL

## Short Answer

**8.** Describe why a negative integer divided by a positive integer results in a negative answer. Use an example to support your answer.

**9.** **a)** Write an ordered pair for each point shown.

**b)** List the quadrant in which each point is found, if possible.

**c)** Are any of the points not located in any of the four quadrants? Explain.

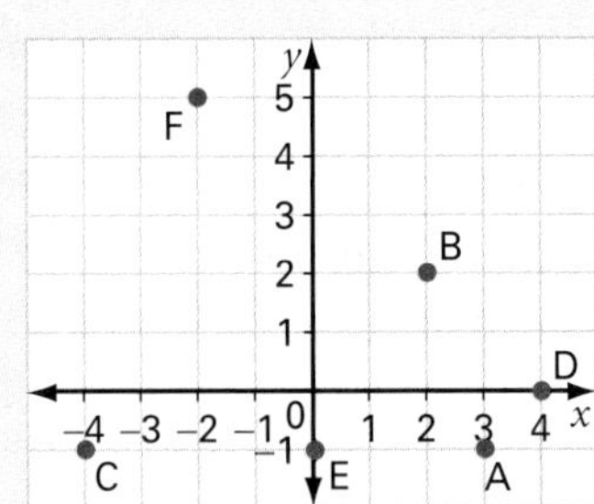

10. Simplify without a calculator. Show all steps. You may check using a calculator.

a) $1\frac{3}{5} \times 1\frac{1}{4}$ b) $\frac{3}{4} - \frac{4}{5}$ c) $4 \times \left(-1\frac{2}{3}\right)$ d) $1\frac{2}{3} + 2\frac{3}{4}$

11. One night the temperature fell from –5°C to –15°C in 3 h. What was the rate of temperature change per hour?

12. To make sour dough pie crust, flour, sour cream, and butter are mixed in the ratio 8:2:1. One cup of flour yields a 23-cm crust. How much sour cream and how much butter should be added to the 1 cup of flour?

## Extended Response

13. **Communication, Thinking/Inquiry/Problem Solving** A study has found that a student's mark is affected by the number of hours of TV watched. The formula $M = -10h$ gives the change in percent mark, $M$, when $h$ hours of TV are watched daily.

a) If a student watched 2 h of TV daily, then $M = -10(2)$, or –20. Describe what –20 means in this context.

b) If you watch $3\frac{3}{4}$ h of TV daily, how will your mark change?

c) If a person watches $8\frac{2}{5}$ h of TV daily, how will their mark change? Is this reasonable? Explain.

**ACHIEVEMENT CHECK** **Knowledge/Understanding Thinking/Inquiry/Problem Solving Communication Application**

14. Norm is a diver who likes to explore shipwrecks. He dives at a rate of 6.3 m/min.

a) How deep will Norm have dived after $2\frac{1}{2}$ min?

b) Norm plans a dive to explore a wreck that is 25 m deep. If his air tank holds enough air for a 30 min dive, how long will it take Norm to dive to the wreck? How long will he be able to explore before he starts to return to the surface?

c) What is the maximum depth that Norm could reach in one dive if he needs to stop to allow his body to adjust for 7 min at 30.5 m while descending, and while surfacing, for 5 min at 23 m, and 5 min at 6 m? Explain and justify how you solved the problem.

d) Norm fills his empty air tank with compressed air before his dive. If the tank can hold 2.3 $m^3$ of air and the tank fills at a rate of 0.07 $m^3$/min, how long will it take for the tank to fill?

# Cumulative Review

## Chapters 4 and 5

1. Is each of the following a primary or a secondary source of data?
   a) a table of data found in a textbook
   b) conducting a telephone survey to gather people's opinions
   c) counting the number of cars that enter the school parking lot in one day

2. **Juice preferences** Joanna surveyed the students in her class to determine their favourite type of juice. The students' responses were:

| | | | | | | | |
|---|---|---|---|---|---|---|---|
| orange | apple | grape | cranberry | apple | grape | grapefruit | orange |
| grape | grape | cranberry | orange | orange | apple | orange | orange |
| orange | apple | apple | grape | grapefruit | cranberry | apple | orange |

   a) State a hypothesis for student preference.
   b) Organize the data into a frequency table.
   c) Identify Joanna's data-gathering method.
   d) If Joanna wants to buy two types of juice for a fundraising pancake breakfast, which two types should she choose? Explain your answer.

3. Identify the population suggested in each statement.
   a) What is the most popular music group for students in your school?
   b) What percent of Canadians like to ski?
   c) What section of a particular newspaper do readers read first?

4. **Communication** Describe a suitable stratified random sampling technique that you could use to determine which school sport is the most popular.

5. **Communication** Describe a suitable systematic sampling technique that could be used to determine how many kilometres a week the average jogger runs.

6. **Magazine purchases** The data represent the number of magazines purchased in the past month by 25 different students.

   1, 4, 3, 2, 0, 3, 3, 2, 1, 0, 7, 5, 4, 2, 3, 3, 6, 5, 3, 2, 1, 1, 3, 4, 4

   a) Make a bar graph of the data.
   b) Describe the graph and what it shows.

7. For each set of data, calculate the mean, median, and mode. Identify any outliers.

a) 70, 30, 45, 52, 11, 70
b) 6, 14, 26, 51, 14, 9, 6, 7, 13
c) 24, 22, 29, 26, 4, 29, 31, 62
d) 23, 27, 29, 28, 27

8. **Wolf population** The table shows the wolf population in a national park over a 12-year period.

| Year | 1 | 2 | 3 | 4 | 5 | 6 | 7 | 8 | 9 | 10 | 11 | 12 |
|---|---|---|---|---|---|---|---|---|---|---|---|---|
| Population | 135 | 192 | 294 | 385 | 413 | 362 | 262 | 168 | 133 | 177 | 272 | 318 |

a) Make a scatter plot of the data.
b) Describe any trends or relationships.
c) **Communication** Why might the wolf population change in this manner?

9. **Average temperature** The daily high temperatures in one town are given for one week. Calculate the average daily high temperature.

6°C, 8°C, 4°C, 0°C, –3°C, –3°C, 2°C

10. Evaluate.

a) $7 \times (-8)$
b) $(-63) \div (-9)$
c) $(-12)(-3)$
d) $\frac{56}{-8}$

11. **Thinking/Inquiry/Problem Solving** Mt. Columbia, the highest mountain in Alberta, is 3747 m at its highest peak. Derek and Michel are hiking near the base of the mountain at an elevation of 750 m. They record the temperature to be 12°C. They have been told that the temperature drops 2°C for every 300 m increase in altitude. What would the temperature be at the top of Mt. Columbia? Show your work.

12. a) Plot the following points on a Cartesian plane.
A(4, 3), B(–3, 3), C(–3, –1), D(4, –5)
b) Connect the points to create a figure.
c) Calculate the area of the figure.

13. Evaluate each expression. Use a calculator to confirm your answers.

a) $9 \times \frac{-2}{5}$
b) $-2\frac{2}{3} \times \left(\frac{-3}{4}\right)$
c) $7\frac{1}{2} \div \frac{7}{3}$
d) $\frac{5}{7} - \frac{2}{7}$
e) $-\frac{5}{8} + \frac{3}{4}$
f) $2\frac{1}{2} - 3\frac{2}{3}$

14. **Application** A teaspoon is a common unit of measure for baking. A set of three small measuring spoons is labelled: 1 teaspoon, $\frac{1}{4}$ teaspoon, and $\frac{1}{2}$ teaspoon. Describe two ways to use the spoons to measure out $\frac{3}{4}$ teaspoon of salt.

# Tasks

## GASOLINE MIXTURES

Vicki has a 5-m long boat with a 20-L gas tank. The gas tank is a square-based prism of length 50 cm. The boat is powered by a motor that uses a gasoline/oil mixture in the ratio of 50:1.

**a)** If Vicki buys 10 L of gas, how much oil should she add to the tank?

**b)** If the trip from the dock to Vicki's cottage uses 1.6 L of the gasoline/oil mixture, how many trips can she make on one full tank?

**c)** What are the dimensions of the gasoline tank? Explain your method and justify your solution.

**d)** If gasoline costs 78¢/L and oil costs $2.99 for a 500-mL container, how much will it cost Vicki if she expects to make 48 dock to cottage trips over the summer?

## STOCK MARKET FUTURES

A person who buys *futures* commodities, such as oil, wheat, sugar, and corn, is hoping that the price increases in the future, when the commodity can be sold at a profit. Some futures markets, such as the Chicago Board of Trade, use rational numbers in their reports.

**a)** Copy and complete the table to show the closing prices and changes for each day.

**b)** Celine bought 5000 bushels of wheat on February 17. How much did she pay?

**c)** How much had she gained or lost on February 19 and on February 20?

**d)** What percent gain or loss did the price of wheat futures make during the week of February 17 –21? Explain how you arrived at your answer.

| Wheat: Cents Per Bushel | | |
|---|---|---|
| **Date** | **Closing Price** | **Change** |
| February 17 | $313\frac{1}{2}$ | +3 |
| February 18 | $315\frac{1}{4}$ | |
| February 19 | $314\frac{1}{2}$ | |
| February 20 | | $-2\frac{3}{4}$ |
| February 21 | | $+3\frac{1}{4}$ |

**Did You Know?**

A bushel basket holds a volume of about 30 000 $cm^3$ of apples or about 27.27 kg of wheat.

## Ball Bounce Heights

Amin and Cheryl measured the height to which a ball bounced when it was dropped from different heights and got the results shown.

| Drop Height (m) | Rebound Height (m) |
|---|---|
| 5.0 | 3.9 |
| 4.5 | 3.6 |
| 4.0 | 3.5 |
| 3.5 | 2.7 |
| 3.0 | 2.4 |
| 2.5 | 1.9 |
| 2.0 | 1.6 |
| 1.5 | 1.1 |
| 1.0 | 0.9 |
| 0.5 | 0.3 |

**a)** What hypothesis could they have made for conducting this experiment?

**b)** Draw a scatter plot of the data, using a graphing calculator or grid paper. Identify and analyse any outliers.

**c)** From the data and the scatter plot, describe any trends or relationships between the drop height and the rebound height. Justify your conclusions.

**d)** Predict what height the ball would rebound to if it were dropped from a height of 6.0 m. Justify your prediction.

**e)** From what height would the ball have been dropped if it rebounded to a height of 6.0 m? Justify your answer.

# CHAPTER 6

# Linear and Non-Linear Relations

You have heard the expression "a picture is worth a thousand words." Graphs are the pictures that describe mathematical relationships. In this chapter, you will learn how to

- connect patterns in data to a graph
- connect types of equations for relations to the shape of their graphs

## Chapter Problem

Ally is a competitive skateboarder who has won a number of trophies. She will be showing her skills at the "Extreme Boards" tournament. At this tournament, all boarders must:

- wear approved protective equipment including helmet, elbow pads, knee pads, and gloves
- complete two mandatory programs
- complete two custom programs of their choice
- compete in a 1-km Rocket Race

# Get Ready

## Working With Rates

A rate is a comparison of two quantities having different units.
Write the following as a unit rate.

| | |
|---|---|
| 140 km in 2 h | \$4.50 for 5 kg |
| $140 \div 2 = 70$ | $4.50 \div 5 = 0.90$ |
| The unit rate is 70 km/h. | The unit rate is \$0.90/kg. |

**1.** Write as a unit rate.
- **a)** 5 m in 2 s
- **b)** \$45 for 6 h
- **c)** \$3.98 for 4 L

**2.** Juan is paid hourly. He earns \$76 for an 8-h shift.
- **a)** Determine Juan's rate of pay.
- **b)** How much will Juan earn in a 40-h work week?

## Rational Numbers and the Order of Operations

Use BEDMAS and operations with rational numbers carefully.

$$8 \times (-2) - \frac{1}{2}(2 + 4)$$

$= 8 \times (-2) - \frac{1}{2} \times 6$ **Brackets first.**

$= -16 - 3$ **Multiply.**

$= -19$ **Subtract.**

**3.** Evaluate.
- **a)** $12 - 3(-3)$
- **b)** $5(-2 - 4)$
- **c)** $-2(5) + 4(-1)$
- **d)** $\frac{1}{3}(-8 + 2)$
- **e)** $\frac{3}{4} \times 12 - (-2)$
- **f)** $\frac{2}{5} \times (-15) + (-4) \times (-3)$

## Substituting and Evaluating Expressions

To evaluate an expression for a given value
- substitute the given value
- simplify the expression by following the order of operations

| | |
|---|---|
| $y = -2x$ for $x = 3$ | $y = \frac{2}{3}x - 5$ for $x = -3$ |
| $y = -2(3)$ | $y = \frac{2}{3}(-3) - 5$ |
| $y = -6$ | $y = \left(\frac{2}{\cancel{3}_1}\right)\left(\frac{\cancel{-3}^{-1}}{1}\right) - 5$ |
| | $y = -2 - 5$ |
| | $y = -7$ |

**4.** Substitute the given value of $x$, and determine the value of $y$.

**a)** $y = 3x + 1$ for $x = 3$ **b)** $y = -4x$ for $x = 2$

**c)** $y = -x - 2$ for $x = -4$ **d)** $y = \frac{3}{4}x - 5$ for $x = 4$

## Plotting Points on a Coordinate Grid

To plot an ordered pair $(x, y)$
- start at the origin
- move right if $x$ is positive, left if $x$ is negative
- then, move up if $y$ is positive, down if $y$ is negative

The following points are shown on the coordinate grid.
A(2, 5) B(−3, 4) C(0, −3) D(−4, −2)

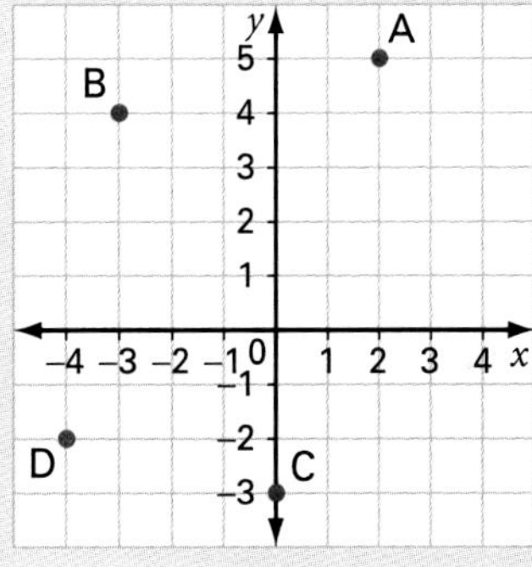


**5.** Write the coordinates of the points P, Q, R, S, T, and V.

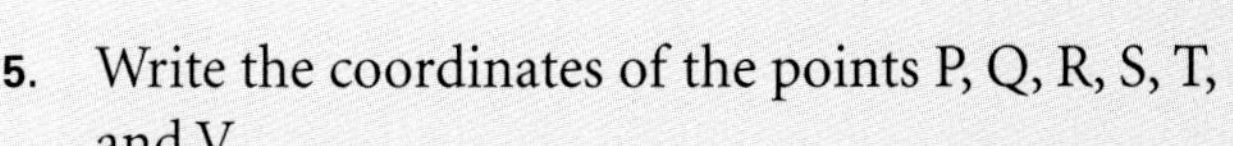

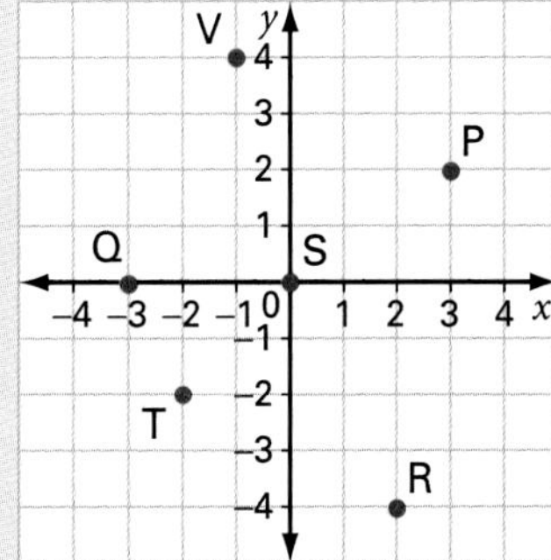


**6.** Plot the following points on a coordinate grid.

A(3, 7) B(2, −5) C(−7, −3) D(0, 4)
E(1, −4) F(0, 0) G(2.5, −6) H(−1.5, −3.5)

# 6.1 Direct Variation

When you get a part-time job, you may be paid by the hour. The more hours you work, the more money you earn. Suppose you start working 8 h per week. What happens to your pay cheque if you increase your time to 16 h per week? The amount you are paid varies directly with the number of hours you work.

In the **Discover** below, you will explore how direct variation occurs in a measurement context.

## Discover

**Materials**
- centimetre grid paper
- ruler

### Exploring a Direct Variation

1. On centimetre grid paper, draw a small square.
2. Measure the side length and the perimeter of the square.

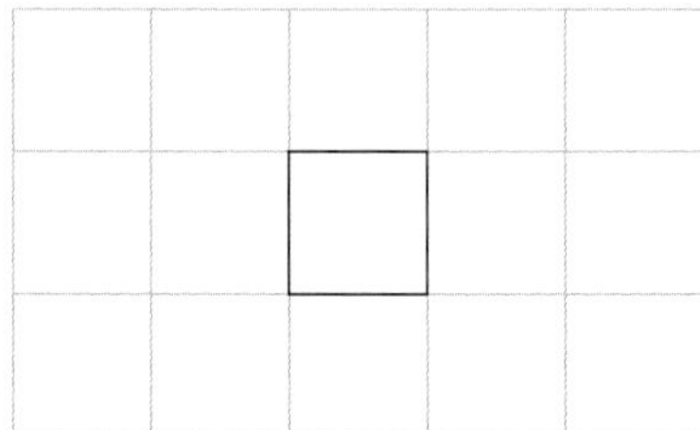

3. a) Predict the value when you divide perimeter by side length.
   b) Divide perimeter by side length. Call this $\frac{P}{s}$.
   c) Compare this result to your prediction. Were you correct? Explain.
4. a) Predict what will happen to the perimeter when you double the side length.
   b) Predict what will happen to $\frac{P}{s}$ when you double the side length.
   c) Draw a new square whose side length is 2 cm, and record the measures.
   d) Compare the results to your predictions. Were you correct? Explain.

5. Repeat step 4, for a square whose side length is triple the original.

6. Repeat steps 1 and 2 for several different-size squares. Determine $\frac{P}{s}$ for each square. Record your results in a table.

| Perimeter (cm) | Side Length (cm) | $\frac{P}{s}$ |
|---|---|---|
| | | |
| | | |
| | | |

7. What do you notice about the values in the third column, $\frac{P}{s}$? Does this value make sense? Explain.

8. a) Predict what a scatter plot of perimeter versus side length will look like.
   b) Create a scatter plot of perimeter versus side length.
   c) Describe the pattern that the scatter plot makes. Compare this to your prediction. Were you correct?

9. Draw a line through the plotted points.

10. Use the graph to predict
   a) the perimeter of a square having a side length of 10 cm
   b) the side length of a square having a perimeter of 10 cm

11. a) Explain how you found your answers to step 10.
   b) Use the formula $P = 4s$ to verify your answers to step 10.

In a **direct variation**, one variable equals a fixed multiple of the other. This multiple is called the **constant of variation**, often represented by $k$.

The relationship between the perimeter and the side length of a square is an example of a direct variation. The equation is $P = 4s$. The constant of variation is 4.

The graph of a direct variation is a straight line that passes through the origin.

The graph can be used as a model to make predictions about the relationship.

**Interpolation** is using a graph to estimate values *inside*, or between, graphed data.

**Extrapolation** is using a graph to estimate values *outside*, or beyond, graphed data.

## EXAMPLE 1

### Using a Graph to Model a Direct Variation

Nicole works part-time at a bookstore. Her earnings for the past three weeks are shown.

| Hours Worked (h) | Pay ($) | Rate of Pay ($/h) |
|---|---|---|
| 6 | 45 | |
| 12 | 90 | |
| 8 | 60 | |

a) Determine Nicole's hourly rate of pay for each week. What does this tell you about the relationship between pay and hours worked?

b) Plot the points and create a graph to model this relationship.

c) Use the graph to find Nicole's earnings if she works 9 h.

d) Use the graph to find how many hours Nicole must work to earn $120.

### Solution

a) Complete the third column in the table by dividing Nicole's pay by the number of hours worked.

| Hours Worked (h) | Pay ($) | Rate of Pay ($/h) |
|---|---|---|
| 6 | 45 | 7.50 |
| 12 | 90 | 7.50 |
| 8 | 60 | 7.50 |

← $45 ÷ 6 h = $7.50/h

Nicole's rate of pay is the same in each case, $7.50/h. Her pay depends on her number of hours worked. So, pay versus hours worked is a direct variation.

b) Graph pay versus hours worked.

**When choosing scales for the axes, look at the values in the table. You need to fit all the data. The scale on each axis must increase by a constant amount.**

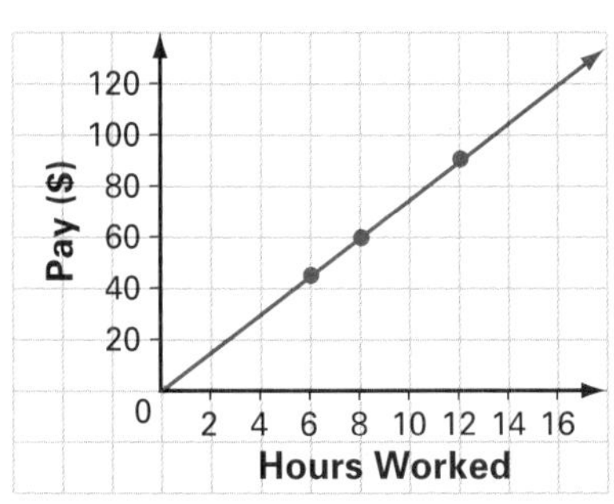


Notice that the points line up. Draw a line through the points.

**c)** Use interpolation to find Nicole's earnings for 9 h of work.

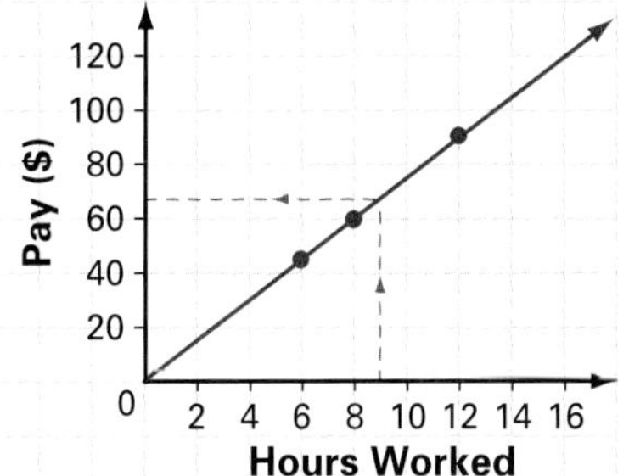


Interpolate: read between the graphed values.

From the graph, Nicole earns approximately \$70 for 9 h of work.
Nicole actually earns 9 × \$7.50, or \$67.50, for 9 h of work.

**d)** Use extrapolation to find how many hours Nicole must work to earn \$120.

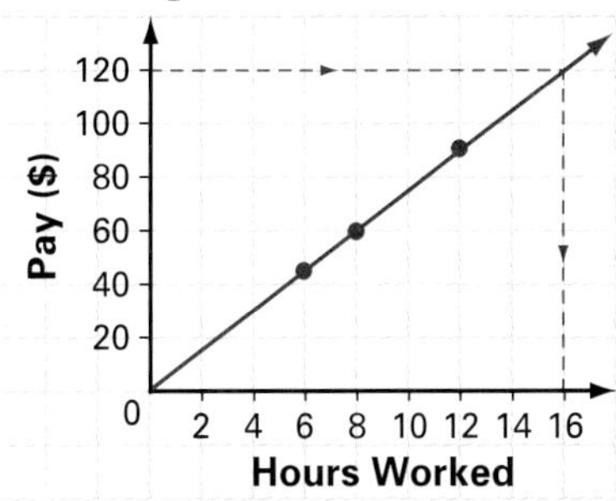


Extrapolate: read beyond the graphed values.

Nicole must work 16 h to earn \$120.

Another way to describe the direct variation in **Example 1** is to say that Nicole's pay, *P*, **varies directly** with the number of hours, *h*, worked.

The **constant of variation**, *k*, is the rate at which the two variables change.

Nicole's rate of pay is \$7.50, so $k = 7.50$.

Another way to write the direct variation is as an equation.
$P = 7.50h$

## EXAMPLE 2

### Using an Equation to Model a Direct Variation

The Alvari family travels 225 km to their cottage. Benny records their progress.

| Time, $t$, (h) | Distance, $d$, (km) |
|---|---|
| 0.5 | 43 |
| 1.5 | 129 |
| 2.0 | 172 |

**a)** Determine the constant of variation. Explain what it means.

**b)** Write an equation that models this direct variation.

**c)** Use the equation to determine how far the Alvari family has travelled after 2.5 h.

**d)** How long will the trip take?

**e)** What assumptions must you make in parts c) and d)?

### Solution

**a)** Divide distance by time.

| Time, $t$, (h) | Distance, $d$, (km) | $k = \frac{d}{t}$ |
|---|---|---|
| 0.5 | 43 | 86 |
| 1.5 | 129 | 86 |
| 2.0 | 172 | 86 |

**The ratio of distance to time is the same in each case.**

Distance varies directly with time. The constant of variation, $k$, is 86. This constant represents the speed, 86 km/h.

**b)** $d = kt$ **Substitute $k = 86$.**

$d = 86t$

The equation that models this direct variation is $d = 86t$.

**c)** In $d = 86t$, substitute $t = 2.5$.

$d = 86(2.5)$

$d = 215$

The Alvari family has travelled 215 km after 2.5 h.

**d)** In $d = 86t$, substitute $d = 225$.

$225 = 86t$ **What number multiplies 86 to give 225?**

$t = 225 \div 86$

$t \doteq 2.6$ **Convert the decimal part to minutes.**

$0.6 \text{ h} = 0.6 \times 60 \text{ min}$, or 36 min

The trip will take about 2 h and 36 min.

**e)** You must assume that the family travels at a constant average speed throughout the trip.

## Key Concepts

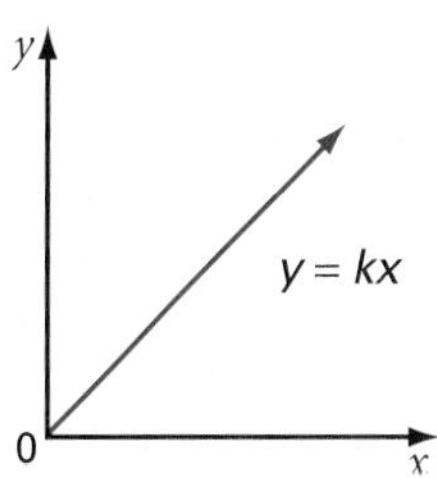


- A direct variation is a relationship in which one variable is a constant multiple of the other.
- The fixed multiple is called the constant of variation, often denoted by $k$.
- The graph of a direct variation is a straight line that passes through the origin.
- The equation $y = kx$ describes a direct variation between two variables, $x$ and $y$.

## Discuss the Concepts

1. Consider the statement: "Distance varies directly with time."
   a) What does this mean?
   b) How can you express this relationship as an equation?
   c) What would a graph of distance versus time look like?

2. The profit earned on the sales of fitness-club memberships varies directly with the number sold.
   a) Explain why this is a direct variation.
   b) What would the graph of this relation look like?

## Practise

**A** ***For help with questions 1 and 2, refer to Example 2.***

1. Write an equation in the form $y = kx$ for each of the following. Choose appropriate letters for the variables. Use $k$ to represent the constant of variation.
   a) cost varies directly with number of units purchased
   b) circumference varies directly with radius

2. Determine the constant of variation for each direct variation.
   a) Brian's pay varies directly with the number of hours he works. He earns $68 in 8 h.
   b) The distance travelled by a train varies directly with time. The train travelled 315 km in 3.5 h.
   c) The number of words typed varies directly with time. Lee typed 180 words in 5 min.

## APPLY THE CONCEPTS

*For help with questions 3 and 4, refer to Example 1.*

3 Claude drives to his cottage, which is 250 km away, at a constant average speed. His distance-time data is given:

| Time, $t$, (h) | Distance, $d$, (km) |
|---|---|
| 0 | 0 |
| 0.5 | 41 |
| 1.0 | 82 |
| 2.0 | 164 |

a) Determine the constant of variation. Explain what it means.
b) Write an equation that relates $d$ and $t$.
c) Use the equation to find how far Claude has driven after 1.5 h.
d) How long will the trip take?
e) What assumptions must you make in parts c) and d)?

4. **Communication** A parking lot charges \$2.50/h.
a) Determine the cost for 1, 2, and 3 h. Make a table of values.
b) Graph cost versus number of hours.
c) Use the graph to determine the cost for 5 h.
d) How long could you park for \$15.00?
e) Determine the cost to park for 16 h. Does this answer seem reasonable? How might the parking lot policy change for long parking times?

5. Neeta's pay varies directly with the number of hours worked. Neeta earns \$45.00 for 5 h.
a) What is the constant of variation?
b) Write an equation relating her pay, $P$, and hours worked, $t$.
c) How much will Neeta earn for 10 h worked?

6. In "Extreme Boards" the first mandatory program is called "Slalom." In this event, competitors must travel back and forth on a curved surface.

| Number of Tricks, $n$ | Style Score, $S$ |
|---|---|
| 0 | 0 |
| 2 | 4 |
| 4 | 8 |
| 6 | 12 |

The boarder can win points for performing trick moves at the top of each swing. The style score varies directly with the number of successful tricks.
a) Determine the constant of variation.
b) Write an equation that relates style score, $S$, and number of tricks, $n$.
c) When Ally's turn comes, the top style score is 12. How many tricks must Ally perform successfully to beat this score?

**Materials**

- *The Geometer's Sketchpad®*

or

- compasses, string, and ruler

7. **Thinking/Inquiry/Problem Solving** The circumference of a circle varies directly with its diameter.
   **a)** Predict the constant of variation.
   **b)** Construct a circle having a diameter of 2 cm. Measure its circumference.
   **c)** Predict the circumference if you draw a new circle having double the original diameter. Draw the new circle and check your prediction.
   **d)** Repeat part c) for a circle having triple the original diameter.
   **e)** For each circle, calculate the ratio of circumference to diameter. Call this $\frac{C}{d}$. Where have you seen this value before?
   **f)** Construct several circles and measure their diameter and circumference. Record diameter, circumference, and the ratio $\frac{C}{d}$ in a table.

| Diameter (cm) | Circumference (cm) | $k = \frac{C}{d}$ |
|---|---|---|
| | | |

   **g)** Predict what a scatter plot of circumference versus diameter will look like. Create the scatter plot and compare it to your prediction.
   **h)** Use the scatter plot to estimate the circumference of a circle with diameter 12 cm.

**Materials**

- paper tubes (toilet paper tube, paper towel tube)
- masking tape
- metre stick

C 8. **Thinking/Inquiry/Problem Solving** Investigate the width of vision seen through a paper tube compared to the distance from the object. Work with a partner.
   **a)** Stick 4 m of tape horizontally on the wall. Mark the centre of the tape. Mark off 5 cm intervals in both directions.
   **b)** How do you think width of vision will vary with distance from the wall?
   **c)** Stand back from the tape, and look through the paper towel tube. Measure your distance from the wall and the width of tape that can be seen looking through the tube. Record the results in a table.

| Distance From Wall (cm) | Width of Vision (cm) |
|---|---|
| | |

   **d)** Repeat step c) at different distances. Keep moving backwards, stopping when you can see both ends of the tape.
   **e)** Graph width of vision versus distance from wall.
   **f)** Does this seem to be a direct variation? Explain why or why not. Explain why the points might not line up perfectly.
   **g)** Discuss how you think the data will differ if you use a different-sized paper roll. Repeat the investigation using a different paper roll. Compare your results with your prediction.

# 6.2 Partial Variation

Some employees are paid in two ways: a fixed amount plus an amount that varies depending on performance. Here are some examples:

- car salesperson
- waiter/waitress
- professional athlete
- computer salesperson

## DISCOVER

### Earning Pay: A Partial-Variation Model

Mayte is a computer salesperson. Her earnings depend on sales performance: the more she sells, the more money she earns. At the end of each month, Mayte is paid $2000 plus 10% commission on sales for the month.

1. Let $S$ represent sales for the month. Determine the 10% commission for each sales amount. Record the results in a table. Leave room for two more columns.

| Sales, *S*, ($) | Commission ($) | |
|---|---|---|
| 0 | 0 | |
| 5 000 | 500 | 10% of $5000 |
| 10 000 | | |
| 15 000 | | |
| 20 000 | | |

2. Let E represent earnings. Add a third column and calculate earnings for each month. Remember, Mayte gets $2000 plus her commission.

| Sales, *S*, ($) | Commission ($) | Earnings, *E*, ($) |
|---|---|---|
| 0 | 0 | 2000 |
| 5 000 | 500 | 2500 |
| 10 000 | | |
| 15 000 | | |
| 20 000 | | |

3. Write Sales and Earnings as ordered pairs $(S, E)$. Record these in a new column.

| Sales, *S*, ($) | Commission ($) | Earnings, *E*, ($) | (*S*, *E*) |
|---|---|---|---|
| 0 | 0 | 2000 | (0, 2000) |
| 5 000 | 500 | 2500 | (5000, 2500) |
| 10 000 | | | |
| 15 000 | | | |
| 20 000 | | | |

4. a) Set up a graph as shown.
   b) Plot the ordered pairs $(S, E)$. Draw a line through the points.
   c) Does the line pass through the origin? Explain.

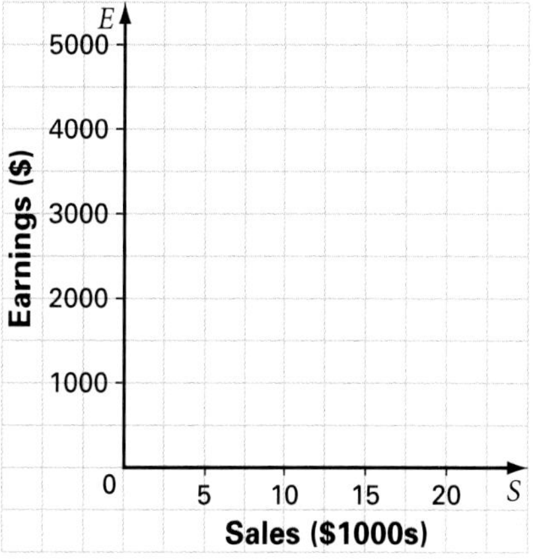


5. Consider the equation $E = 0.1S + 2000$.
   a) Substitute $S = 5000$ and calculate $E$. What do you notice?
   b) Repeat this for the other three values of $S$ that were used in the table. Compare the results with those obtained in step 2.
   c) Explain why this equation works.

6. Use the equation in step 5 to determine Mayte's earnings if she has monthly sales of each amount.
   a) $7500
   b) $25 000

7. Repeat step 6, using the graph instead of the equation. Do these results match? Explain.

8. a) Describe one advantage, and one disadvantage, of using the graph to predict earnings.
   b) Describe one advantage, and one disadvantage, of using the equation to predict earnings.

9. Describe how the graph would change if Mayte were paid
   a) $3000 per month plus 10% of sales
   b) $2000 per month plus 15% of sales

In a **partial variation**, one variable equals a constant multiple of the other, plus a constant value. There is a **fixed part**, which does not change, and a **variable part**, which changes.

Mayte is paid in this way. For each month, her fixed earnings are \$2000. This amount never changes. Her variable earnings are 10% of her sales, or $0.1 \times S$. This amount changes from month to month, depending on how much she sells.

$$E = 0.1S + 2000$$

Variable Part (0.1S) — Fixed Part (2000)

The graph of a partial variation is a straight line that does not pass through the origin.

**Example 1**

## Using a Graph to Model a Partial Variation

A taxicab driver charges \$2.50 plus \$0.50/km for each trip.

**a)** Set up a table of values and graph this relation.

**b)** Use the graph to predict the cost of a 6-km trip.

**c)** Use the graph to predict how far you could travel for \$8.00.

### Solution

**a)** The cost is \$2.50 plus \$0.50 for each kilometre.

| Distance, $d$, (km) | Cost, $C$, (\$) |
|---|---|
| 0 | 2.50 |
| 1 | 3.00 |
| 2 | 3.50 |
| 3 | 4.00 |

Plot the points and draw a line through them.

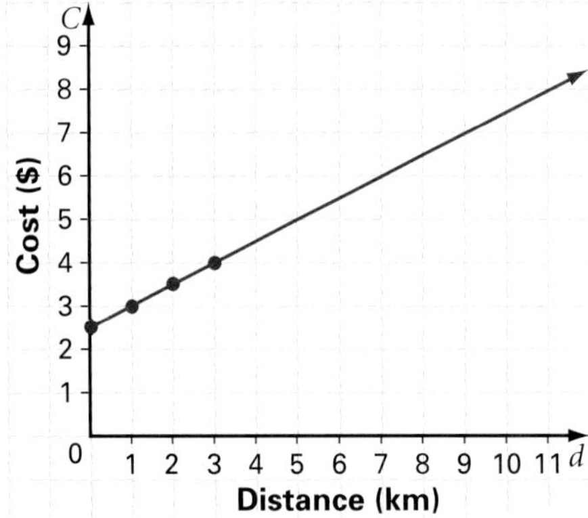

**b)** Use extrapolation to determine the cost of a 6-km trip.
Extend the line.

The cost of a 6-km trip is \$5.50.

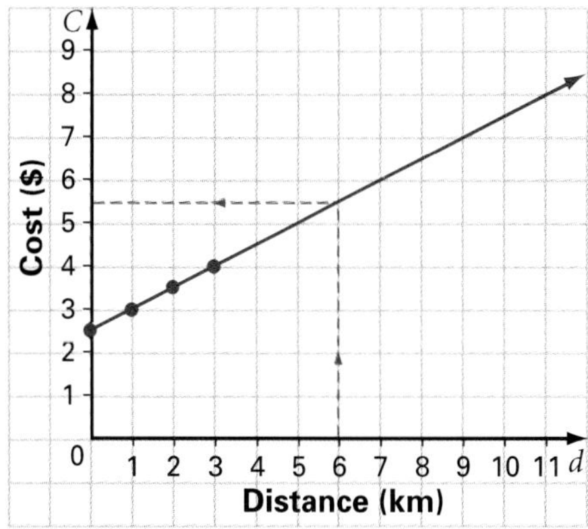

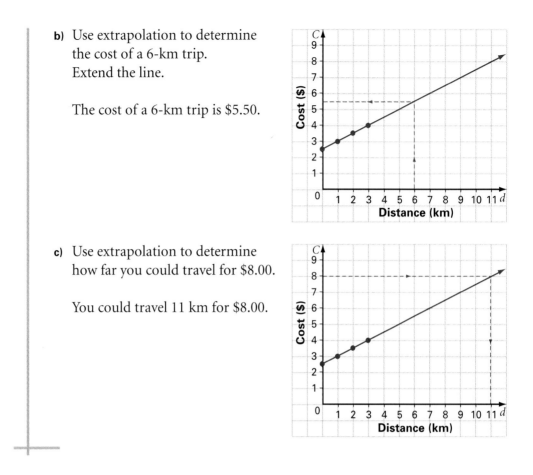

**c)** Use extrapolation to determine how far you could travel for \$8.00.

You could travel 11 km for \$8.00.

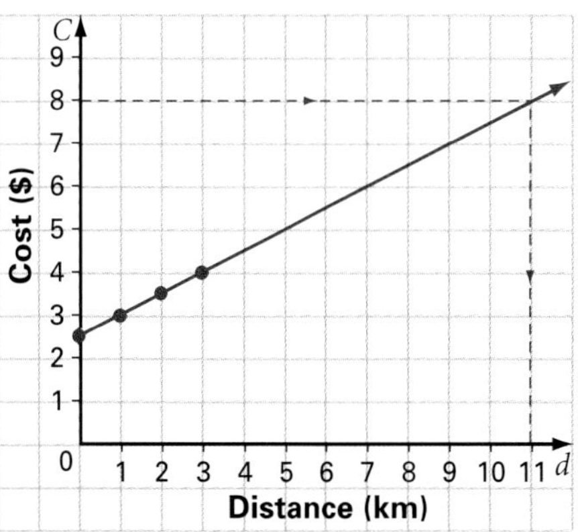


You could also model the partial variation in **Example 1** using the equation:

$C = 0.50d + 2.50$

In this equation, 2.50 is the fixed part of the cost and $0.50d$ is the variable part that depends on the length of the trip.

## EXAMPLE 2

### Using an Equation to Model a Partial Variation

José is a professional baseball pitcher. His contract states that he will be paid \$3 million per season plus \$100 000 for every win he earns.

**a)** Identify the fixed part and the variable part of this partial variation.

**b)** Write an equation that relates José's earnings, $E$, to his number of wins, $W$.

**c)** Use the equation to predict José's earnings if he wins 10 games.

### Solution

**a)** The fixed part is \$3 000 000. The variable part is \$100 000 $\times$ $W$.

**b)** $E = 100\ 000W + 3\ 000\ 000$

**c)** In $E = 100\ 000W + 3\ 000\ 000$, substitute $W = 10$.

$E = 100\ 000(10) + 3\ 000\ 000$

$E = 1\ 000\ 000 + 3\ 000\ 000$

$E = 4\ 000\ 000$

If José wins 10 games, he will earn \$4 million.

## KEY CONCEPTS

- In a partial variation, one variable is a constant multiple of the other, plus a constant value.
- A partial variation consists of two parts:
  - a fixed part that does not change
  - a variable part that changes
- The graph of a partial variation is a straight line that does not pass through the origin.

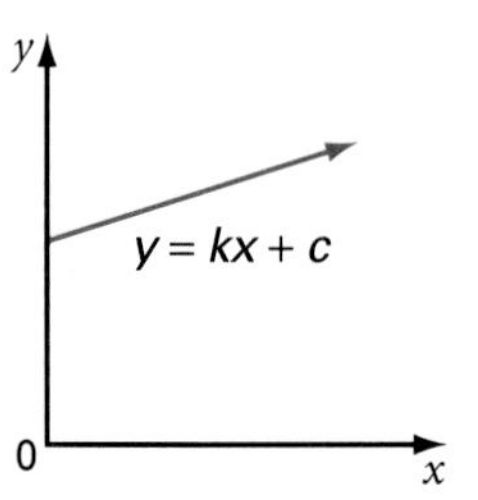

## Discuss the Concepts

1. Think of the graphs of a partial variation and a direct variation. How are they similar? How are they different?
2. When using a partial variation model, identify an advantage and a disadvantage of using
   - **a)** a graph
   - **b)** an equation
3. Discuss the advantages and disadvantages of being paid using a partial-variation model.

## Practise

**A**

1. Classify each relation as a direct variation, a partial variation, or neither. Explain your answer.

**a)**

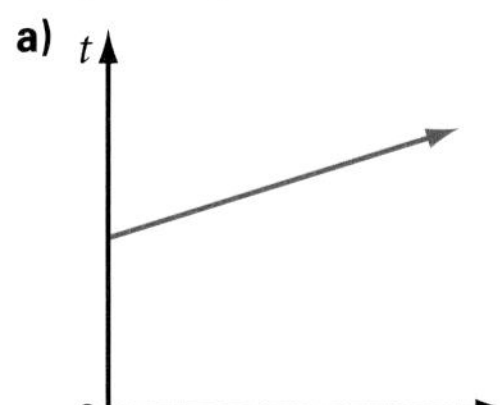


**b)**

y
0
x

**c)**

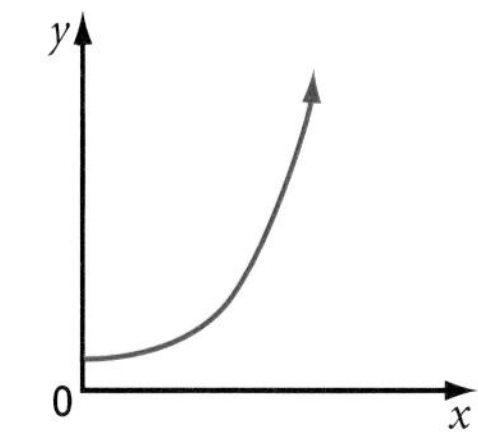


2. Classify each relation as a direct variation, a partial variation, or neither. Explain your answer.
   - **a)** $d = 5t$
   - **b)** $C = 140n + 300$
   - **c)** $v = 2.5t + 4$
   - **d)** $P = 4s$

## Apply the Concepts

**B**

***For help with questions 3-6, refer to Examples 1 and 2.***

3. **Application** Scuba divers experience an increase in pressure as they dive below sea level. The atmospheric pressure (atm) at various depths (metres, below sea level) is shown.

| Depth (m) | Pressure (atm) |
|---|---|
| 0 | 1 |
| 10 | 2 |
| 20 | 3 |
| 30 | 4 |

   - **a)** Graph pressure versus depth.
   - **b)** Is this a direct or partial variation? Explain.
   - **c)** What is the atmospheric pressure at a depth of 25 m?
   - **d)** Scuba divers begin to feel dizzy when pressure exceeds 5 atm. What depth limit would you advise for scuba divers?

**Did You Know?**

The dizzy sensation that divers may feel is nitrogen narcosis, commonly called "rapture of the deep."

4. **Application, Communication** The cost to rent an airplane from a flying school is posted on a board.

| Time (h) | Cost ($) |
|---|---|
| 1 | 120 |
| 2 | 170 |
| 3 | 220 |
| 4 | 270 |
| 5 | 320 |

   **a)** Graph this relation.
   **b)** Use the graph to find the cost of a 7 h rental.
   **c)** Use the graph to find how long you could rent an airplane for $500.
   **d)** Do you think you should round your answer to part c) up or down to the nearest hour? Explain.
   **e)** In this relation, what is the fixed cost? What is the variable cost?
   **f)** How would the graph change if the fixed cost is increased by $30?
   **g)** How would the graph change if the variable cost is increased by $10?

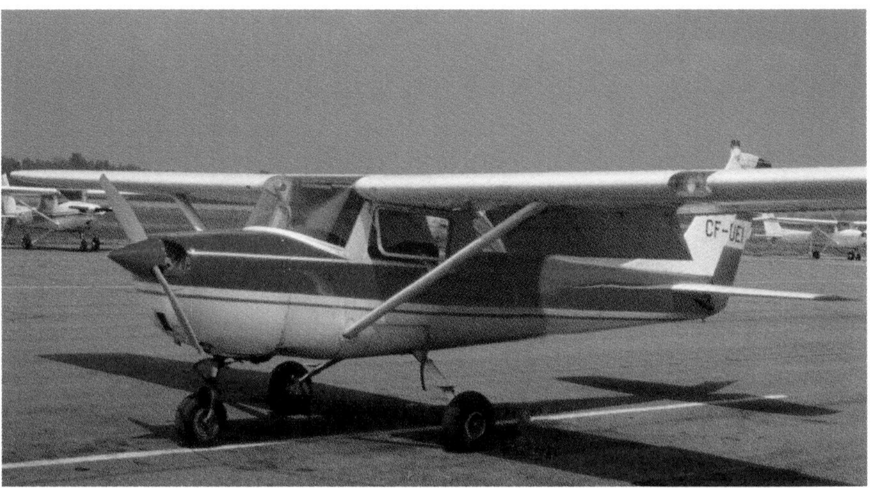

5. **Communication** The cost to rent a snowboard for one day is $40. You can rent it for extra days at a reduced cost, as shown.

| Number of Extra Days | Cost ($) |
|---|---|
| 0 | 40 |
| 1 | 55 |
| 2 | 70 |
| 3 | 85 |

   **a)** What is the cost for each extra day? Explain how you determined this.
   **b)** What is the fixed part of this variation? What is the variable part?
   **c)** Write an equation to express cost, $C$, in terms of additional days, $D$.
   **d)** Use your equation to calculate the rental cost for a total of 8 days.
   **e)** What other option might be worthwhile, instead of renting a snowboard for 8 days?

6. A car entering a highway is accelerating at a constant rate. Its speed is given by $v = 2t + 50$, where $v$ is the speed in kilometres per hour and $t$ is the time in seconds.

a) Identify the fixed part and the variable part.

b) What will the speed be after 15 s?

c) How long will it take for the car to reach the highway speed of 100 km/h? Explain how you obtained your answer.

7. **Communication** To convert centimetres to inches, a carpenter uses the relation $c = 2.54I$, where $c$ is the length in centimetres, and $I$ is the length in inches.

a) Create a table of values and graph this relation.

b) Is this relation a direct or partial variation? Explain.

c) Explain how you can use the graph to
- convert a length in centimetres to a length in inches
- convert a length in inches to a length in centimetres

Support each explanation with an example.

8. The second mandatory event of "Extreme Boards" is an obstacle course. Points are awarded only to competitors who complete the course in 30 s or less. Successful competitors are awarded 10 points plus 2 points for every second under 30 s.

a) Is this relation a direct variation or a partial variation? Explain.

b) Write an equation relating points, $P$, and number of seconds under 30, $n$.

c) Find Ally's score for this event if she completes the course successfully in 27 s.

C 9. On the back of a hotel room door, the following rates are shown.

| Length of Stay (number of nights) | Cost per Night ($) |
|---|---|
| 1 | 120 |
| 2 | 115 |
| 3 | 110 |
| 4 | 105 |

a) Graph total cost, $C$, versus number of nights, $n$.

b) Use the graph to determine the cost per night for a stay of 14 nights.

c) Does your answer to part b) seem reasonable? Explain.

d) Suggest how the hotel's rental policy might cause this model to be inaccurate. How might the sign on the door reflect this?

# 6.3 Graphing Linear Relations

A **linear relation** is a relationship between two variables. Its graph is a straight line. You can create the graph by finding points that satisfy the equation. A table of values is useful in organizing the ordered pairs.

## DISCOVER

### Temperature Scales: Constructing a Linear Graph

The equation $F = 1.8C + 32$ models the relationship between the two common temperature scales. $F$ is temperature in degrees Fahrenheit (°F) and $C$ is temperature in degrees Celsius (°C).

1. Which graph could represent this relationship? Explain your choice.

**A**

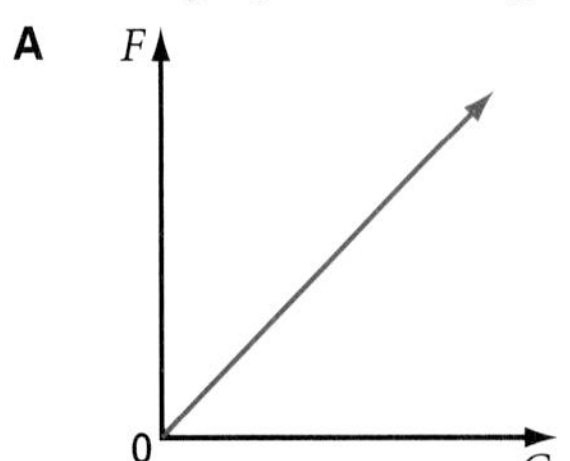


**B**

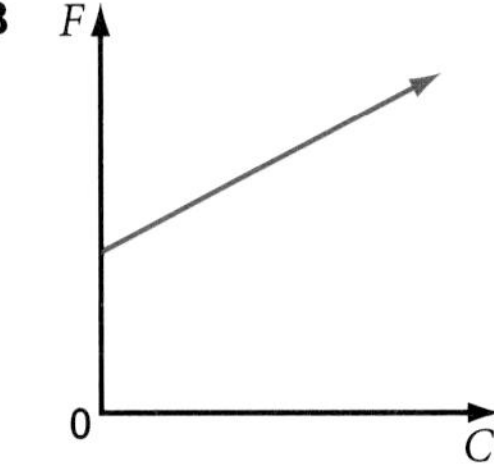


2. a) The freezing point of water is 0°C. Substitute to find the freezing point of water in degrees Fahrenheit.
   b) The boiling point of water is 100°C. Substitute to find the boiling point of water in degrees Fahrenheit.
   c) Determine the temperature in degrees Fahrenheit equivalent to –40°C.

**Did You Know?**

The coldest temperature ever recorded in Ontario was –58.3°C, in Iroquois Falls on January 23, 1935.

3. a) Create a table of values.
   b) Choose any two other temperatures in degrees Celsius. Use at least one negative value. Find their equivalent values in degrees Fahrenheit and complete the table.

| Degrees Celsius | Degrees Fahrenheit |
|---|---|
| 0 | 32 |
| 100 | |
| –40 | |
| | |
| | |

4. a) Set up a graph using appropriate scales. Since negative values are involved, use four quadrants.
   b) Plot the ordered pairs. You may have to approximate some points.
   c) Join the points and extend the line through the graph.

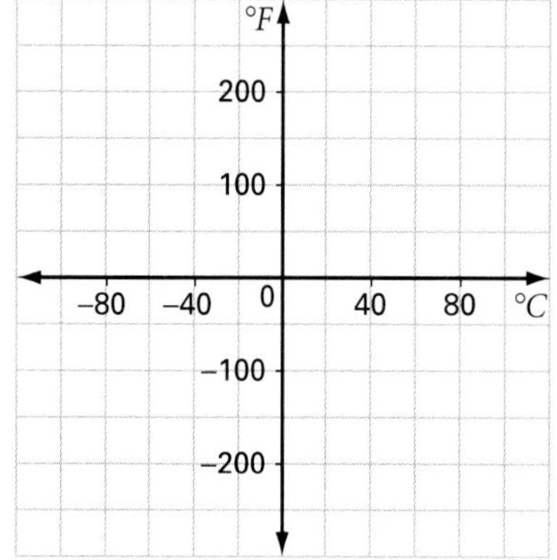


5. Compare the graph with your answer in step 1. Were you correct?

6. a) Use the graph to find the temperature in degrees Fahrenheit equivalent to 60°C.
   b) Explain how you found your answer.

7. a) A Detroit radio station says the overnight low will be 0°F. Use the graph to find the equivalent temperature in degrees Celsius.
   b) Explain how you found your answer.

Any direct or partial variation can be represented by a linear graph. To construct a graph

- create a table of values
- use substitution to find ordered pairs that satisfy the equation
- choose appropriate scales for the axes
- plot the ordered pairs
- join the points with a straight line
- label the line with the equation

**EXAMPLE 1**

## Graphing a Linear Relation Using a Table of Values

Create a table of values and graph the linear relation $y = -4x + 5$.

### Solution

Set up a table of values. Choose any three values for $x$. Use easy numbers.

Substitute $x = 0$.

$y = -4x + 5$
$y = -4(0) + 5$
$y = 0 + 5$
$y = 5$

| x | y |
|---|---|
| 0 | 5 |
| 1 | |
| 2 | |

This means that $x = 0$, $y = 5$ satisfies the equation. The point (0, 5) is on the line.

Substitute $x = 1$.

$y = -4x + 5$
$y = -4(1) + 5$
$y = -4 + 5$
$y = 1$

Substitute $x = 2$.

$y = -4x + 5$
$y = -4(2) + 5$
$y = -8 + 5$
$y = -3$

Complete the table.

| x | y |
|---|---|
| 0 | 5 |
| 1 | 1 |
| 2 | -3 |

Plot the ordered pairs and graph the line.

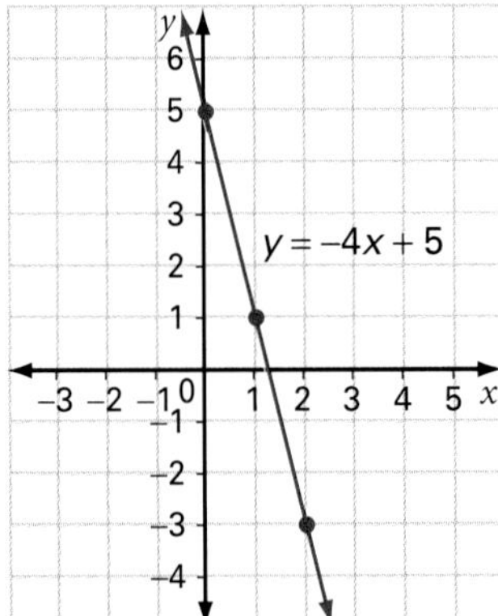


**If the three points do not line up, check your calculations for errors.**

Label the line with its equation.

## EXAMPLE 2

### Graphing a Linear Relation Involving Fractions

Create a table of values and graph the linear relation $y = \frac{2}{3}x - 4$.

### Solution

Choose values for $x$. Look at the denominator of the fraction multiplying $x$. Using multiples of 3 will simplify the calculations.

| x | y |
|---|---|
| 0 | |
| 3 | |
| 6 | |

Substitute $x = 0$.

$y = \frac{2}{3}x - 4$

$y = \frac{2}{3}(0) - 4$

$y = -4$

Substitute $x = 3$.

$y = \frac{2}{3}x - 4$

$y = \frac{2}{3}(3) - 4$

$y = \frac{2}{\cancel{3}_1}\left(\frac{\cancel{3}^1}{1}\right) - 4$

$y = 2 - 4$

$y = -2$

Substitute $x = 6$.

$y = \frac{2}{3}x - 4$

$y = \frac{2}{3}(6) - 4$

$y = \frac{2}{\cancel{3}_1}\left(\frac{\cancel{6}^2}{1}\right) - 4$

$y = 4 - 4$

$y = 0$

Complete the table.

| x | y |
|---|---|
| 0 | –4 |
| 3 | –2 |
| 6 | 0 |

Plot the ordered pairs and graph the relation.
Label the line with its equation.

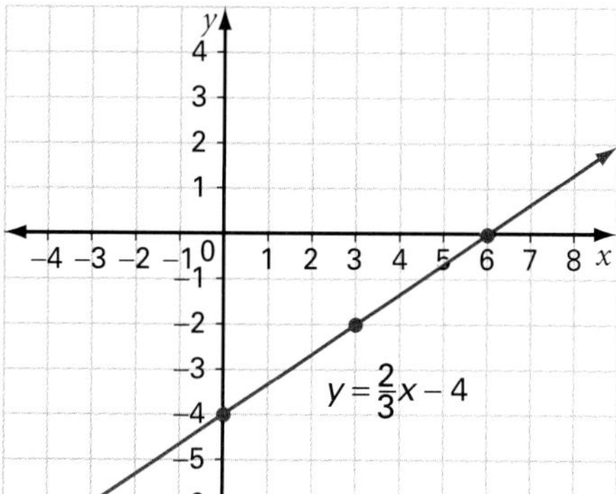


Notice that, by choosing values of $x$ carefully, you avoid plotting points involving fractions.

# EXAMPLE 3

## Graphing a Linear Relation Using a Graphing Calculator

The surface area of a cylindrical can is given by: $S = 2\pi rh + 2\pi r^2$.
If the radius is fixed at 2.5 cm, then the equation becomes
$S = 2\pi(2.5)h + 2\pi(2.5)^2$
or, to one decimal place,
$S = 15.7h + 3.9$

**a)** Use a graphing calculator to graph this linear relation.
**b)** Adjust the window settings to produce a clear graph.
**c)** Determine the surface area when the height is 4 cm.

**Make Connections**

You worked with the formula for surface area of a cylinder in section 3.4.

Refer to the Technology Appendix for help with **Graphing Relations and Equations**.

## Solution

**a)** Press the Y= key.
Check that all highlighted Plots (at the top of the screen) are turned off, by placing the cursor on them and pressing ENTER.
Clear any equations, by placing the cursor on them and pressing CLEAR.

GRAPHING CALCULATOR
Plot1 Plot2 Plot3
\Y1=
\Y2=
\Y3=
\Y4=
\Y5=
\Y6=
\Y7=

Instead of *S*, you will use Y. Instead of *h* you will use X.
Beside Y1, enter 15.7X + 3.9.

GRAPHING CALCULATOR
Plot1 Plot2 Plot3
\Y1=15.7X+3.9
\Y2=
\Y3=
\Y4=
\Y5=
\Y6=
\Y7=

From the ZOOM menu, choose **6:ZStandard**.
The line should appear.

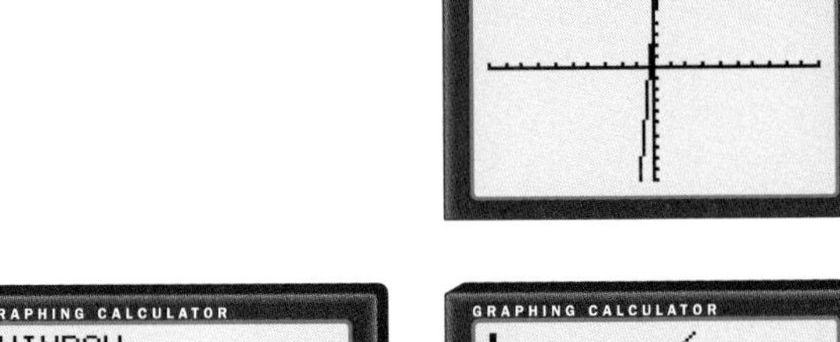


**b)** To get a better view, press WINDOW and set as shown.

Press GRAPH.

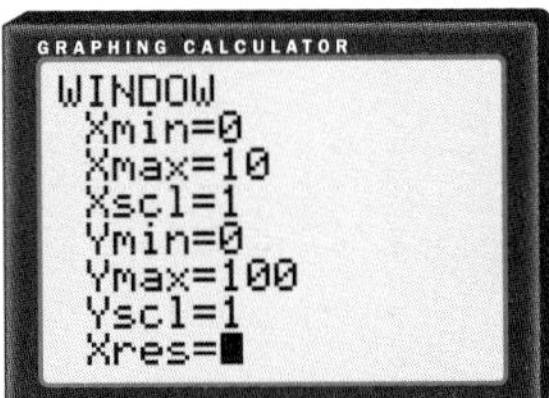


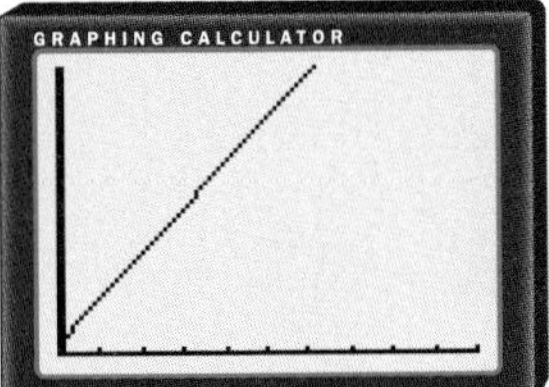

**c)** To find the surface area of the cylinder when the height is 4 cm, you can use the trace feature. Press TRACE.
Coordinates should appear that give the position of the cursor.

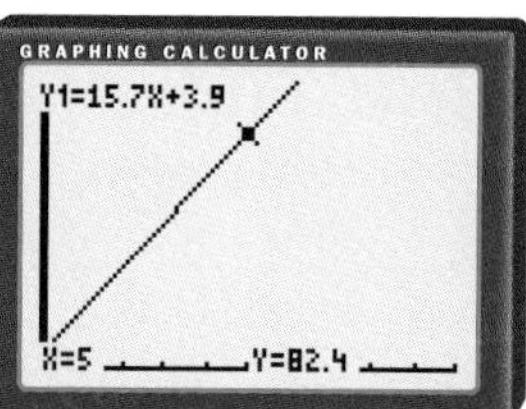


Use the left and right arrow keys to move the cursor until the $x$-coordinate reads approximately 4.

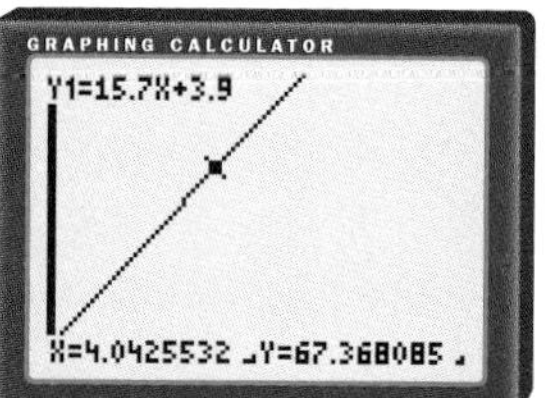


You can zoom in to achieve greater accuracy:

- From the ZOOM menu, choose **2:Zoom In** and press ENTER.
- Press TRACE.
- Use the cursor keys to move closer to X = 4.
- Repeat as necessary.

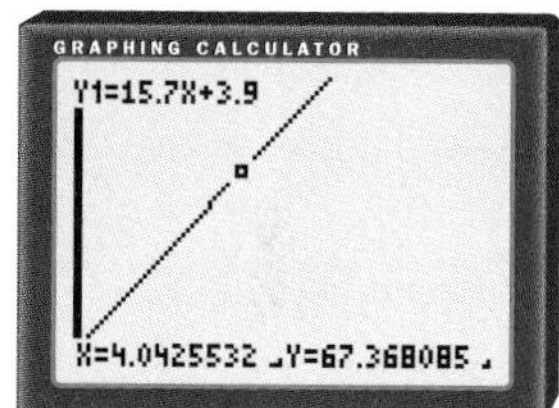


When the height is 4 cm, the surface area is approximately 67 cm$^2$.

## Key Concepts

- You can use a table of values to graph a linear relation.
- Substitute easy values of $x$ into the equation to determine the corresponding $y$-values.
- By selecting $x$-values carefully, you can make calculations involving fractions easier.
- The coordinates of any point on the line satisfy the equation.

## Discuss the Concepts

**1.** **a)** Why is it possible to choose any $x$-values you wish when making a table of values for a linear equation?
**b)** Why should you choose easy values of $x$?

**2.** For each linear relation, suggest values of $x$ that should be used in making a table of values. Explain your choices.

**a)** $y = \frac{3}{2}x - 4$ **b)** $y = -\frac{3}{4}x + 1$

## PRACTISE

*For help with questions 1 and 2, refer to Example 1.*

1. For each linear relation, copy and complete the table of values. Then, graph the line.

   a) $y = 2x$  b) $y = x + 3$  c) $y = -x$

| x | y |
|---|---|
| 0 | |
| 1 | |
| 2 | |

2. For each linear relation, copy and complete the table of values. Then, graph the line.

   a) $y = \frac{1}{2}x + 3$

| x | y |
|---|---|
| 0 | |
| 2 | |
| 4 | |

   b) $y = \frac{2}{5}x - 4$

| x | y |
|---|---|
| 0 | |
| 5 | |
| 10 | |

## APPLY THE CONCEPTS

*For help with questions 3 to 5, refer to Example 2.*

3. For each linear relation, complete a table of values using at least three ordered pairs. Graph the line.

   a) $y = 2x + 1$  b) $y = 3x - 4$  c) $y = 5x$

   d) $y = -2x$  e) $y = 4x - 1$  f) $y = -x - 5$

4. For each linear relation, choose three easy $x$-values to use to make a table of values. Then, graph the line.

   a) $y = \frac{1}{3}x$  b) $y = \frac{3}{2}x + 1$  c) $y = \frac{3}{4}x - 2$

   d) $y = -\frac{1}{2}x$  e) $y = -\frac{3}{5}x$  f) $y = -\frac{4}{5}x + 5$

5. Graph each line.

   a) $y = -2x + 5$  b) $y = 7x - 2$  c) $y = \frac{2}{5}x - 8$

   d) $y = -\frac{5}{6}x + 4$  e) $y = 1.5x - 4$  f) $y = -0.75x$

To zoom in to a point that is *outside* of the viewing window
- zoom out first
- move the cursor close to the desired point
- zoom in

*Use a graphing calculator for questions 6 and 7. For help refer to Example 3.*

6. a) Graph the line $y = 3x + 2$.

   b) Use the TRACE and ZOOM features to determine which of the following points are on this line.

   P(0, 2)  Q(0, −1)  R(−4, −10)  S(2.5, 9.4)

Use the (−) key to enter leading negative signs.

7. a) Graph the line $y = -2x - 5$.
   b) Use the TRACE and ZOOM features to determine which of the following points are on this line:
   V(2, −9) W(−2, −1) X(5.5, −15) Y(−6.6, −17.2)

**Chapter Problem**

8. "Ally's Trolley" is Ally's first custom event. In this event, Ally rides her skateboard down a narrow 5-m inclined bar. The wheels of the skateboard straddle on either side of the bar. Points are awarded for style and grace. Ally sets the angle of the bar so that she slides at a constant speed. Ally's position on the bar is given by the relation $P = -t + 5$, where $t$ is time in seconds and $P$ is position in metres.

   $P = 5$

   $P = 0$

   a) Create a table of values and graph this relation.
   b) How long will Ally be on the bar? Explain.

9. **Thinking/Inquiry/Problem Solving** The table shows points that satisfy the linear relation $y = 3$.

| x | y |
|---|---|
| 0 | 3 |
| 1 | 3 |
| 2 | 3 |

   a) Use these ordered pairs to graph the line.
   b) Describe this line.
   c) Create a table of values for the linear relation $y = -2$.
   d) Graph the line $y = -2$.
   e) Describe what the graph of the line $y = 10$ looks like.
   f) What is the equation that describes the $x$-axis?
   g) Check your answers to parts d), e), and f) using a graphing calculator.

10. **Thinking/Inquiry/Problem Solving** The table shows points that satisfy the linear relation $x = -1$.

| x | y |
|---|---|
| −1 | 0 |
| −1 | 1 |
| −1 | 2 |

   a) Use these ordered pairs to graph the line.
   b) Describe this line.
   c) Create a table of values for the linear relation $x = 4$.
   d) Graph the line $x = 4$.
   e) What is the equation that describes the $y$-axis?
   f) Describe what the graph of the line $x = -3$ looks like.

# 6.4 Graphing Non-Linear Relations

A farmer has a fenced pen, in the shape of a square, for his sheep. He is going to purchase more sheep and needs to double the area of the sheep pen. Which will be cheaper:

- expanding the existing pen? or
- building a second pen the same size as the first?

After completing the **Discover**, you will be able to answer this question.

## DISCOVER A

### Perimeter and Area: Constructing a Non-Linear Graph

***Using The Geometer's Sketchpad®***

1. Open *The Geometer's Sketchpad®* and begin a new sketch.

2. a) From the **Graph** menu, choose **Show Grid**.
   b) From the **Graph** menu, choose **Snap Points**.

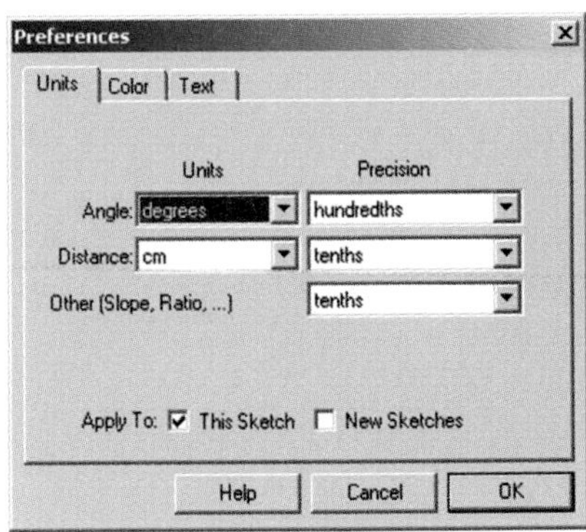


3. a) From the **Edit** menu, choose **Preferences**.
   b) Choose the **Units** tab.
   c) Set the preferences as shown.
   d) Click **OK**.

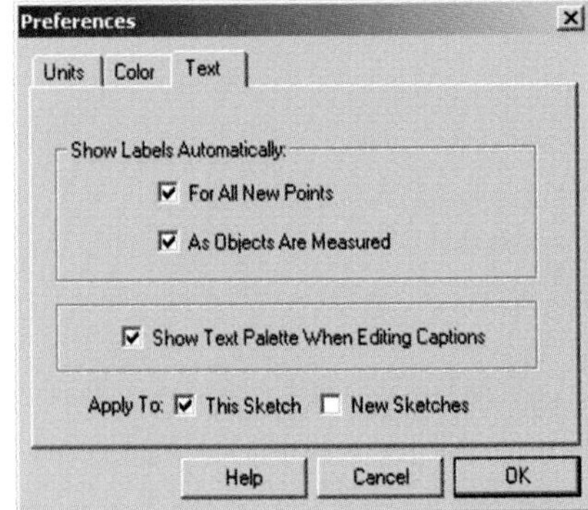


4. a) From the **Edit** menu, choose **Preferences**.
   b) Choose the **Text** tab.
   c) Set the preferences as shown.
   d) Click OK.

5. Create a 1 cm by 1 cm square near the top-left corner of the screen:

a) Plot points A, B, C, and D as shown.

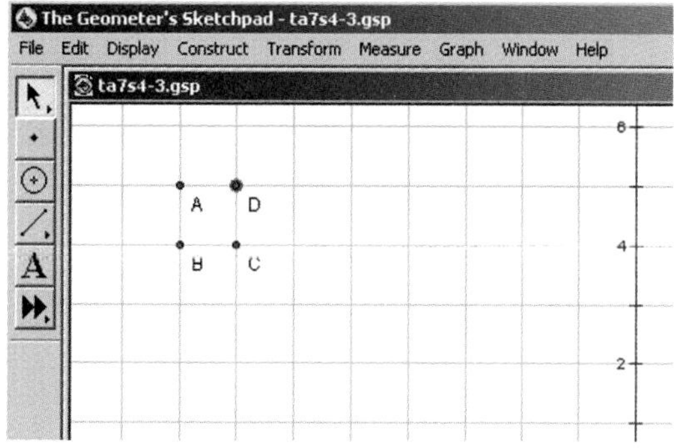


**Be careful to plot the points in a clockwise or counterclockwise order to get a square.**

b) Select all four points by using the **Arrow Tool**. Click and drag to form a dashed box around the four points.

c) From the **Construct** menu, choose **Segments**. A square should appear.

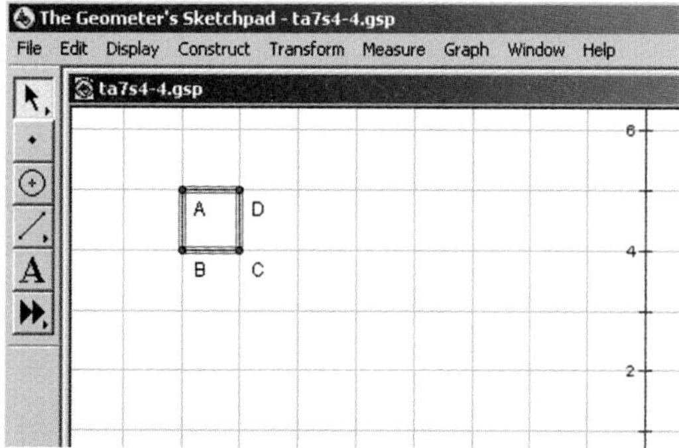


6. Measure the perimeter and area of the square:

a) Select, in order, A, B, C, and D. From the **Construct** menu, choose **Quadrilateral Interior**.

b) From the **Measure** menu, choose **Perimeter**.

c) Select the interior of the square. From the **Measure** menu, choose **Area**.

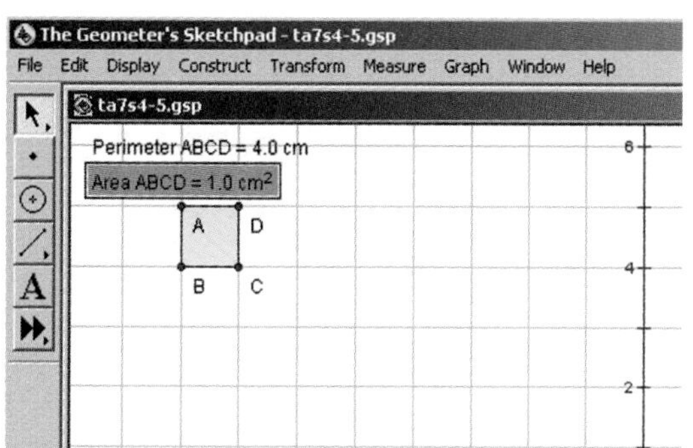


**Remember to deselect before making new selections.**

7. Create a table of values for perimeter and area:
   a) Select, in order, the perimeter measure and the area measure.
   b) From the **Graph** menu, choose **Tabulate.** A table should appear.
   c) Click and drag the table to a convenient location. Double-click in the table to make an entry.

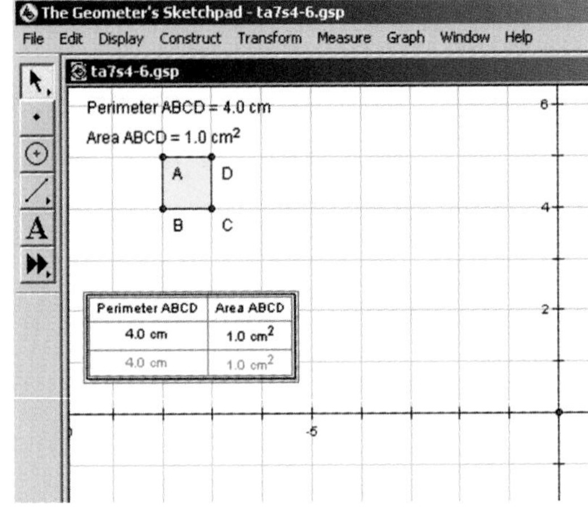


8. If you were to double the side length of the square, predict what will happen to
   a) the perimeter
   b) the area

9. a) Click and drag the points to form a 2 cm by 2 cm square.
   b) Double-click in the table to enter the new perimeter and area.
   c) Compare these values with your predictions in step 8. Were you correct? Explain.

10. a) Repeat step 9 for several different-size squares.
    b) Examine the data in the table. What do you think a graph of perimeter versus area will look like?

11. a) Create a scatter plot of perimeter versus area:
       • Select the table.
       • From the **Graph** menu, choose **Plot Table Data.**
    b) Click and drag the "handle points" near the origin so that you can see all the points.
    c) Describe the pattern formed by the points. Compare this graph to your prediction in step 10. Were you correct? Explain.

12. a) Based on this investigation, if you were to double the perimeter of a square pen, which would you expect the new area to be?
       • less than double the original area
       • double the original area
       • more than double the original area
    b) Explain your choice.

# DISCOVER B

- centimetre grid paper
- ruler

## Perimeter and Area: Constructing a Non-Linear Graph

***Using Paper and Pencil***

1. Use a blank sheet of centimetre grid paper. Draw a 1 cm by 1 cm square.

2. Create a table of values for perimeter and area.

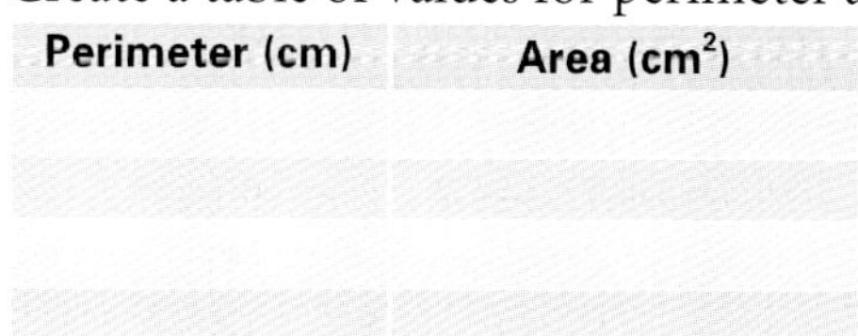

| Perimeter (cm) | Area (cm$^2$) |
|---|---|
| | |
| | |
| | |
| | |

Record the values for perimeter and area of the first square.
- Apply $P = 4s$ for the perimeter, where $s$ is the side length.
- Apply $A = s^2$ for the area.

3. If you were to double the side length of the square, predict what will happen to
   **a)** the perimeter
   **b)** the area

4. **a)** Draw a 2 cm by 2 cm square.
   **b)** Calculate the perimeter and area. Record these values in your table.
   **c)** Compare these values with your predictions in step 3. Were you correct? Explain.

5. **a)** Repeat step 4 for several different-size squares.
   **b)** Examine the data in your table. What do you think a graph of area versus perimeter will look like?

6. **a)** Create a scatter plot of perimeter versus area.
   **b)** Describe the pattern formed by the points. Compare this graph to your prediction. Were you correct? Explain.

7. **a)** Based on this investigation, if you were to double the perimeter of a square pen, which would you expect the new area to be?
   - less than double the original area
   - double the original area
   - more than double the original area

   **b)** Explain your choice.

Area versus perimeter is a non-linear relation. The graph is not a straight line. In this case, the graph is a curve.

## EXAMPLE 1

### Graphing a Non-Linear Relation

Use the relation $y = x^2$.

**a)** Complete the table of values.

| $x$ | $y$ |
|---|---|
| 0 | |
| 1 | |
| 2 | |
| 3 | |

**b)** Plot the points on a graph with four quadrants. Join them with a smooth curve. Describe the graph.

**c)** Add some negative values of $x$ to the table, and calculate $y$.

**d)** Plot these points. Join all the points with a smooth curve. Describe the graph.

### Solution

**a)** Substitute $x = 0$.

$y = x^2$

$y = (0)^2$

$y = 0$

This means that (0, 0) is on the curve.

Verify, by substitution, that (1, 1), (2, 4), and (3, 9) are also on the curve.

Enter these values into the table.

| $x$ | $y$ |
|---|---|
| 0 | 0 |
| 1 | 1 |
| 2 | 4 |
| 3 | 9 |

**b)** Plot the points. Join them with a smooth curve.

The graph curves upward as you move to the right.

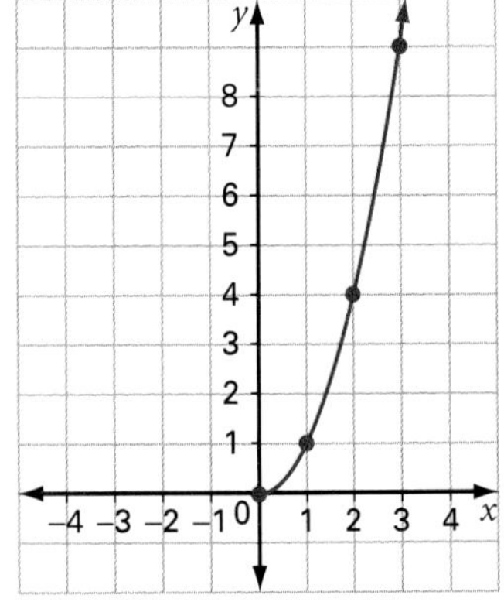

**c)** Choose $x = -1$, $x = -2$, $x = -3$.
Substitute $x = -1$.
$y = x^2$
$y = (-1)^2$ **Substitute integers carefully.**
$y = 1$ **Take care with integer calculations: $(-1)^2 = (-1) \times (-1)$**

This means that $(-1, 1)$ is on the curve.

Similarly, $(-2, 4)$ and $(-3, 9)$ are on the curve.

Enter these values in the table.

| *x* | *y* |
|---|---|
| −1 | 1 |
| −2 | 4 |
| −3 | 9 |

**d)** Plot the points. Join them with a smooth curve.

The graph is a U-shaped curve. The graph curves upward on either side of the origin.

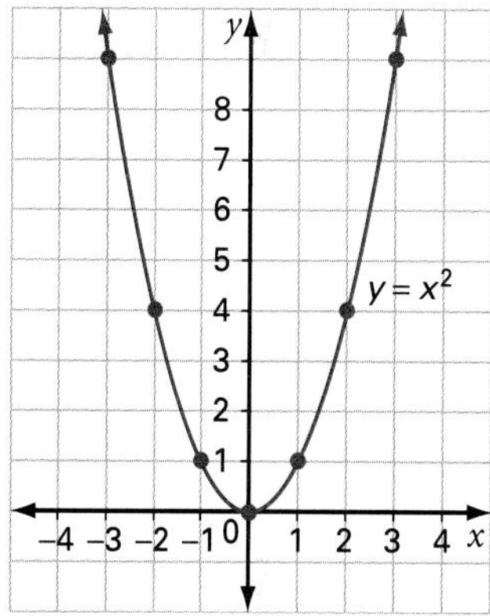


**Did You Know?**

This shape of graph is called a parabola.

When graphing non-linear relations, use both positive and negative values of $x$ to get a good idea of the shape of the graph. Sometimes, you need to use more points in the table to see the shape.

## EXAMPLE 2

### Graphing Non-Linear Relations Using a Graphing Calculator

Graph each relation, using a graphing calculator. Use a standard viewing window. Classify the graph as linear or non-linear.

**a)** $y = 0.5x^3$ **b)** $y = -x^2 + 5$

### Solution

Check that you have a standard viewing window.
Press WINDOW.
If you do not see the window shown, press ZOOM and choose **6:ZStandard**.

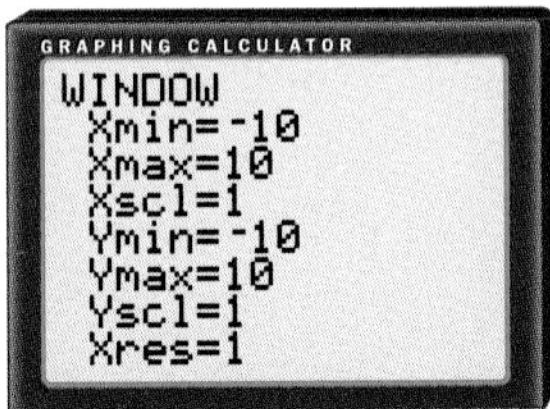


**a)** Use the equation editor to enter the equation $y = 0.5x^3$.
Press Y=.
Enter 0.5 X,T,θ,n ^ 3.

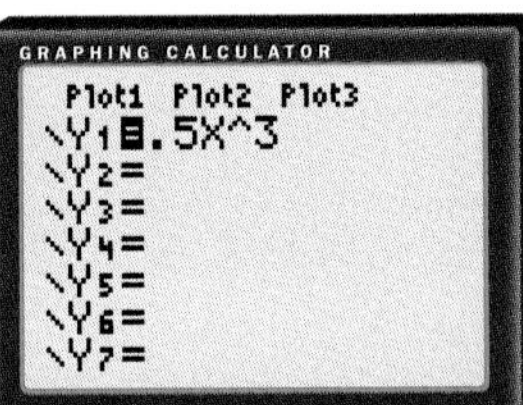


Press GRAPH.
A curved line appears.

Since the graph is not a straight line, the relation is non-linear.

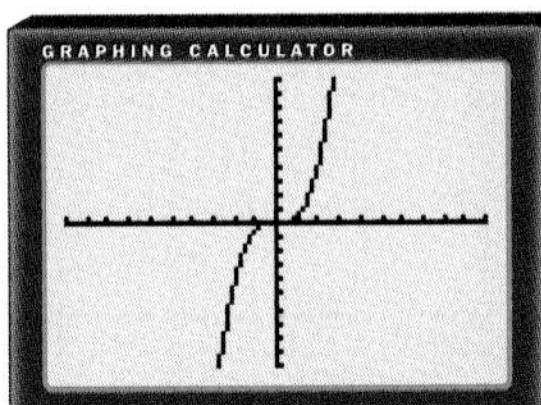


**b)** Clear the previous equation as follows.
Press Y=, and with the cursor on the Y1 = line, press CLEAR.

Enter (-) X,T,θ,n $x^2$ + 5.

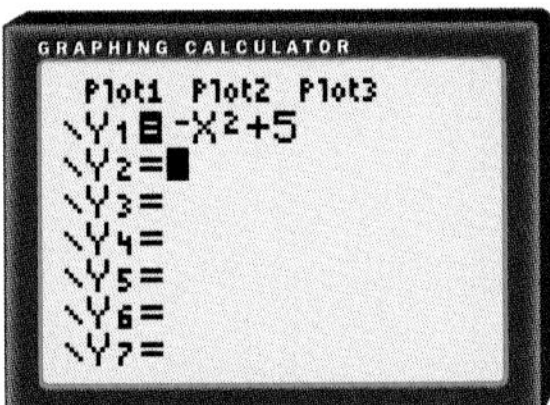


Press GRAPH.

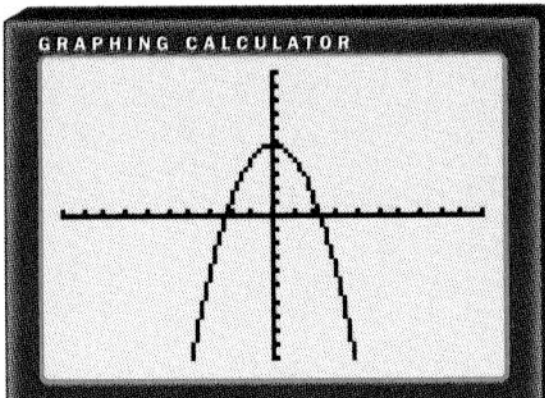


Since the graph is not a straight line, the relation is non-linear.

## Key Concepts

- The graph of a non-linear relation is not a straight line.
- Use both positive and negative values of $x$ when plotting a non-linear relation. You may need to use more points to see the shape.

## Discuss the Concepts

1. Why is it important to use both positive and negative values when graphing a non-linear relation?
2. Classify the following as linear or non-linear.

a) 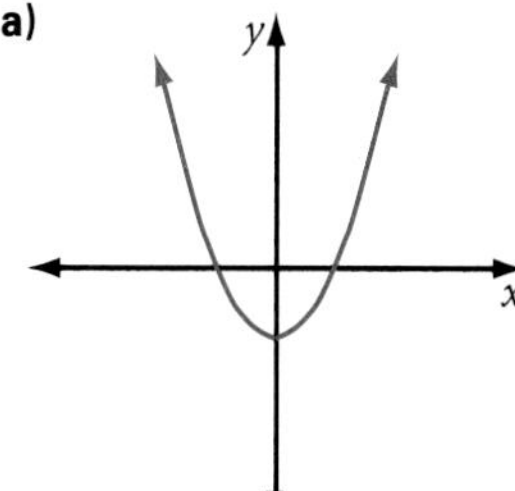


b) 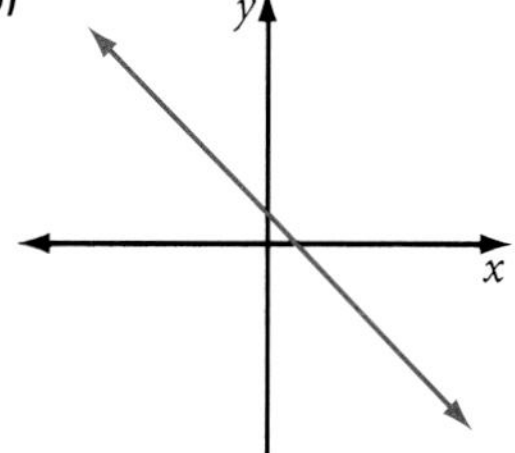


c) 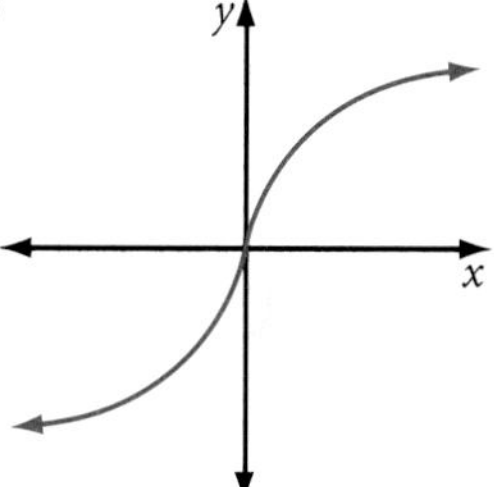


## Practise

***For help with questions 1 and 2, refer to Example 1.***

1. For each non-linear relation, copy and complete the table of values. Then, graph the relation.

a) $y = x^2 + 1$ b) $y = x^3$ c) $y = -x^2$

| $x$ | $y$ |
|---|---|
| 0 | |
| 1 | |
| 2 | |
| 3 | |
| −1 | |
| −2 | |
| −3 | |

2. For each non-linear relation, make a table of values using at least three positive and three negative values of $x$. Then, graph the relation.

a) $y = x^2 - 2$ b) $y = x^2 + 3$ c) $y = x^3 + 2$
d) $y = -x^2 - 3$ e) $y = -x^2 + 5$ f) $y = -x^3$

***For help with question 3, refer to Example 2.***

3. Graph each non-linear relation. You may use a graphing calculator.

a) $y = 2x^2$ b) $y = -3x^2 + 5$ c) $y = -\frac{1}{2}x^3$

## Apply the Concepts

4. **Communication** Vina has a square pen, 20 m by 20 m, for her pigs. She is going to purchase more pigs and needs to double the area of the pen. Vina is considering two options
   - expanding the existing pen, or
   - building a second pen the same size as the first

   What advice would you give to Vina regarding the cost of fencing material? Apply the perimeter-area relationship to explain your reasoning. Hint: Refer to your results from the **Discover** in this section.

5. **Application** Investigate the relationship between the area of a circle and the radius. Use either *The Geometer's Sketchpad®*, or paper and pencil.
   a) Draw five circles with radius, 2 cm, 4, cm, 5 cm, 6 cm, and 7 cm.
   b) Determine the area of each circle. Record your results in a table.

   | Radius (cm) | Area (cm$^2$) |
   |---|---|
   | | |
   | | |

   c) Plot area versus radius. Join the points.
   d) Classify the relation as linear or non-linear.
   e) Use the graph to estimate the area of a circle with radius 12 cm.
   f) Check your answer to part e) by applying the formula $A = \pi r^2$.
   g) Use the graph to predict the radius of a circle whose area is 75 cm$^2$.

**Make Connections**

You worked with the formula for the area of a circle in Chapters 1 and 2. If you are not using *The Geometer's Sketchpad®* for question 5, use the formula $A = \pi r^2$.

6. **Application** When you drop an object, the speed with which it hits the ground depends on the height from which it was dropped. The relationship is $s = 4.4\sqrt{h}$, where $h$ is the height in metres and $s$ is the impact speed in metres per second.
   a) Copy and complete the table of values.

   | Height (m) | Impact Speed (m/s) |
   |---|---|
   | 1 | 4.4 |
   | 2 | 6.2 |
   | 3 | |
   | 4 | |
   | 5 | |
   | 6 | |

   b) Graph impact speed versus height. Join the points.
   c) Is this graph linear or non-linear?
   d) How fast will a rock hit the water if it is dropped from a bridge 3.5 m above a stream?
   e) How fast will a rock hit the ground if it is dropped from a height of 10 m?
   f) Will your answer to part e) be the same if you drop a styrofoam ball? Explain.

7. "Ally Oop" is one of Ally's custom events. In Ally Oop, Ally jumps over an obstacle using a ramp. Points are awarded for a boarder's maximum height and hang time (length of time in the air). Ally's height, $h$, at any time, $t$, is given by $h = -4.9t^2 + 3.5t$.

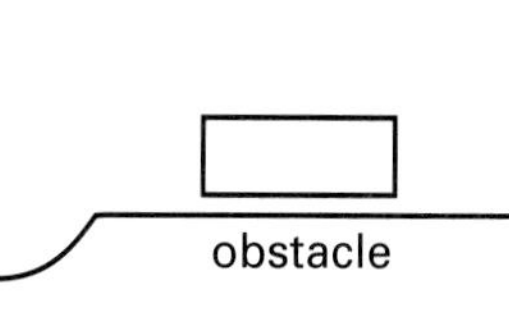


a) Copy and complete the table of values.
b) Graph height versus time. Join the points with a smooth curve.
c) Classify this relation as linear or non-linear.
d) Use the graph to estimate Ally's maximum height.
e) Use the graph to estimate Ally's hang time.

| Time (s) | Height (m) |
|---|---|
| 0 | 0 |
| 0.2 | 0.5 |
| 0.4 | |
| 0.6 | |
| 0.8 | |
| 1.0 | |

**Materials**
- TI-83 Plus graphing calculator
- CBR™
- link cable
- ball (e.g. basketball or volleyball)

C 8. **Ball-Bounce Investigation** In this investigation, you will drop a ball from a height of 1.5 m, and then measure the maximum height after each bounce. Work with a partner.

a) Predict what a graph of bounce height versus bounce number would look like. Explain your reasoning.
b) Use the Ball Bounce program in the calculator using these steps.
   - Turn the calculator on.
   - Press (APPS).
   - Select **2:CBL/CBR.**
   - Press (ENTER).
   - Select **3:RANGER.**
   - Press (ENTER).
   - Select **3:APPLICATIONS.**
   - Select **1:METERS.**
   - Select **3:BALL BOUNCE.**

d) Firmly connect the calculator to the CBR™ with a link cable. Follow the instructions on the calculator screen to collect your data.
e) Use the **TRACE** feature to measure the maximum height of each bounce. Record your results in a table.
f) Graph maximum height versus bounce number. How does this graph compare with your prediction?
g) Based on your graph, approximately how many bounces will it take for the ball to stop bouncing? Explain.

| Bounce Number | Maximum Height (m) |
|---|---|
| 0 | |
| 1 | |
| 2 | |
| 3 | |
| 4 | |
| 5 | |

# 6.5 First Differences

The table of values for a linear relation has a pattern. If the values of *x* go up by a constant amount, you can tell whether a relation is linear by examining the pattern in the corresponding *y*-values. You will see how the pattern works in the following **Discover**.

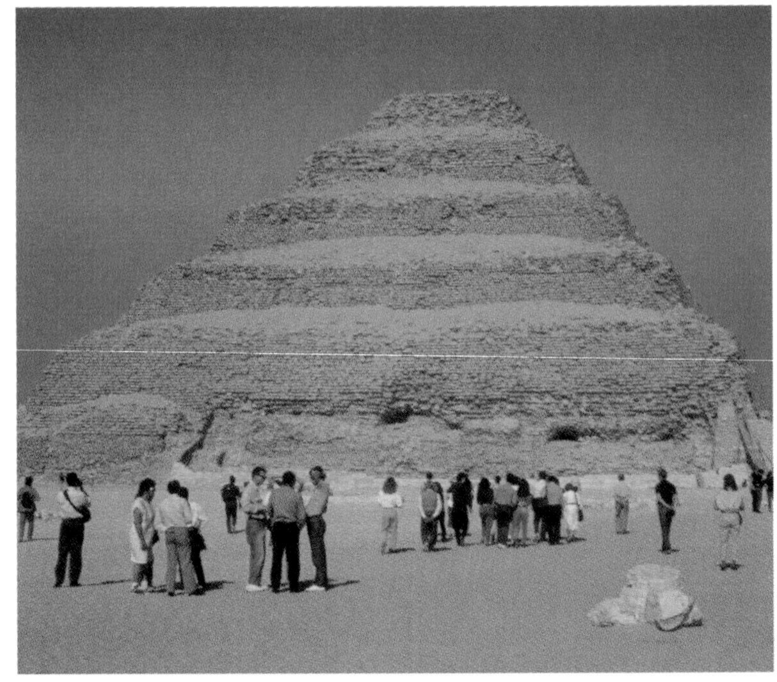

## DISCOVER

### Finding Patterns in First Differences

1. Use the relation $y = 2x + 1$.
   a) Copy and complete the table of values.
   b) Graph the relation.
   c) Classify the relation as linear or non-linear.
   d) Can you see a pattern in the *y*-values? If so, describe the pattern.

| *x* | *y* |
|---|---|
| 0 | 1 |
| 1 | 3 |
| 2 | 5 |
| 3 | |
| 4 | |

2. Add a third column to your table, to record the change in *y*. Calculate each entry by subtracting consecutive values of *y*. For example, the first value is $3 - 1 = 2$.

| *x* | *y* | Change in *y* | |
|---|---|---|---|
| 0 | 1 | | |
| 1 | 3 | 2 | ← 3 – 1 = 2 |
| 2 | 5 | | ← 5 – 3 |
| 3 | | | |
| 4 | | | |

The values in the third column are called **first differences**.

3. What do you notice about the values in the third column?

4. Use the relation $y = x^2 + 2$.

| $x$ | $y$ |
|---|---|
| −3 | 11 |
| −2 | 6 |
| −1 | 3 |
| 0 | |
| 1 | |
| 2 | |
| 3 | |

a) Copy and complete the table of values.
b) Graph the relation.
c) Classify the relation as linear or non-linear.
d) Can you see a pattern in the $y$-values? If so, describe the pattern.

5. a) Add a column to your table from step 4. Calculate each entry by subtracting consecutive values of $y$.

| $x$ | $y$ | First Differences | |
|---|---|---|---|
| −3 | 11 | | |
| −2 | 6 | −5 | ← 6 − 11 = −5 |
| −1 | 3 | | ← 3 − 6 |
| 0 | | | |
| 1 | | | |
| 2 | | | |
| 3 | | | |

b) Describe what you notice about the values in the third column for this relation.

6. Make a prediction about what is true for the first differences of
a) a linear relation
b) a non-linear relation

7. For each linear relation below
- create a table of values
- graph the relation
- add a third column to the table and calculate the first differences
- describe any pattern that you see in the $y$-values

a) $y = 3x$
b) $y = -x + 2$

8. For each non-linear relation below
- create a table of values
- graph the relation
- add a third column to the table and calculate the first differences
- describe any pattern that you see in the $y$-values

a) $y = 2x^2$
b) $y = x^2 - 3x$

9. Compare your results from steps 7 and 8. Do your results agree with the predictions you made in step 6? Explain.

For a table of values in which $x$-values increase by a constant, you can calculate first differences by subtracting consecutive values of $y$.

- If the first differences are constant, then the relation is linear.
- If the first differences are not constant, then the relation is non-linear.

## EXAMPLE 1

### First Differences of a Linear Relation

If you ride the "Drop Zone" at Paramount Canada's Wonderland, you will free-fall toward the ground at speeds in excess of 100 km/h, or 28 m/s. The table gives the riders' speed, before the brakes are applied.

| Time (s) | Speed (m/s) |
|---|---|
| 0 | 0 |
| 0.5 | 4.9 |
| 1.0 | 9.8 |
| 1.5 | 14.7 |
| 2.0 | 19.6 |
| 2.5 | 24.5 |

**a)** Calculate the first differences for speed.

**b)** Classify the relation as linear or non-linear.

**c)** Create a scatter plot of speed versus time.

**d)** If the brakes are applied once riders reach a speed of 28 m/s, how long are the riders in free-fall?

### Solution

**a)** The independent variable, time, increases in constant steps of 0.5 s. You can see if a pattern exists in the first differences of the dependent variable, speed. Use a third column.

| Time (s) | Speed (m/s) | First Differences |
|---|---|---|
| 0 | 0 | |
| 0.5 | 4.9 | 4.9 |
| 1.0 | 9.8 | 4.9 |
| 1.5 | 14.7 | 4.9 |
| 2.0 | 19.6 | 4.9 |
| 2.5 | 24.5 | 4.9 |

← **The first differences are the change in speed.**

← **4.9 − 0 = 4.9**

← **9.8 − 4.9 = 4.9**

**b)** The first differences are constant. This is a linear relation.

c)

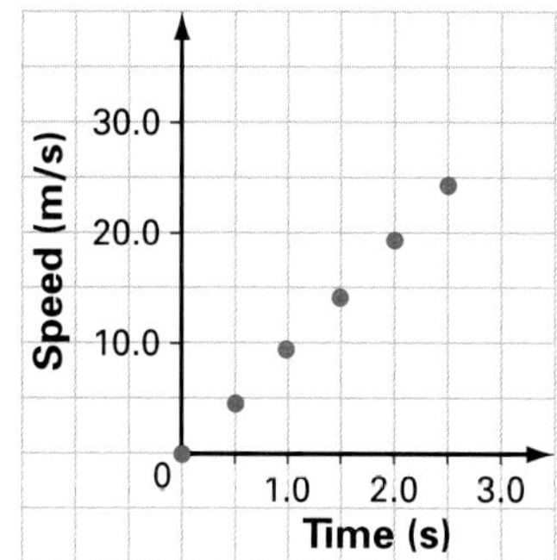


d) To estimate the elapsed time when the riders reach 28 m/s, extend the graph and apply extrapolation.

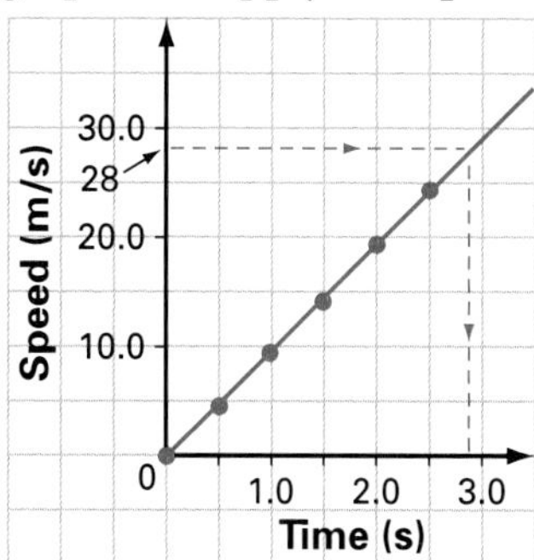


From the graph, the riders are in free-fall for about 2.8 s.

For help, refer to the Technology Appendix items on **Entering Data in Lists** and **Clearing Lists**.

You can use a graphing calculator to calculate first differences.

Using the table editor, enter the table of values into L1 and L2:

- Press (STAT).
- Choose **1:Edit**.
- Clear any existing lists by placing the cursor on the list header and pressing (CLEAR).
- Enter the time values in the L1 column.
- Enter the speed values in the L2 column.

Generate the first differences for speed:

- Place the cursor over L3.
- Press (2nd) [LIST].
- From the **OPS** menu, choose **7:ΔList(**.
- Press (2nd) **[L2]** ( ) ).
- Press (ENTER).

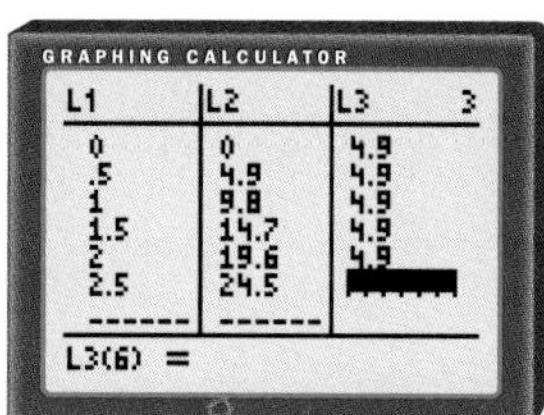

## Example 2

### First Differences of a Non-Linear Relation

The growing number of students at a new school is shown.

| Year | Students |
|---|---|
| 1998 | 200 |
| 1999 | 320 |
| 2000 | 450 |
| 2001 | 600 |
| 2002 | 780 |

**a)** Calculate the first differences for students.

**b)** Classify the relation as linear or non-linear.

**c)** Create a scatter plot of students versus year.

**d)** Estimate the number of students in 2003, based on this growth pattern.

### Solution

**a)** The independent variable, year, increases in constant steps of one year. So the first differences of the dependent variable, students, can be used.

| Year | Students | First Differences |
|---|---|---|
| 1998 | 200 | |
| 1999 | 320 | 120 |
| 2000 | 450 | 130 |
| 2001 | 600 | 150 |
| 2002 | 780 | 180 |

← 320 − 200 = 120

**b)** The first differences are not constant. This relation is non-linear.

**c)**

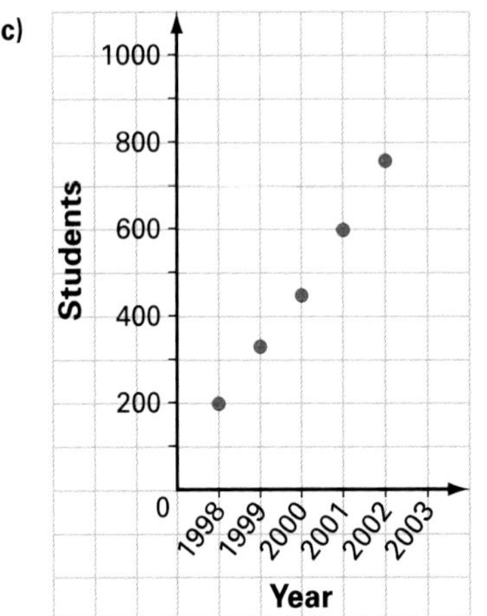


**d)**

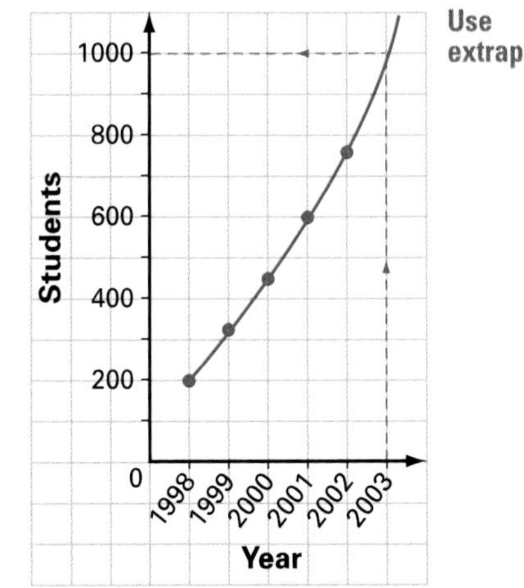


Use extrapolation.

From the graph, provided the same growth pattern continues, the number of students in 2003 would be about 1000.

## Key Concepts

- To find a pattern in first differences, the values of the independent variable must change by a constant amount.
- First differences of a linear relation are constant.
- First differences of a non-linear relation are not constant.

## Discuss the Concepts

1. Is it possible to use first differences to tell whether each relation is linear or non-linear? Explain why or why not.

a)

| $x$ | $y$ |
|---|---|
| 1 | 1 |
| 2 | 3 |
| 5 | 8 |
| 7 | 15 |
| 10 | 18 |

b)

| $x$ | $y$ |
|---|---|
| 1 | 2 |
| 2 | 3 |
| 3 | 4 |
| 4 | 5 |
| 5 | 6 |

2. A traveller's distance is related to time by the equation $D = 95t$.
   a) Is this a linear or a non-linear relation? Explain why.
   b) What is true about the first differences for distance? Explain why.
   c) What can you conclude about the traveller's speed?

## Practise

1. Decide whether you can use first differences to tell whether each relation is linear or non-linear. Explain why or why not.

a)

| $x$ | $y$ |
|---|---|
| 1 | 2 |
| 2 | 4 |
| 3 | 8 |
| 4 | 16 |
| 5 | 32 |

b)

| $x$ | $y$ |
|---|---|
| 1 | 1 |
| 2 | 3 |
| 4 | 5 |
| 8 | 7 |
| 11 | 9 |

c)

| $x$ | $y$ |
|---|---|
| 2 | 4 |
| 4 | 5 |
| 6 | 6 |
| 8 | 7 |
| 10 | 8 |

*For help with questions 2–5, refer to Examples 1 and 2.*

**2.** Copy each table and include a third column to record first differences. Classify the relation as linear or non-linear.

**a)**

| $x$ | $y$ |
|---|---|
| 1 | 0 |
| 2 | 4 |
| 3 | 8 |
| 4 | 12 |
| 5 | 16 |

**b)**

| $x$ | $y$ |
|---|---|
| 0 | 0 |
| 2 | 4 |
| 4 | 16 |
| 6 | 36 |
| 8 | 64 |

**c)**

| $x$ | $y$ |
|---|---|
| −1 | 1 |
| 0 | −2 |
| 1 | −5 |
| 2 | −8 |
| 3 | −11 |

## Apply the Concepts

**3.** For each relation below
- complete a table of values, using at least four values for $x$
- calculate first differences
- classify the relation as linear or non-linear

**a)** $y = 3x - 5$ **b)** $y = x^2 + 2$ **c)** $y = x^3 - 6$ **d)** $y = -x + 6$

**B**

**4.** **Communication** Jay gets paid $8.50/h.

| Hours Worked | Pay ($) |
|---|---|
| 1 | |
| 2 | |
| 3 | |
| 4 | |

**a)** Copy and complete the table of values.
**b)** Calculate first differences.
**c)** Is pay versus hours worked a linear or a non-linear relation? Explain.
**d)** What is the relationship between the first differences and Jay's rate of pay?
**e)** Is this a direct or a partial variation? Explain.
**f)** Calculate the constant of variation. How is this related to Jay's rate of pay?

**5.** **Application** Automobile engines burn fuel less efficiently at greater speeds. The rate of fuel consumption for one vehicle is given.

| Speed (km/h) | Fuel Consumption (km/L) |
|---|---|
| 60 | 19 |
| 80 | 17 |
| 100 | 15 |
| 120 | 13 |
| 140 | 11 |

**a)** Calculate first differences. Classify the relation as linear or non-linear.
**b)** Model this relation with a graph or an equation.
**c)** Use your model to determine the fuel consumption when the car travels at 50 km/h.
**d)** What driving habits can you use in order to save money on fuel?

6. In the "Rocket Race" event, the two Extreme Boards finalists race a distance of 1 km. Ally's rival, Vanessa, likes to go at a constant speed. Ally prefers to increase her speed gradually throughout the race.

| Vanessa | |
|---|---|
| Time (s) | Distance (m) |
| 0 | 0 |
| 30 | 90 |
| 60 | 180 |
| 120 | 270 |
| 150 | 360 |
| 180 | 450 |

| Ally | |
|---|---|
| Time (s) | Distance (m) |
| 0 | 0 |
| 30 | 60 |
| 60 | 130 |
| 120 | 210 |
| 150 | 300 |
| 180 | 400 |

a) Calculate first differences for each relation.
b) Classify each relation as linear or non-linear.
c) Predict who you think will win the race.

7. As you free-fall through the "Drop Zone," the distance you travel keeps increasing at a faster and faster rate. The table below gives the distance fallen before the brakes are applied.

| Time (s) | Distance (m) |
|---|---|
| 0 | 0 |
| 0.5 | 1.23 |
| 1.0 | 4.90 |
| 1.5 | 11.03 |
| 2.0 | 19.60 |
| 2.5 | 30.63 |

a) Calculate the first differences for distance.
b) Classify the relation as linear or non-linear.
c) Create a scatter plot of distance versus time.
d) Compare the shape of this graph to the shape of the graph in **Example 1.** Why are they different?
e) If the brakes are applied after 2.8 s, use your graph to find approximately how far the riders have fallen at this point.

# 6.6 Characteristics of Linear and Non-Linear Relations

Linear and non-linear relations can be identified from the shape of their graphs. You can also recognize them by calculating first differences. You may have noticed that you can also tell whether a relation is linear or non-linear by looking at its equation.

## DISCOVER

### Exploring Linear and Non-Linear Equations Using a Graphing Calculator

In this investigation, you will examine linear and non-linear graphs in all four quadrants.

For help, refer to **Graphing Relations and Equations** in the Technology Appendix.

1. Graph each relation using a standard viewing window. Examine the graphs and classify each one as either linear or non-linear.
   **a)** $y = 2x - 3$ **b)** $y = -3x$ **c)** $y = 0.5x + 4$

2. Repeat step 1 for the following relations.
   **a)** $y = x^2$ **b)** $y = x^3 + x + 3$ **c)** $y = x - 0.5x^4 - 4$

3. Examine the two sets of equations in steps 1 and 2. Focus on the terms containing $x$. What feature seems to determine whether a relation will have a linear or non-linear graph?

4. Predict whether the following relations will have linear or non-linear graphs.
   **a)** $y = 3x^2$ **b)** $y = 5x - 2$ **c)** $y = -2x$
   **d)** $y = 3x - x^3$ **e)** $y = 0.2x^4$ **f)** $y = 0.6x + 3$

5. Test your predictions in step 4 by graphing each relation. Were your predictions correct? Explain.

6. Describe how, by looking at the equation, you can decide whether a relation is linear or non-linear.

You can usually tell if a relation is linear or non-linear by looking at the equation.

If the equation contains $x$ raised to some exponent other than 1, then the relation is non-linear.

## Example 1

### Identifying Linear and Non-Linear Relations From Equations

For each equation, classify the relation as linear or non-linear.

**a)** $y = 4x^2$
**b)** $y = -3x + 5$
**c)** $y = 7x - 3x^3$
**d)** $y = 2.5x + 8$

### Solution

**a)** $x$ is raised to the exponent 2. The relation is non-linear.
**b)** The exponent in $-3x$ is 1. The relation is linear.
**c)** $x$ appears twice. In one case, $x$ is raised to the exponent 3. The relation is non-linear.
**d)** $x$ is not raised to a power other than one. The relation is linear.

The graph of a linear relation is a straight line. The graph of a non-linear relation is not a line. It may be a curve.

## Example 2

### Identifying Linear and Non-Linear Relations From Graphs

Examine each graph and classify the relation as linear or non-linear.

**a)**

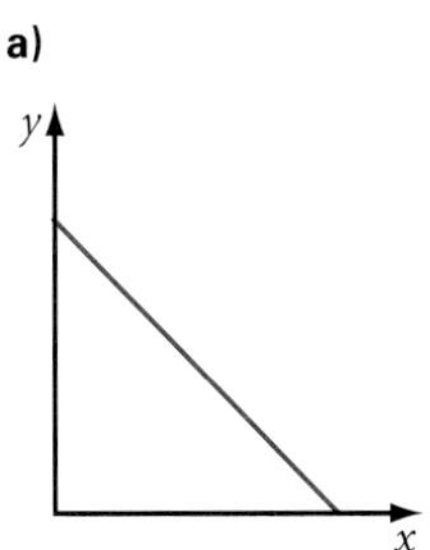


**b)**

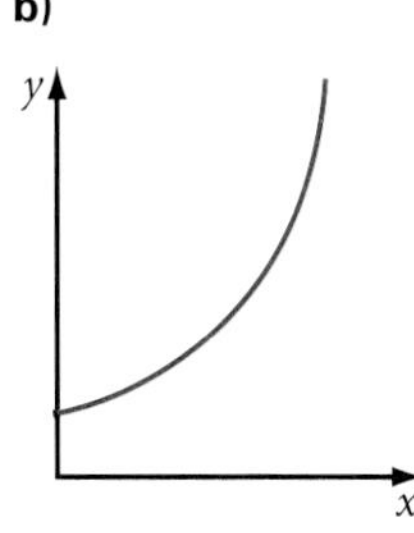


**c)**

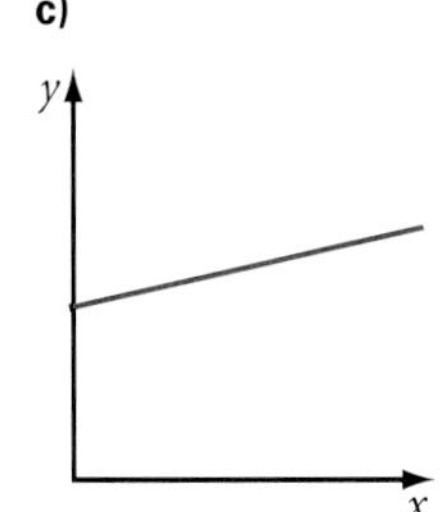


**d)**

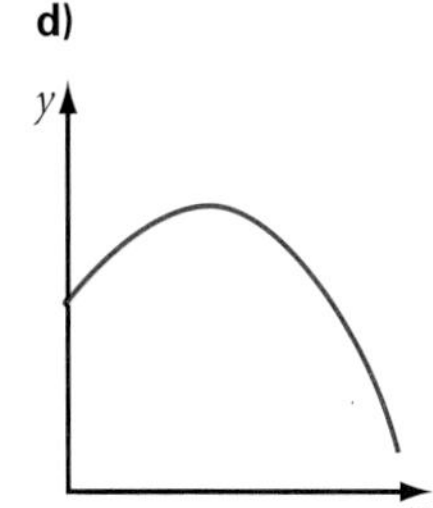


### Solution

The graphs in a) and c) are straight lines. These are linear relations. The graphs in b) and d) are curves. These are non-linear relations.

The first differences of a linear relation are constant. The first differences of a non-linear relation are not constant.

## EXAMPLE 3

### Identifying Linear and Non-Linear Relations Using First Differences

For each relation
- calculate the first differences
- classify the relation as linear or non-linear

a)

| Number | Cost ($) |
|---|---|
| 0 | 250 |
| 100 | 300 |
| 200 | 350 |
| 300 | 400 |
| 400 | 450 |

b)

| Cube Side-Length (cm) | Cube Volume (cm$^3$) |
|---|---|
| 1 | 1 |
| 2 | 8 |
| 3 | 27 |
| 4 | 64 |
| 5 | 125 |

### Solution

In each table, the independent variable is increasing at a constant rate, so first differences can be used. Add a third column. Subtract successive values of the dependent variable to find first differences.

a)

| Number | Cost ($) | First Differences | |
|---|---|---|---|
| 0 | 250 | | |
| 100 | 300 | 50 | ← 300 − 250 = 50 |
| 200 | 350 | 50 | |
| 300 | 400 | 50 | |
| 400 | 450 | 50 | |

The first differences are constant. This is a linear relation.

b)

| Cube Side-Length (cm) | Cube Volume (cm$^3$) | First Differences | |
|---|---|---|---|
| 1 | 1 | | |
| 2 | 8 | 7 | ← 8 − 1 = 7 |
| 3 | 27 | 19 | ← 27 − 8 = 19 |
| 4 | 64 | 37 | |
| 5 | 125 | 61 | |

The first differences are not constant. This is a non-linear relation.

## KEY CONCEPTS

The table summarizes the features of linear and non-linear relations of the form "$y$ = an expression involving $x$."

| | Graph | Equation | First Differences |
|---|---|---|---|
| **Linear relation** | straight line | $x$ is not raised to an exponent other than 1 | constant |
| **Non-linear relation** | not a straight line | $x$ is raised to an exponent other than 1 | not constant |

## DISCUSS THE CONCEPTS

1. Describe three ways to identify whether a relation is linear or non-linear.
2. Explain how you can recognize whether an equation represents a linear or a non-linear relation.
3. Describe the shape of the graph of a
   **a)** linear relation **b)** non-linear relation
4. How can you tell if a relation is linear or non-linear from looking at first differences?

## PRACTISE

***For help with question 1, refer to Example 1.***

1. Classify each equation as linear or non-linear.
   **a)** $y = -x^2$
   **b)** $y = 3x + 2$
   **c)** $2x - 3y = 15$
   **d)** $y = 2x^2$

***For help with question 2, refer to Example 2.***

2. Classify each graph as linear or non-linear.

**a)**
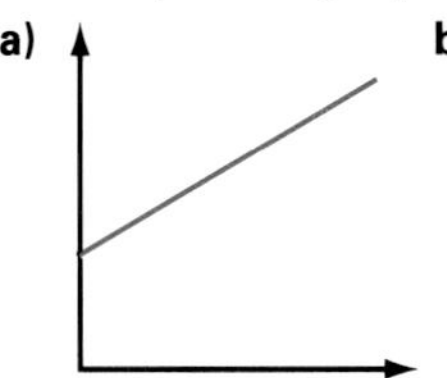

**b)**
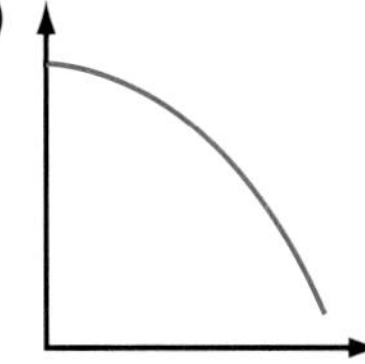

**c)**
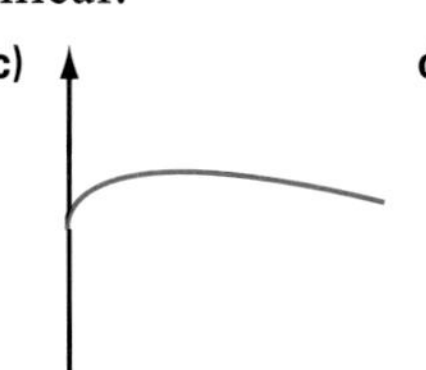

**d)**
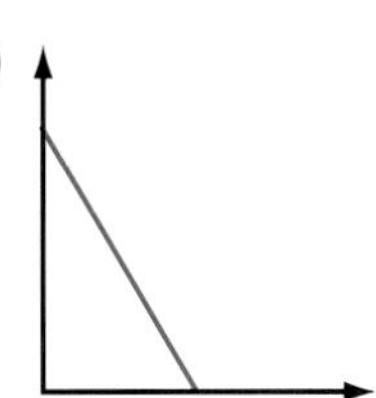

*For help with question 3, refer to Example 3.*

3. Use first differences to classify each relation as linear or non-linear.

a)

| x | y |
|---|---|
| 1 | 2 |
| 2 | 5 |
| 3 | 8 |
| 4 | 11 |
| 5 | 14 |

b)

| x | y |
|---|---|
| 2 | –1 |
| 4 | 0 |
| 6 | 1 |
| 8 | 4 |
| 10 | 9 |

c)

| x | y |
|---|---|
| –2 | 9 |
| 1 | 5 |
| 4 | 1 |
| 7 | –3 |
| 10 | –7 |

4. Examine the equation for each relation and classify it as linear or non-linear. Give reasons for your answer.
   **a)** $y = 3x - 7$ **b)** $y = 2x^2$ **c)** $y = -x^3$
   **d)** $y = -x + 3$ **e)** $y = x^2 - 2x + 1$ **f)** $y = x^2 - 5$

## APPLY THE CONCEPTS

5. The population growth of three towns is shown. Classify each growth rate as linear or non-linear.

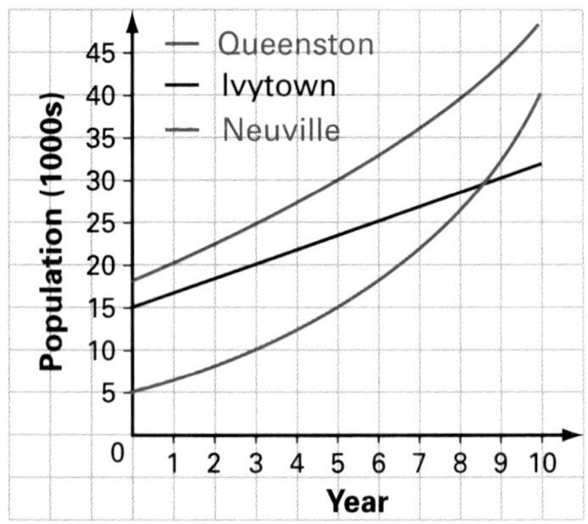


6. **Communication** Consider each relation below.
   - Classify it as linear or non-linear by looking at the equation.
   - Create a table of values using four points and determine the first differences. Do these results support how you classified the relation? Explain.

   **a)** $y = 3x - 1$ **b)** $y = x^2$ **c)** $y = -x + 2$

7. **Application** A skydiver is dropped from an airplane. Her distance fallen versus time is recorded.

| Time (s) | Distance (m) |
|---|---|
| 0 | 0 |
| 1 | 5 |
| 2 | 19 |
| 3 | 42 |
| 4 | 74 |
| 5 | 115 |

   **a)** Calculate first differences.
   **b)** Classify this relation as linear or non-linear. Explain.
   **c)** Predict the shape of the distance-time graph.
   **d)** Graph the relation and compare it with your prediction. Were you correct? Explain.

8. **Communication** Refer to Question 7. More data were gathered for the skydiver.

| Time (s) | Distance (m) |
|---|---|
| 10 | 330 |
| 11 | 371 |
| 12 | 412 |
| 13 | 453 |
| 14 | 494 |
| 15 | 535 |

   a) Calculate first differences.
   b) Classify this relation as linear or non-linear. Explain.
   c) Is this the same type of relation as found in question 7? Explain.
   d) Predict the shape of the distance-time graph for this set of data.
   e) Graph the relation and compare it with your prediction. Were you correct? Explain.
   f) What do you think happened to the skydiver to account for the two different distance-time relations?

**Chapter Problem**

9. Ally and Vanessa are competing in the final 1-km "Rocket Race" event to determine the Extreme Boards skateboarding champion.

| Vanessa | | Ally | |
|---|---|---|---|
| Time (s) | Distance (m) | Time (s) | Distance (m) |
| 0 | 0 | 0 | 0 |
| 30 | 90 | 30 | 60 |
| 60 | 180 | 60 | 130 |
| 90 | 270 | 90 | 210 |
| 120 | 360 | 120 | 300 |
| 150 | 450 | 150 | 400 |

   a) Predict who will win the race.
   b) Graph both relations on the same grid.
   c) Classify each graph as linear or non-linear.
   d) Use extrapolation to determine who will win the race.
   e) Compare this result to your earlier prediction. What assumptions must you make?

**C**

***Use a graphing calculator for question 10.***

10. **Thinking/Inquiry/Problem Solving** Consider the relation $y = 0.2x^3 + 8x$.
   a) Is this relation linear or non-linear? Explain.
   b) Graph this relation on a graphing calculator using a standard viewing window.
   c) Does this relation appear to be linear or non-linear? Does this agree with your answer to part a)? Explain.
   d) Change the viewing window settings. See if you can determine for certain whether the graph is linear or non-linear based on its appearance. State your conclusion.

# Review

## 6.1 Direct Variation, pages 224–231

1. Suzanne's pay for the past three weeks is shown.
   a) Determine Suzanne's hourly rate of pay for each week. What does this tell you about the relationship between pay and hours worked?
   b) Graph pay versus hours worked.
   c) Is this a direct variation? Explain how you can tell.
   d) Use the graph to find Suzanne's earnings if she works
      - 10 h
      - 25 h
   e) How many hours must Suzanne work to earn $250?

| Hours Worked | Pay ($) |
|---|---|
| 20 | 180 |
| 15 | 135 |
| 22 | 198 |

## 6.2 Partial Variation, pages 232–239

2. A car rental costs $60 per day plus $0.50 for each kilometre driven.
   a) Copy the table. Find the rental cost for one day for each distance.
   b) Graph cost versus distance.
   c) Is this a direct or a partial variation? Explain how you can tell.
   d) Determine the cost to drive 250 km.
   e) How far could you drive if you could afford $380 for the rental?

| Distance (km) | Cost ($) |
|---|---|
| 0 | |
| 50 | |
| 100 | |
| 200 | |
| 500 | |

3. Rydel works in a factory. Each week he earns $400 plus $5 for every machine part he assembles.
   a) Identify the fixed part and the variable part of this partial variation.
   b) Write an equation relating pay, $p$, and number of parts, $n$.
   c) Determine Rydel's pay for the week if he assembles
      - 32 parts
      - 50 parts

## 6.3 Graphing Linear Relations, pages 240–247

4. For each linear relation, create a table of values using at least three ordered pairs. Then, graph the line.
   a) $y = 4x - 7$ b) $y = -x + 3$ c) $y = \frac{1}{2}x - 3$

## 6.4 Graphing Non-Linear Relations, pages 248–257

5. The volume of a cylindrical can with a fixed height of 32 cm is given by the formula $V = 100r^2$.
   a) Copy and complete the table of values.
   b) Graph volume versus radius. Describe the shape of the graph.
   c) Use the graph to estimate the volume of a can with radius 55 cm.
   d) Use the graph to estimate the radius of a can whose volume is 25 600 cm$^3$.

| Radius, $r$, (cm) | Volume, $V$, (cm$^3$) |
|---|---|
| 10 | |
| 20 | |
| 30 | |
| 40 | |

## 6.5 First Differences, pages 258–265

6. An amount of \$1000 is left in two different types of savings account. The money accumulated, with interest, is shown.

| Simple Interest Account | |
|---|---|
| Number of Years | Amount (\$) |
| 0 | 1000 |
| 1 | 1100 |
| 2 | 1200 |
| 3 | 1300 |

| Compound Interest Account | |
|---|---|
| Number of Years | Amount (\$) |
| 0 | 1000 |
| 1 | 1100 |
| 2 | 1210 |
| 3 | 1331 |

   a) Calculate first differences in each case. Classify each relation as linear or non-linear.
   b) Graph each relation.
   c) Which account appears to be a better savings account? Explain.

## 6.6 Characteristics of Linear and Non-Linear Relations, pages 266–271

7. Classify each relation as linear or non-linear. Explain your answers.

a) 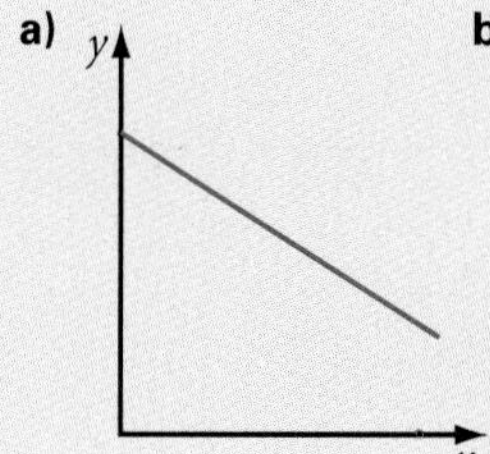


b) 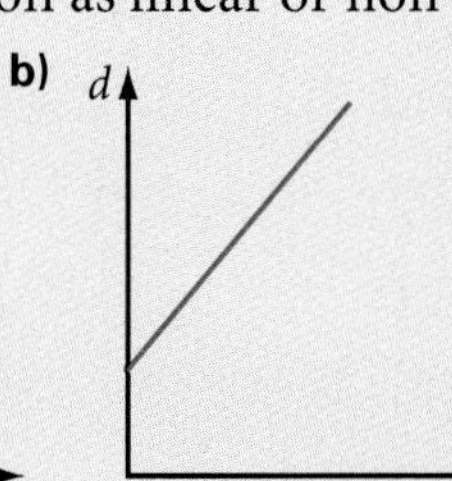


c) 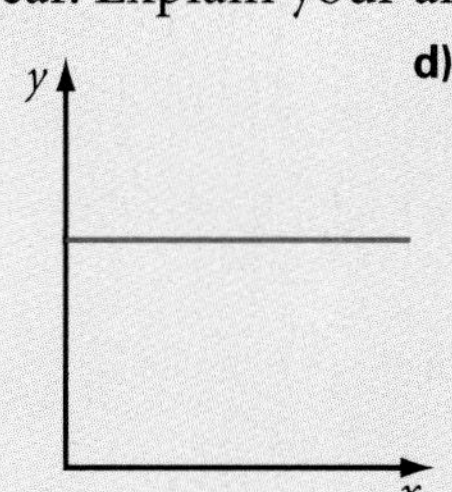


d) 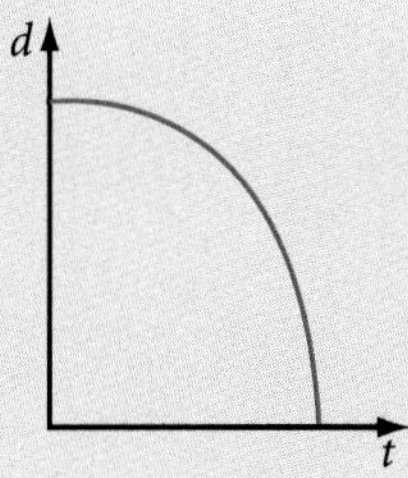


8. Classify each relation as either linear or non-linear. Explain your answers.
   a) $y = 3x - 5$  b) $y = 2x^2 - 3x$  c) $y = x^3$

# Practice Test

## Multiple Choice

***For questions 1 to 7, select the best answer.***

1. Distance varies directly with time. What is the constant of variation?

| Time (s) | Distance (m) |
|---|---|
| 0 | 0 |
| 1 | 2 |
| 2 | 4 |

**A** 0 **B** 0.5
**C** 1 **D** 2

2. Samad's pay varies directly with the number of hours he works. He earns $48 for a 6-h shift. Which of the following relates Samad's pay, $P$, with hours worked, $t$?

**A** $P = 6t$ **B** $P = 8t$ **C** $P = 6t + 48$ **D** $P = 8t + 48$

3. Tia gets paid $500 per week plus 15% of her sales, $S$, for the week. What is the fixed part and the variable part of this partial variation?

**A** fixed part = 500, variable part = $0.15S$
**B** fixed part = 500, variable part = $15S$
**C** fixed part = $15S$, variable part = 500
**D** fixed part = 15, variable part = $500S$

4. The cost of a taxi ride is $3.00 plus $0.70 for each kilometre. What is the cost of a 5-km trip?

**A** $3.50 **B** $3.70 **C** $6.50 **D** $7.00

5. Which relation is non-linear?

**A** **B** **C** 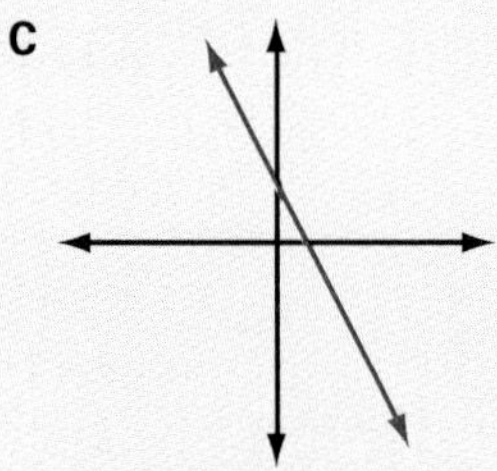 **D** 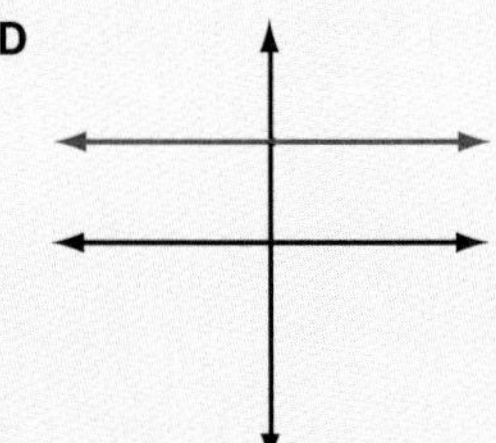

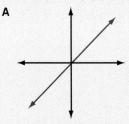

6. Which relation is linear?

**A**

| $x$ | $y$ |
|---|---|
| 1 | 12 |
| 2 | 24 |
| 3 | 48 |
| 4 | 64 |

**B**

| $x$ | $y$ |
|---|---|
| 0 | 11 |
| 3 | 12 |
| 6 | 14 |
| 9 | 17 |

**C**

| $x$ | $y$ |
|---|---|
| −2 | −3 |
| −1 | 1 |
| 0 | 5 |
| 1 | 9 |

**D**

| $x$ | $y$ |
|---|---|
| −2 | 3 |
| −1 | 2 |
| 0 | 3 |
| 1 | 2 |

7. Which relation is non-linear?

**A** $y = 3x - 5$ **B** $y = 6x^2$ **C** $y = 3 - x$ **D** $y = -6.5x$

## Short Answer

8. Graph each relation. Classify each relation as linear or non-linear.

**a)** $y = 4x - 3$ **b)** $y = x^2 - 5$ **c)** $y = -\frac{1}{2}x + 3$

9. Leah claims that this relation is linear, based on the fact that the first differences are constant.

| x | y |
|---|---|
| 0 | 0 |
| 1 | 1 |
| 4 | 2 |
| 9 | 3 |
| 16 | 4 |

**a)** Explain the flaw in Leah's reasoning.

**b)** Determine whether the relation is linear or non-linear. Explain your method.

## Extended Response

10. **Communication, Application** The cost of renting a banquet hall depends on how many people attend.

| Number Attending | Cost ($) |
|---|---|
| 0 | 225 |
| 50 | 275 |
| 100 | 325 |
| 150 | 375 |
| 200 | 425 |

**a)** Is this a fixed or partial variation? Explain how you can tell.

**b)** Graph cost, *C*, versus number attending, *n*.

**c)** Write an equation relating cost and number attending.

**d)** Determine the rental cost if 325 people attend. Explain your method.

**e)** Santino wants to invite 500 people to a banquet. He can afford to spend $750. Can Santino afford this banquet hall? Explain your answer.

**ACHIEVEMENT CHECK** Knowledge/Understanding Thinking/Inquiry/Problem Solving Communication Application

11. Students conducted experiments to see how heating effects the volume of three different gases. The tables show the results of their experiments.

| Gas A | |
|---|---|
| **Temperature (°C)** | **Volume (mL)** |
| 10 | 60 |
| 15 | 80 |
| 20 | 95 |
| 25 | 105 |
| 30 | 110 |

| Gas B | |
|---|---|
| **Temperature (°C)** | **Volume (mL)** |
| 10 | 849 |
| 15 | 864 |
| 20 | 879 |
| 25 | 894 |
| 30 | 905 |

| Gas B | |
|---|---|
| **Temperature (°C)** | **Volume (mL)** |
| 10 | 100 |
| 15 | 105 |
| 20 | 110 |
| 25 | 120 |
| 30 | 130 |

**a)** Graph the data for each gas tested.

**b)** By examining each graph, or using any other method that you have learned, classify each relation as linear or non-linear.

**c)** Estimate the volume of each gas when the temperature is 35°C.

# CHAPTER 7
# Analysing Linear Relations

In this chapter, you will

- investigate distance-time graphs using a motion sensor
- investigate the properties of the slope and *y*-intercept of a linear relation
- graph lines using intercepts
- graph and write equations of lines in the form $y = mx + b$
- construct a line of best fit
- investigate parallel and perpendicular lines

## Chapter Problem

*Runaround* is a television show where teams find clues in a number of races that take them around the globe. After each leg of the race, the last team to finish is eliminated. The winning team gets $1 000 000, to be donated to a charity of their choice. In this chapter, you will examine the races of three teams.

# Get Ready

## Writing Fractions in Lowest Terms

A fraction can be reduced to lowest terms by dividing the numerator and the denominator by a common factor.

To express the fraction $\frac{9}{12}$ in lowest terms, divide the numerator and the denominator by the common factor, 3.

$$\frac{9}{12} = \frac{3}{4} \qquad \begin{matrix} \leftarrow 9 \div 3 = 3 \\ \leftarrow 12 \div 3 = 4 \end{matrix}$$

To express the fraction $\frac{50}{150}$ in lowest terms, divide the numerator and the denominator by the common factor, 50.

$$\frac{50}{150} = \frac{1}{3} \qquad \begin{matrix} \leftarrow 50 \div 50 = 1 \\ \leftarrow 150 \div 50 = 3 \end{matrix}$$

**1.** Express each fraction in lowest terms.

**a)** $\frac{5}{20}$ **b)** $\frac{18}{30}$ **c)** $\frac{10}{50}$

**d)** $\frac{14}{4}$ **e)** $\frac{24}{9}$ **f)** $\frac{250}{75}$

## Operations With Integers and Fractions

To simplify an expression,

- simplify the numerator and the denominator
- apply the rules for integer operations
- apply the techniques for fraction operations

$$\frac{8-4}{15-3} = \frac{4}{12} = \frac{1}{3} \qquad \frac{3-(-12)}{-2-8} = \frac{15}{-10} = -\frac{3}{2}$$

**2.** Evaluate each expression.

**a)** $\frac{10-2}{9-5}$ **b)** $\frac{4-(-6)}{5-10}$ **c)** $\frac{-9-3}{-2-2}$

**d)** $\frac{-3-(-6)}{3-9}$ **e)** $\frac{2-8}{9-5}$ **f)** $\frac{9-(-1)}{-2-2}$

## Evaluating Expressions

To evaluate the expression $3x - 2$ for $x = -4$, substitute $-4$ for $x$ in the expression. Then, simplify using the order of operations.

$$\begin{aligned} 3x - 2 &= 3(-4) - 2 \\ &= -12 - 2 \\ &= -14 \end{aligned}$$

3. Evaluate $4x$ for each value of $x$.

   a) $3$  b) $-5$  c) $\frac{1}{2}$  d) $-\frac{1}{4}$

4. Evaluate $3x - 5$ for each value of $x$.

   a) $1$  b) $0$  c) $2$  d) $-3$

5. Evaluate each expression for $x = -2$.

   a) $4x + 1$  b) $-2x - 3$  c) $-x - 5$
   d) $6x - 3$  e) $x + 4$  f) $3x + 5$

## Solving Simple Equations

To solve an equation is to find the value of the variable that makes the equation true.

Solve $3x = 12$ for $x$.

$$\begin{aligned} 3x &= 12 \\ \frac{3x}{3} &= \frac{12}{3} \quad \text{Divide both sides by 3.} \\ x &= 4 \end{aligned}$$

Solve $-2y = 6$ for $y$.

$$\begin{aligned} -2y &= 6 \\ \frac{-2y}{-2} &= \frac{6}{-2} \quad \text{Divide both sides by } -2. \\ y &= -3 \end{aligned}$$

6. Solve for $x$.

   a) $5x = 20$  b) $8x = 24$  c) $-3x = 18$  d) $-x = 7$

7. Solve for $y$.

   a) $3y = 15$  b) $-y = -2$  c) $-3y = -12$  d) $2y = -16$

# 7.1 Motion Sensors and Distance-Time Graphs

Speeding on the highway can be very dangerous and costly. Police can use radar motion sensors to accurately measure speeds from a distance.

Motion sensors also can be used to graph distance versus time. This type of graph is called a **distance-time graph**. Since the distance travelled depends on time, distance is the dependent variable and is placed on the vertical axis. Time is the independent variable and is placed on the horizontal axis.

## Discover 1

**Materials**
- TI-83 Plus graphing calculator
- CBR™
- metre stick
- masking tape

### Exploring Distance-Time Graphs

***Using a graphing calculator and CBR™***

Work with a partner or in a small group.

In this activity, you will use a motion sensor to record movements. You will transfer the data to a graphing calculator where it will be stored and analysed.

1. Find a clear location where you have plenty of room to move, such as a hallway.

2. Using masking tape, mark off 1-m intervals from the wall on the floor.

3. Turn on the graphing calculator and load the Ranger program:
   - Press the APPS key.
   - Select **2:CBL/CBR**.
   - Press ENTER.
   - Select **3:RANGER**.
   - Press ENTER.

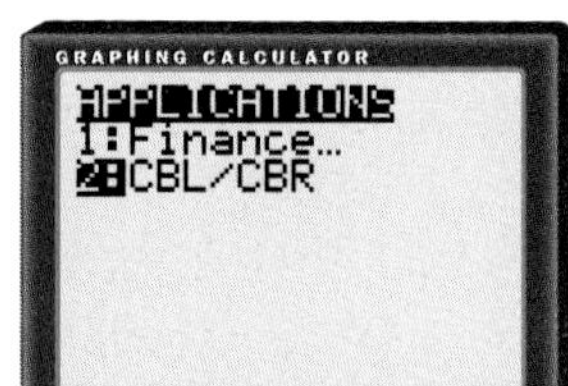


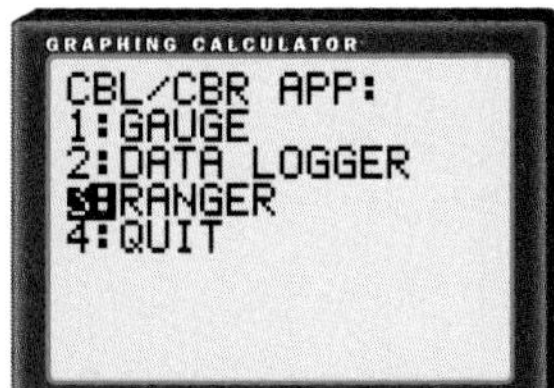

4. Now set up the Ranger program:
   • Select **1:SETUP/SAMPLE.**
   • Make sure that the settings are as shown below:

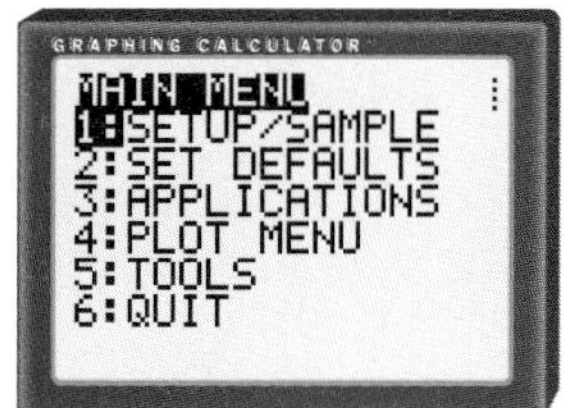


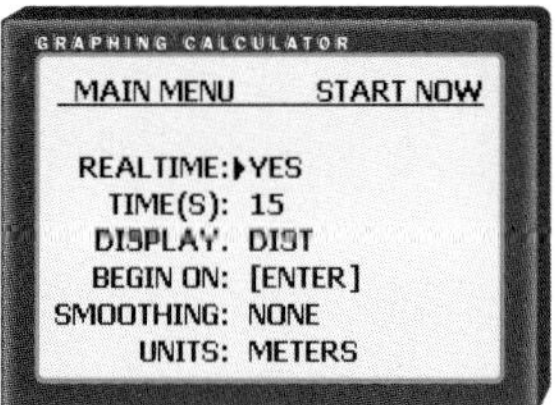


5. Connect the CBR™ to the calculator using the link cable. Insert the cable firmly.

6. Move the cursor to **START NOW** at the top of the screen. Press ENTER.

7. Stand with your back against the wall. Have your partner start at the 2-m mark, facing you. Hold the CBR™ so that the sensor is directly facing your partner. Hold the calculator in your other hand. Make sure that no objects or people are standing between you and your partner.

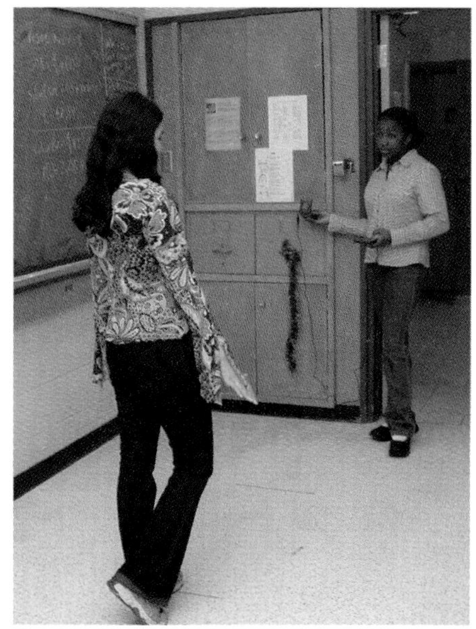

8. Press ENTER. You should hear a ticking sound from the CBR™. Have your partner start walking backwards from you at a slow, steady pace. A graph will begin to form on the calculator screen.

9. a) Use the blue arrow keys to trace along the graph. You will see the coordinates of each data point appear at the bottom of the screen.
   b) The left-most point is called the $y$-intercept. Write down the coordinates of this point.
   c) What do you notice about the $y$-value of this point? Why might this value not be exactly what you expect?
   d) Use a ruler or other straightedge to sketch this graph. Call it Graph A.

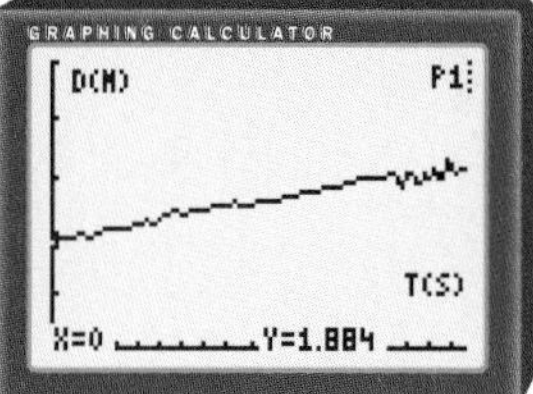

10. a) Now, collect a new set of motion data:
    - Press ENTER and select **3:REPEAT SAMPLE**.
    - Have your partner start at the 5-m mark.
    - Press ENTER on the calculator and have your partner walk at a slow, steady pace toward you.

    b) Repeat step 9 for this graph. Call it Graph B.

    c) Compare Graph A and Graph B. Describe any similarities and differences.

11. a) Collect a new set of data. Have your partner start at the 4-m mark and walk at a steady, faster pace toward you.

    b) Use a ruler or other straightedge to sketch this graph. Call it Graph C.

    c) Compare Graph B and Graph C. Describe any similarities and differences.

**The maximum range of the CBR™ is about 5 or 6 m. Your readings may become distorted at this distance.**

12. a) Collect a new set of data. Have your partner start at the 2-m mark and carefully back away from you, slowly at first, and gradually increase speed.

    b) Sketch this graph. Call it Graph D.

    c) Compare Graph A and Graph D. Describe any similarities and differences.

## EXAMPLE 1

### Describing Distance-Time Graphs

A person walks in front of a motion sensor. Describe the motion that would produce each of the following graphs.

a) 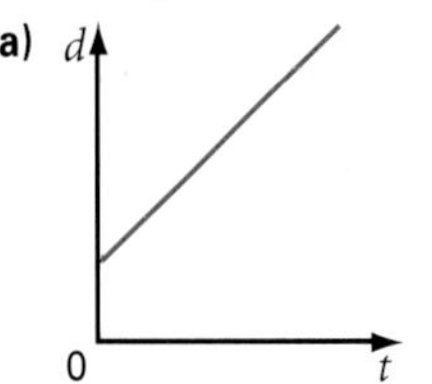


b) 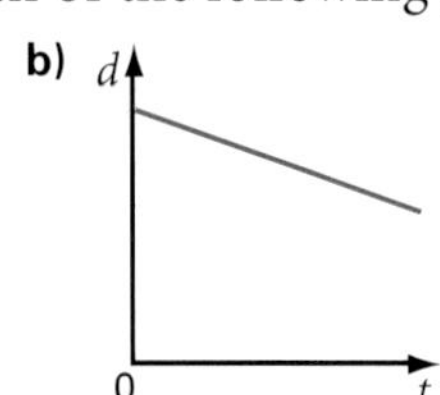


c) 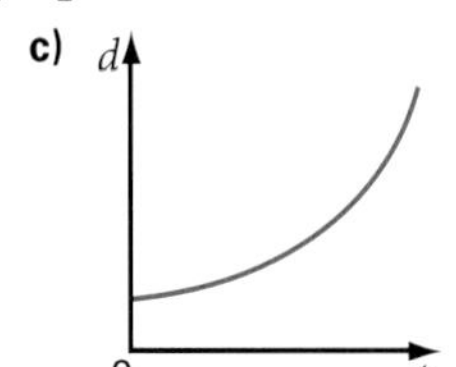


d) 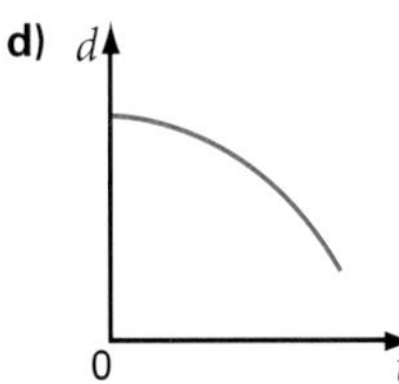


### Solution

a) This line is steep. The person moves at a fast, steady pace away from the sensor.

b) The person moves at a slow, steady pace toward the sensor.

c) The curve indicates a change in speed. The person moves away from the sensor, slowly at first, and then gradually picks up speed.

d) The person moves toward the sensor, slowly at first, and then gradually picks up speed.

## DISCOVER 2

**Materials**
- TI-83 Plus graphing calculator
- CBR™
- metre stick
- masking tape

### Matching Distance-Time Graphs

Work with a partner or in a small group.

In this activity, you will view a random distance-time (d-t) graph. Then, you will perform a series of motions to try to reproduce the graph.

1. a) Find a location with plenty of room.
   b) Use masking tape to mark 1-m intervals on the floor.

2. Connect the graphing calculator to the CBR™, using the link cable.

3. Load the Ranger program:
   - Press APPS.
   - Select **2:CBL/CBR**.
   - Press ENTER.
   - Select **3:RANGER**.
   - Press ENTER.

4. Generate a random distance-time graph:
   - Select **3:APPLICATIONS**.
   - Select **1:METERS**.
   - Select **1:DIST MATCH**.
   - Press ENTER.

5. Study the graph with your partner(s). Discuss what movements should be performed in order to reproduce the same graph.

6. a) Position the person with the CBR™ facing you.
   b) Press ENTER, and begin moving.
   c) Watch the screen as you move. Adjust your speed and direction, as necessary.

7. a) Stop moving when the CBR™ stops ticking.
   b) Examine the two graphs and discuss how accurate you were.
   c) Press ENTER and select **1:SAME MATCH** to try the same graph again, or **2:NEW MATCH** to try a new graph.

## EXAMPLE 2

### Analysing Distance-Time Graphs

A person walks in front of a motion sensor.
Describe the motion represented by each graph.

**a)**

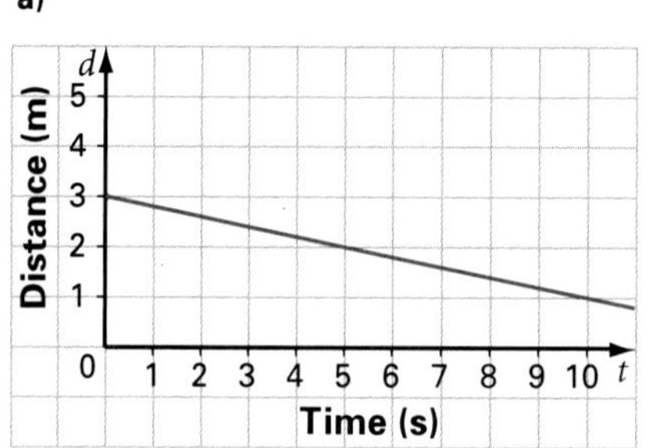


**b)**

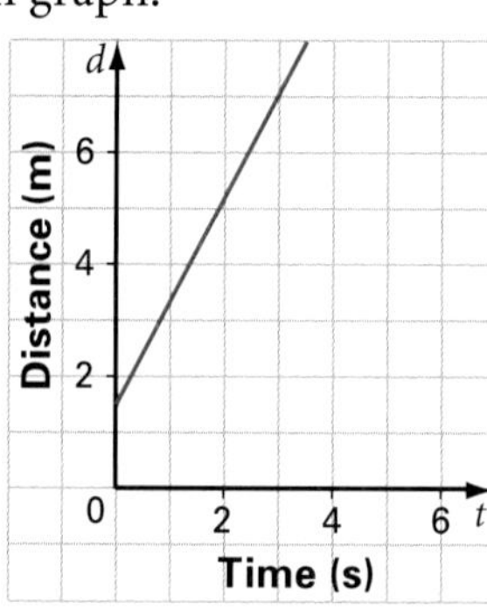


**c)**

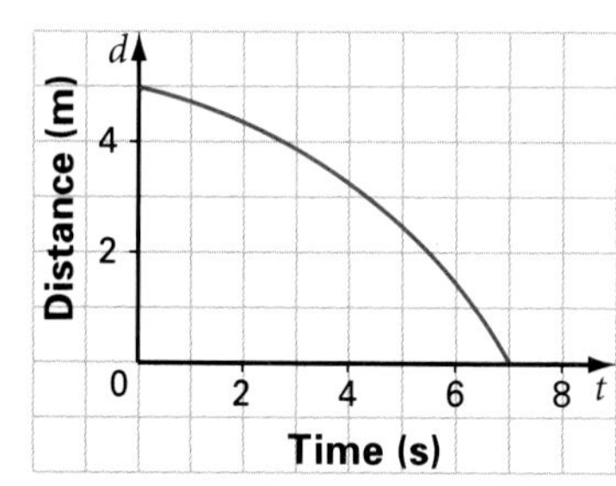


**d)**

### Solution

**a)** The person starts at a distance of 3 m from the sensor and walks toward it at a slow, steady pace.

**b)** The person starts at a distance of 1.5 m from the sensor and walks away from it at a fast, steady pace.

**c)** The person starts at a distance of 5 m from the sensor and walks toward it, slowly at first, and then gradually picks up speed.

**d)** The person starts at a distance of 2 m from the sensor, takes 5 s to walk at a slow, steady pace to the 4-m mark, pauses for 2 s, and then walks at a fast, steady pace to the sensor.

- A motion sensor can be used to collect and display distance-time data.
- A linear graph is produced when a person walks at a constant speed.
- The speed of the person affects the steepness of the graph.
- The direction of motion affects which way the line is directed.
- A non-linear graph is produced when a person changes speed.

## Discuss the Concepts

1. When moving in front of a motion sensor, describe how to produce
   a) a linear graph
   b) a non-linear graph
   c) a horizontal line

2. A person is walking at a constant speed toward a motion sensor. How will the distance-time graph change if the person
   a) speeds up?
   b) slows down?
   c) reverses direction?

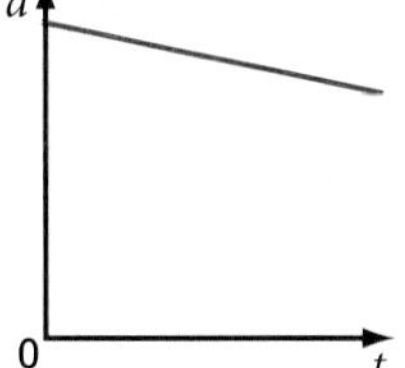


3. For each of the following, describe what the distance-time graph would look like. Then, sketch the graph.
   a) A person moves slowly at a constant speed toward the sensor.
   b) A person moves quickly at a constant speed away from the sensor.
   c) A person does not move.
   d) A person moves toward a sensor, slowly at first, then gradually picks up speed.

## Practise

**A** ***For help with questions 1 and 2, refer to Example 1.***

1. Four distance-time graphs are shown. Rank the graphs from slowest to fastest motion.

a) 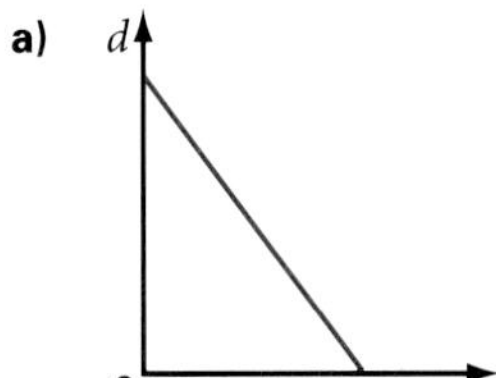


b) 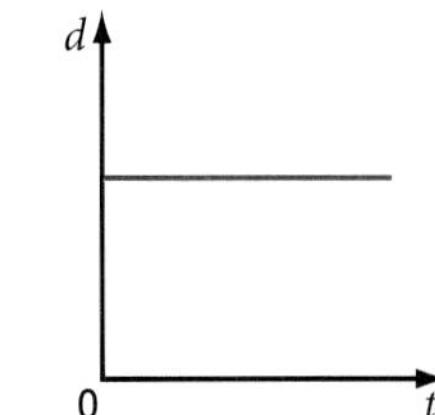


c) 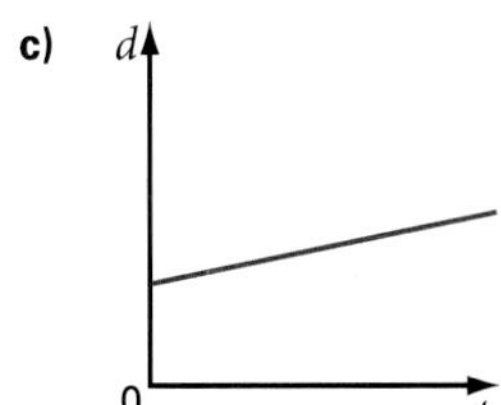


d) 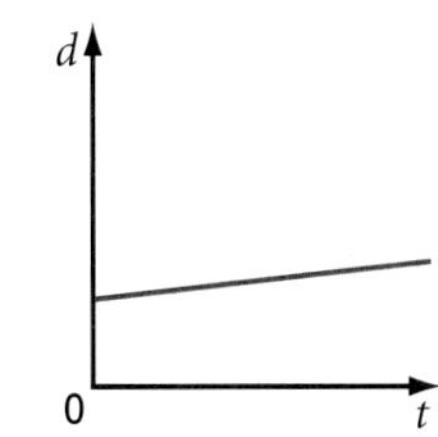

2. Match each distance-time graph with its description.

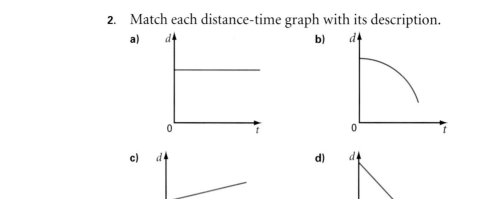

a)

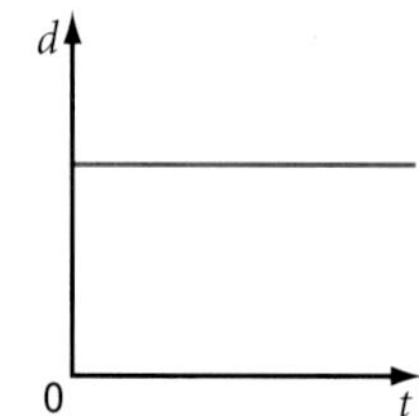


b)

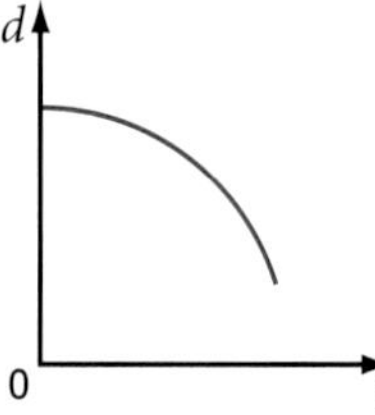


c)

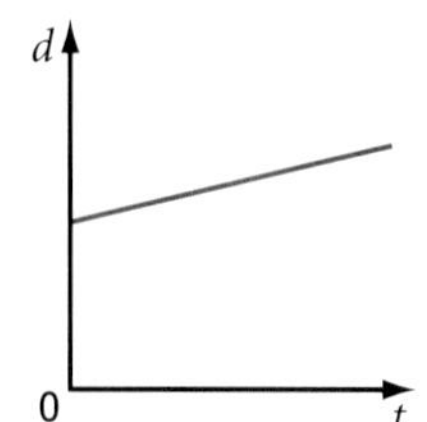


d)

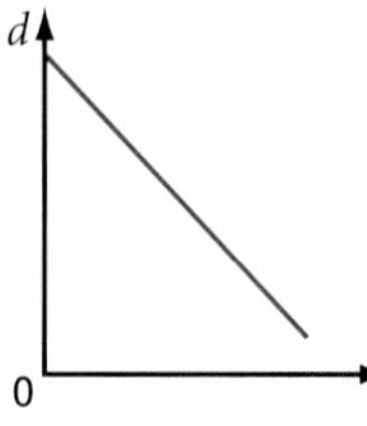


A) Walk quickly toward the sensor.
B) Walk slowly away from the sensor.
C) Remain still.
D) Walk toward the sensor, slowly at first, then gradually speed up.

## Apply the Concepts

*For help with question 3, refer to Example 2.*

3. **Application** Sketch a distance-time graph for each motion.
   a) Start at 2 m and walk slowly away from the sensor.
   b) Start at 4 m and walk quickly toward the sensor.
   c) Start at 1 m and walk slowly away from the sensor for 5 s. Then, immediately walk slowly back toward the sensor for 5 s.
   d) Start at 1 m and walk away from the sensor. Start slowly, then gradually pick up speed.
   e) Start at 6 m and walk toward the sensor. Start quickly, then gradually slow down.

4. **Communication** For each graph in question 3, classify the distance-time relationship as either linear or non-linear. Explain your choices.

**Chapter Problem**

5. ***Runaround*** The first leg of *Runaround* is a 45-m foot race to the top of the great pyramid at Chichen Itza in Mexico. Distance-time graphs are shown for three of the teams.

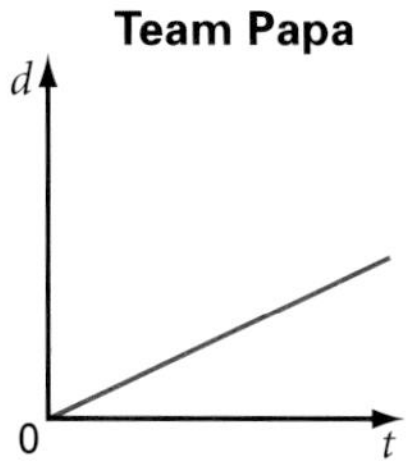


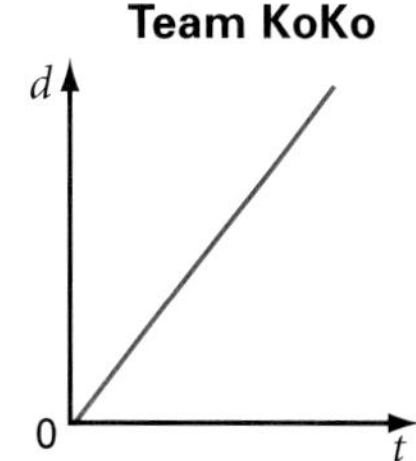


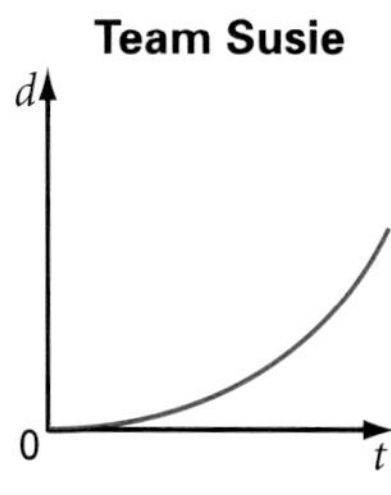


**a)** Classify each graph as linear or non-linear.

**b)** Which team ran at the fastest constant rate?

**c)** Which team increased their speed throughout the first leg of the race?

6. **Thinking/Inquiry/Problem Solving** The distance-time graph shows the motion of a car as it starts from a stopped position at an intersection. Describe what is happening during each interval of time.

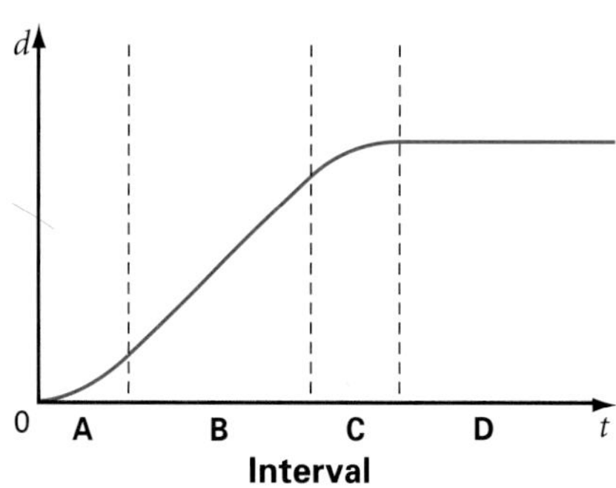

# 7.2 Slope

Why do the roofs of chalets have very steep slopes?

Why do homes in tropical countries often have flat roofs?

There are many situations where the steepness of a roof, ramp, staircase, or incline is an important consideration for builders.

Skiers and snowboarders are often concerned about the steepness and condition of ski hills.

In mathematics, slope is the measure of steepness.

**Slope** is the ratio of rise to run.
**Rise** is the vertical distance between two points.
**Run** is the horizontal distance between two points.

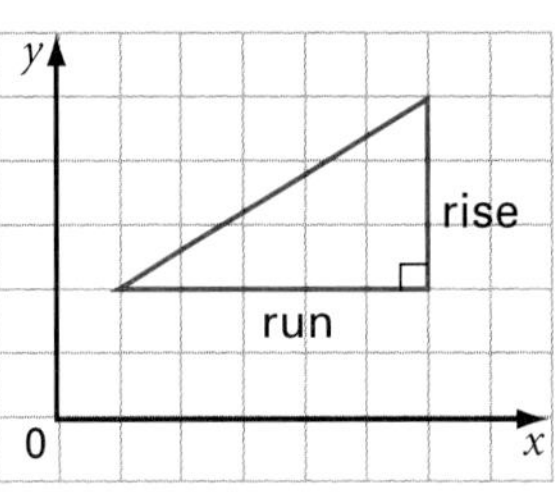


Slope, $m = \frac{\text{rise}}{\text{run}}$ **The letter *m* is often used to represent slope.**

## EXAMPLE 1

### Measuring the Slope of a Physical Object

Determine the slope of each object.

**a)**

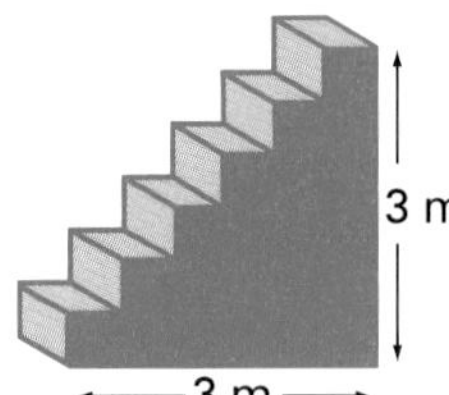


**b)**

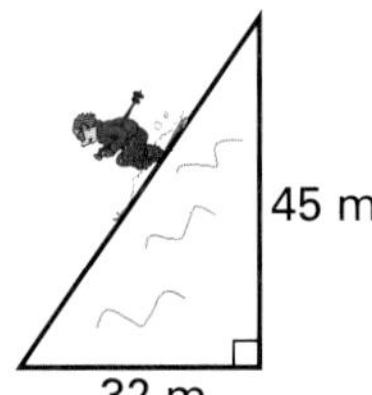


**c)**

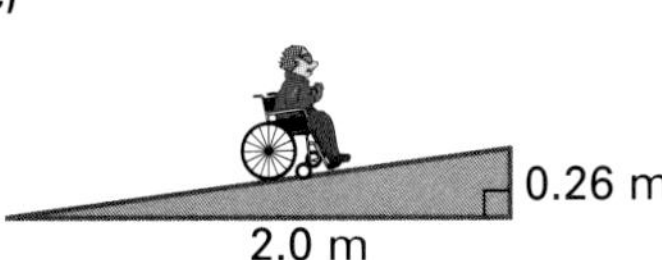


### Solution

**a)** $m = \frac{\text{rise}}{\text{run}}$

$= \frac{3}{3}$

$= 1$

The slope of the staircase is 1.

**b)** $m = \frac{\text{rise}}{\text{run}}$

$= \frac{45}{32}$

$= 1.406$ **Round to 1.4.**

The slope of the ski hill is 1.4.

**c)** $m = \frac{\text{rise}}{\text{run}}$

$= \frac{0.26}{2.0}$

$= 0.13$

The slope of the wheelchair ramp is 0.13.

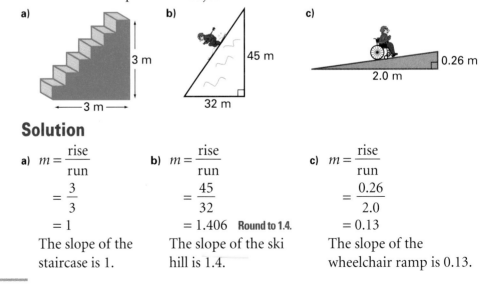

The speed at which a person walks affects the slope of the distance-time graph.

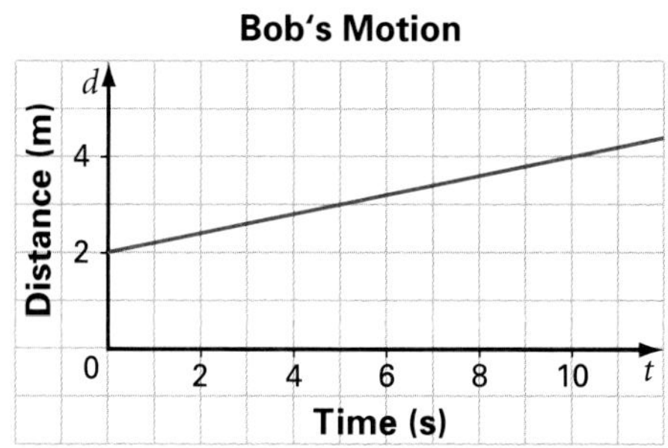


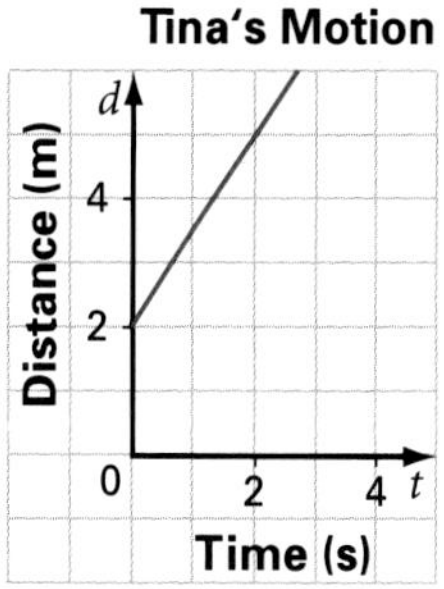


A slow walker produces a shallow line. A fast walker produces a steep line.

**EXAMPLE 2**

## Measuring Slope of a Line Segment

**a)** Determine the slope of Bob's distance-time graph.

**b)** Determine the slope of Tina's distance-time graph.

**c)** Who walks faster? Explain your reasoning.

### Solution

**a)** $m = \dfrac{\text{rise}}{\text{run}}$

$= \dfrac{2}{10}$

$= \dfrac{1}{5}$ or 0.2

**Slope can be expressed as a fraction or as a decimal.**

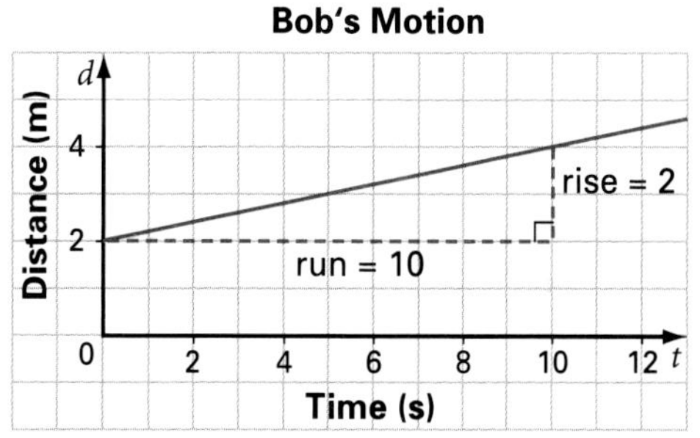


**b)** $m = \dfrac{\text{rise}}{\text{run}}$

$= \dfrac{3}{2}$ or 1.5

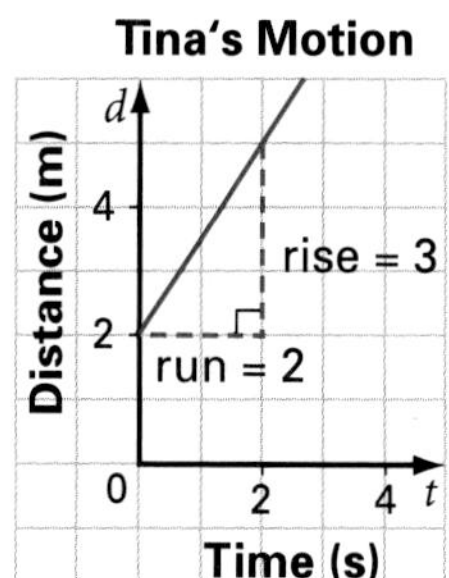


**c)** Tina walks faster than Bob does. The line on Tina's graph has a steeper slope than the line on Bob's.

The direction a person walks affects the direction of the distance-time graph.
• When moving away from the target, the line *rises to the right*.
• When moving toward the target, the line *falls to the right*.

If a line *rises* to the right, it has a **positive slope**.

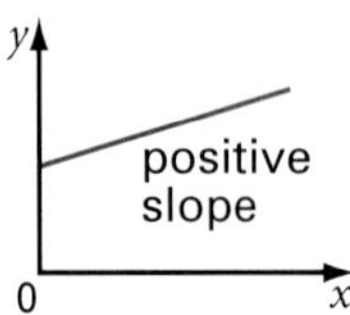


If a line *falls* to the right, it has a **negative slope**.

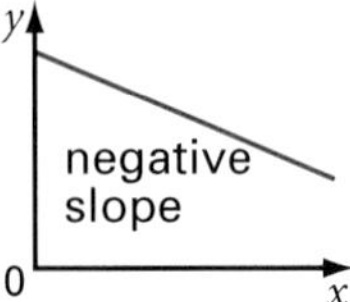


This concept applies to *all* types of linear graphs, not just distance-time graphs.

### Slope as a Rate of Change

The slope of a distance-time graph measures a *change in distance* compared to a *change in time*. This rate of change is called **speed**.

$$\text{speed} = \frac{\Delta d}{\Delta t}$$

$\frac{\Delta d}{\Delta t}$ **is read as "delta *d* over delta *t*." Delta means "change in."**

## EXAMPLE 3

### Positive and Negative Slope

Each distance-time graph was created by walking in front of a motion sensor. Determine the slope of each graph and explain what it means.

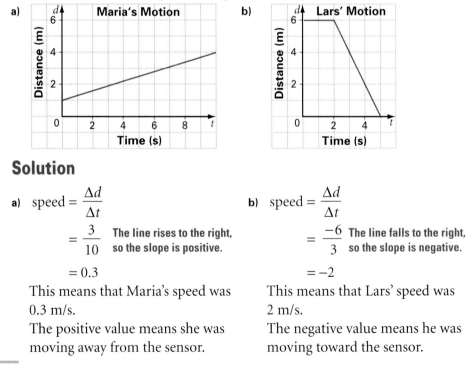

**a)**

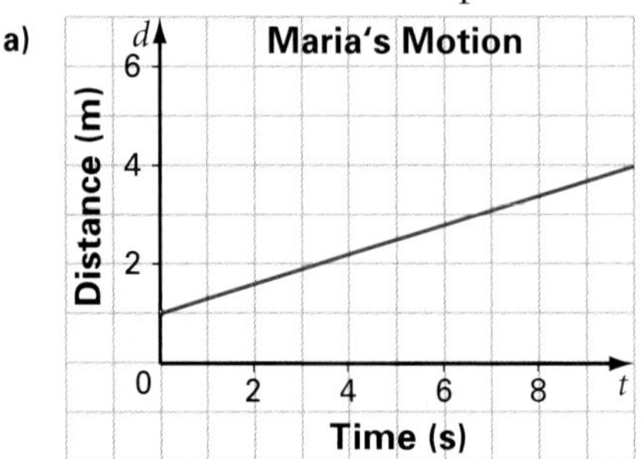


**b)**

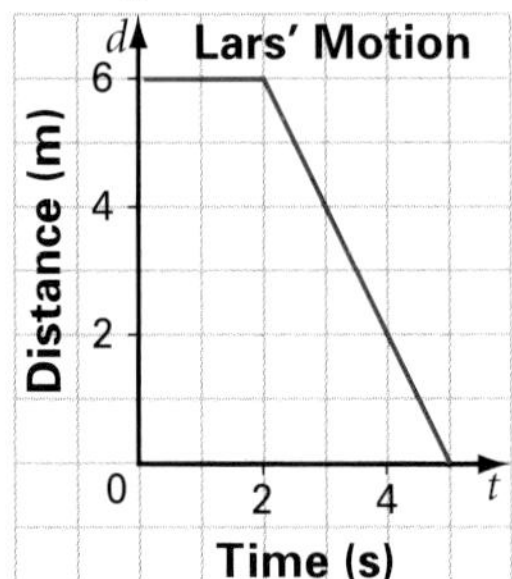


### Solution

**a)** $\text{speed} = \frac{\Delta d}{\Delta t}$

$= \frac{3}{10}$ **The line rises to the right, so the slope is positive.**

$= 0.3$

This means that Maria's speed was 0.3 m/s.

The positive value means she was moving away from the sensor.

**b)** $\text{speed} = \frac{\Delta d}{\Delta t}$

$= \frac{-6}{3}$ **The line falls to the right, so the slope is negative.**

$= -2$

This means that Lars' speed was 2 m/s.

The negative value means he was moving toward the sensor.

In the last two examples, the slope of a distance-time graph gives a measure of speed. Slope can also be applied to other relations with different variables.

- Slope, $m$, is a measure of steepness of a straight object or line segment.
- $m = \frac{\text{rise}}{\text{run}}$
- Slope measures the ratio of how two variables change.
- If a line rises to the right, it has a positive slope.
- If a line falls to the right, it has a negative slope.
- On a distance-time graph, slope is a measure of speed and direction.

## Discuss the Concepts

1. a) What does slope measure?
   b) Give some examples where you might measure the slope of a physical object.
2. a) What does the sign of a slope indicate?
   b) How can you tell, by looking at a line on a graph, whether the line has a positive or a negative slope?

## Practise

**A** ***For help with question 1, refer to Example 1.***

1. Determine the slope of each object.

a)

b)

**Did You Know?**

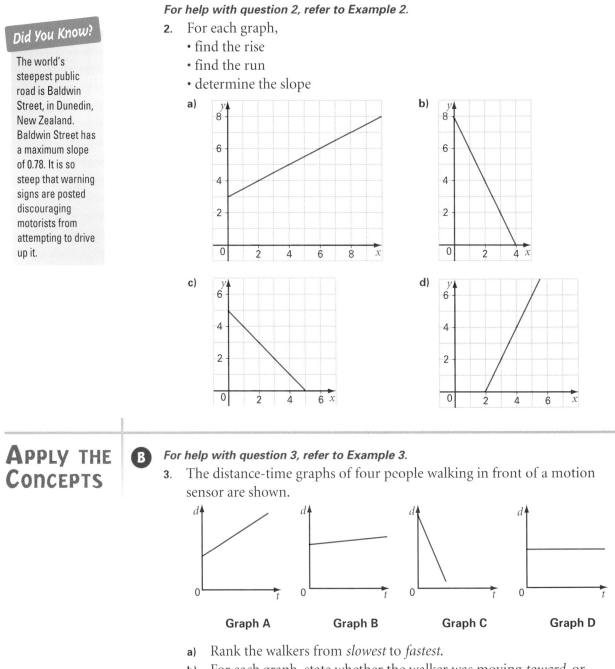

The world's steepest public road is Baldwin Street, in Dunedin, New Zealand. Baldwin Street has a maximum slope of 0.78. It is so steep that warning signs are posted discouraging motorists from attempting to drive up it.

***For help with question 2, refer to Example 2.***

2. For each graph,
   - find the rise
   - find the run
   - determine the slope

**a)**

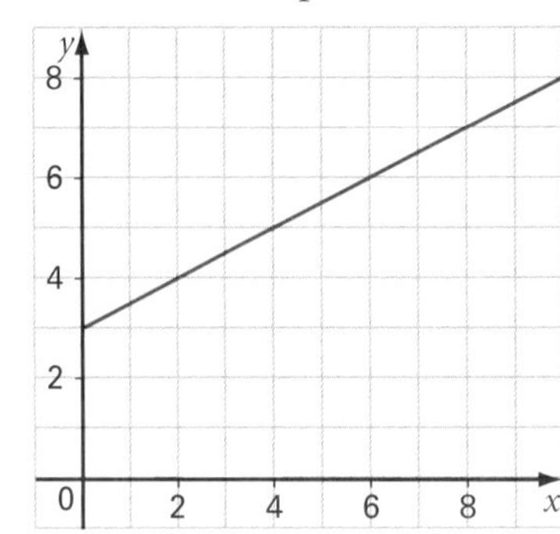


**b)**

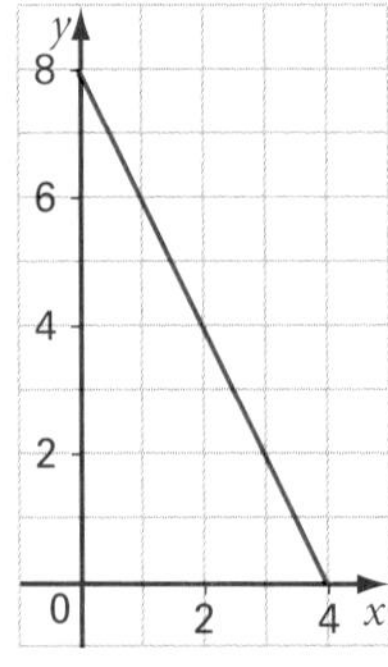


**c)**

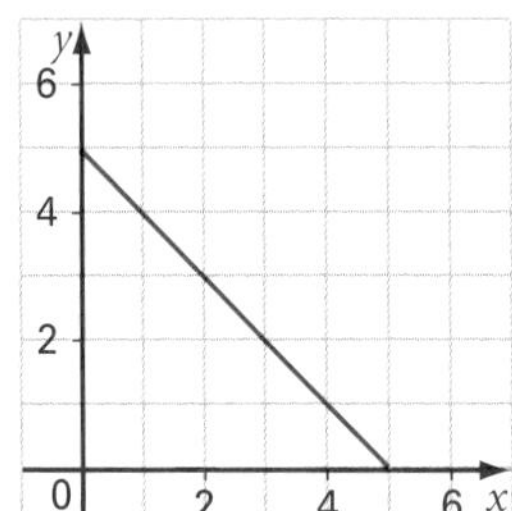


**d)**

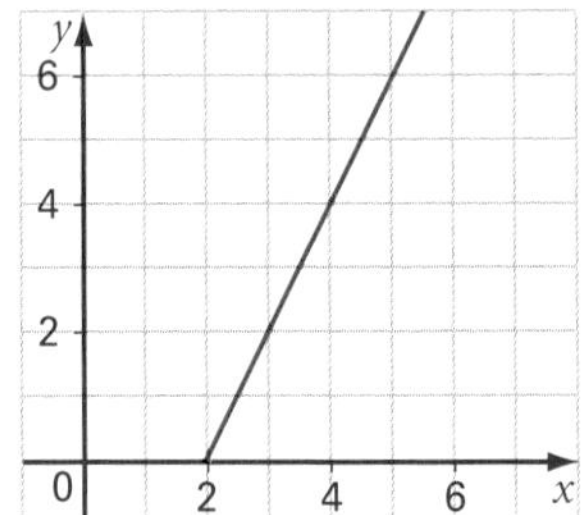


## Apply the Concepts

***For help with question 3, refer to Example 3.***

3. The distance-time graphs of four people walking in front of a motion sensor are shown.

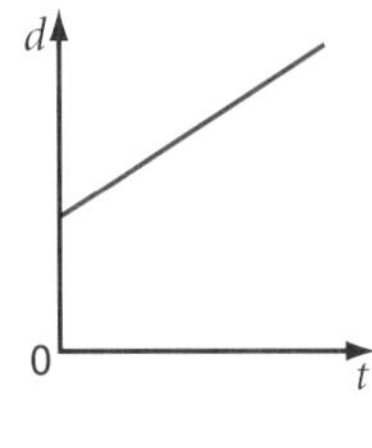


**Graph A**

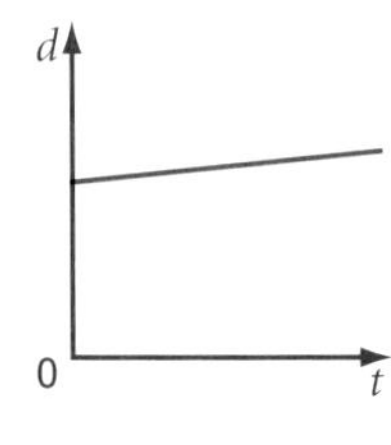


**Graph B**

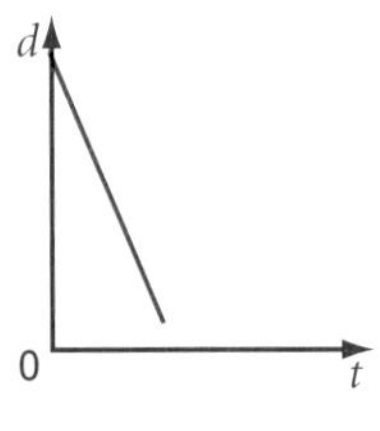


**Graph C**

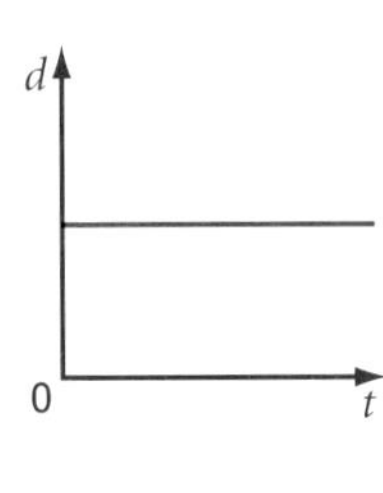


**Graph D**

a) Rank the walkers from *slowest* to *fastest.*

b) For each graph, state whether the walker was moving *toward*, or *away from*, the sensor.

**Chapter Problem**

4. ***Runaround*** In this leg of *Runaround*, teams face a "fork" where the team must choose between two paths *Step* or *Stroll*. Both paths lead from the top to the bottom of Mount Sinai, in Egypt. In *Step*, teams walk down a steep staircase containing 3000 steps. In *Stroll*, teams walk down a gentler, but longer, camel path. Determine the slope of each route.

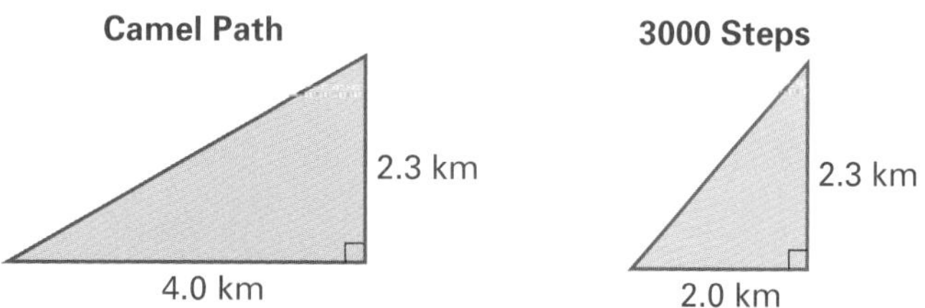

**C** 5. **Communication** A person moves in front of a motion sensor to produce the distance-time graph shown. Accurately describe the movements. Discuss speed and direction.

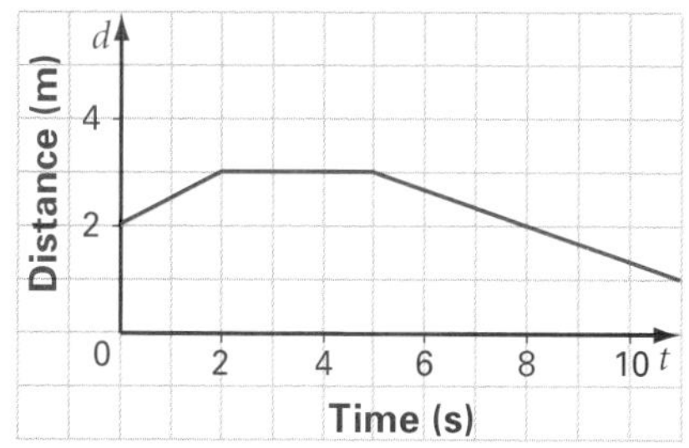


6. **Thinking/Inquiry/Problem Solving**
Pinder and Naomi are in a 100-m race. Naomi gives Pinder a 20-m head start. Naomi runs at a constant speed of 6 m/s while Pinder runs at a constant speed of 4.5 m/s.
   a) Create a distance-time graph for each runner.
   b) Who will win the race? Explain your answer.

# 7.3 Applying the Slope Formula

The slope of a line is the ratio of rise over run. If you know the coordinates of two points on the line, you can measure slope without a graph, using a formula.

## DISCOVER

### The Slope Formula

1. a) On a piece of grid paper, set up coordinate axes.
   b) Plot and label points A(1, 2) and B(5, 5). Join line segment AB.
   c) Form a right-angled triangle as shown.

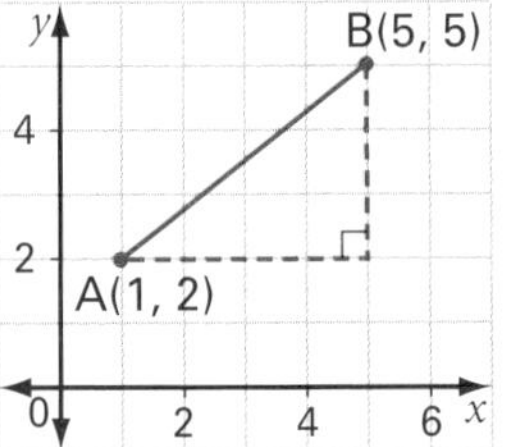


2. a) Measure the rise of AB by counting squares.
   b) What is the $y$-coordinate of B? Call this $y_B$.
   c) What is the $y$-coordinate of A? Call this $y_A$.
   d) Subtract $y_B - y_A$. How is this answer related to the rise of AB?

3. a) Measure the run of AB by counting squares.
   b) What is the $x$-coordinate of B? Call this $x_B$.
   c) What is the $x$-coordinate of A? Call this $x_A$.
   d) Subtract $x_B - x_A$. How is this answer related to the run of AB?

4. a) Determine the slope of AB, using the formula $m = \frac{\text{rise}}{\text{run}}$.
   b) Evaluate the expression $\frac{y_B - y_A}{x_B - x_A}$.
   c) Explain how the answers to a) and b) are related.

5. Repeat steps 1 to 4 for the points A(−1, 3) and B(5, −2).

6. Repeat steps 1 to 4 for two points of your choice.

7. Write the formula for the slope of the line segment that joins two points $A(x_A, y_A)$ and $B(x_B, y_B)$.

When a line appears on a coordinate grid, the slope can be calculated using any two points on the line, $A(x_A, y_A)$ and $B(x_B, y_B)$.

$$m = \frac{y_B - y_A}{x_B - x_A}$$

$y_B - y_A$ **represents the rise of AB.**
$x_B - x_A$ **represents the run of AB.**

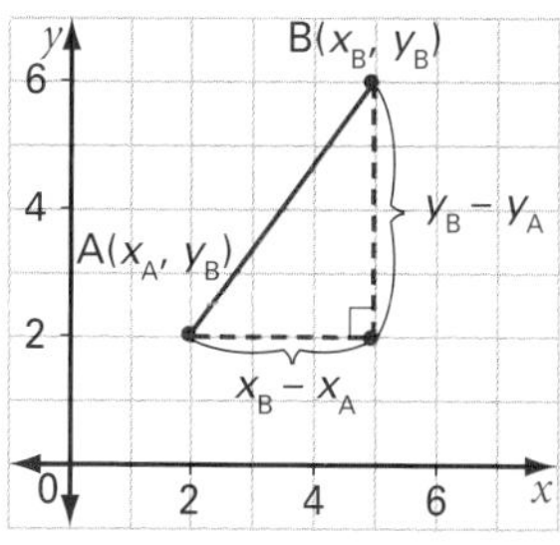


**$\frac{\Delta y}{\Delta x}$ is read as "delta $y$ over delta $x$."**

Sometimes the formula is written as $m = \frac{\Delta y}{\Delta x}$.

$\Delta y$ means the change in $y$-coordinates or $y_B - y_A$.

$\Delta x$ means the change in $x$-coordinates or $x_B - x_A$.

## EXAMPLE 1

### Calculating Slope Using a Formula

Calculate the slope of the line segment joining each pair of points.

**a)** A(3, 7) and B(8, 2)
**b)** P(−1, −3) and Q(5, −1)

### Solution

**a)** Label each coordinate.

$\overset{x_A\ y_A}{A(3, 7)}$ $\quad$ $\overset{x_B\ y_B}{B(8, 2)}$

Substitute these values into the formula.

$$\begin{aligned} m &= \frac{y_B - y_A}{x_B - x_A} \\ &= \frac{2 - 7}{8 - 3} \\ &= \frac{-5}{5} \\ &= -1 \end{aligned}$$

**rise = −5, run = 5**

The slope of AB is −1.

**b)** Label each coordinate.

$\overset{x_P\ y_P}{P(-1, -3)}$ $\quad$ $\overset{x_Q\ y_Q}{Q(5, -1)}$

Substitute these values into the formula.

$$\begin{aligned} m &= \frac{y_Q - y_P}{x_Q - x_P} \\ &= \frac{-1 - (-3)}{5 - (-1)} \\ &= \frac{-1 + 3}{5 + 1} \\ &= \frac{2}{6} \\ &= \frac{1}{3} \end{aligned}$$

**Substitute integers carefully.**

**Simplify integer calculations.**

**rise = 2, run = 6**

The slope of PQ is $\frac{1}{3}$.

## EXAMPLE 2

### Chapter Problem

## Applying the Slope Formula

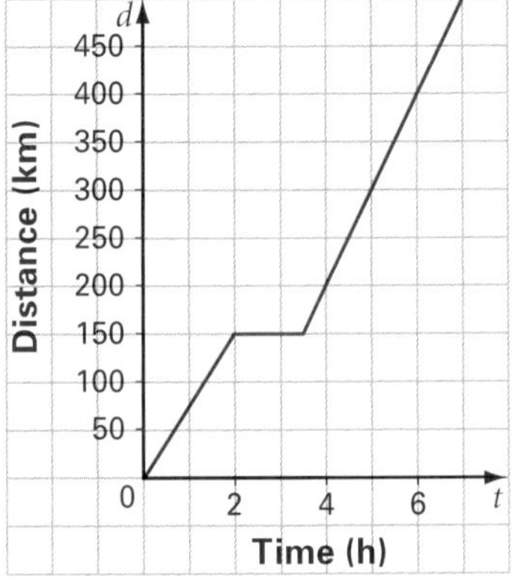


In the *Road-Race* leg of *Runaround*, teams must drive 500 km across the Serengeti Plain, in Tanzania. The distance-time graph for Team Susie is shown.

At one point, Team Susie had a flat tire.

**a)** When did this happen? How long did it take to repair?

**b)** Find the team's speed before the flat tire.

**c)** Find the team's speed after the flat tire.

**d)** How long did it take Team Susie to complete this leg of the race?

## Solution

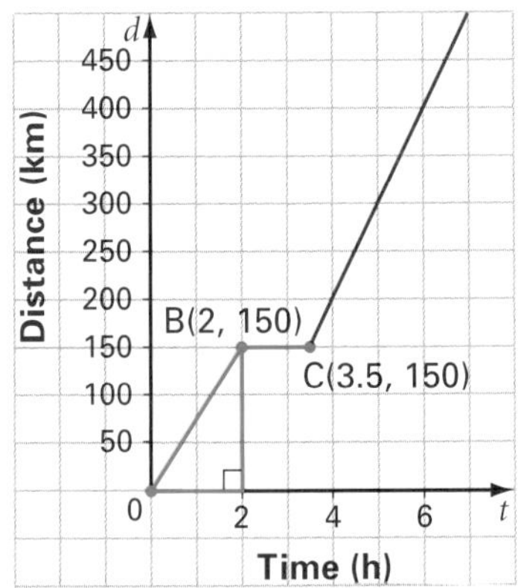


**a)** The slope of the distance-time graph is the team's speed. Look at the flat region of the graph. The speed during this interval is 0 km/h. The flat occurred at 2 h. The team started again at 3.5 h. The repair took 1.5 h.

**b)** Look at the region of the graph between 0 s and 2 s.

$$m = \frac{d_B - d_A}{t_B - t_A}$$
$$= \frac{150 - 0}{2 - 0}$$
$$= 75$$

Team Susie was travelling at 75 km/h before the flat.

**c)**
$$m = \frac{d_D - d_C}{t_D - t_C}$$
$$= \frac{500 - 150}{7 - 3.5}$$
$$= \frac{350}{3.5}$$
$$= 100$$

Team Susie was travelling at 100 km/h after the flat.

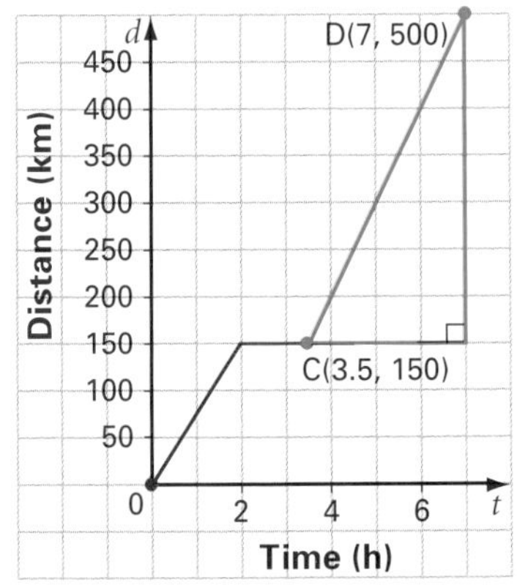


**d)** The ordered pair (7, 500) means that Team Susie completed the 500-km leg in 7 h.

## Key Concepts

- The slope of a line segment joining two points, A and B, can be calculated using $m = \frac{\text{rise}}{\text{run}} = \frac{y_B - y_A}{x_B - x_A}$.
- On a distance-time graph, slope represents speed. The formula becomes $m = \frac{d_B - d_A}{t_B - t_A}$.

## Discuss the Concepts

1. What is the formula for the slope of a line segment joining two points, A and B?
2. a) What is the slope of a horizontal line?
   b) Why is this true? Hint: Think of $\frac{\text{rise}}{\text{run}}$.

## Practise

**A**

***For help with questions 1 and 2, refer to Example 1.***

1. Determine the slope of the line segment joining each pair of points.
   a) A(2, 3) and B(5, 9) b) P(3, 1) and Q(7, 9)
   c) G(4, 4) and H(6, 2) d) U(8, 0) and V(0, 6)

2. Determine the slope of the line segment joining each pair of points.
   a) R(−1, 0) and S(2, −3) b) C(−10, −4) and D(−2, 6)
   c) T(0, 0) and W(−5, 6) d) K(−8, 3) and L(−5, 8)
   e) P(3, −1) and Q(−4, −6) f) G(−2, −5) and H(−6, −2)

## Apply the Concepts

**B**

3. **Communication**
   a) Write the coordinates of the three points, A, B, and C as shown.
   b) Find the slope of AB.
   c) Predict values for the slopes of BC and AC.
   d) Find the slopes of BC and AC. Compare these values with your prediction. Were you correct?
   e) When calculating the slope of a line, does it matter which two points you choose? Explain.

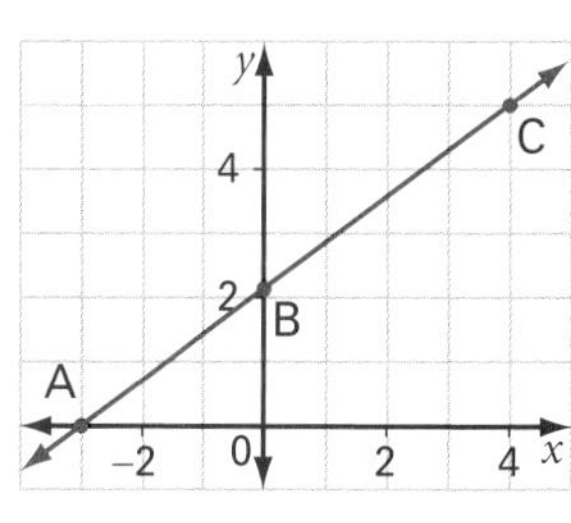

4. **Application** A student, in front of a motion sensor, starts at the 2-m mark and walks at a constant speed to the 5-m mark in 6 s. Determine the speed of the student. Verify your answer by drawing a sketch.

***For help with question 5, refer to Example 2.***

**Chapter Problem**

5. ***Runaround*** Distance-time graphs of two teams for the *Road-Race* leg are shown.

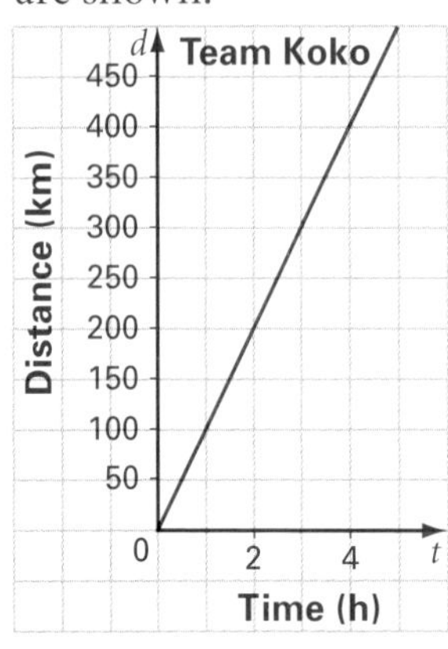


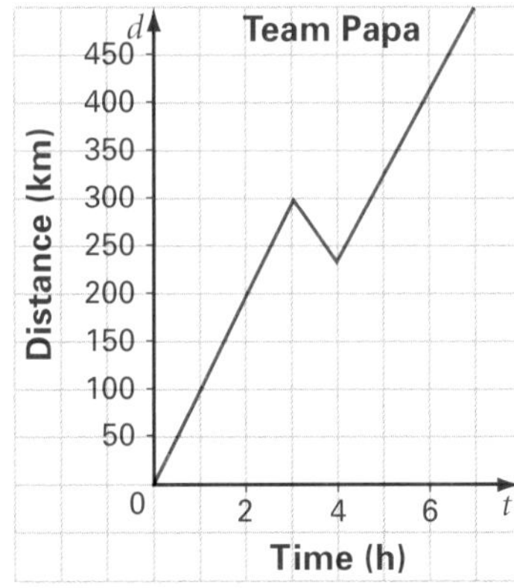


a) Which team travelled at a constant speed for the entire distance?
b) Determine this speed.
c) How long did it take for this team to complete this leg of the race?
d) What might have happened to Team Papa to account for their graph?
e) Determine their speed and direction for each interval of their graph.
f) How long did it take them to finish this leg of the race?

**C**

Refer to the Technology Appendix for help with using the TI-83 graphing calculator or *The Geometer's Sketchpad*®.

6. **Thinking/Inquiry/Problem Solving** Suppose these points are plotted on a grid.
A(−1, 3) B(2, 1) P(−4, 1) Q(−1, −1) U(−1, 1) V(5, −3)
a) Calculate the slopes of line segments AB, PQ, and UV.
b) Compare the slope values. What do you notice?
c) Predict what you expect to see when you graph these segments.
d) Plot line segments AB, PQ, and UV on the same grid.
e) What interesting feature do the line segments have in common? Compare this to your prediction. Were you correct? Explain.

7. **Thinking/Inquiry/Problem Solving** What is the slope of a vertical line? Use a graphing calculator or *The Geometer's Sketchpad*® to investigate what happens to the slope of a line as it becomes steeper and steeper. Write a brief report on your findings and how you approached this problem.

# 7.4 Graphing Lines Using Intercepts

In Chapter 6, you learned how to graph a linear relation using a table of values. For example, you can graph $y = 2x + 3$ by substituting values of $x$ into the equation and finding ordered pairs.

| $x$ | $y$ |
|---|---|
| 1 | 5 |
| 0 | 3 |
| −1 | 1 |

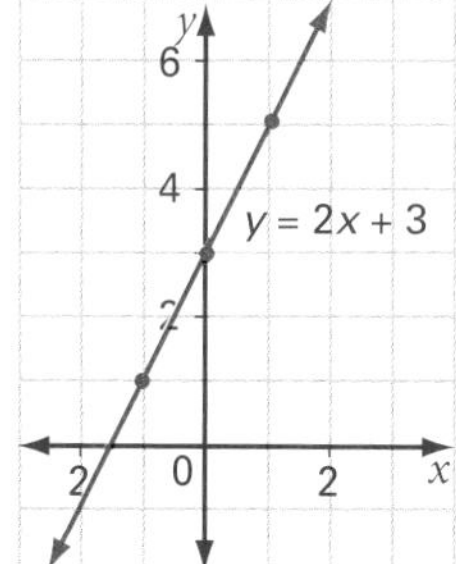


Each ordered pair represents a point on the line.

Linear relations may occur in different forms, such as $2x + 3y = 18$. In this section, you will learn how to graph linear relations in this form.

## Discover

### Finding a Meaning for Intercepts

Lily is at a baseball game with her nephew, Paul. Hot dogs cost \$3 and soft drinks cost \$2. Lily spends a total of \$18 on hot dogs and soft drinks.

1. If Lily buys only hot dogs and no soft drinks, how many can she purchase?

2. If Lily buys only soft drinks and no hot dogs, how many can she purchase?

3. Let $x$ be the number of hot dogs. Let $y$ be the number of soft drinks. Write each combination in steps 1 and 2 as an ordered pair $(x, y)$.

4. Plot the ordered pairs from step 3 on a graph. Join the points with a straight line.

5. a) If Lily buys a combination of hot dogs and soft drinks, what combinations can Lily buy?
   b) Explain how you found these combinations.
   c) Look at your graph. Explain how the graph can be used to discover combinations that work.

The **x-intercept** is the $x$-coordinate of the point where a line or curve crosses the $x$-axis. At this point, $y = 0$.

The **y-intercept** is the $y$-coordinate of the point where a line or curve crosses the $y$-axis. At this point, $x = 0$.

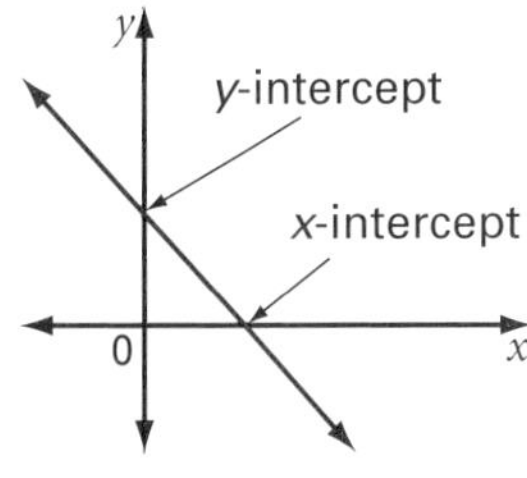


## Example 1

### Calculating Intercepts

The following equation can be used to model the situation in the **Discover** on page 299.

| $3x$ | + | $2y$ | = | 18 |
|---|---|---|---|---|
| \$3 × (number of hot dogs) | + | \$2 × (number of soft drinks) | = | Total Spent, \$18 |

a) Determine the $x$- and $y$-intercepts of the equation $3x + 2y = 18$.

b) Use the intercepts to graph the line.

### Solution

a) Find the $x$-intercept.
At the $x$-intercept, the value of $y$ is 0.

$3x + 2(0) = 18$ **Substitute $y = 0$.**

$3x = 18$ **Simplify.**

$\frac{3x}{3} = \frac{18}{3}$ **Divide both sides by 3.**

$x = 6$

The $x$-intercept is 6.
The point (6, 0) is on the line.

Find the $y$-intercept.
At the $y$-intercept, the value of $x$ is 0.

$3(0) + 2y = 18$ **Substitute $x = 0$.**

$2y = 18$ **Simplify.**

$\frac{2y}{2} = \frac{18}{2}$ **Divide both sides by 2.**

$y = 9$

The $y$-intercept is 9.
The point (0, 9) is on the line.

b) Plot the intercepts to graph this linear relation.

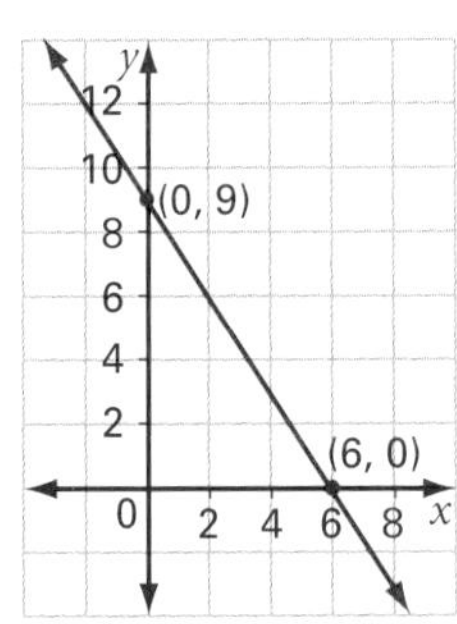


You can use this graph to find other points that satisfy the equation, such as (4, 3) and (2, 6).

Be careful when using a linear model. In this example, the point (5, 1.5) has no meaning, even though it is on the line. Why not?
Hint: What does $y$ represent?

## EXAMPLE 2

### Using Intercepts to Graph a Line

For each linear relation, determine the $x$- and $y$-intercepts and graph the line.

**a)** $3x - 4y = 12$ **b)** $-x + 2y = 5$

### Solution

**a)** Find the $x$-intercept. Let $y = 0$.

$$3x - 4(0) = 12$$
$$3x = 12$$
$$\frac{3x}{3} = \frac{12}{3} \quad \text{Divide both sides by 3.}$$
$$x = 4$$

The $x$-intercept is 4.
The point (4, 0) is on the line.

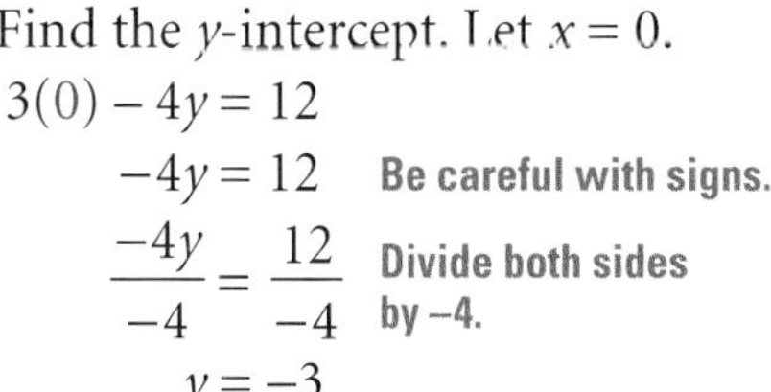

Find the $y$-intercept. Let $x = 0$.

$$3(0) - 4y = 12$$
$$-4y = 12 \quad \text{Be careful with signs.}$$
$$\frac{-4y}{-4} = \frac{12}{-4} \quad \text{Divide both sides by } -4.$$
$$y = -3$$

The $y$-intercept is $-3$.
The point $(0, -3)$ is on the line.

Plot the intercepts.
Draw the line through the intercepts.
Label the line with the equation.

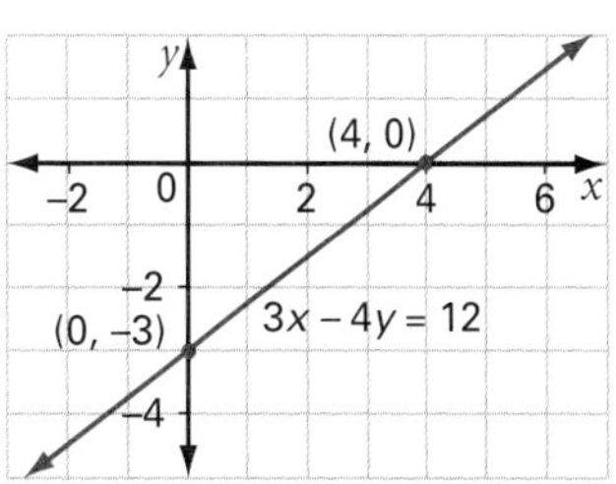


**b)** Find the $x$-intercept. Let $y = 0$.

$$-x + 2(0) = 5$$
$$-x = 5 \quad \text{Remember } -x \text{ means } -1x.$$
$$\frac{-x}{-1} = \frac{5}{-1} \quad \text{Divide both sides by } -1.$$
$$x = -5$$

The $x$-intercept is $-5$.
The point $(-5, 0)$ is on the line.

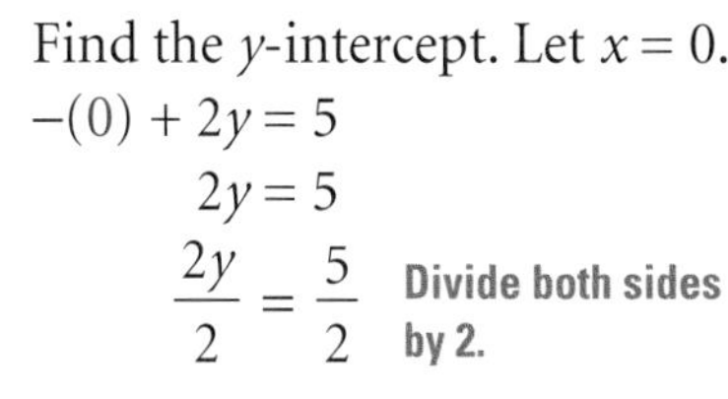

Find the $y$-intercept. Let $x = 0$.

$$-(0) + 2y = 5$$
$$2y = 5$$
$$\frac{2y}{2} = \frac{5}{2} \quad \text{Divide both sides by 2.}$$
$$y = 2.5$$

The $y$-intercept is 2.5.
The point (0, 2.5) is on the line.

Plot the intercepts.
Draw the line through the intercepts.
Label the line with the equation.

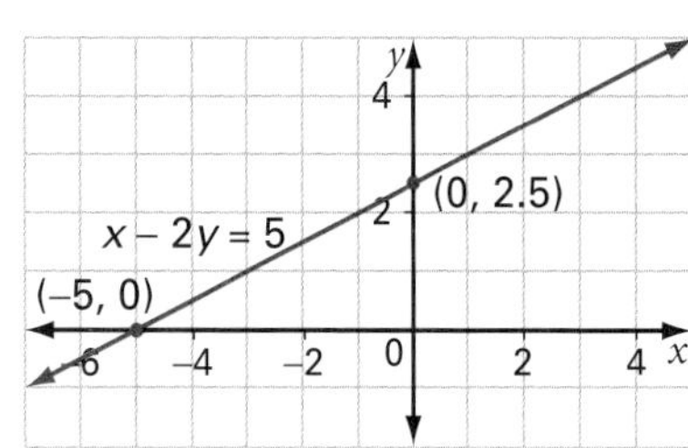

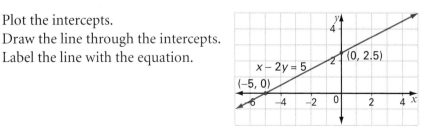

Fractional or decimal intercepts can be used to graph lines. Whether these points have meaning depends on the type of relationship they describe.

You can use the intercepts to find the slope of a line.

## Example 3

### Finding the Slope Using the Intercepts

Determine the slope of the line whose $x$-intercept is $-2$ and $y$-intercept is 8.

#### Solution

Graph the line by plotting the intercepts.
Label the two points A(−2, 0) and B(0, 8).
Count squares vertically from A to B.
The rise is 8 up, or 8.
Count squares horizontally from A to B.
The run is 2 right, or 2.

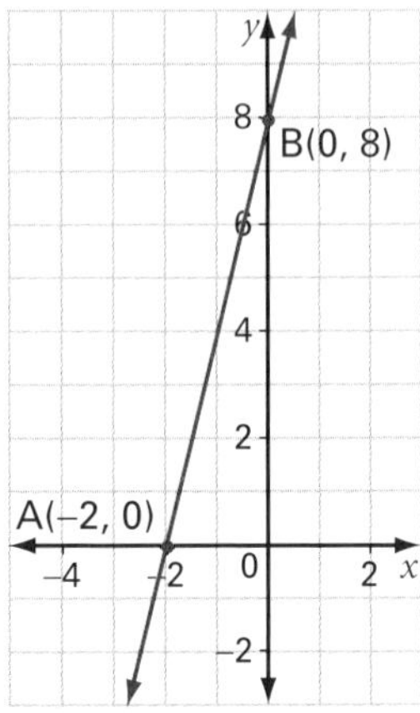


$$\begin{aligned}\text{slope } (m) &= \frac{\text{rise}}{\text{run}}\\ &= \frac{8}{2}\\ &= 4\end{aligned}$$

The slope of the line is 4.

## Key Concepts

- The **$x$-intercept** is the $x$-coordinate of the point where a line crosses the $x$-axis. At this point, $y = 0$.
- The **$y$-intercept** is the $y$-coordinate of the point where a line crosses the $y$-axis. At this point, $x = 0$.
- For some equations, it is easy to graph a line using intercepts.

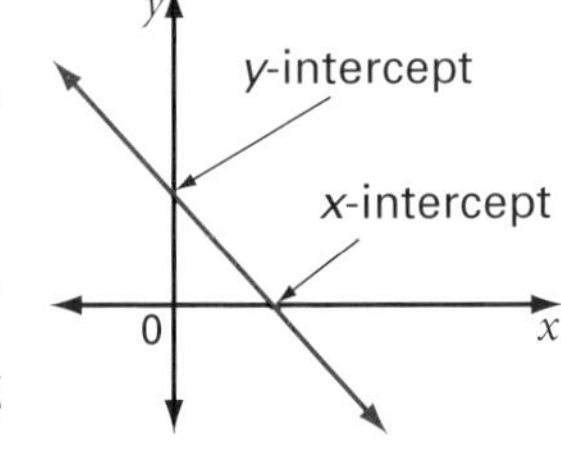


## Discuss the Concepts

1. a) What is the value of $x$ at the $y$-intercept of a graph? Why is this always true?
   b) What is the value of $y$ at the $x$-intercept of a graph? Why is this always true?
2. Is it possible for a line to have no $x$-intercept? Describe such a line.
3. A line has an $x$-intercept of 3 but no $y$-intercept. Describe the line.

## PRACTISE

**A** ***For help with question 1, refer to Example 1.***

1. Identify the $x$- and $y$-intercepts of each graph.

a) 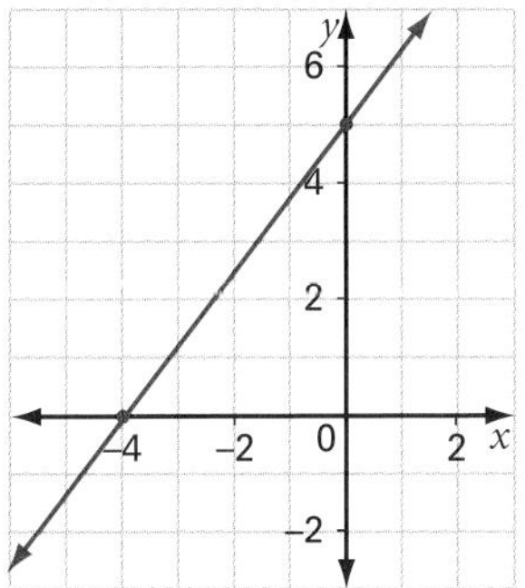

b) 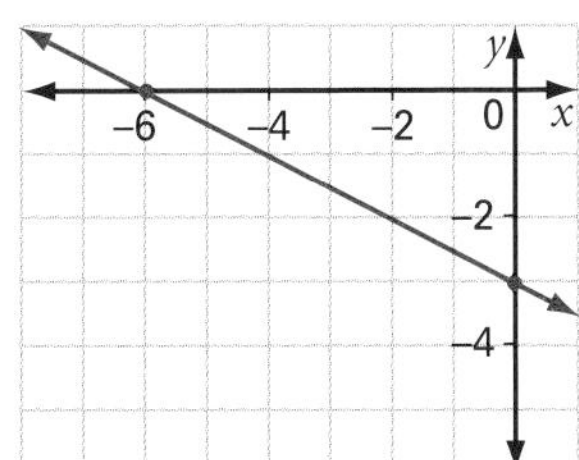

c) 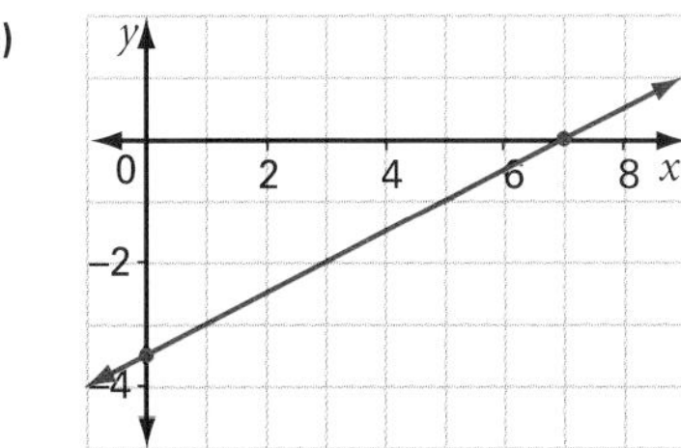

***For help with questions 2 and 3, refer to Example 2.***

2. For each of the following, plot the intercepts and graph the line.

| | x-intercept | y-intercept |
|---|---|---|
| a) | 4 | 7 |
| b) | −3 | 1 |
| c) | 1 | −4 |
| d) | −5.5 | −2 |

3. Determine the $x$- and $y$-intercepts and use them to graph each line.

a) $2x + 5y = 10$

b) $-2x - 3y = 12$

c) $3x + 6y = -9$

d) $4x - y = 6$

e) $3y - 7x = 21$

f) $y - x = 11$

## Apply the Concepts

**B** ***For help with question 4, refer to Example 3.***

**4.** Draw a graph and determine the slope of each line whose $x$- and $y$-intercepts are given.

**a)** $x$-intercept = 2; $y$-intercept = 4

**b)** $x$-intercept = −3; $y$-intercept = 5

**c)** $x$-intercept = 6; $y$-intercept = −3

**d)** no $x$-intercept; $y$-intercept = 3

**5. Application** The distance-time graph shows Kyla's motion in front of a motion sensor.

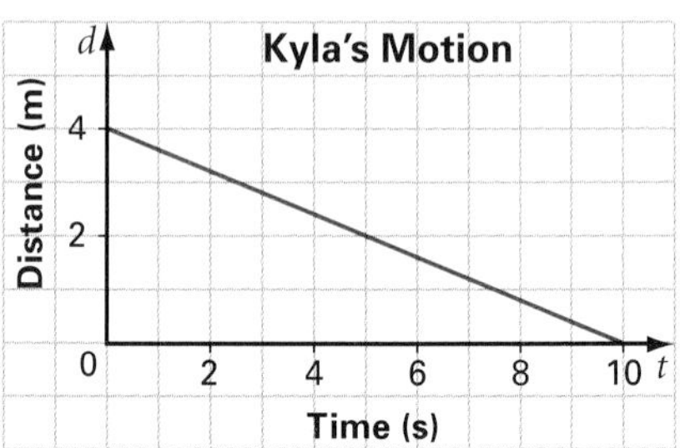


**a)** What is the $d$-intercept?

**b)** What is the $t$-intercept?

**c)** What information does each intercept give about Kyla's motion?

**d)** Use the graph or the slope formula to determine Kyla's speed. Remember the speed is the slope on a distance-time graph.

**Chapter Problem**

**6. *Runaround*** The next leg of *Runaround* involves a 500-m canoe race on Lake Louise in the Canadian Rockies. Each team paddles at a different constant rate.
Starting line: $d = 500$
Finish line: $d = 0$

| Team | Finish Time (s) |
|---|---|
| Papa | 38 |
| Susie | 30 |
| Koko | 35 |

**a)** Set up a distance-time graph for each team. Plot each $d$-intercept and each $t$-intercept. Graph each line.

**b)** Which team was the fastest? Which team was the slowest?

7. **Communication**

   a) Determine the $x$- and $y$-intercepts of $y + 2x = 6$.

   b) Use the intercepts to graph the line.

   c) Make a table of values for this equation. Substitute three different values of $x$ and solve for $y$.

   d) Graph the line using the table of values.

   e) How do the graphs in b) and d) compare?

   f) Which method for graphing the line do you prefer in this case? Explain.

8. **Thinking/Inquiry/Problem Solving** A candle burns at a constant rate of 2 cm/h. The candle is 12 cm tall when it is first lit.

   a) State the dependent and the independent variables.

   b) Set up a graph of length, $l$, in centimetres versus time, $t$, in hours.

   c) Plot points to represent the length of candle remaining after 0, 1, 2 h.

   d) Join the points and extend the line so that it crosses the $t$-axis.

   e) What is the $l$-intercept? What information does it give?

   f) What is the $t$-intercept? What information does it give?

   g) Why does this linear model have no meaning below the $t$-axis?

   h) Why does this linear model have no meaning to the left of the $l$-axis?

9. **Thinking/Inquiry/Problem Solving**

   a) How many $x$-intercepts does the graph have? What are they?

   b) How many $y$-intercepts does the graph have? What are they?

   c) Sketch a graph of a relation that has two $y$-intercepts.

   d) Sketch a graph of a relation that has three $x$-intercepts.

   e) Sketch a graph of a relation that has two $x$-intercepts and two $y$-intercepts.

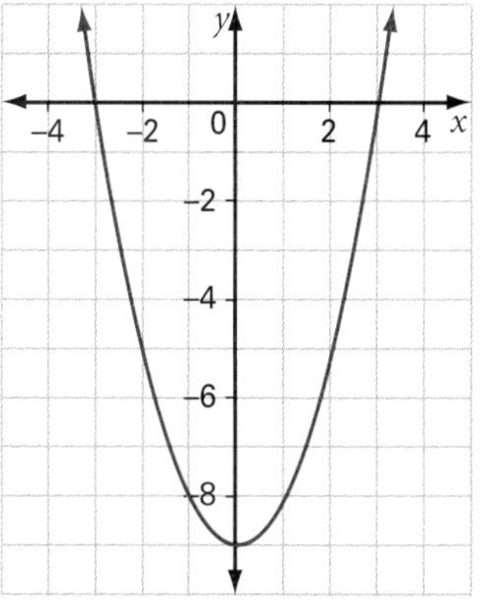


10. **Communication** Explain and use sketches to support your answers to each question.

   a) Is it possible for a line to have no $x$-intercept?

   b) Is it possible for a line to have no $y$-intercept?

   c) Is it possible for a line to have neither an $x$-intercept nor a $y$-intercept?

# 7.5 The Equation of a Line: $y = mx + b$

You have learned two methods for graphing lines:

- using a table of values
- using $x$- and $y$-intercepts

You can also graph a line if you know the slope and the $y$-intercept. These values also can be used to generate the equation of a line.

## DISCOVER A

### Exploring the Properties of $m$ and $b$

***Using a graphing calculator***

1. Turn the calculator on. Press the Y= key.

2. Graph the line $y = mx + b$. Start with values of $m = 1$ and $b = 1$:
   - Beside **Y1**, enter 1X + 1.
   - From the **ZOOM** menu, select **6:ZStandard**.
   - From the **ZOOM** menu, select **5:ZSquare**.

   A graph of the line should appear.

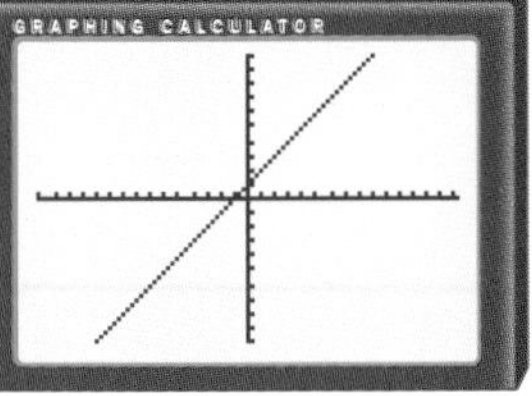


3. a) Predict what will happen when you enter values of 2, 0.5, and −1 for the slope, $m$.
   b) Press Y= and change the value of $m$ by typing over the original value. Use the values from part a).
   c) Were your predictions correct? Explain.

4. a) Predict how can you change $m$ to create
      - a horizontal line
      - a vertical line
   b) Test your hypotheses and describe any difficulties you encounter. Were your predictions correct? Explain.

5. a) Predict what will happen to the line when you
      - increase the value of the $y$-intercept, $b$
      - decrease the value of the $y$-intercept, $b$
   b) Press Y= and change the value of $b$ by typing over the original value.
   c) Were your predictions correct? Explain.

## DISCOVER B

## Exploring the Properties of *m* and *b*

***Using The Geometer's Sketchpad®***

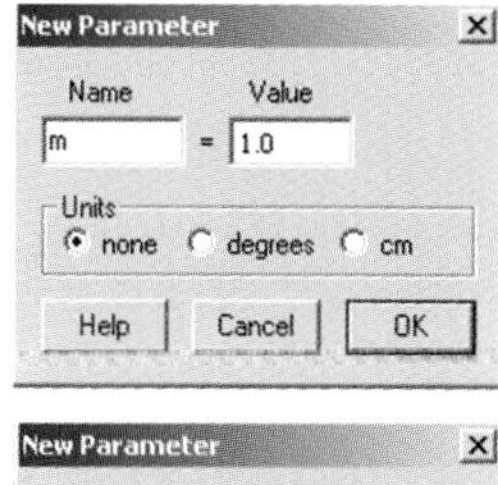


1. Open *The Geometer's Sketchpad®* and begin a new sketch.

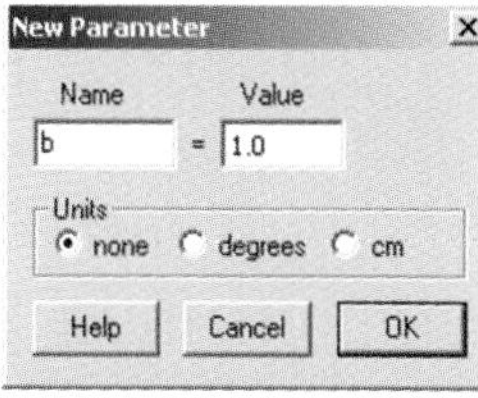


2. Plot the line $y = mx + b$:
   - From the **Graph** menu, choose **Plot New Function.**
   - Click on **Values** and choose **New Parameter.**
   - Type **m** in the **Name** field. Click **OK.**
   - Click on *, **x** , + from the keypad.
   - Click on **Values** and choose **New Parameter.**
   - Type **b** in the **Name** field. Click **OK.**

   Click **OK.**

   A line should appear on a coordinate grid.

* means "times".

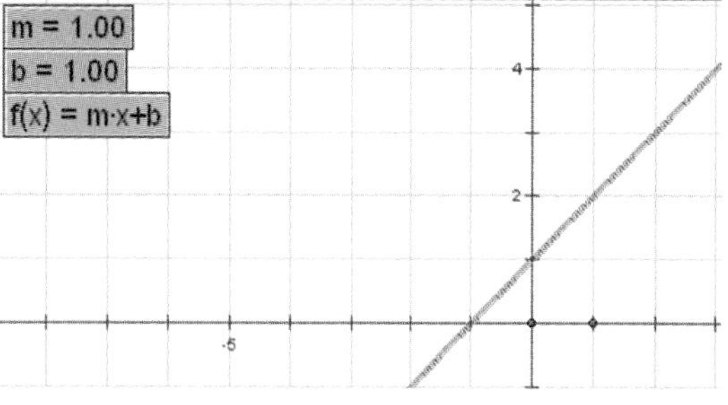


3. **a)** Predict what will happen when you enter the values of 2, 0.5, and −1 for the slope, *m*.
   **b)** Change the value of *m* by double-clicking on its measure. Use the values from part a). Were your predictions correct? Explain.

4. **a)** Animate the value of *m*:
   - Select the measure of *m*.
   - From the **Display** menu, choose **Animate Parameter.**
   - Use the **Motion Controller** window to change the speed or direction of the motion.

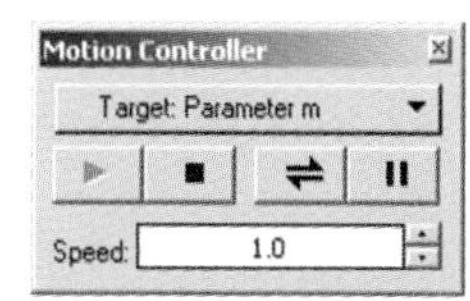


   **b)** Describe what happens when $m = 0$.
   **c)** What happens to the value of *m* when the line becomes almost vertical?
   **d)** Does this observation make sense? Explain.

5. **a)** Predict what will happen to the line when you
   - increase the value of the *y*-intercept, *b*
   - decrease the value of the *y*-intercept *b*

   **b)** Change the value of *b* by entering new values or by animating the parameter. Were your predictions in part a) correct? Explain.

## Discover C

### Materials

- grid paper
- several different coloured pencils or pens
- ruler

## Exploring the Properties of *m* and *b*

***Using paper and pencil***

1. On a piece of grid paper, set up a coordinate grid.

2. a) Graph the line $y = x + 1$.
   b) What is the slope and the $y$-intercept?

3. a) Predict how the line will change when you use the values of 2, 0.5, and $-1$ for the slope, $m$.
   b) Change the value of $m$ and graph each line on the same grid. Use a different colour for each line.
   c) Were your predictions correct? Explain.

4. a) Draw a horizontal line and a vertical line through (0, 1).
   b) State the slope and $y$-intercept for each line.
   c) How many $y$-intercepts does the vertical line have? Explain.

5. Set up a new grid and graph $y = x + 1$.

6. a) Predict what will happen to the line when you
      - increase the value of the $y$-intercept, $b$
      - decrease the value of the $y$-intercept, $b$
   b) Use various values of $b$ and graph each line on the same grid. Use a different colour for each line.
   c) Were your predictions in part a) correct? Explain.

Most linear relations can be described by the **slope-intercept form** of the equation of a line.

$y = mx + b$ is the equation of a line having a slope, $m$, and $y$-intercept, $b$.

The equation $y = mx + b$ relates two variables $x$ and $y$. The same method can be used to relate any pair of variables, such as Sales, $S$, and Earnings, $E$.

## Example 1

### Identifying the Slope and *y*-Intercept From an Equation

For each linear relation, identify the slope, $m$, and the $y$-intercept, $b$.

**a)** $C = 1.25n + 5.5$

**b)** $d = -t - 5$

**c)** $y = \frac{2}{3}x - 11$

**d)** $y = -\frac{5}{4}x$

### Solution

**a)** $C = 1.25n + 5.5$
Although different variables are used, the equation is in the form $y = mx + b$.
So, $m = 1.25$ and $b = 5.5$.

**b)** $y = \frac{2}{3}x - 11$ is the same as $y = \frac{2}{3}x + (-11)$.
So, $m = \frac{2}{3}$ and $b = -11$.

**c)** $y = -\frac{5}{4}x$ is the same as $y = -\frac{5}{4}x + 0$.
So, $m = -\frac{5}{4}$ and $b = 0$.

**d)** $d = -t - 5$ is the same as $d = (-1)t + (-5)$.
So, $m = -1$ and $b = -5$.

## Example 2

### Determining the Slope and *y*-Intercept From a Graph

For each graph,

- identify the slope and the *y*-intercept
- write the equation of the line

**a)**

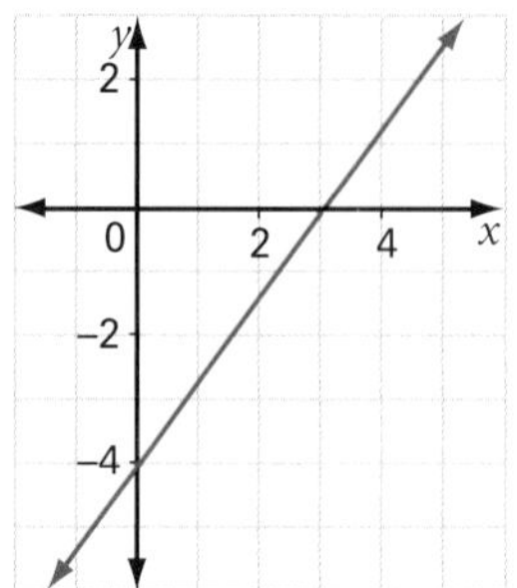


**b)**

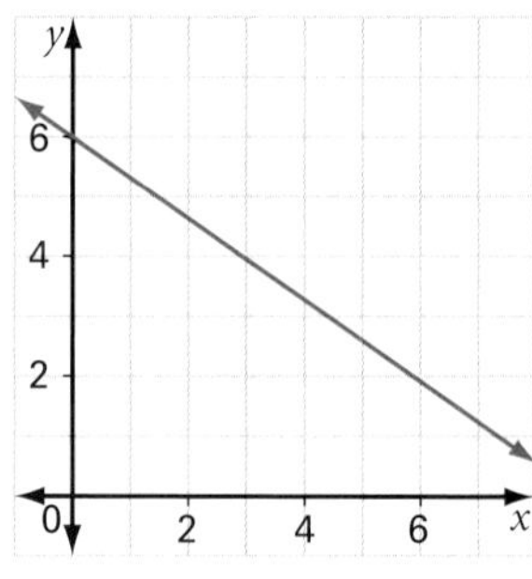


### Solution

**a)** The *y*-intercept is −4. To find the slope, *m*, use any two points on the line, in this case, the intercepts.

$$m = \frac{\text{rise}}{\text{run}}$$
$$= \frac{4}{3}$$

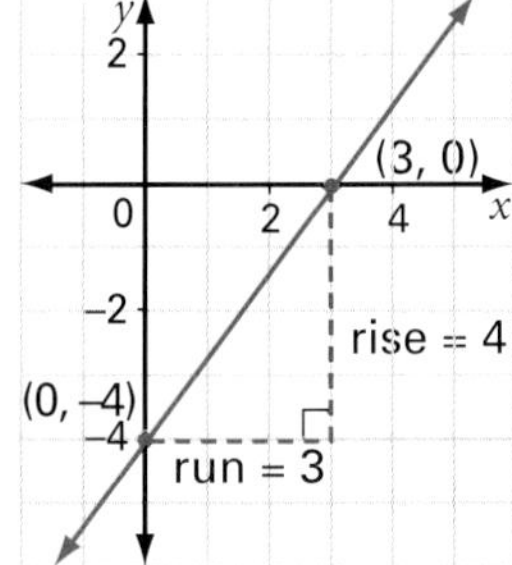


Substitute $m = \frac{4}{3}$ and $b = -4$ into $y = mx + b$.

The equation of the line is $y = \frac{4}{3}x - 4$.

**b)** The *y*-intercept is $b = 6$.
To find the slope, *m*, use any two points on the line, such as (0, 6) and (6, 2).

$$m = \frac{\text{rise}}{\text{run}}$$
$$= \frac{-4}{6}$$
$$= \frac{-2}{3}$$

**Since the line falls to the right, the "rise" is a negative value.**

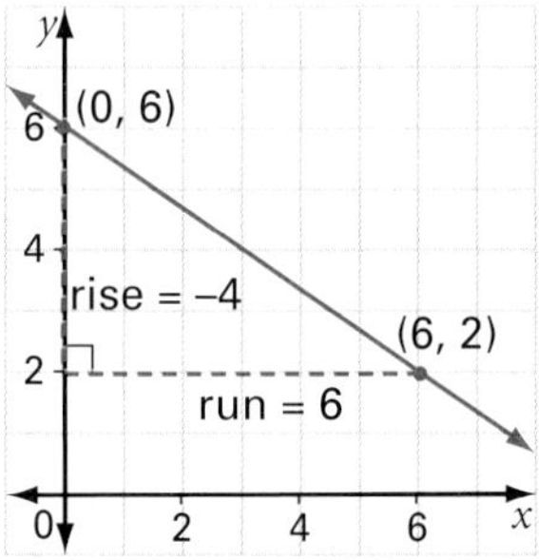


Substitute $m = -\frac{2}{3}$ and $b = 6$ into $y = mx + b$.

The equation of the line is $y = -\frac{2}{3}x + 6$.

## EXAMPLE 3

### Graphing a Line Using the Slope and *y*-Intercept

For each linear relation, the slope and *y*-intercept are given. Write the equation and graph the line.

**a)** $m = \frac{2}{3}$; $b = -3$ **b)** $m = -3$ ; $b = 0$

### Solution

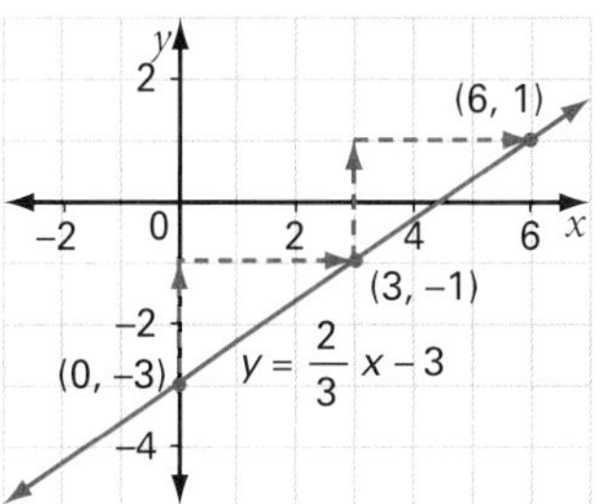


**a)** Substitute $m = \frac{2}{3}$ and $b = -3$ into $y = mx + b$.

The equation of the line is $y = \frac{2}{3}x - 3$.

Plot the *y*-intercept, which is at the point $(0, -3)$.

Since $m = \frac{\text{rise}}{\text{run}}$, from the *y*-intercept, rise 2 units and run 3 units to find additional points on the line.
Draw the line and label it with the equation.

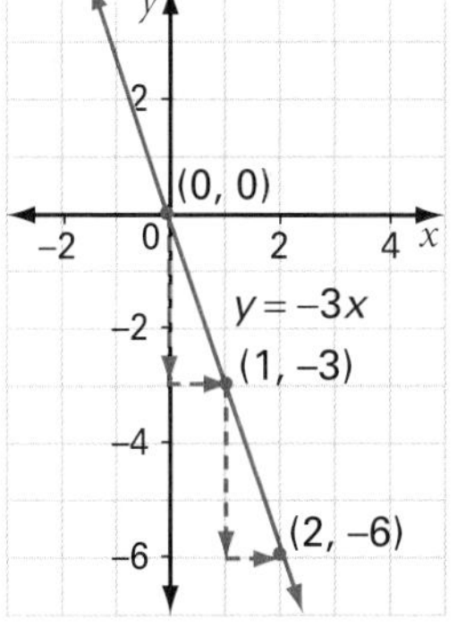


**b)** Substitute $m = -3$ and $b = 0$ into $y = mx + b$.

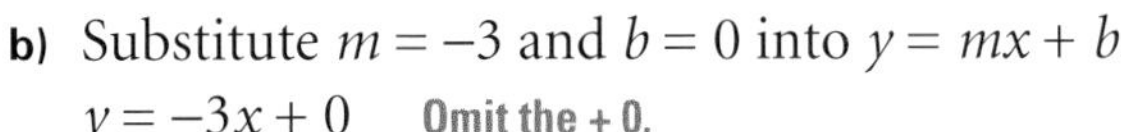

$y = -3x + 0$ **Omit the + 0.**

The equation of the line is $y = -3x$.
Plot the *y*-intercept, which is at $(0, 0)$.

$m = -3$ **Express *m* as a fraction: $\frac{\text{rise}}{\text{run}}$.**

$m = \frac{-3}{1}$ **−3 means 3 in a negative direction, which is down.**

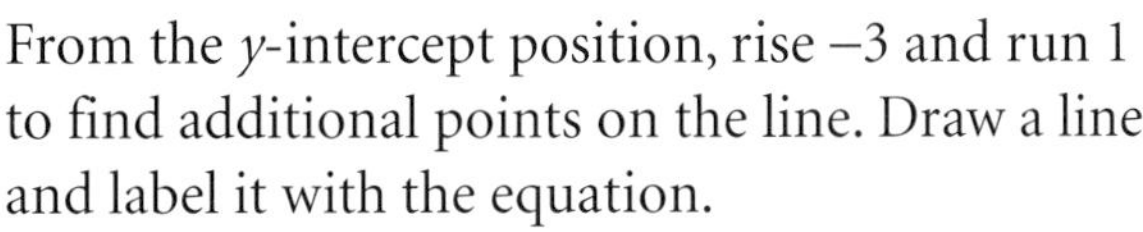

From the *y*-intercept position, rise −3 and run 1 to find additional points on the line. Draw a line and label it with the equation.

The equation $y = b$, where $b$ is a number, represents a horizontal line. The slope is 0. Equations such as $y = 2$ and $y = -3$ represent horizontal lines.

The equation $x = a$, where $a$ is a number, represents a vertical line. The slope is undefined. Equations such as $x = 4$ and $x = -1$ represent vertical lines.

## Key Concepts

- Most linear relations can be described by the slope-intercept form of the equation of a line $y = mx + b$, where $m$ is the slope and $b$ is the $y$-intercept.
- The equation of a horizontal line has the form $y = b$. The slope is 0.
- The equation of a vertical line has the form $x = a$. The slope is undefined.

## Discuss the Concepts

1. Explain how you can identify the slope and $y$-intercept by looking at the equation of a line in the form $y = mx + b$.
2. What happens to the line $y = mx + b$ when you
   a) increase the value of $m$?
   b) decrease the value of $m$?
   c) increase the value of $b$?
   d) decrease the value of $b$?
3. Explain how to graph a line using the slope, $m$, and the $y$-intercept, $b$.
4. a) Describe the equation of a vertical line. Why does it look like this?
   b) Describe the equation of a horizontal line. Why does it look like this?

## Practise

*For help with question 1, refer to Example 1.*

1. Identify the slope and $y$-intercept of each relation.
   a) $y = 6x + 5$ b) $y = -\frac{3}{4}x + 3$ c) $y = -4 + x$ d) $y = -x$

*For help with question 2, refer to Example 2.*

2. For each linear relation,
   - determine the slope and $y$-intercept
   - write the equation of the line

a)

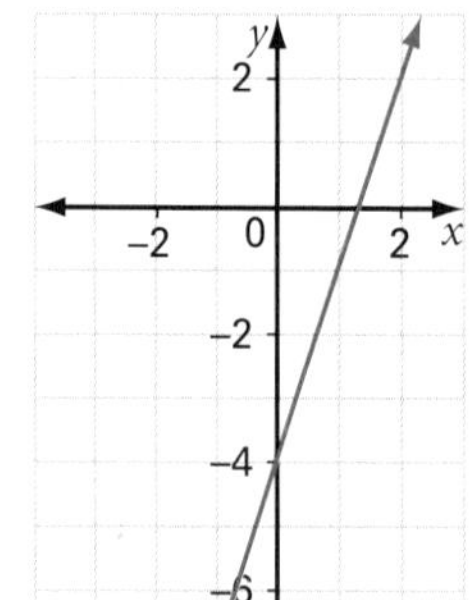


b)

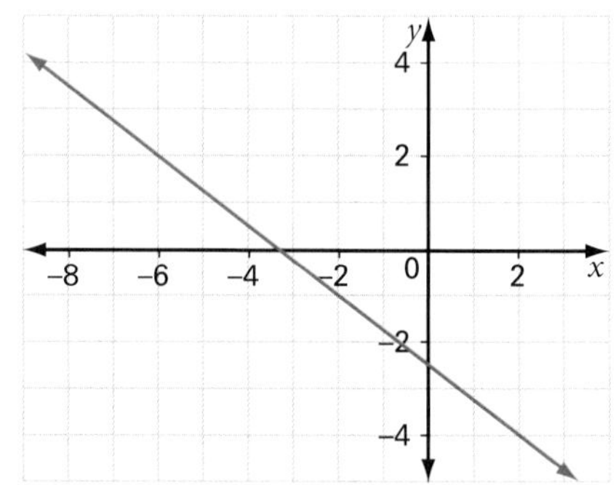

## APPLY THE CONCEPTS

**B** *For help with question 3, refer to Example 3.*

3. Write the equation and graph the line for each slope and $y$-intercept.

   a) $m = 2$ ; $b = -5$    b) $m = \frac{1}{3}$; $b = 2$    c) $m = -\frac{3}{4}$; $b = 0$

**Make Connections**

This linear relation is a partial variation.

4. **Application** The cost of a banquet can be represented by $C = 11p + 250$, where $p$ is the number of people attending.
   a) What is the meaning of 11 and 250?
   b) If the cost was $C = 11p + 350$, how would the graph change?
   c) If the cost per person was $20, how would the equation change?

**Chapter Problem**

5. Partway through one leg of *Runaround*, the position and speed of each team is measured. A negative speed means the distance to the next clue is decreasing.

| Team | Distance From Clue (m) | Speed (m/s) |
|---|---|---|
| Papa | 20 | –2 |
| Koko | 25 | –3 |
| Susie | 30 | –2.5 |

   a) Predict who will win this leg.
   b) On the same grid, plot a distance-time graph for each team. Use “Distance From Clue” as the $d$-intercept and “Speed” as the slope.
   c) Substitute into $d = mt + b$ to generate the equation of each line.
   d) Determine the $t$-intercept of each graph.
   e) From the graph, who won the race? Explain your answer.

6. Write the equation of each line.

   a) 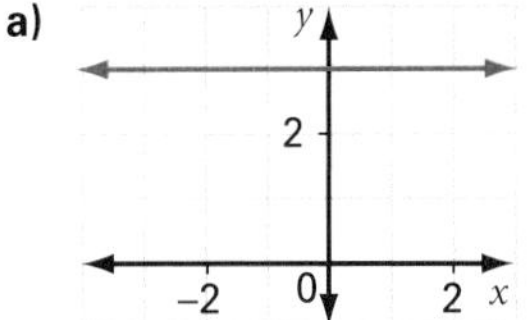


   b) 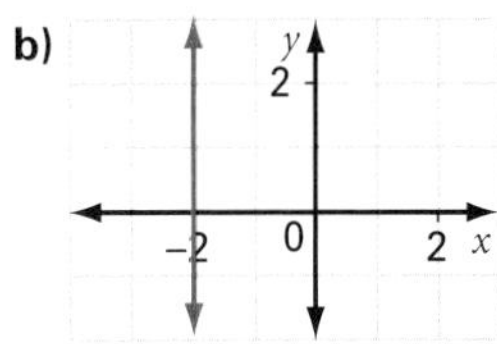


   c) 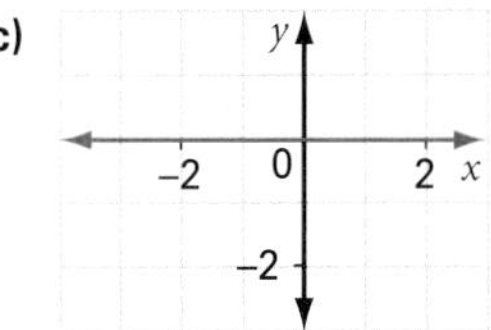


7. **Communication**
   a) What is the equation that describes the $y$-axis?
   b) What is the slope of this line?
   c) How many $y$-intercepts does it have? Explain.

**C** 8. **Thinking/Inquiry/Problem Solving**
   a) Graph the line $y = 3x – 6$ using three different methods:
      • Use a table of values.
      • Use $m$ and $b$.
      • Use the $x$- and $y$-intercepts.
   b) Which method do you think is the best in this situation? Explain.
   c) Explain when you would use each of the other two methods.

# 7.6 Constructing Linear Models: The Line of Best Fit

In real situations, you often observe data that shows a clear, but imperfect, linear trend. In such cases, often you still use a straight line to make reasonable predictions.

## DISCOVER A

### Finding a Line of Best Fit

***Using a graphing calculator***

Is there a relationship between grade 12 marks and first year college marks? Overall averages were collected for ten students.

| Student | Grade 12 | First Year College |
|---|---|---|
| Henrik | 80 | 83 |
| Sena | 78 | 74 |
| Larry | 64 | 66 |
| Nicole | 83 | 82 |
| Shannon | 60 | 54 |
| Jordan | 80 | 75 |
| Rhiannon | 96 | 91 |
| Fumio | 55 | 48 |
| Vashal | 72 | 68 |
| Laura | 90 | 88 |

1. Predict what a graph of this data might look like.

2. Before you begin, make sure there are no equations stored in the Y= editor.
   Press 2nd **[STAT PLOT] 4:PlotsOff** ENTER to turn off all plots.
   Press 2nd + **4:ClrAllLists** ENTER to clear all lists.

3. Enter the data into a table:
   - Press STAT.
   - Select **1:Edit.**
   - Enter the Grade 12 scores into **L1**.
   - Enter the First Year College scores into **L2.**

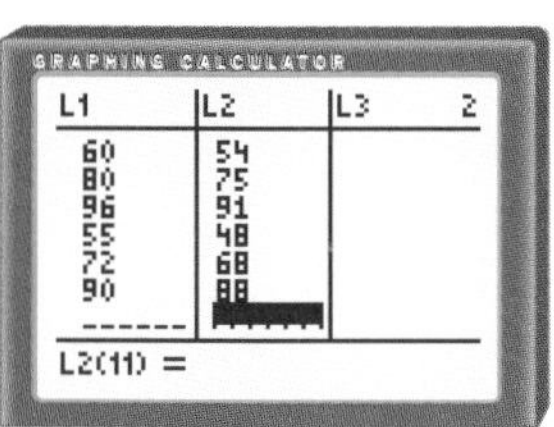

**Make Connections**

**Scatter plots** were introduced in section **4.5 Data Analysis: Trends and Relationships**.

For help with **Creating a Scatter Plot**, refer to the Technology Appendix.

4. Create a scatter plot for the data:
   - Press 2nd [**STAT PLOT**].
   - Select **1:Plot1**.
   - Set up **Plot1** as shown.

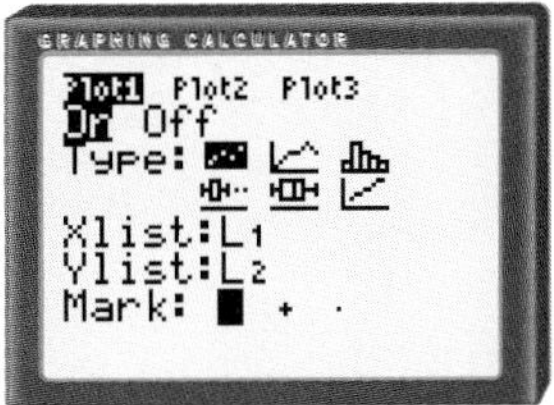


   - From the **ZOOM** menu, select **9:ZoomStat**.

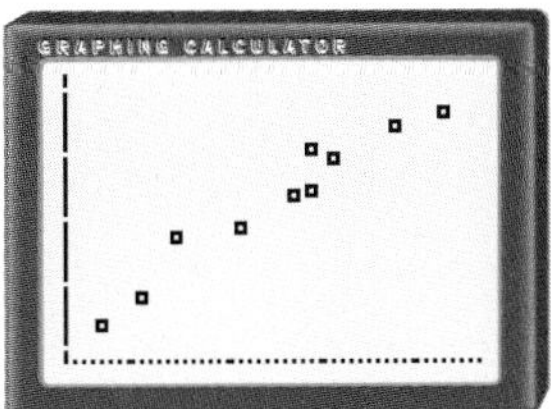


5. Describe any pattern the points make. Is the pattern perfect? Explain.

6. Graph the line $y = x + 1$:
   - Press Y= .
   - Type 1X + 1 and press ENTER .
   - Press GRAPH .

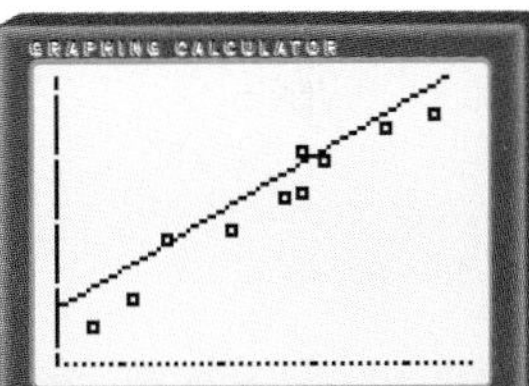


7. a) Adjust the values of $m$ and $b$ to create a line of best fit. This line should pass through or near as many points as possible.
   b) Record the values of $m$ and $b$.
   c) Substitute these values to write your line of best fit, $y = mx + b$. This equation is a linear model. It can be used to predict scores for other students.

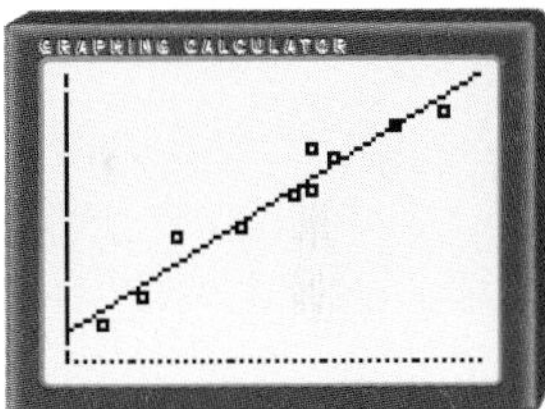


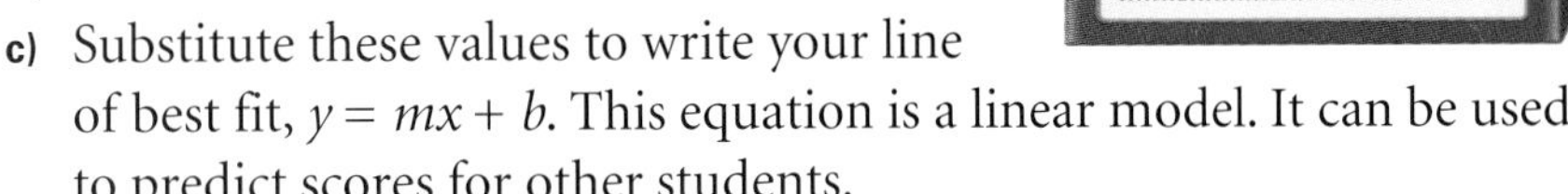

8. Average marks for three other grade 12 students are given.

| Student | Grade 12 |
|---|---|
| Maggie | 67 |
| Tom | 74 |
| Jean | 88 |

   a) Use your equation to predict each student's first year college average:
      - Substitute their grade 12 mark for $x$.
      - Solve for $y$.
   b) How accurate do you think these predictions are?
   c) What factors could affect the accuracy of this linear model?

# Discover B

## Finding a Line of Best Fit

**Materials**
- grid paper
- clear ruler

***Using paper and pencil***

Is there a relationship between grade 12 marks and first year college marks?

Use the data in the table in **Discover A**, page 314.

1. Predict what a graph of these data might look like.
2. Set up a grid as shown.

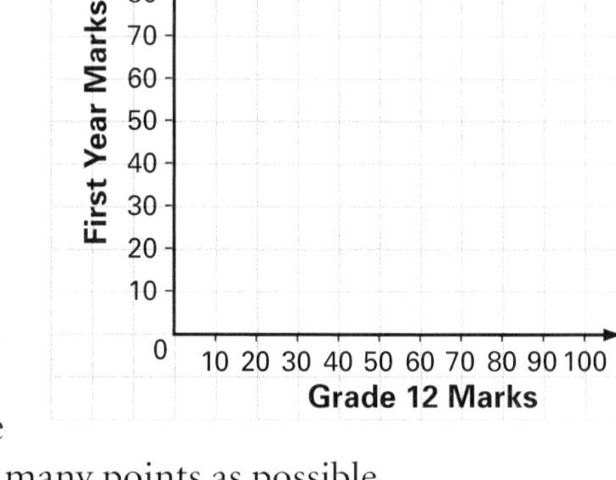


3. Plot each ordered pair to create a scatter plot for the data.
4. Describe any pattern the points make. Is the pattern perfect? Explain.
5. **a)** Place a clear ruler on the graph and adjust it so that you can draw a **line of best fit**. This line should pass through or near as many points as possible.
   **b)** Record the $y$-intercept.
   **c)** Pick two points on the line that are not close together. Use them to determine the slope of the line.
   **d)** Substitute these to write your line of best fit, $y = mx + b$. This equation is a linear model. It can be used to predict scores for other students.
6. Average marks for three other grade 12 students are given.

| Student | Grade 12 |
|---|---|
| Maggie | 67 |
| Tom | 74 |
| Jean | 88 |

   **a)** Use your equation to predict each student's first year college average:
   - Substitute their grade 12 mark for $x$.
   - Solve for $y$.

   **b)** How accurate do you think these predictions are?
   **c)** What factors could affect the accuracy of this linear model?

**Make Connections**

Scatter plots were introduced in section **4.5 Data Analysis: Trends and Relationships**.

Make Connections

**Interpolation** and **extrapolation** were introduced in section **6.1 Direct Variation**.

Linear relationships frequently occur in two-variable data analysis. In real situations, the data often do not line up perfectly. If the relationship is strong, a line of best fit can be used as a model to make reasonable predictions by using the techniques of interpolation and extrapolation.

## Example

### Applying a Line of Best Fit

| Time (s) | Distance (m) |
|---|---|
| 0 | 0 |
| 1.8 | 10 |
| 3.4 | 20 |
| 4.7 | 30 |
| 6.0 | 40 |
| 7.2 | 50 |
| 8.6 | 60 |
| 10.0 | 70 |
| 12.5 | 80 |

Rico is trying to run at a constant speed on a track. His partners collect distance-time data, using distance markers and stopwatches.

**a)** Create a scatter plot for distance versus time.

**b)** Draw a line of best fit.

**c)** For the line of best fit, determine the $d$-intercept. What does this value tell you about Rico's motion?

**d)** For the line of best fit, determine the slope. What does this value tell you about Rico's motion?

**e)** Write the equation relating distance and time.

**f)** Apply this linear model to predict how far Rico had run after 5 s.

**g)** Can Rico run 100 m in 15 s or less? Explain.

### Solution

**a)** Plot distance versus time.

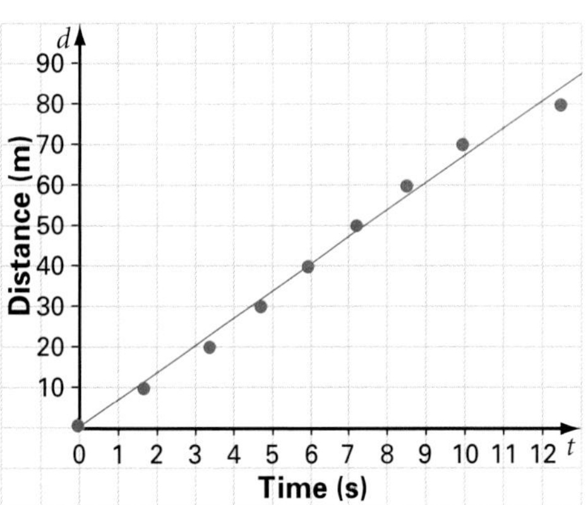


**b)** Add a line of best fit that passes through or near to as many points as possible.

**c)** The $d$-intercept is approximately 0. This means at time = 0 s, Rico had travelled 0 m.

**d)** Choose two points on the line of best fit that are reasonably far apart. (0, 0) and (11, 75) are on the line of best fit. Find the slope.

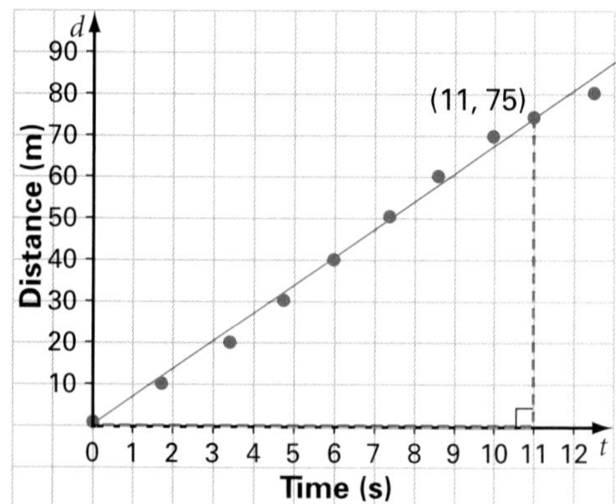


$$m = \frac{\text{rise}}{\text{run}}$$
$$= \frac{75}{11}$$
$$\doteq 6.8$$

The slope of a distance-time graph gives speed. Rico ran at 6.8 m/s.

**e)** To write the equation relating distance and time, substitute the values of $m$ and $b$ into $d = mt + b$.

$d = 6.8t + 0$ **Omit the + 0.**

The equation is $d = 6.8t$.

**f)** To determine how far Rico had run after 5 s, substitute $t = 5$ into the equation.

$d = 6.8(5)$

$d = 34$

Rico had run 34 m after 5 s.

**g)** To determine how far Rico had run after 15 s, substitute $t = 15$ into the equation.

$d = 6.8(15)$

$d = 102$

Rico had run 102 m after 15 s. So, Rico can run 100 m in 15 s or less.

## KEY CONCEPTS

- In real situations, linear relationships are usually not perfect.
- A line of best fit can model a linear relationship and be used to make predictions.

## DISCUSS THE CONCEPTS

1. In many real situations, data from linear relationships do not line up perfectly. Why is this so?
2. a) What is a line of best fit? b) How is it useful?
3. a) Explain how to draw a line of best fit.
   b) Explain how you can determine the equation of a line of best fit.

## PRACTISE

***For help with question 1, refer to Example 1.***

1. For each set of data,
   - create a scatter plot and draw a line of best fit
   - determine the slope and $y$-intercept
   - write the equation of the line of best fit

a)

| $x$ | $y$ |
|---|---|
| 2 | 4 |
| 3 | 5 |
| 5 | 7 |
| 7 | 10 |
| 9 | 13 |
| 12 | 15 |

b)

| $x$ | $y$ |
|---|---|
| 1 | 7 |
| 2 | 4 |
| 4 | 1 |
| 6 | –2 |
| 7 | –4 |
| 9 | –7 |

c)

| $x$ | $y$ |
|---|---|
| –5 | –2 |
| –3 | –1 |
| –2 | 3 |
| 0 | 8 |
| 3 | 9 |
| 6 | 15 |

## APPLY THE CONCEPTS

2. Is there a relationship between height and arm span?
   a) Measure the height and arm span for at least six friends and/or family members. Record the results in a table.

| Height (cm) | Arm Span (cm) |
|---|---|
| | |
| | |

   b) Create a scatter plot for the data and construct a line of best fit.
   c) Determine $m$ and $b$.
   d) Determine the equation of the line of best fit.
   e) Predict the arm span of a 175-cm-tall person.
   f) Predict the height of a person having an arm span of 150 cm.

3. **Application** For each scatter plot, explain how you should change $m$ and $b$ to create a better line of best fit.

a)

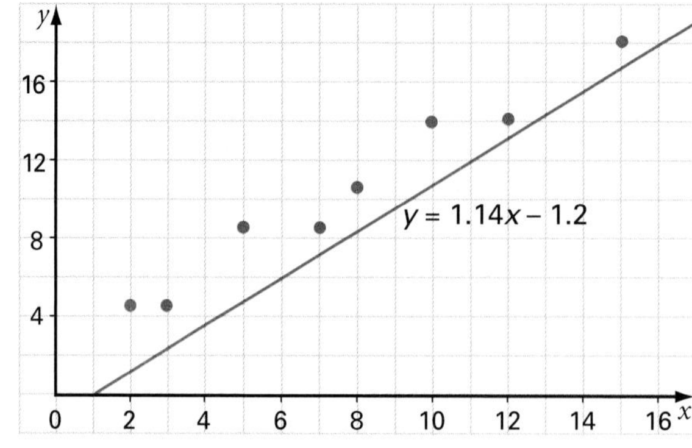


b)

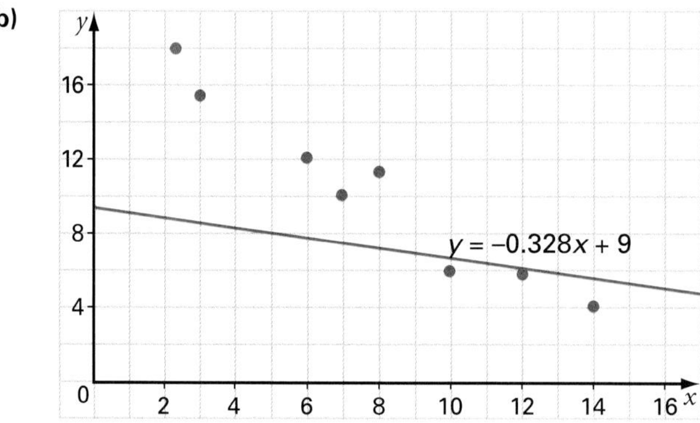


**Chapter Problem**

4. *Runaround* In this leg of *Runaround*, teams cycle along a 70-km section of the Tour de France bicycle route. Team Koko are tracking their *Runaround* progress by measuring their elapsed time at each 10-km marker.

| Time (min) | Distance (km) |
|---|---|
| 0 | 0 |
| 24 | 10 |
| 46 | 20 |
| 71 | 30 |
| 94 | 40 |
| 116 | 50 |

If you are using a graphing calculator, refer to the Technology Appendix for help with **Creating a Scatter Plot**.

a) Create a scatter plot of distance versus time.

b) Construct a line of best fit.

c) Use this linear model to estimate Team Koko's elapsed time at the midpoint of this leg of the race.

d) Use this linear model to estimate Team Koko's elapsed time at the end of this leg.

Refer to the Technology Appendix for help with **Creating a Scatter Plot**.

Refer to the Technology Appendix for help with **Changing Line Style**.

**C** 5. **Thinking/Inquiry/Problem Solving** Use a graphing calculator. Graphing calculators (and certain graphing software) will determine the line of best fit, using a mathematical process called **linear regression**. Use the linear-regression feature of a graphing calculator to produce a line of best fit for the data shown.

| Time (h) | Distance (km) |
|---|---|
| 1 | 100 |
| 2 | 190 |
| 3 | 240 |
| 4 | 350 |
| 5 | 465 |
| 6 | 520 |

**a)** Create a scatter plot for these data:
- Press STAT.
- Select **1:Edit.**
- Enter the $x$-values into **L1.**
- Enter the $y$-values into **L2.**
- Press ZOOM.
- Select **9:ZoomStat.**

**b)** Press Y=. In **Y1**, use trial and error to try to determine the equation of the line of best fit.

**c)** Determine the line of best fit, using linear regression:
- Press STAT.
- From the **CALC** menu, select **4:LinReg(ax+b)**.
- Press 2nd [L1] , 2nd [L2] , VARS ▶.
- From the **Y-VARS** menu, select **1:Function.**
- Select **2:Y2.**
- Press ENTER.

**d)** Under the line $y = ax + b$, you will see two values. "$a$" is the slope and "$b$" is the $y$-intercept for this line of best fit. Press Y=. The equation for the linear-regression equation appears in **Y2.**

**e)** Compare this equation with the one you discovered in part b). How close are they?

**f)** Press GRAPH to view the scatter plot and the two equations. You can change the line style of one of the lines to distinguish it from the other.

**g)** Compare the two line graphs. How close are they?

# 7.7 Investigating Parallel and Perpendicular Lines

The slope of a line is a measure of its steepness.

Is there a relationship between the slopes of parallel lines?

What about perpendicular lines?

## DISCOVER 1

(optional)
- grid paper
- ruler

### Comparing Parallel Lines

***Using The Geometer's Sketchpad® or paper and pencil***

1. Verify that the two points A(0, 3) and B(1, 5) are on the line $y = 2x + 3$. Call this line $L_1$.

2. Open *The Geometer's Sketchpad®* and begin a new sketch.

3. *The Geometer's Sketchpad®*: Graph $L_1$:
   - From the **Graph** menu, choose **Plot Points.**
   - Plot A(0, 3) and B(1, 5).
   - Click **Done.** The two points should appear on a grid.
   - Select A and B.
   - From the **Construct** menu, choose **Line.** A line through points A and B should appear.

   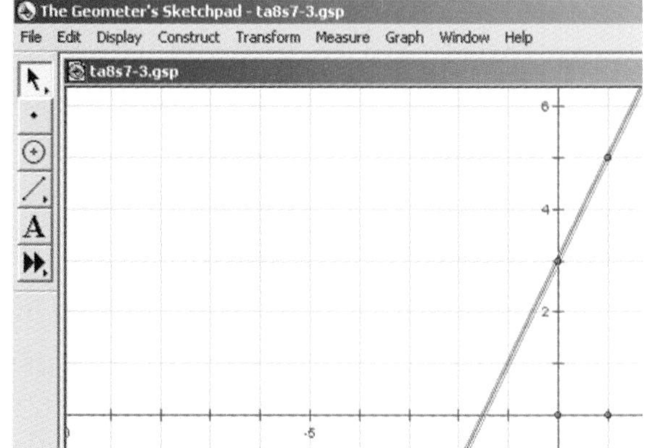
   

   *Paper and Pencil:* Graph the line $y = 2x + 3$ on a piece of grid paper. Label this line $L_1$.

4. a) Look at the equation. What is the slope of this line?
   b) *The Geometer's Sketchpad®*: From the **Measure** menu, choose **Slope**. Does this value make sense? Explain.
   *Paper and Pencil*: Use rise and run to calculate the slope of $L_1$. Does this value make sense? Explain.

Remember to "deselect" an object before making a new selection.

5. You will construct a number of lines parallel to $L_1$.
   a) Predict how you think the slopes of these lines will be related.
   b) *The Geometer's Sketchpad®*:
   - Plot a point anywhere on the graph, not on $L_1$.
   - Select the point and $L_1$.
   - From the **Construct** menu, choose **Parallel Line**.
   - Repeat to create two more parallel lines.

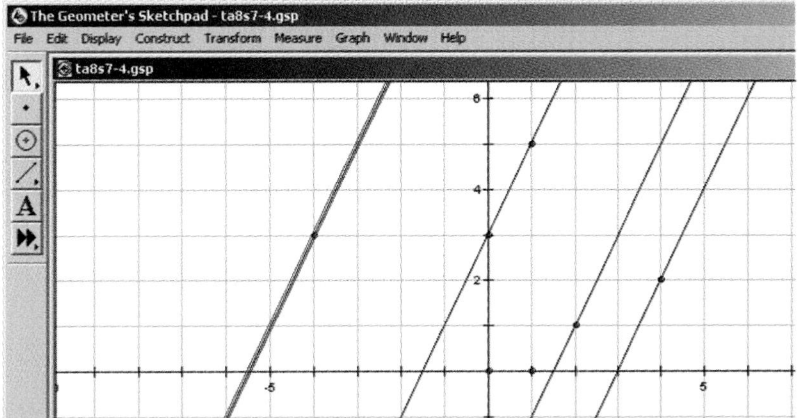


   *Paper and Pencil*:
   - Plot a point anywhere on the graph, not on $L_1$.
   - Use a ruler to draw a line through the point that is parallel to $L_1$.
   - Repeat to create two more parallel lines.

6. a) *The Geometer's Sketchpad®*:
   - Select one line.
   - From the **Measure** menu, choose **Slope**.
   - Repeat for each line.

   *Paper and Pencil*:
   - Select one line.
   - Draw a right triangle and find its slope.
   - Repeat for each line.

   b) Compare the slopes of the lines. Is this what you predicted in step 5? Explain.

7. a) *The Geometer's Sketchpad*®: Determine the equation of each line:
   - Select one line.
   - From the **Measure** menu, choose **Equation**.
   - Repeat for each line.

   *Paper and Pencil*: Determine the equation of each line:
   - Select one line.
   - Identify its $y$-intercept.
   - Substitute $m$ and $b$ into $y = mx + b$.
   - Repeat for each line.

   b) Compare the equations of the lines. Describe the similarities and differences.

8. Describe the relationship between the slopes of parallel lines.

# DISCOVER 2

(optional)
- grid paper
- ruler
- protractor

## Comparing Perpendicular Lines

***Using The Geometer's Sketchpad® or paper and pencil***

1. Verify that the two points A(6, 0) and B(0, –4) are on the line $y = \frac{2}{3}x - 4$. Call this line $L_1$.

2. Open *The Geometer's Sketchpad*® and begin a new sketch.

3. *The Geometer's Sketchpad*®:
   - From the **Graph** menu, choose **Plot Points.**
   - Plot A(6, 0) and B(0, –4).
   - Click **Done.** The two points should appear on a grid.
   - Select A and B.
   - From the **Construct** menu, choose **Line.**

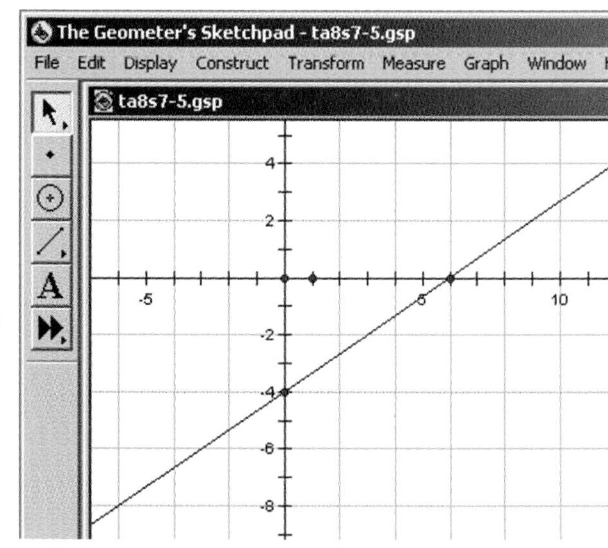


*Paper and Pencil*: Graph the line $y = \frac{2}{3}x - 4$ on a piece of grid paper. Label this line $L_1$.

Remember to "deselect" an object before making a new selection.

4. a) Look at the equation. What is the slope of this line?
   b) *The Geometer's Sketchpad®*: From the **Measure** menu, choose **Slope**. Does this value make sense? Explain.
   *Paper and Pencil*: Use rise and run to calculate the slope of $L_1$. Does this value make sense? Explain.

5. You will construct a line perpendicular to $L_1$.
   a) Predict how you think the slopes of these lines will be related.
   b) *The Geometer's Sketchpad®*:
   - Plot a point anywhere not on $L_1$.
   - Select this point and $L_1$.
   - From the **Construct** menu, select **Perpendicular Line**.
   - Call this line $L_2$.

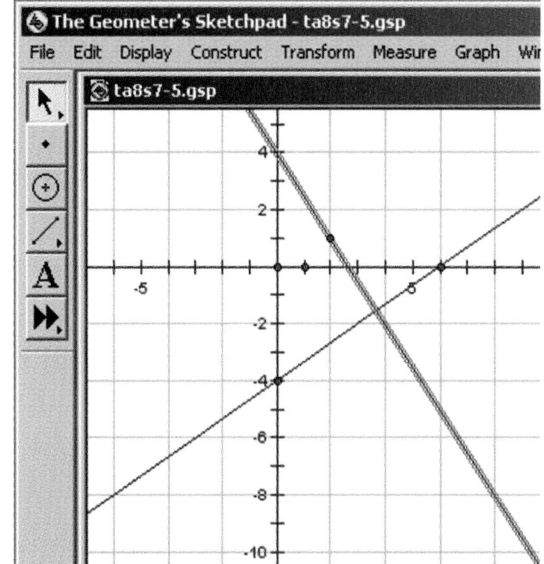


   *Paper and Pencil*:
   - Pick a point, P, on $L_1$.
   - From P, draw a point Q, not on $L_1$, so that the line segment joining PQ is at a 90° angle to $L_1$.
   - Use a ruler to draw a line through P and Q that is perpendicular to $L_1$. Call this $L_2$.

6. Measure the slope and find the equation of $L_2$.

7. Compare the slopes of $L_1$ and $L_2$. Is this what you predicted in step 5? Explain.

8. Repeat steps 1 to 7 for the line $y = -\frac{3}{4}x + 2$. You will need to determine two points on the line to begin the construction.

9. Describe the relationship between the slopes of perpendicular lines.

# Review

## 7.1 Motion Sensors and Distance-Time Graphs, pages 280–287

1. Describe the motion in front of a sensor that will produce each distance-time graph.

a) 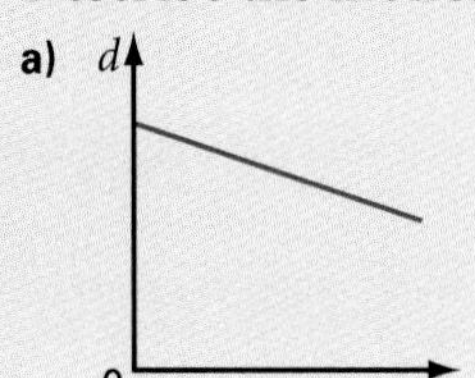


b) 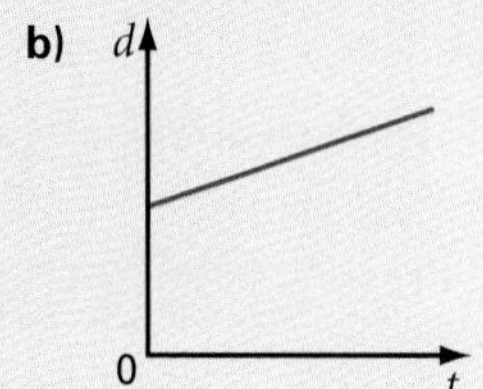


c) 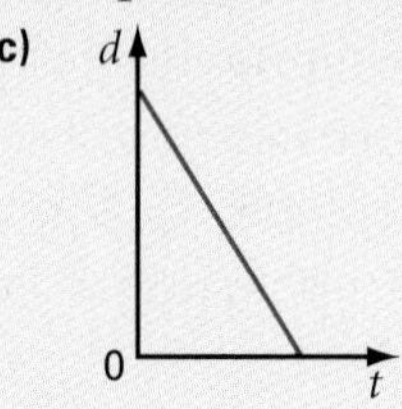


d) 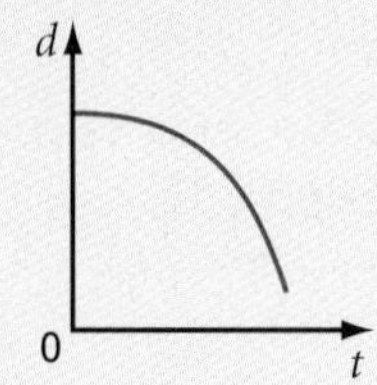


2. Sketch a distance-time graph for motion in front of a motion sensor.
   a) Start at 5 m and walk quickly away from the sensor.
   b) Start at 4 m and do not move.
   c) Start at 6 m, walk slowly toward the sensor for 4 s, then immediately walk away from the sensor quickly for 2 s.

## 7.2 Slope, pages 288–293

3. Determine the slope of each object.

a) 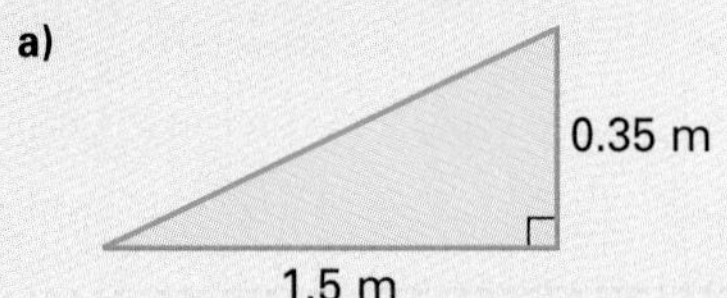


b) 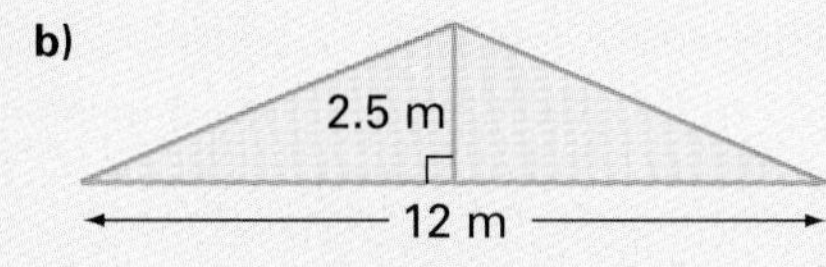


4. Describe the series of movements in front of a motion sensor that will produce the distance-time graph shown. Discuss both speed and direction in your answer.

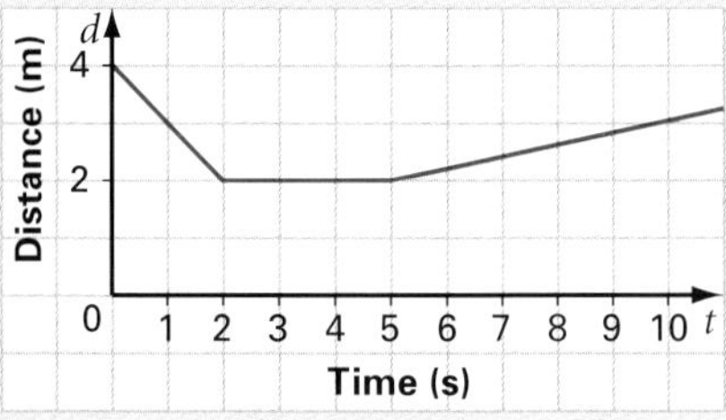


## 7.3 Applying the Slope Formula, pages 294–298

5. Determine the slope of the line segment joining each pair of points.
   a) A(3, –2) and B(9, 4)
   b) P(–3, 0) and Q(5, –4)

## 7.4 Graphing Lines Using Intercepts, pages 299–305

6. Determine the $x$- and $y$-intercepts and use them to graph each line.
   a) $5x + 3y = 15$
   b) $2x - 3y = 12$
   c) $3x - y = -6$

## 7.5 The Equation of a Line: $y = mx + b$, pages 306–313

7. The slope and $y$-intercept are given. Write the equation and graph the line.

   a) $m = \frac{1}{5}$; $b = -4$  b) $m = -3$ ; $b = 0$

8. The amount of cat food remaining in Nala's bowl, $A$, as she eats her lunch, is shown.

   a) Does Nala eat her food at a constant rate? Explain.
   b) What is the slope and $A$-intercept?
   c) What do the slope and $A$-intercept tell you about Nala's lunch?
   d) What does the $t$-intercept tell you about Nala's lunch?

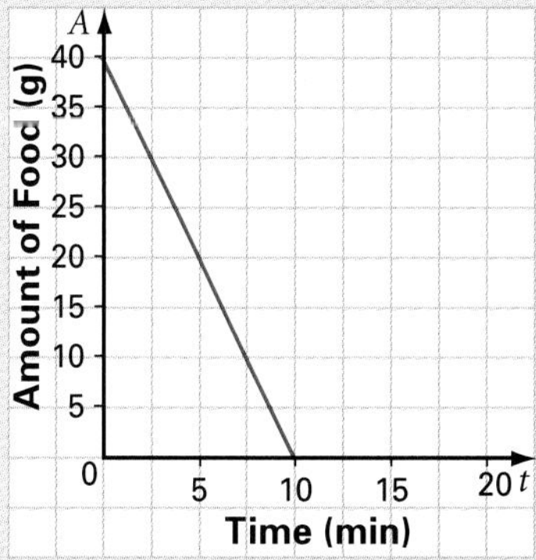


9. In the final sprint of *Runaround*, the three finalists are running at the same speed of 5 m/s. When Team Papa reaches the final 50-m mark, they have a 10-m lead over Team Susie and a 15-m lead over Team Koko.

   **Chapter Problem**

   a) Substitute $m$ and $b$ into $d = mt + b$ to determine the equation of each team's distance-time graph.
   b) Graph all three lines on the same grid.
   c) If no team changes their speed, who will win?
   d) How many seconds behind will the other two teams finish?
   e) How fast must Team Susie run the final 50 m in order to catch Team Papa at the finish line? Explain how you arrived at your answer.
   f) Repeat part e) for Team Koko.

## 7.6 Constructing Linear Models: The Line of Best Fit, pages 314–321

10. Various masses are suspended from a spring. The distance the spring is stretched is measured for each mass.

   a) Create a scatter plot of distance versus mass.
   b) Draw a line of best fit.
   c) Determine the equation of the line of best fit.
   d) Use the linear model to predict the amount the spring will stretch if a mass of 600 g is suspended.
   e) Use the linear model to predict the amount the spring will stretch if a mass of 10 000 g is suspended.
   f) Suggest why the answer to part e) may not be accurate.

| Mass (g) | Distance (cm) |
|---|---|
| 0 | 0 |
| 100 | 5 |
| 250 | 13 |
| 500 | 23 |
| 750 | 44 |
| 1000 | 52 |

# Practice Test

## Multiple Choice

***For each question, select the best answer.***

**1.** A person walks in front of a motion sensor. Which statement best describes the motion shown in the distance-time graph?

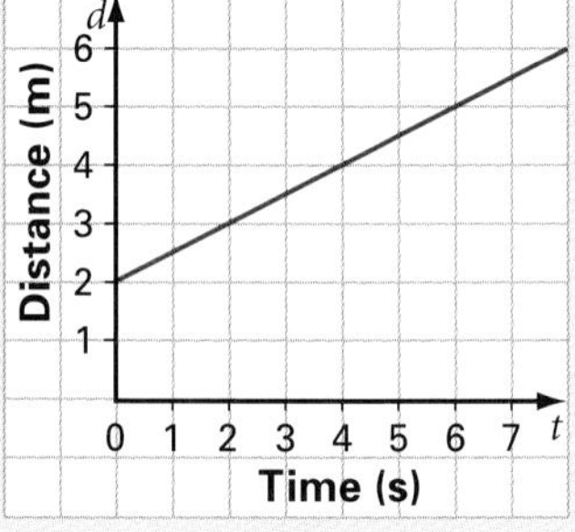


**A** Start at 2 m and walk toward the sensor at 0.5 m/s.

**B** Start at 2 m and walk away from the sensor at 0.5 m/s.

**C** Start at 2 m and walk toward the sensor at 2 m/s.

**D** Start at 2 m and walk away from the sensor at 2 m/s.

**2.** What is the slope of the ramp shown?

**A** 0.04 **B** 0.4

**C** 4 **D** 40

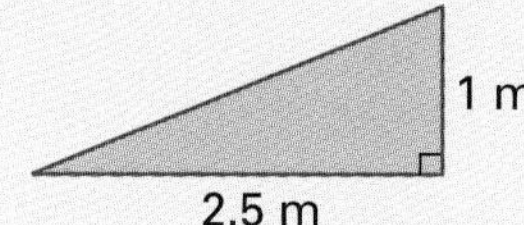

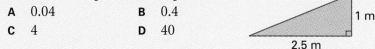

**3.** For the line, $3x - 4y = 12$, which statement is true?

**A** The $x$-intercept is 3 and the $y$-intercept is 4.

**B** The $x$-intercept is 3 and the $y$-intercept is $-4$.

**C** The $x$-intercept is 4 and the $y$-intercept is 3.

**D** The $x$-intercept is 4 and the $y$-intercept is $-3$.

**4.** What is the equation of the line having a slope of 3 and a $y$-intercept of $-5$?

**A** $y = 3x + 5$ **B** $y = 5x + 3$ **C** $y = 3x - 5$ **D** $y = 5x - 3$

**5.** What are the slope and the $y$-intercept of the line shown?

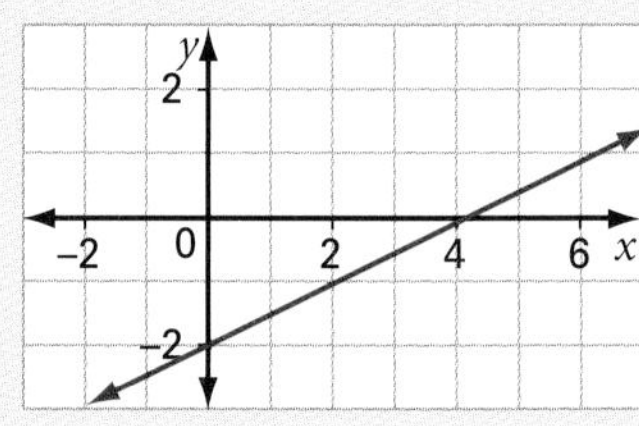


**A** $m = 2$ and $b = 4$ **B** $m = \frac{1}{2}$ and $b = -2$

**C** $m = \frac{1}{2}$ and $b = 4$ **D** $m = 4$ and $b = -2$

## Short Answer

**6.** Sheila was explaining to her classmate how she graphed the line $3x - 5y = 15$. "First I made up a table of values. I used $x = 1$, 2, and 3. Then, I worked out the $y$-value for each $x$-value. I used trial and error on my calculator and came up with some decimals. Then I plotted the points and joined them to make the line".

**a)** Describe a different method that Sheila could have used.

**b)** Use this method to graph the line.

7. Two koala bears, Rocco and Biff, are competing in a race. Because one of them is a faster runner, the other gets a head start. Their distance-time graphs are shown.
   a) Determine the slope and $d$-intercept of each graph.
   b) Who got a head start? How much of a head start did he get?
   c) How fast did each bear run?
   d) Who will win a 10-m race? Explain your answer.
   e) Who will win a 20-m race? Explain your answer.
   f) For what distance race will the bears tie? Explain your answer.

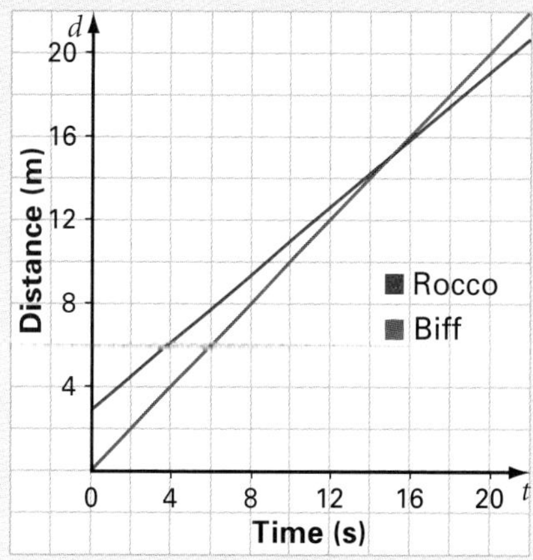


## Extended Response

8. **Application** Owen is an NHL hockey player. Here are some of his statistics for the past six years.
   a) Create a scatter plot of goals versus games played.
   b) Draw a line of best fit.
   c) Determine the equation of the line of best fit.
   d) Use your linear model to predict how many goals Owen will score next season, assuming he plays 50 games.
   e) Use your linear model to predict how many goals Owen will score next season, assuming he plays 82 games.
   f) How many games might he need to play to score 20 goals?

| Games Played | Goals |
|---|---|
| 28 | 4 |
| 60 | 25 |
| 44 | 14 |
| 65 | 26 |
| 70 | 33 |
| 72 | 36 |

**ACHIEVEMENT CHECK** Knowledge/Understanding Thinking/Inquiry/Problem Solving Communication Application

9. The values of rare antiques and works of art increase over time. The tables show the values for an oriental vase and a wildlife print over the last 20 years.

| Oriental Vase | Value |
|---|---|
| When purchased | $425 |
| After 5 years | $450 |
| After 10 years | $475 |
| After 15 years | $500 |
| After 20 years | $525 |

| Wildlife Print | Value |
|---|---|
| When purchased | $550 |
| After 5 years | $600 |
| After 10 years | $650 |
| After 15 years | $700 |
| After 20 years | $750 |

   a) Use a graphing calculator to graph the data given in each table.
   b) Find the equation of the line for each graph. Explain how you found each equation.
   c) What is the slope of each line and what does the slope represent?
   d) Predict the value of the oriental vase after 30 years. Explain your answer.
   e) Predict the value of the wildlife print after 23 years. Explain your answer.

# Cumulative Review

## Chapters 6 and 7

**1.** The perimeter of a regular hexagon varies directly with its side length.

| Side Length (cm) | Perimeter (cm) |
|---|---|
| 1 | 6 |
| 2 | 12 |
| 3 | 18 |
| 4 | 24 |
| 5 | 30 |

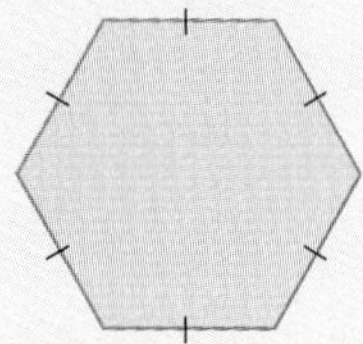

**a)** Is this a direct or partial variation? Explain.
**b)** Write an equation relating perimeter, $P$, and side length, $s$.
**c)** Use the equation to find the perimeter of a regular hexagon with a side length of 8 cm.

**2.** **Towing costs** A tow truck operator's charges for towing a vehicle are shown.

| Distance Towed (km) | Cost ($) |
|---|---|
| 0 | 40 |
| 10 | 50 |
| 20 | 60 |
| 30 | 70 |
| 40 | 80 |

**a)** Is this a direct or partial variation? Explain.
**b)** Write an equation relating cost, $C$, and distance towed, $d$.
**c)** Graph the relation.
**d)** How much would it cost to have your car towed 15 km?
**e)** If a car owner was charged $86, how far was her car towed?

**3.** For each relation, construct a table of values using at least five ordered pairs. Calculate the first differences and classify the relation as linear or non-linear. Graph the relation to check.
**a)** $y = 4x - 3$ **b)** $y = x^2 - 3$ **c)** $y = -\frac{1}{2}x + 1$

**4.** Draw a distance-time graph to show the following motions.
**a)** Jamaal was walking at a constant speed of 1.5 m/s away from home.
**b)** Marissa was walking at a constant speed of 3 m/s toward home.

**5.** Determine the $x$- and $y$-intercepts and use them to graph each line.
**a)** $3x - 4y = 12$ **b)** $-5x + 3y = 15$ **c)** $4x - 6y = -18$

6. Find the slope and $y$-intercept and write the equation of each line shown.

a) 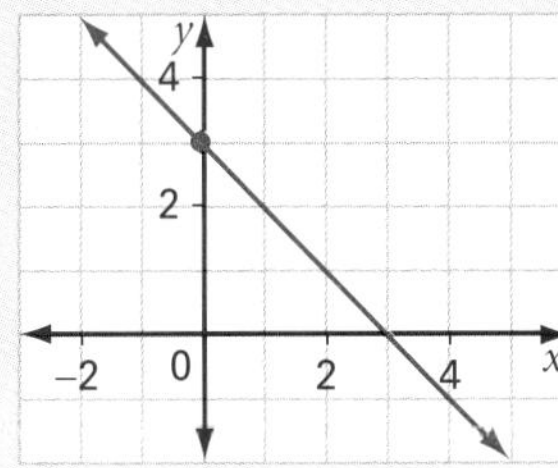

b) 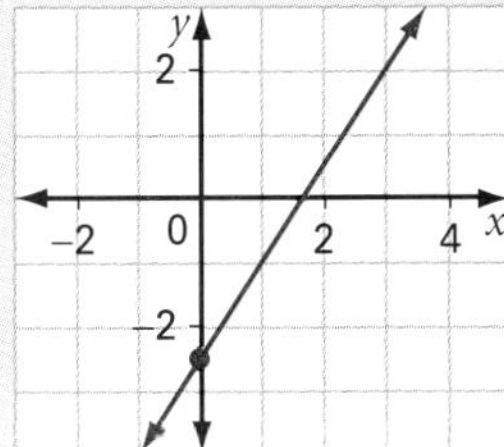

7. Graph each line. Identify the slope and $y$-intercept, if possible.

a) $x = 3$ b) $y = 2$ c) $y = -4$ d) $x = 0$

8. **Car acceleration** A car is travelling at a speed of 30 km/h and begins to accelerate at a rate of 5 km/h per second. The speed of the car is given by $s = 5t + 30$, where $s$ is the speed, in kilometres per hour, and $t$ is the time, in seconds.

a) Construct a graph of speed versus time.

b) State the slope and the $s$-intercept of this linear relation.

c) State the variable part and the fixed part of this partial variation.

d) Describe the relationship between the slope and the variable part.

e) Describe the relationship between the $s$-intercept and the fixed part.

9. **Application** The cost of renting a car for one day is \$50 plus \$0.25/km driven. Let $C$ represent the cost and $d$ represent the distance driven.

a) Copy and complete the table of values.

b) Construct a graph of cost versus distance.

c) If the distance driven is 0 km, what is the cost? Plot this point.

d) State the slope and the $C$-intercept of this relation. Substitute these values into $C = md + b$ to create a linear model.

e) Use the equation to determine the cost if the car is driven 175 km.

f) Use the equation to determine the cost if the car is driven 450 km.

| Distance (km) | Cost (\$) |
|---|---|
| 100 | |
| 200 | |
| 300 | |

10. For each set of data,

- create a scatter plot and draw a line of best fit
- determine the slope and $y$-intercept
- write the equation of the line of best fit

a)

| $x$ | $y$ |
|---|---|
| 1 | 3 |
| 2 | 4 |
| 4 | 6 |
| 6 | 9 |
| 8 | 12 |
| 11 | 14 |

b)

| $x$ | $y$ |
|---|---|
| 2 | 6 |
| 3 | 3 |
| 5 | 0 |
| 7 | −3 |
| 8 | −5 |
| 10 | −8 |

# Tasks

## Surface Area and Volume of a Cube

What is the relationship between the side length of a cube and its surface area?
What is the relationship between the side length of a cube and its volume?

For a cube of side length, $s$:
- the surface area is $S = 6s^2$
- the volume is $V = s^3$

**a)** Copy and complete the table.

| Side Length, $s$ (cm) | Surface Area, $S = 6s^2$ (cm$^2$) | Volume, $V = s^3$ (cm$^3$) |
|---|---|---|
| 1 | 6 | 1 |
| 2 | 24 | 8 |
| 3 | | |
| 4 | | |
| 5 | | |

**b)** Sketch what you think a graph of surface area versus side length will look like.

**c)** Graph the relation. Call this Graph 1.

**d)** Sketch what you think a graph of volume versus side length will look like.

**e)** Graph the relation. Call this Graph 2. Explain how your sketch is similar to and how is it different from Graph 2.

**f)** Sketch what you think a graph of volume versus surface area will look like.

**g)** Graph the relation. Call this Graph 3. Explain how your sketch is similar to and how is it different from Graph 3.

**h)** From Graph 3, suggest a reason why a 2-L box of detergent usually costs less than two 1-L boxes.

## Bridge Design

The diagram below represents two suspension cables that run from the top of a support tower 50 m high to points on the bridge below.

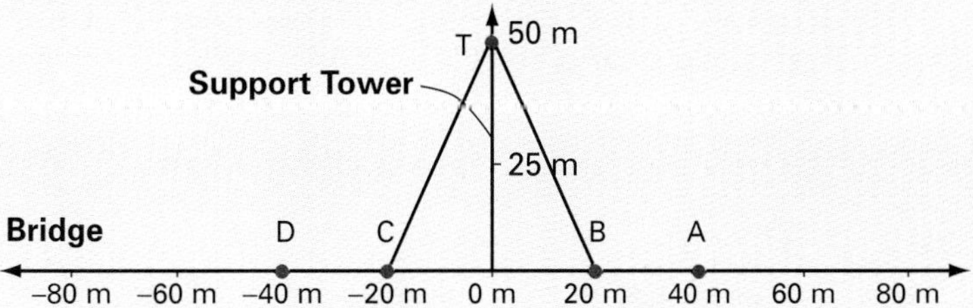


**a)** Make your own drawing showing two more suspension cables attached from the same point T on the support tower to the bridge at points A and D.

**b)** Find the slope of each of the four cables.

**c)** Determine the equations of the lines representing each of the four cables.

**d)** An engineer wants to use longer cables, attached from the same point on the support tower to the bridge at 80 m from either side of the tower. Find the slope of each of these cables.

## Salary and Commission

Leisle works a 40-h week selling electronic equipment. She earns a base salary of $11/h and receives a commission of 5¢ for every dollar of sales she makes.

**a)** What is Leisle's base salary?

**b)** Copy and complete the table showing weekly sales, commission, and total salary.

| Weekly Sales ($) | Commission ($) | Total Salary ($) |
|---|---|---|
| 0 | 0 | |
| 1000 | 50 | |
| 2000 | | |
| 3000 | | |
| 4000 | | |

**c)** Draw a graph of total salary, $T$, versus weekly sales, $S$. What type of relation is this?

**d)** What is the equation of the relation?

**e)** What is the slope of the relation? What does the slope represent?

**f)** Leisle usually has weekly sales of about $5000. She is offered a new sales position that pays $17/h, but does not include commission. Should she take the new job? Justify your answer.

# CHAPTER 8

# Applying Exponents

An optic fibre can be as thin as a human hair, yet long enough to lay across a city. In this chapter, you will

- study exponents
- combine exponents in calculations
- use exponents to handle very large and very small numbers, such as the dimensions of optic fibres

## Chapter Problem

In Canada, as in most countries, we recycle a lot of material. We also produce a large amount of garbage. In 2000, Canadians generated 25 200 000 000 000 kg of waste. Of that, only 1 280 000 000 000 kg was recycled. In this chapter, you will learn quick ways to calculate with large numbers like these.

# Get Ready

## Powers

You can evaluate these powers using repeated multiplication.

$5^3 = 5 \times 5 \times 5$
$= 125$

Scientific calculator: C 5 $y^x$ 3 =

Graphing calculator: 5 ^ 3 ENTER

$3^4 = 3 \times 3 \times 3 \times 3$
$= 81$

**1.** Evaluate each power.

**a)** $2^3$ **b)** $5^2$ **c)** $10^4$
**d)** $8^3$ **e)** $7^4$ **f)** $3^5$
**g)** $2^6$ **h)** $6^2$ **i)** $9^3$

## Order of Operations

Use the order of operations (BEDMAS) to evaluate expressions.

$4^2 + 3(15 - 9) = 16 + 3(6)$
$= 16 + 18$
$= 34$

Scientific calculator: C 4 $x^2$ + 3 × ( 15 − 9 ) =

Graphing calculator: 4 $x^2$ + 3 ( 15 − 9 ) ENTER

$7(5^2 - 3^2) = 7(25 - 9)$
$= 7(16)$
$= 112$

Scientific calculator: C 7 × ( 5 $x^2$ − 3 $x^2$ ) =

Graphing calculator: 7 ( 5 $x^2$ − 3 $x^2$ ) ENTER

**2.** Use the order of operations to evaluate each expression.

**a)** $5(17 + 3)$ **b)** $(2 + 4) + (8 - 3)$
**c)** $(6 + 4)(9 + 11)$ **d)** $5 - 2(3^2 + 1)$
**e)** $10 + 7(36 - 5^2)$ **f)** $(9 - 6)^2$
**g)** $12 \div 3 + 15 \div 5$ **h)** $6^2 \div 3^2$
**i)** $\frac{10^3}{5^2}$ **j)** $\frac{4^3}{(3 - 1)^2}$

## Adding and Subtracting Integers

Evaluate these integer expressions.

$3 + (-7)$
$= -4$

$8 + (-2)$
$= 6$

$(-1) + 5$
$= 4$

$6 - 7$
$= -1$

$(-6) + (-2)$
$= -8$

$6 - (-2)$
$= 6 + 2$
$= 4$

**3.** Evaluate each integer expression.

**a)** $5 + (-9)$ **b)** $6 + (-15)$ **c)** $10 + (-2)$

**d)** $7 - 12$ **e)** $2 - 10$ **f)** $-3 + (-4)$

**g)** $-7 + (-8)$ **h)** $-18 + 10$ **i)** $-12 + 15$

## Multiply Fractions

Multiply fractions by multiplying the numerators and multiplying the denominators.

$$\frac{2}{3} \times \frac{2}{3} = \frac{2 \times 2}{3 \times 3} = \frac{4}{9}$$

$$\frac{1}{2} \times \frac{1}{2} \times \frac{1}{2} = \frac{1 \times 1 \times 1}{2 \times 2 \times 2} = \frac{1}{8}$$

**4.** Evaluate.

**a)** $\frac{3}{4} \times \frac{3}{4}$ **b)** $\frac{1}{3} \times \frac{1}{3} \times \frac{1}{3}$

**c)** $\frac{4}{5} \times \frac{4}{5}$ **d)** $\frac{2}{3} \times \frac{2}{3} \times \frac{2}{3} \times \frac{2}{3}$

**e)** $\frac{1}{2} \times \frac{1}{2} \times \frac{1}{2} \times \frac{1}{2} \times \frac{1}{2}$ **f)** $\frac{7}{8} \times \frac{7}{8} \times \frac{7}{8}$

# 8.1 Powers With Rational Bases

Recall that a repeating expression like $3 \times 3 \times 3 \times 3$ can be rewritten as a power:

$3^4$

4 is the exponent: the number of times 3 is repeated

3 is the base: the number being repeated

In this section, you will combine fractions with exponents.

## DISCOVER

### Exponents With Fractional Bases

1. In expanded form, $6^4 = 6 \times 6 \times 6 \times 6$.
   a) Write $\left(\frac{2}{5}\right)^4$ in expanded form.
   b) Evaluate the answer to a) by multiplying. Leave your answer in fraction form.

2. a) Evaluate $2^4$.  b) Evaluate $5^4$.
   c) Use your answers from parts a) and b) to evaluate $\frac{2^4}{5^4}$. Leave your answer in fraction form.
   d) Compare your answers from step 2c) and step 1b).

3. Describe two ways of evaluating powers when the base is a fraction.

4. Use one method from step 3 to evaluate each expression.
   a) $\left(\frac{1}{2}\right)^3$  b) $\left(\frac{2}{3}\right)^2$  c) $\left(\frac{3}{4}\right)^4$

When a power has a fraction as its base, you can evaluate it by

- *either* writing the power in expanded form first:
  $\left(\frac{2}{3}\right)^3 = \frac{2}{3} \times \frac{2}{3} \times \frac{2}{3} = \frac{8}{27}$
- *or* placing the exponent on both the numerator and the denominator:
  $\left(\frac{2}{3}\right)^3 = \frac{2^3}{3^3} = \frac{2 \times 2 \times 2}{3 \times 3 \times 3} = \frac{8}{27}$

This rule can be expressed by the formula $\left(\frac{a}{b}\right)^c = \frac{a^c}{b^c}$.

## Example 1

### Powers of Fractions

Evaluate these powers.

a) $\left(\frac{1}{7}\right)^2$

b) $\left(\frac{3}{4}\right)^5$

### Solution

a) $\left(\frac{1}{7}\right)^2 = \frac{1}{7} \times \frac{1}{7}$

$= \frac{1}{49}$

b) $\left(\frac{3}{4}\right)^5 = \frac{3^5}{4^5}$

$= \frac{243}{1024}$

## Example 2

### Evaluating Powers of Fractions With a Calculator

Use a calculator to evaluate $\left(\frac{2}{3}\right)^4$.

### Solution

**Method 1: Scientific Calculator**

Press the following key sequence: C ( 2 a b/c 3 ) $y^x$ 4 =

The result will look like this:

You can change back and forth between the decimal and fraction forms of the answer by pressing the F◂▸D key.

**Method 2: Graphing Calculator**

Press the following key sequence:

( 2 ÷ 3 ) ^ 4 MATH 1:Frac ENTER

The result will be:

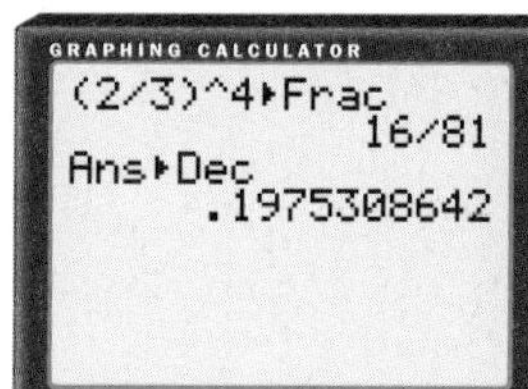


You can change to a decimal answer by pressing:

MATH 2:Dec ENTER

## Key Concepts

- An exponent gives how many times the base is multiplied by itself. For example, $4^3$ means $4 \times 4 \times 4$, and $\left(\frac{2}{5}\right)^3$ means $\frac{2}{5} \times \frac{2}{5} \times \frac{2}{5}$.
- A power with a fractional base $\left(\frac{a}{b}\right)^c$ can be rewritten as $\frac{a^c}{b^c}$.

  For example, $\left(\frac{2}{5}\right)^3 = \frac{2^3}{5^3}$.

## Discuss the Concepts

1. A common mistake when evaluating a power such as $1^5$ is to write $1^5 = 5$. Explain why this is not correct.
2. When should you use a scientific or graphing calculator to solve questions in this section? When should you rely on your mental math skills?

## Practise

***For help with questions 1 and 2, refer to Example 1.***

1. Express each power in expanded form.

   For example: $\left(\frac{2}{3}\right)^3 = \frac{2}{3} \times \frac{2}{3} \times \frac{2}{3}$. Then, evaluate.

   **a)** $\left(\frac{1}{4}\right)^2$ **b)** $\left(\frac{1}{6}\right)^3$ **c)** $\left(\frac{2}{11}\right)^4$

   **d)** $\left(\frac{3}{10}\right)^1$ **e)** $\left(\frac{4}{15}\right)^3$ **f)** $\left(\frac{2}{9}\right)^5$

2. Apply the rule $\left(\frac{a}{b}\right)^c = \frac{a^c}{b^c}$ to these powers. Then, evaluate.

   **a)** $\left(\frac{4}{5}\right)^3$ **b)** $\left(\frac{1}{5}\right)^5$ **c)** $\left(\frac{5}{12}\right)^6$

   **d)** $\left(\frac{2}{7}\right)^1$ **e)** $\left(\frac{9}{4}\right)^5$ **f)** $\left(\frac{8}{3}\right)^3$

*For help with question 3, refer to Example 2.*

3. Evaluate, using a calculator.

a) $\left(\frac{1}{2}\right)^2$ b) $\left(\frac{6}{5}\right)^4$ c) $\left(\frac{2}{5}\right)^4$

d) $\left(\frac{5}{3}\right)^2$ e) $\left(\frac{7}{2}\right)^3$ f) $\left(\frac{5}{2}\right)^4$

**B** 4. **Thinking/Inquiry/Problem Solving, Communication** Compare the methods you used in questions 1 to 3. Give an advantage of each one.

5. Rewrite each power using the rule $\left(\frac{a}{b}\right)^c = \frac{a^c}{b^c}$.

a) $\left(\frac{p}{q}\right)^2$ b) $\left(\frac{m}{n}\right)^3$ c) $\left(\frac{x}{y}\right)^5$

## Apply the Concepts

6. **Thinking/Inquiry/Problem Solving** You cut a 4-kg block of cheese in half, then the remaining piece in half, and so on. The expression $4 \times \left(\frac{1}{2}\right)^x$ gives the mass, in kilograms, of the smallest piece of cheese, after $x$ cuts. For example, after 1 cut,

$$\begin{aligned} 4 \times \left(\frac{1}{2}\right)^1 &= 4 \times \frac{1^1}{2^1} \\ &= 4 \times \frac{1}{2} \\ &= 2 \end{aligned}$$

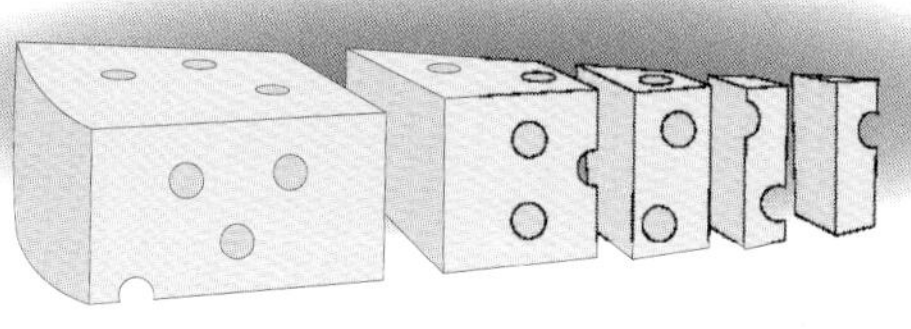

The mass of the smallest piece after 1 cut is 2 kg. What is the mass of the smallest piece of cheese, as a decimal, after each number of cuts?

a) 2 cuts b) 3 cuts c) 5 cuts d) 10 cuts

**C** 7. **Thinking/Inquiry/Problem Solving** Evaluate these powers.

a) $(-2)^2$ b) $\left(\frac{-2}{3}\right)^2$ c) $\left(-\frac{2}{3}\right)^2$

d) $(-5)^3$ e) $\left(\frac{-5}{2}\right)^3$ f) $\left(-\frac{5}{2}\right)^3$

g) $\left(-\frac{3}{5}\right)^2$ h) $\left(-\frac{3}{4}\right)^3$ i) $\left(-\frac{2}{3}\right)^5$

# 8.2 Exponent Rules

What happens when powers are combined in different ways? Expressions can have a combination of different powers. There is a set of rules for evaluating expressions involving powers.

## DISCOVER

### Exploring Exponent Rules

1. Set up a table, as shown below.
   - Evaluate the powers in columns A and B. You may use a calculator.
   - Multiply the results to get the product in column C.
   - Evaluate the powers in column D.

| A | B | C | D |
|---|---|---|---|
| $5^2 =$ | $5^4 =$ | $5^2 \times 5^4 = (5 \times 5) \times (5 \times 5 \times 5 \times 5)$<br>$=$ | $5^6 = 5 \times 5 \times 5 \times 5 \times 5 \times 5$<br>$=$ |
| $2^3 =$ | $2^5 =$ | $2^3 \times 2^5 =$ | $2^8 =$ |
| $3^3 =$ | $3^2 =$ | $3^3 \times 3^2 =$ | $3^5 =$ |

2. a) Compare your results in columns C and D.
   b) How do the exponents in column C relate to the exponents in column D?
   c) Based on your results, state a rule for multiplying two powers with the same base.

3. Set up a table, as shown below.
   - Evaluate the powers in columns A and B. You may use a calculator.
   - Divide the results to get the quotient in column C.
   - Evaluate the powers in column D.

| A | B | C | D |
|---|---|---|---|
| $2^5 =$ | $2^3 =$ | $2^5 \div 2^3 = \frac{2 \times 2 \times 2 \times 2 \times 2}{2 \times 2 \times 2}$<br>$=$ | $2^2 = 2 \times 2$<br>$=$ |
| $5^3 =$ | $5^2 =$ | $5^3 \div 5^2 =$ | $5^1 =$ |
| $3^5 =$ | $3^2 =$ | $3^5 \div 3^2 =$ | $3^3 =$ |

4. a) Compare your results in columns C and D.
   b) How do the exponents in column C relate to the exponents in column D?
   c) State a rule for dividing two powers with the same base.

5. Set up a table, as shown below.
   - Evaluate the powers in columns A and B. You may use a calculator.
   - Evaluate the power in column C by evaluating the power inside the brackets first.
   - Evaluate the power in column D. You may use a calculator.

| A | B | C | D |
|---|---|---|---|
| $2^3 =$ | $8^2 =$ | $(2^3)^2 =$ | $2^6 =$ |
| $5^2 =$ | $25^2 =$ | $(2^2)^2 =$ | $5^4 =$ |
| $3^4 =$ | $81^3 =$ | $(3^4)^3 =$ | $3^{12} =$ |

6. a) Compare your results in columns C and D.
   b) How do the exponents in column C relate to the exponents in column D?
   c) State a rule for the power of a power.

To multiply powers with the same base, add the exponents and keep the base the same.

$$a^b \times a^c = a^{b+c}$$

## EXAMPLE 1

### Multiplying Powers

Simplify, by writing as a single power.

a) $4^2 \times 4^3$  b) $(10^4)(10^3)$  c) $(y^2)(y^7)$

### Solution

a) $4^2 \times 4^3 = 4^{2+3}$
$= 4^5$
$= 1024$

b) $(10^4)(10^3) = 10^{4+3}$
$= 10^7$
$= 10\ 000\ 000$

**$(10^4)(10^3)$ means to multiply the powers, so add the exponents (keep the base the same).**

c) $(y^2)(y^7) = y^{2+7}$
$= y^9$

To divide powers with the same base, subtract the exponents and keep the base the same.

$$\frac{a^b}{a^c} = a^{b-c}$$

## EXAMPLE 2

### Dividing Powers

Simplify, by writing as a single power.

**a)** $\frac{6^7}{6^5}$ **b)** $10^9 \div 10^6$ **c)** $k^6 \div k^5$

### Solution

**a)** $\frac{6^7}{6^5} = 6^{7-5}$
$= 6^2$
$= 36$

**b)** $10^9 \div 10^6 = 10^{9-6}$
$= 10^3$
$= 1000$

**c)** $k^6 \div k^5 = k^{6-5}$
$= k^1$
$= k$

To raise a power to another exponent, multiply the exponents and keep the base the same.

$$(a^b)^c = a^{b \times c}$$

## EXAMPLE 3

### Powers of Powers

Simplify, by writing as a single power.

**a)** $(2^3)^2$ **b)** $(m^3)^4$ **c)** $(2^3)^2 \times 2^3$

### Solution

**a)** $(2^3)^2 = 2^{3\times2}$
$= 2^6$
$= 64$

**b)** $(m^3)^4 = m^{3\times4}$
$= m^{12}$

**c)** $(2^3)^2 \times 2^3 = 2^{3\times2} \times 2^3$
$= 2^6 \times 2^3$
$= 2^{6+3}$
$= 2^9$
$= 512$

Scientific calculator:

Graphing calculator:

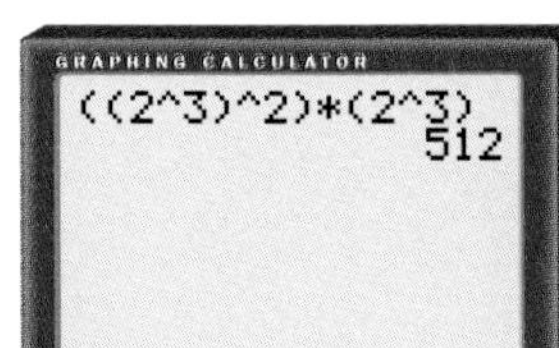

## Key Concepts

The exponent rules are:

- To multiply powers with the same base, add the exponents. Keep the base the same.

  $a^b \times a^c = a^{b+c}$

- To divide powers with the same base, subtract the exponents. Keep the base the same.

  $\frac{a^b}{a^c} = a^{b-c}$

- To raise a power to another exponent, multiply the exponents. Keep the base the same.

  $(a^b)^c = a^{b \times c}$

## Discuss the Concepts

1. This incorrect solution was written for a quiz:

   $2^3 \times 2^2 = 2^6$
   $= 64$

   a) What was the mistake?   b) What is the correct solution?

2. Describe the steps you need to evaluate each expression.

   a) $5^7 \div 5^4$   b) $(7^2)^3$   c) $(3^3)^2 \div 3^4$

## Practise

***For help with questions 1 to 3, refer to Examples 1, 2, and 3.***

1. Simplify, by writing as a single power.

   a) $5^2 \times 5^3$   b) $(8^5)(8^4)$   c) $7^{10} \div 7^4$

   d) $\frac{3^8}{3^2}$   e) $(4^3)^9$   f) $(10^2)^2$

2. Write as a single power.

   a) $b^2 \times b^8$   b) $y^5 \times y^2$   c) $w^6 \div w^3$

   d) $\frac{x^4}{x^3}$   e) $(n^2)^4$   f) $(c^5)^3$

3. Use the exponent rules to simplify. Then, use a calculator to evaluate.

   a) $2^2 \times 2^5$   b) $5^1 \times 5^2$   c) $(4^2)(4^3)$   d) $6^5 \div 6^2$

   e) $10^8 \div 10^5$   f) $\frac{11^7}{11^4}$   g) $(5^2)^3$   h) $(2^4)^5$

## Apply the Concepts

4. **Thinking/Inquiry/Problem Solving** Find the value of the unknown exponent.
   a) $2^3 \times 2^5 = 2^x$
   b) $9^6 \times 9^y = 9^7$
   c) $4^k \times 4^2 = 4^8$
   d) $(10^m)(10^3) = 10^9$

5. Determine the unknown exponent.
   a) $8^7 \times 8^6 = 8^y$
   b) $15^3 \div 15^x = 15^1$
   c) $4^m \div 4^2 = 4^6$
   d) $\dfrac{7^k}{7^3} = 7^5$

6. Determine the unknown exponent.
   a) $(5^6)^7 = 5^w$
   b) $(3^2)^y = 3^8$
   c) $(6^x)^4 = 6^{12}$
   d) $(8^y)^5 = 8^{15}$

7. Simplify.
   a) $(2^3)^2 \div 2^5$
   b) $6^4 \times 6^5 \div 6^7$
   c) $(x^2)^5(x^3)$
   d) $\dfrac{y^2 \times y^4}{y^6}$
   e) $\dfrac{k^5}{(k^2)^2}$
   f) $\dfrac{(n^7)^3}{n^{15}}$

**Did You Know?**

Paper was invented by Ts'ai Lun in China, around the year 100. The art of folding paper may also have begun in China, but became known as origami in Japan.

8. **Paper folding** Tara folded a sheet of paper 5 times and ended up with a stack $2^5$ layers thick. Wayne folded a sheet of paper 2 times and ended up with a stack $2^2$ layers thick. How many times thicker is Tara's stack than Wayne's?

9. **Thinking/Inquiry/Problem Solving** Simplify.
   a) $(-2)^2$
   b) $(-2)^5$
   c) $(-2)^2 \times (-2)^5$
   d) $(-2)^5 \div (-2)^2$
   e) $((-3)^3)^2$
   f) $\dfrac{((-2)^2)^5}{(-4)^3}$

**Chapter Problem**

10. Canada's population produces about $2^{43}$ kg of waste per year. Canadians recycle about $5 \times 2^{31}$ kg of material per year. Canada's population is about $15 \times 2^{21}$ people.
    a) What fraction of waste is recycled in Canada?
    b) How many kilograms of waste are produced per person per year?
    c) How many kilograms of material are recycled per person per year?
    d) If Canadians doubled their recycling, how much material would the average Canadian recycle per year? Write your answer using a power of 2.

# 8.3 Zero and Negative Exponents

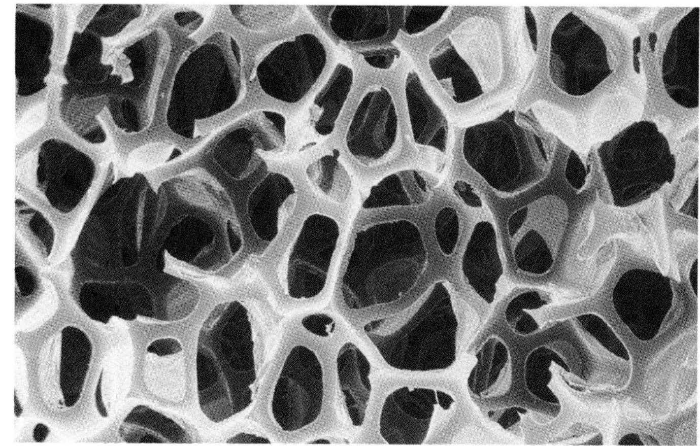

This polystyrene packing foam has been magnified 55 times. Its lattice structure gives it strength. The actual foam is $55^{-1}$ times the photograph size. In this section you will learn the meaning of negative exponents like this, and of zero exponents.

## DISCOVER

### The Meaning of Zero and Negative Exponents

1. Evaluate each expression.

   a) $\frac{2^3}{2^3} = 2^{3-3} = \square$ b) $\frac{5^4}{5^4} = 5^{4-4} = \square$ c) $\frac{7^9}{7^9} = 7^{9-9} = \square$

2. a) Describe the patterns you saw in question 1.
   b) What can you conclude about raising a number to an exponent 0?

3. Evaluate each expression.

$$5^{-1} = 5^{3-4} = \frac{5 \times 5 \times 5}{5 \times 5 \times 5 \times 5} = \square$$

$$5^{-2} = 5^{3-5} = \frac{5 \times 5 \times 5}{5 \times 5 \times 5 \times 5 \times 5} = \square$$

$$5^{-3} = 5^{3-6} = \frac{5 \times 5 \times 5}{5 \times 5 \times 5 \times 5 \times 5 \times 5} = \square$$

4. Evaluate each expression.

$$2^{-1} = \frac{2 \times 2 \times 2 \times 2}{2 \times 2 \times 2 \times 2 \times 2} = \square$$

$$2^{-2} = \frac{2 \times 2 \times 2 \times 2}{2 \times 2 \times 2 \times 2 \times 2 \times 2} = \square$$

$$2^{-3} = \frac{2 \times 2 \times 2 \times 2}{2 \times 2 \times 2 \times 2 \times 2 \times 2 \times 2} = \square$$

5. a) Describe the patterns you saw in questions 3 and 4.
   b) What can you conclude about raising a number to a negative exponent?

A number, to an exponent of 0, equals 1.

$a^0 = 1$

When a base has a negative exponent, the power is the reciprocal of the base to the positive of the exponent.

$a^{-b} = \frac{1}{a^b}$ **A reciprocal is "one over" the original number.**

## EXAMPLE 1

### Evaluating With Zero and Negative Exponents

Write each power with a positive exponent, if possible. Then, evaluate the power.

**a)** $3^2$ **b)** $3^{-2}$ **c)** $5^{-3}$ **d)** $7^0$ **e)** $1^{-2}$

### Solution

**a)** $3^2 = 9$

**b)** $3^{-2} = \frac{1}{3^2}$

$= \frac{1}{9}$

Verify using a scientific calculator: C 3 $y^x$ 2 (−) = F◂▸D

If your scientific calculator does not have the F◂▸D button, your answer will be in decimal form.

**c)** $5^{-3} = \frac{1}{5^3}$

$= \frac{1}{125}$

Graphing calculator keystrokes:

5 ^ (−) 3 MATH 1:Frac ENTER

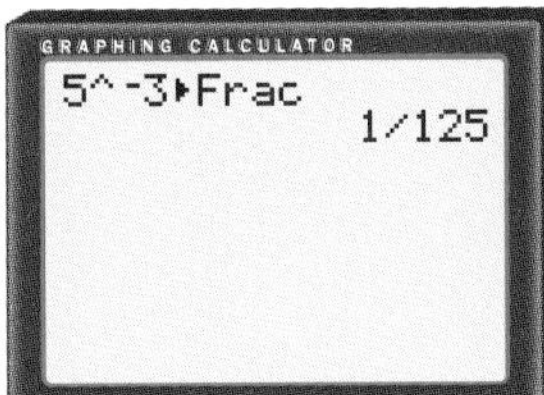


**d)** $7^0 = 1$

**e)** $1^{-2} = \frac{1}{1^2}$

$= \frac{1}{1}$

$= 1$

## EXAMPLE 2

### Rewriting Powers With Negative Exponents

Write each power with a negative exponent.

**a)** $\frac{1}{4^7}$ **b)** $\frac{1}{2^5}$ **c)** $\frac{1}{6^1}$

### Solution

**a)** $\frac{1}{4^7} = 4^{-7}$ **b)** $\frac{1}{2^5} = 2^{-5}$ **c)** $\frac{1}{6^1} = 6^{-1}$

## KEY CONCEPTS

- A number, to an exponent of 0, equals 1.
  $a^0 = 1$
- A number, to a negative exponent, is the reciprocal of the base to the positive of the exponent.
  $a^{-b} = \frac{1}{a^b}$

## DISCUSS THE CONCEPTS

1. Explain why $2^{-3}$ is not a negative number.
2. Explain why $5^0 = 1$.

## PRACTISE

***For help with questions 1 and 2, refer to Example 1.***

1. Rewrite each power with a positive exponent. Leave your answer in power form.

**a)** $6^{-2}$ **b)** $9^{-5}$ **c)** $4^{-1}$
**d)** $7^{-3}$ **e)** $15^{-6}$ **f)** $1^{-4}$

2. Evaluate each power. Check your answers by using a calculator.

**a)** $7^{-2}$ **b)** $3^{-3}$ **c)** $2^{-3}$ **d)** $6^0$
**e)** $4^{-5}$ **f)** $9^{-1}$ **g)** $1^0$ **h)** $10^{-1}$

*For help with question 3, refer to Example 2.*

3. Write the correct exponent for each power.

   a) $3^{\blacksquare} = \frac{1}{3^4}$  b) $5^{\blacksquare} = \frac{1}{5^6}$  c) $10^{\blacksquare} = 1$

   d) $4^{-3} = \frac{1}{4^{\blacksquare}}$  e) $8^{-2} = \frac{1}{8^{\blacksquare}}$  f) $6^{\blacksquare} = 1$

## Apply the Concepts

4. a) Using a graphing calculator, enter the values as shown into list L1. Enter the powers of 2 into list L2 so that the entry in L1 is the exponent. The first one is shown for you.

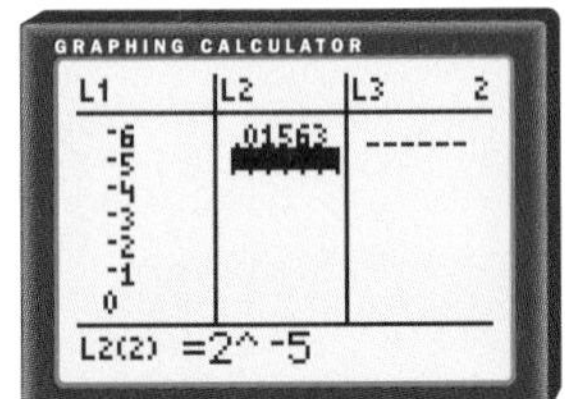


   b) Make sure **Plot1** is on. Select the **scatter plot**, with **Xlist** set to **L1** and **Ylist** set to **L2**.

For help with **Entering Data Into Lists** or **Creating a Scatter Graph**, refer to the Technology Appendix.

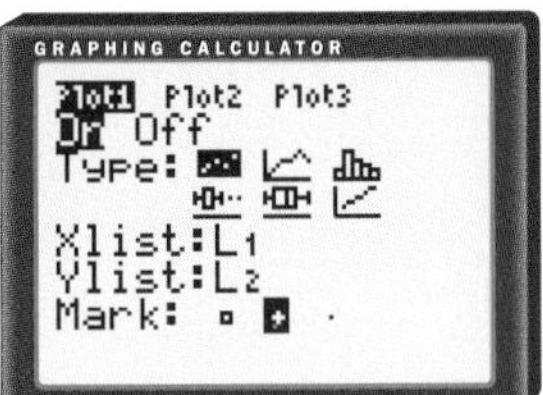


   c) Press **ZOOM 9:Zoomstat** to view the graph. Describe the graph.

   d) Press **TRACE** and use the ◄ key to scroll across the graph. This will show the value of $2^x$ for each value of $x$ in your chart. Describe what is happening to the value of $2^x$ as you scroll to the left.

   e) Will the value of $2^x$ ever equal zero? Explain.

5. a) Write the first five positive powers of 3 ($3^1$ up to $3^5$). Evaluate each one.

   b) Write the first five negative powers of 3 ($3^{-1}$ down to $3^{-5}$). Evaluate each one. Leave your answers in fraction form.

   c) Compare your answers in parts a) and b).

6. **Communication** Copy the table into your notebook. Write each power of 10 in fraction form and then in decimal form. Describe the pattern.

| | Exponential Form | Fraction Form | Decimal Form |
|---|---|---|---|
| a) | $10^{-1}$ | $\frac{1}{10}$ | 0.1 |
| b) | $10^{-2}$ | | |
| c) | $10^{-3}$ | | |
| d) | $10^{-4}$ | | |
| e) | $10^{-5}$ | | |
| f) | $10^{-6}$ | | |

7. Copy the table into your notebook. Complete the table.

| | Expression | Expanded Form | Exponential Form | Resulting Value |
|---|---|---|---|---|
| a) | $3^3 \times 3^{-2}$ | $(3 \times 3 \times 3) \times \left(\frac{1}{3} \times \frac{1}{3}\right)$ | $3^1$ | 3 |
| b) | $5^4 \times 5^{-2}$ | | | |
| c) | $7^6 \div 7^8$ | | | |
| d) | $10^6 \times 10^{-9}$ | | | |
| e) | | $(8 \times 8) \times \left(\frac{1}{8} \times \frac{1}{8} \times \frac{1}{8}\right)$ | | |
| f) | | $\frac{6 \times 6 \times 6 \times 6 \times 6}{6 \times 6 \times 6 \times 6 \times 6 \times 6 \times 6 \times 6}$ | | |

8. Use the exponent rules to simplify, and then evaluate, each expression. (See page 345.)

a) $4^5 \times 4^{-2}$
b) $5^{-1} \times 5^{-2}$
c) $2^5 \times 2^{-6}$
d) $3^{-1} \times 3^0$
e) $(2^{-2})^2$
f) $(4^{-1})^{-2}$
g) $12^7 \times 12^{-7}$
h) $125^{-18} \times 125^{17}$
i) $10^4 \times 10^{-3}$
j) $10^{-7} \times 10^5$
k) $10^{-3} \times 10^{-6}$
l) $10^5 \div 10^8$

9. Evaluate each power. Then, write them in order, from least to greatest.

$$7^{-2} \quad 6^{-3} \quad 5^{-4} \quad 4^{-5} \quad 3^{-6} \quad 2^{-7}$$

C

10. **Thinking/Inquiry/Problem Solving** Evaluate each power.

a) $(-2)^3$
b) $(-2)^{-3}$
c) $(-2)^3 \times (-2)^{-3}$
d) $(-2)^0$
e) $(-3)^{-2}$
f) $(-5)^{-1}$
g) $(-10)^0$
h) $(-125)^{-18} \times (-125)^{17}$

**Did You Know?**

The radioactive decay of carbon-14, which exists in every living thing on Earth, can be used to calculate the age of ancient relics, as far back as about 50 000 years. This is about four times as long as human civilization has existed.

11. **Radioactive decay** A sample of iodine-135 decays to $\frac{1}{2}$ or $2^{-1}$ of its original mass after 8 days. After 16 days, it decays to $\frac{1}{4}$ or $2^{-2}$ of its original mass.

a) What fraction of its original mass will remain after 24 days?
b) What fraction of its original mass will remain after 240 days?
c) Write each fraction as a power with a negative exponent.

# 8.4 Scientific Notation

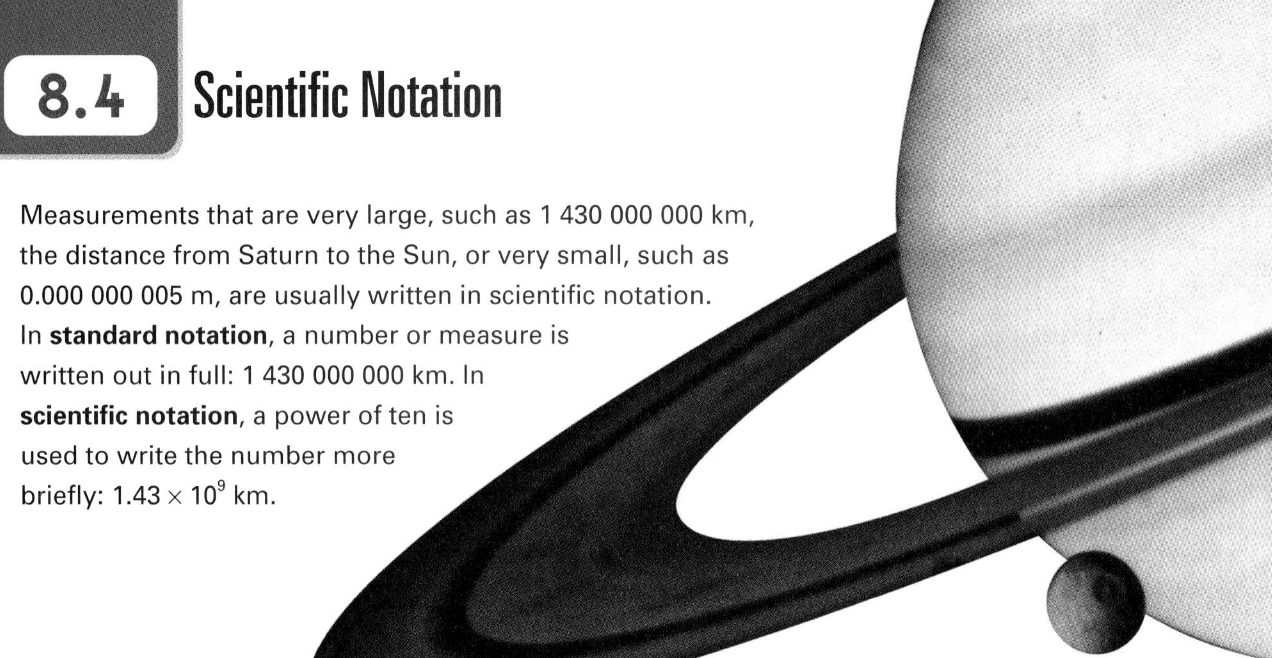

Measurements that are very large, such as 1 430 000 000 km, the distance from Saturn to the Sun, or very small, such as 0.000 000 005 m, are usually written in scientific notation. In **standard notation**, a number or measure is written out in full: 1 430 000 000 km. In **scientific notation**, a power of ten is used to write the number more briefly: $1.43 \times 10^9$ km.

## DISCOVER

**Did You Know?**

Why "scientific notation"? Very small or very large numbers are often used in science. Scientific notation makes it easier to calculate with these numbers.

### The Meaning of Scientific Notation

1. Expand each power of 10. Then, multiply by the first number and write the result in standard form.
   a) The distance from Mercury to the Sun is $5.79 \times 10^7$ km.
   b) The distance from Earth to the Sun is $1.50 \times 10^8$ km.
   c) The distance from Pluto to the Sun is $5.91 \times 10^9$ km.

2. For each result in question 1, compare the exponent of 10 to the number of spaces the decimal point has shifted. What do you notice?

3. Write each power of 10 in decimal form. Then, multiply by the first number and write the result in standard form.
   a) The diameter of an amoeba is $1.0 \times 10^{-4}$ m.
   b) The time it takes for light to travel one metre is $3.336 \times 10^9$ s.
   c) The diameter of a helium atom is $2.56 \times 10^{-10}$ m.

4. For each result in question 3, compare the exponent of 10 to the number of spaces the decimal point has shifted. What do you notice?

5. In questions 1 and 3, the expressions are given in scientific notation. Describe how to convert from scientific notation to standard form.

Scientific notation expresses large and small numbers as a number between 1 and 9.999…, multiplied by a power of 10. For example,

$57\ 910\ 000 = 5.791 \times 10^7$ **The decimal point moves 7 spaces to the left.**

## EXAMPLE 1

### Writing Numbers in Scientific Notation

Write each number in scientific notation. Explain your answers.

**a)** 14 500 000 **b)** 0.000 000 000 014

### Solution

**a)** $14\ 500\ 000 = 1.45 \times 10^7$. The decimal point moves 7 spaces to the left.

**b)** $0.000\ 000\ 000\ 014 = 1.4 \times 10^{-11}$. The decimal point moves 11 spaces to the right.

A scientific calculator displays answers in scientific notation if there are too many digits for the display. The number after the space represents the exponent of 10.

## EXAMPLE 2

### Converting Back to Standard Form

The scientific calculator screens represent numbers in scientific notation. Write each number in standard form. Explain your method.

**a)** 

**b)** 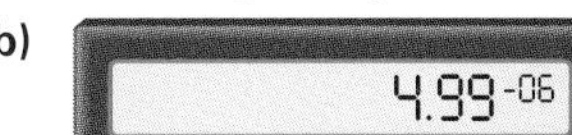

### Solution

**a)** $7.519 \times 10^{15} = 7\ 519\ 000\ 000\ 000\ 000$. Move the decimal point 15 spaces to the right. Fill in the blanks with zeros.

**b)** $4.99 \times 10^{-6} = 0.000\ 004\ 99$. Move the decimal point 6 spaces to the left.

## Example 3

### Scientific Notation and Exponent Rules

Use exponent rules to evaluate $(5.4 \times 10^6) \times (2.5 \times 10^7)$.
Go to page 345 if you need a reminder.

### Solution

$(5.4 \times 10^6) \times (2.7 \times 10^7)$

$= 5.4 \times 10^6 \times 2.7 \times 10^7$ **Remove brackets because it is all multiplying.**

$= 5.4 \times 2.7 \times 10^6 \times 10^7$ **Rearrange.**

$= 14.58 \times 10^{13}$ **Multiply the decimals. Add the exponents.**

$= (1.458 \times 10^1) \times 10^{13}$ **Rewrite 14.58 in scientific notation.**

$= 1.458 \times 10^{14}$ **Add the exponents**

## Example 4

**Did You Know?**

In 2002, China had the world's largest population, $1.28 \times 10^9$ people. The most densely populated country or territory in the world is Macau, with $2.08 \times 10^4$ people per square kilometre.

### Population Density

The population of Earth is estimated at $6.3 \times 10^9$ people. Earth's land area is $1.5 \times 10^8$ km$^2$. What is the population density in people per square kilometre?

### Solution

To find population density, divide the population by the land area.

**The word "per" tells you to divide by the second quantity.**

Evaluate using the exponent laws.

$$\frac{6.3 \times 10^9}{1.5 \times 10^8} = (6.3 \div 1.5) \times (10^9 \div 10^8)$$

$$= 4.2 \times 10^1$$

$$= 42$$

Earth's population density is about 42 people per square kilometre.

Scientific calculator:

C ( 6.3 ÷ 1.5 ) × 10 =

Graphing calculator:

( 6.3 EE 9 ) ÷
( 1.5 EE 8 ) ENTER

## Key Concepts

To express a number in scientific notation:

- Place or move the decimal to the right of the first non-zero digit.
- For the exponent, count the number of places the decimal point moves.
- If the decimal was moved to the left, the exponent is positive.
- If the decimal was moved to the right, the exponent is negative.

To multiply or divide numbers in scientific notation, use the exponent rules from Section 8.2 (page 345).

## Discuss the Concepts

1. Decide if each number is in scientific notation. Explain your reasoning.
   a) $4.51 \times 10^{5}$ b) $0.026 \times 10^{-3}$ c) $1562 \times 10^{8}$
2. For each kind of number in scientific notation, will the number in standard form be large or small? Explain your reasoning.
   a) The exponent of 10 is positive.
   b) The exponent of 10 is negative.

## Practise

*For help with questions 1 and 2, refer to Example 1.*

1. Determine the missing exponents.
   a) $2387 = 2.387 \times 10^{\boxed{?}}$
   b) $691\ 000\ 000 = 6.91 \times 10^{\boxed{?}}$
   c) $20\ 000\ 000\ 000\ 000\ 000 = 2.0 \times 10^{\boxed{?}}$
   d) $0.782 = 7.82 \times 10^{\boxed{?}}$
   e) $0.000\ 000\ 63 = 6.3 \times 10^{\boxed{?}}$
   f) $0.000\ 000\ 000\ 000\ 214\ 9 = 2.149 \times 10^{\boxed{?}}$

2. Express each measure in scientific notation.
   a) 5688.4 m b) 27 881 664 $km^2$
   c) 0.000 2 g d) 0.000 000 000 351 mg
   e) 341 000 000 000 000 000 km
   f) 0.000 000 000 000 000 000 008 mm

*For help with questions 3 to 5, refer to Example 2.*

3. Express each measure in standard form.
   a) $3.4 \times 10^{6}$ cm b) $6.0 \times 10^{3}$ L
   c) $9.112 \times 10^{12}$ km d) $4.5 \times 10^{-5}$ mm
   e) $1.0 \times 10^{-8}$ g f) $6.7325 \times 10^{-10}$ mg

4. **Scientific measures** Write in standard form.
 a) The distance from Jupiter to the Sun is $7.78 \times 10^8$ km.
 b) The diameter of a flu virus is $1.2 \times 10^{-4}$ m.
 c) The speed of sound in air is $3.4 \times 10^2$ m/s.
 d) Life has existed on Earth for over $3.5 \times 10^9$ years.

5. **Application** Write the number in each calculator screen in both scientific notation and standard form.

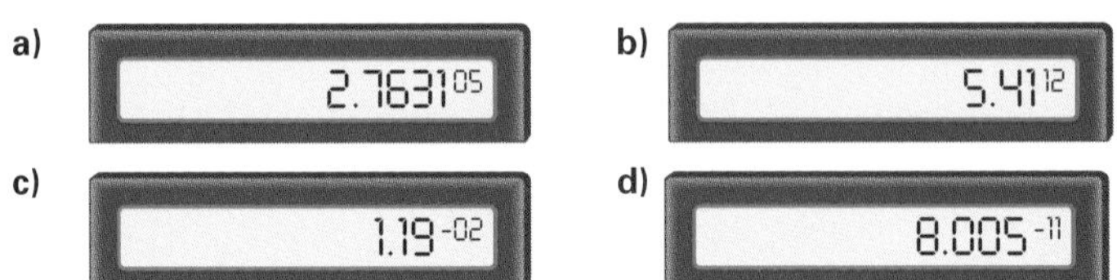


***For help with questions 6 and 7, refer to Example 3.***

6. **Communication** Use the exponent rules to evaluate. Express your answer in scientific notation. Compare and explain your results.
 a) $2.3 \times 3.5 \times 10^3 \times 10^4$
 b) $2.3 \times 10^3 \times 3.5 \times 10^4$
 c) $(2.3 \times 10^3) \times (3.5 \times 10^4)$

**B**

7. Use a calculator and the exponent laws to evaluate. Express your answer in scientific notation.
 a) $(6.3 \times 10^2) \times (5.1 \times 10^7)$
 b) $(8.5 \times 10^4) \times (2.43 \times 10^6)$
 c) $(5.4 \times 10^{-2}) \times (1.2 \times 10^{-6})$
 d) $(1.02 \times 10^{-5}) \times (3.3 \times 10^{-1})$
 e) $(4.8 \times 10^7) \times (8.2 \times 10^{-4})$
 f) $(6.6 \times 10^{-2}) \times (5.1 \times 10^9)$
 g) $\dfrac{6.5 \times 10^7}{1.3 \times 10^4}$
 h) $\dfrac{7.2 \times 10^5}{8.0 \times 10^{13}}$
 i) $\dfrac{3.5 \times 10^{-7}}{4.2 \times 10^9}$

8. a) Express 25 831 443 mm in scientific notation.
 b) Express 25 831 443 mm, in centimetres, using scientific notation.
 c) Express 25 831 443 mm, in metres, using scientific notation.
 d) Express 25 831 443 mm, in kilometres, using scientific notation.

## Apply the Concepts

***For help with question 9, refer to Example 4.***

9. **Population density** The population of Canada is $3.15 \times 10^7$ people. Canada's land area is $9.09 \times 10^6$ km$^2$. What is Canada's population density in people per square kilometre?

10. An answer was incorrectly given as $3.58 \times 10^{12}$. It should have been $3.58 \times 10^{-12}$. How many times too large was the incorrect answer?

Chapter Problem

Did You Know?

The kilowatt-hour or kW·h is the unit of energy you see on hydro bills. You use 1 kW·h if you draw a kilowatt of power for 1 h, or if you leave a 100-W light bulb on for 10 h.

**11.** By recycling a tonne (1 t) of newspaper, a school can save

**a)** 19 trees **b)** 3 $m^3$ of landfill

**c)** 4000 kW·h of energy **d)** 29 000 L of water

**e)** 30 kg of air pollution

There are about 4800 schools in Ontario. How much of each resource above could be saved, if each school recycled 1 t of newspaper? Express your answers in both standard form and scientific notation.

**12.** **Application** The smallest computer chips are about $9.0 \times 10^{-8}$ m wide. A human hair is about $2.0 \times 10^{-4}$ m wide.

**a)** If you placed 100 small chips side-by-side, would they be as wide as a human hair? Explain.

**b)** If you placed 1000 small chips side-by-side, would they be as wide as a human hair? Explain.

**c)** Express the width of a small computer chip as a fraction of the width of a human hair.

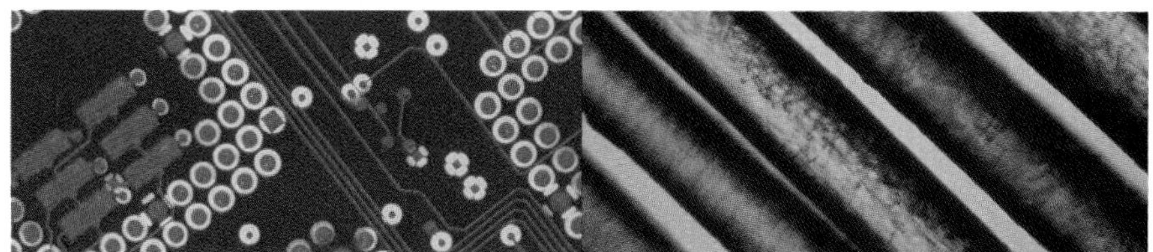

C

**13.** **Thinking/Inquiry/Problem Solving** The speed of light in space is about $3.0 \times 10^5$ km/s.

**a)** Earth is about $1.5 \times 10^8$ km from the Sun. How long does it take for light from the Sun to reach Earth? Express your answer in minutes and seconds, to the nearest second.

**b)** Pluto is about $6.0 \times 10^9$ km from the Sun. How long does it take for light from the Sun to reach Pluto? Express your answer in hours and minutes, to the nearest minute.

**14.** **Fermi problems** In Fermi problems, use reasonable estimates for quantities in the question to calculate an approximate answer. Select one of these five Fermi problems. Use your estimation skills to answer it. Then, express your answer in scientific notation.

**A** How many paper clips, end to end, equal the length of your school?

**B** How many hairs are on your head?

**C** How many pieces of paper will be handed out to all the students in your math class this year?

**D** How many ping pong balls would it take to fill your classroom (assuming that the room is empty)?

# Review

## 8.1 Powers With Rational Bases, pages 338–341

1. Evaluate each power.

   a) $\left(\frac{2}{3}\right)^3$   b) $\left(\frac{4}{5}\right)^2$   c) $\left(\frac{3}{10}\right)^3$

   d) $\left(\frac{1}{4}\right)^4$   e) $\left(\frac{3}{2}\right)^5$   f) $\left(\frac{7}{8}\right)^3$

2. **Application** Under shallow water, most of the Sun's light is visible, but deeper water reduces the amount of sunlight. The fraction of sunlight visible under water in a particular river can be found using the formula $S = \left(\frac{4}{5}\right)^d$. In this formula, $S$ is the fraction of sunlight and $d$ is the depth, in metres, under water. What fraction of sunlight is visible under each depth of water?

   a) 2 m

   b) 3 m

## 8.2 Exponent Rules, pages 342–346

3. Simplify by writing as a single power. Then, use a calculator to evaluate.

   a) $4^2 \times 4^1$   b) $2^3 \times 2^2$   c) $(5^2)(5^2)$

   d) $8^6 \div 8^4$   e) $5^7 \div 5^4$   f) $\frac{10^8}{10^3}$

   g) $(2^2)^4$   h) $(3^2)^2$   i) $(4^3)^0$

4. Simplify by writing as a single power.

   a) $(5^4)^3 \times 5^3$   b) $7^8 \div 7^6 \times 7^3$   c) $(m^3)^2(m^5)$

   d) $\frac{(x^2)^4}{x^5}$   e) $\frac{g^5 \times g^6}{g^7}$   f) $\frac{a^{10}}{(a^3)^3}$

5. **Communication** Using an example, explain why you add the exponents when multiplying powers with the same base.

## 8.3 Zero and Negative Exponents, pages 347–351

6. What is the missing exponent in each power?

**a)** $7^{■} = \frac{1}{7^3}$ **b)** $5^{-6} = \frac{1}{5^{■}}$ **c)** $y^{■} = \frac{1}{y^5}$ **d)** $m^{-7} = \frac{1}{m^{■}}$

7. Evaluate each power. Leave your answer as a whole number or a fraction.

**a)** $3^{-2}$ **b)** $5^{-3}$ **c)** $7^{-1}$
**d)** $8^0$ **e)** $10^{-3}$ **f)** $9^{-1}$
**g)** $5^{-4}$ **h)** $7^0$ **i)** $5^{-5}$

8. Use the exponent rules to evaluate each expression. Check using a calculator.

**a)** $3^4 \times 3^{-2}$ **b)** $8^{-2} \times 8^2$ **c)** $5^4 \times 5^{-6}$
**d)** $7^{-2} \times 7^0$ **e)** $(6^{-1})^2$ **f)** $(7^{-2})^{-1}$
**g)** $8^7 \times 8^{-8}$ **h)** $10^{-9} \times 10^{-15}$ **i)** $125^{12} \times 125^{-13}$

## 8.4 Scientific Notation, pages 352–357

9. Express each number in standard form.

**a)** $5.3 \times 10^8$ m **b)** $7.12 \times 10^4$ g
**c)** $3.9901 \times 10^{10}$ L **d)** $6.2 \times 10^{-4}$ L
**e)** $3.0 \times 10^{-10}$ m **f)** $4.001 \times 10^{-8}$ g

10. Express each number in scientific notation.

**a)** 600 000 000 m **b)** 56 000 000 000 L
**c)** 6 519 000 000 000 000 $m^2$ **d)** 0.000 03 m
**e)** 0.000 000 067 L **f)** 0.000 000 000 000 000 091 g

11. **Communication** Measurements used in science often have many decimal places or many zeros.

**a)** The mass of an electron is $9.11 \times 10^{-31}$ kg. How many zeros would you need after the decimal point to write this mass in standard form? Explain.

**b)** Scientists have estimated the mass of the universe at about $1.00 \times 10^{41}$ kg. How many zeros would you need after the "1" in order to write this in standard form? Explain.

12. **Application** The population of Sudbury, in 2001, was $1.552 \times 10^5$ people. Sudbury's land area is $2.8 \times 10^3$ $km^2$. What was Sudbury's population density in 2001?

**Did You Know?**

Scientists think that most of the universe is made up of dark matter (23%) and dark energy (73%). Dark matter makes galaxies revolve more quickly. Dark energy is accelerating the growth of the universe. However, no one is really sure yet what dark matter or dark energy actually are!

# Practice Test

## Multiple Choice

***For questions 1 to 4, select the best answer.***

**1.** To evaluate $\left(\frac{2}{3}\right)^5$, you could use

**A** $\frac{2}{3} \times \frac{2}{3} \times \frac{2}{3} \times \frac{2}{3} \times \frac{2}{3}$

**B** $\frac{2^5}{3^5}$

**C** $\frac{2 \times 2 \times 2 \times 2 \times 2}{3 \times 3 \times 3 \times 3 \times 3}$

**D** any of the above

**2.** The number $3^{-4}$ is equivalent to

**A** $-12$

**B** $\frac{1}{3^4}$

**C** 0.0003

**D** none of the above

**3.** When a number is converted into scientific notation

**A** it always represents a very large number

**B** it always represents a very small number

**C** it usually represents a very large or very small number

**D** all of the above

**4.** $8^9 \times 8^7$ can be rewritten as

**A** $8^2$ **B** $64^{16}$ **C** $8^{63}$ **D** $8^{16}$

## Short Answer

**5.** Write each power in expanded form. Then, evaluate the power.

**a)** $\left(\frac{3}{5}\right)^2$ **b)** $\left(\frac{7}{3}\right)^3$ **c)** $\left(\frac{5}{8}\right)^6$

6. Rewrite using positive exponents. Then evaluate.

a) $8^{-1}$ b) $5^{-2}$
c) $4^{-3}$ d) $10^{-5}$

7. Rewrite in scientific notation.

a) 248 875 000 b) 7 349 000 000 000
c) 0.000 0002 d) 0.000 000 000 000 000 043

8. Simplify each expression. Then, evaluate.

a) $5^2 \times 5^4$ b) $7^8 \times 7^{-6}$ c) $\frac{12^5}{12^6}$
d) $9^7 \times 9^{-7}$ e) $(2^3)^2$ f) $(5^2)^{-1}$

## Extended Response

9. **Application** Lake Superior's surface area is $8.14 \times 10^{10}$ m$^2$. Lake Simcoe's surface area is $3.58 \times 10^9$ m$^2$. How many times would Lake Simcoe fit into Lake Superior? Express your answer in scientific notation.

10. **Thinking/Inquiry/Problem Solving** A tonne is $1.0 \times 10^3$ kg. A quarterpounder hamburger has a mass of about $1.1 \times 10^{-1}$ kg. How many quarterpounders would have a mass of one tonne? Express your answer in standard form, rounded to the nearest hamburger.

**ACHIEVEMENT CHECK** Knowledge/Understanding Thinking/Inquiry/Problem Solving Communication Application

11. A package of 500 sheets of computer printing paper is 5 cm thick. The sheets are 21.6 cm wide by 27.9 cm long. The paper has a mass of 75 g per square metre. "Computers and Connections" store has just had a delivery of a pallet of 48 boxes of paper, each box containing 12 packages.

a) How thick is one sheet of paper?
b) What is the area of one sheet of paper?
c) How many sheets of paper are there in the delivery? Give your answer in scientific notation.
d) What is the total area of the paper in the delivery? Give your answer in scientific notation.
e) What is the mass of the paper in the delivery? Give your answer in scientific notation.

Y20T3

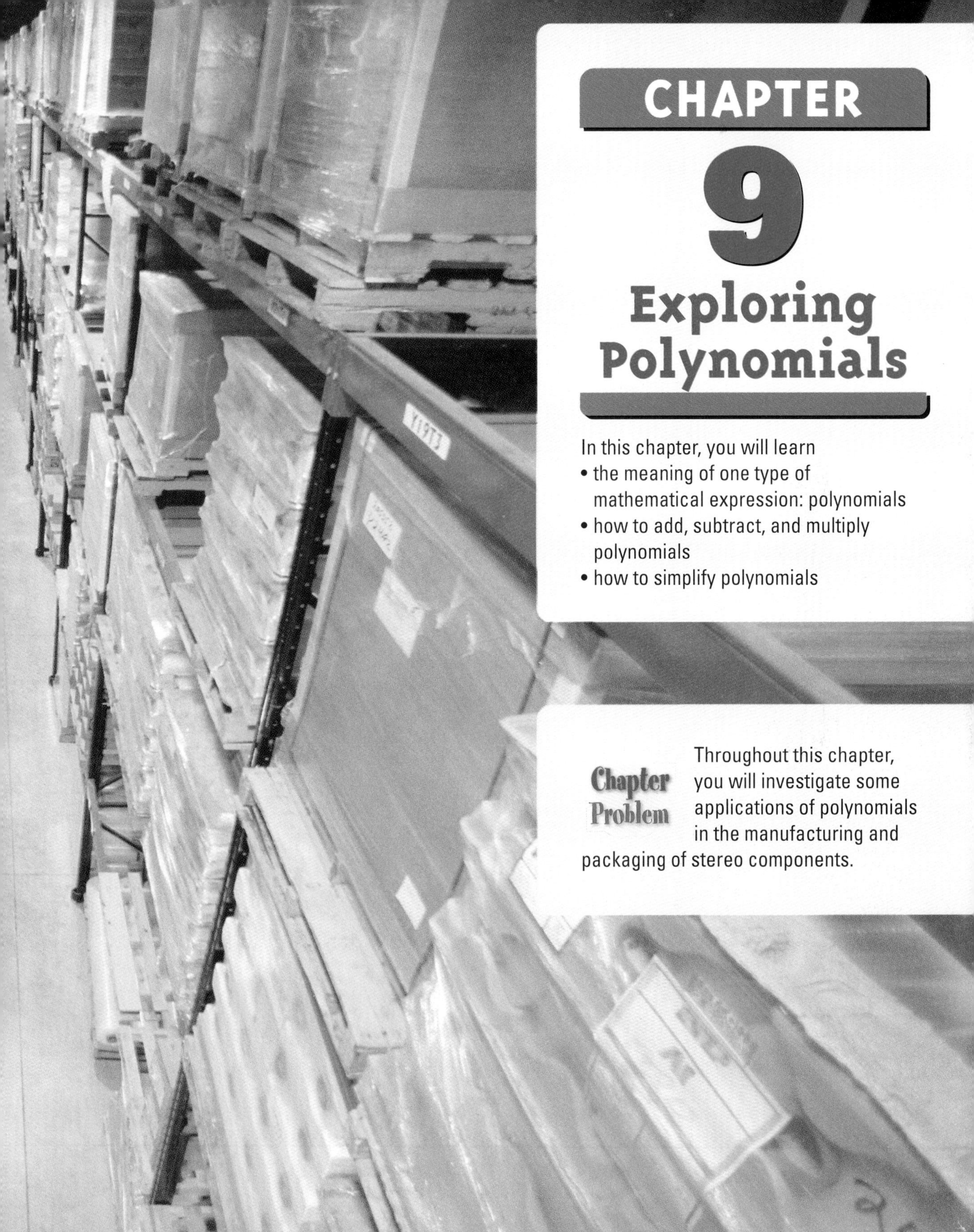

# CHAPTER 9
# Exploring Polynomials

In this chapter, you will learn

- the meaning of one type of mathematical expression: polynomials
- how to add, subtract, and multiply polynomials
- how to simplify polynomials

**Chapter Problem**

Throughout this chapter, you will investigate some applications of polynomials in the manufacturing and packaging of stereo components.

# Get Ready

## Using Algebra Tiles

Tiles can be used to model algebraic expressions.

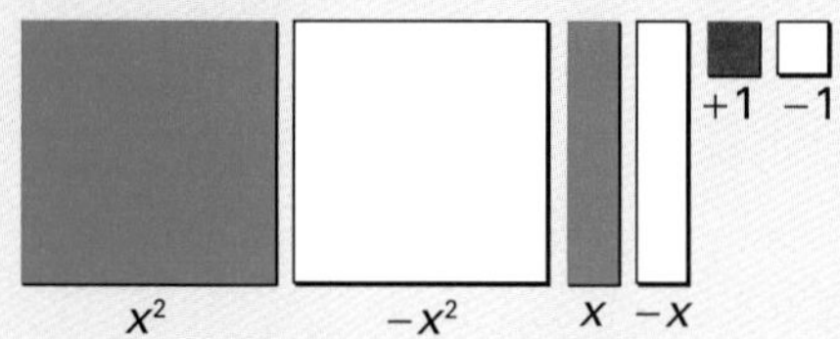


Algebra tiles are used to represent expressions.

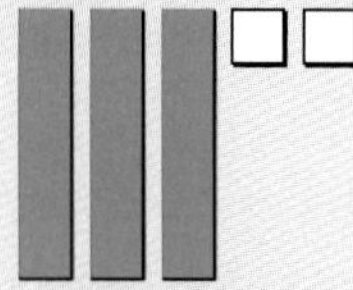

represents $3x - 2$

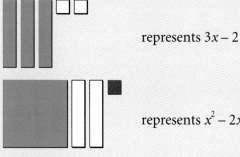

represents $x^2 - 2x + 1$

**1.** Write the expression that each group of algebra tiles represents.

**a)**  **b)** **c)** 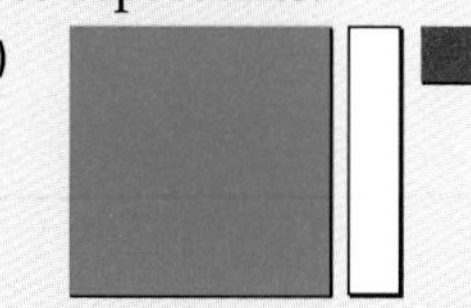

**2.** Use algebra tiles or diagrams to model each expression.

**a)** $2x + 1$ **b)** $x^2 + x + 3$ **c)** $x^2 - 3x - 2$

## Exponent Rules

You can use the exponent rules to simplify products of powers.

$$\begin{aligned}&(7x)(4x)\\&= 7 \times 4 \times x^2\\&= 28x^2\end{aligned}$$

$$\begin{aligned}&(k)(k^2)\\&= k^3\end{aligned}$$

$$\begin{aligned}&5n^2(7n^3)\\&= 5 \times 7 \times n^5\\&= 35n^5\end{aligned}$$

**3.** Simplify.

**a)** $(2x)(3x)$ **b)** $(y^2)(y)$ **c)** $-8(5k^2)$

**d)** $-5n(-3n)$ **e)** $\left(\frac{x}{y}\right)^2$ **f)** $-5(2c^2)(3c)$

## Perimeter and Area

Find the perimeter and the area of the rectangle using the appropriate formulas.

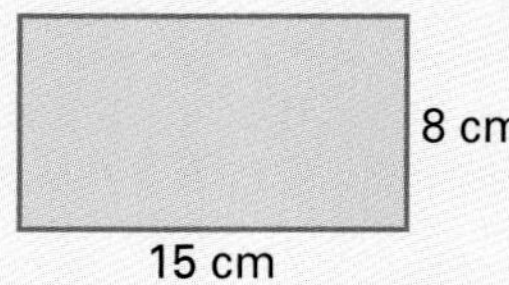


$P = 2(l + w)$
$P = 2(15 + 8)$
$P = 2(23)$
$P = 46$
The perimeter of the rectangle is 46 cm.

$A = l \times w$
$A = 15 \times 8$
$A = 120$
The area of the rectangle is 120 $cm^2$.

**4.** Find the perimeter and area of the rectangle.

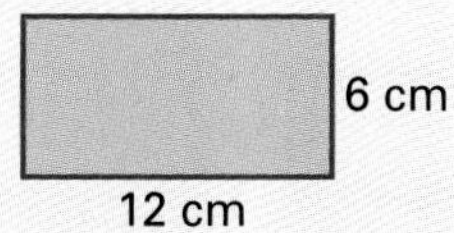


**5.** Calculate the area of the triangle.

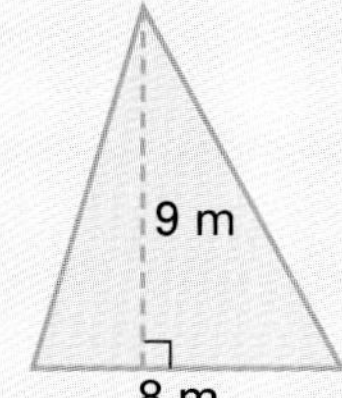


## Surface Area and Volume

Determine the surface area and the volume of the rectangular prism.

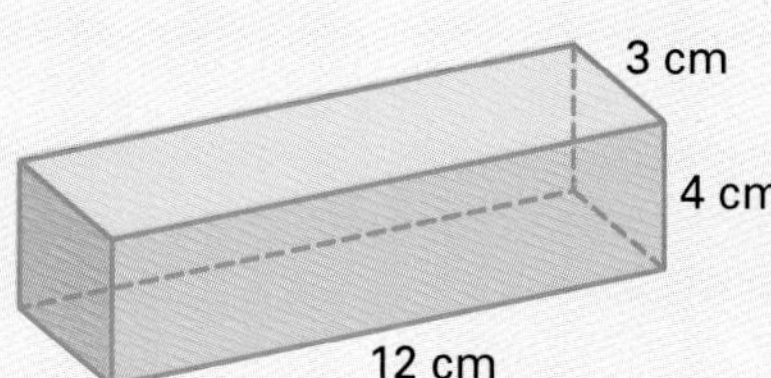


$S = 2lw + 2lh + 2wh$
$= 2(12)(3) + 2(12)(4) + 2(3)(4)$
$= 72 + 96 + 24$
$= 192$
The surface area is 192 $cm^2$.

$V = lwh$
$= (12)(3)(4)$
$= 144$
The volume is 144 $cm^3$.

**6.** Determine the surface area and the volume of each rectangular prism.

**a)**

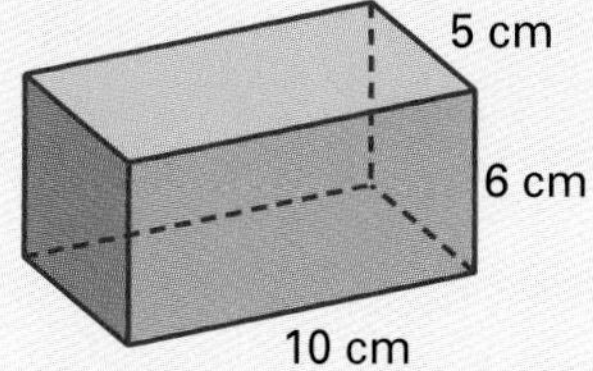


**b)**

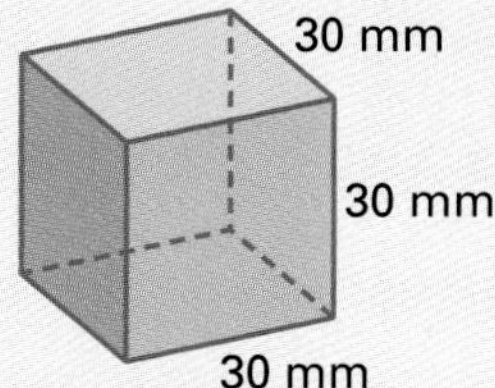

# 9.1 Introducing to Polynomials

In previous chapters, you used variables to graph and study relationships in measurement formulas and in work with exponents. Here, you will investigate variable expressions called polynomials.

## DISCOVER

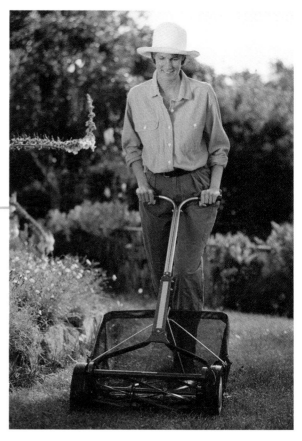

### Applying Algebraic Expressions

Jenna has a summer job working for a landscaping company. She earns \$50 per day plus \$15 for each lawn she cuts.

1. Copy and complete the table to show Jenna's earnings on one day.

| Number of Lawns Cut | 0 | 1 | 2 | 3 | 4 | 5 | 6 |
|---|---|---|---|---|---|---|---|
| Daily Earnings (\$) | | | | | | | |

2. The letter $n$ represents the number of lawns Jenna cuts in one day. Which expression represents her earnings that day? Explain.
   **A** $50n + 15$ **B** $50 + 15n$ **C** $50(n + 15)$ **D** $65 + n$

3. Use your formula to determine Jenna's earnings on one day. Use a table such as the one below.

| Number of Lawns Cut | 6 | 10 | 15 |
|---|---|---|---|
| Daily Earnings (\$) | | | |

4. The following expressions represent different people's earnings per day at the same landscaping company. Describe each person's earnings in words.
   **a)** $45 + 18n$ **b)** $60 + 12n$

In the **Discover**, $n$ represents the number of lawns cut. Because $n$ can take any integer value greater than 0, it is known as a **variable**. Any letter can be used as a variable.

Algebraic expressions are made up of several parts, which are defined in the table below.

The coefficient of the term $x$ is 1, and the coefficient of the term $-x$ is $-1$.

| | Definition | Examples |
|---|---|---|
| **variable** | • a letter that represents a value that can change, or vary, in an expression | $x, p, y, l, w$ |
| **term** | • a number<br>• a variable<br>• a power of a variable<br>• a product of a number and a power of a variable | 6<br>$x$<br>$x^2$<br>$5y$ |
| **coefficient** | • the number that is multiplied by the variable in a term | 5 in $5y$<br>$-4$ in $-4x^2$ |
| **variable term** | • a term that contains a variable<br>• its value changes when the value of the variable changes | $15n$<br>$2x^2$ |
| **constant term** | • a term that contains no variables<br>• its value does not change | 5<br>$-22$ |

An expression such as $2x^2 - 5x + 3$ is called a **polynomial**. A polynomial is made up of terms separated by addition or subtraction.

The polynomial $2x^2 - 5x + 3$ can be modelled using algebra tiles as shown.

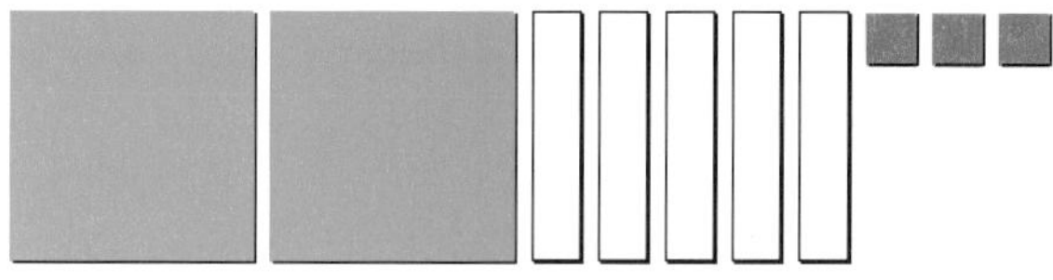

Polynomials are usually written in **descending order**. The exponents on the variables are in order from greatest to least. For example, $4a^2 + 5a - 8$ is written in descending order.

The table shows three special types of polynomials.

| Type of Polynomial | Number of Terms | Examples |
|---|---|---|
| monomial | 1 | $5x$, $7y^2$, 50 |
| binomial | 2 | $2x + 3$, $5n^2 - 7n$ |
| trinomial | 3 | $4a^2 + 5a - 8$, $2p^3 + 3p + 1$ |

A polynomial with more than three terms has no special name. For example, $5y^3 - 3y^2 + 2y + 9$ is a polynomial.

## Example 1

### Finding the Number of Terms in a Polynomial

State the number of terms in each polynomial. Which polynomial is a binomial?

**a)** $5k - 3$ **b)** $7m^2$
**c)** $10x^2 - 6x + 1$ **d)** $-7a^3 - 7a^2 + a + 1$

### Solution

| | Polynomial | Number of Terms |
|---|---|---|
| a) | $5k - 3$ | 2 |
| b) | $7m^2$ | 1 |
| c) | $10x^2 - 6x + 1$ | 3 |
| d) | $-7a^3 - 7a^2 + a + 1$ | 4 |

The first polynomial, $5k - 3$, is a binomial because it has two terms.

## Example 2

### Substituting and Evaluating

Evaluate $x^2 - 5x + 3$ when

**a)** $x = 2$ **b)** $x = -1$

### Solution

**a)** Substitute $x = 2$ for each $x$ in $x^2 - 5x + 3$. Then, evaluate.

$$x^2 - 5x + 3$$
$$= (2)^2 - 5(2) + 3$$
$$= 4 - 10 + 3$$ **Use BEDMAS to evaluate.**
$$= -3$$

**b)**
$$x^2 - 5x + 3$$
$$= (-1)^2 - 5(-1) + 3$$ **Substitute –1 for *x*.**
$$= 1 + 5 + 3$$
$$= 9$$

## Example 3

### Writing Expressions for Word Phrases

Write an expression for each phrase.

**a)** two years younger than a person's age
**b)** double the mass of the brick
**c)** five dollars more than the cost

## Solution

**a)** Let $a$ represent the person's age.
Then, two years younger is represented by $a - 2$.

**b)** Let $m$ represent the mass of the brick.
Then, double the mass is $2m$.

**c)** Let $c$ represent the cost.
Then, five dollars more than the cost is represented by $c + 5$.

Polynomial expressions can sometimes be simplified by adding or subtracting like terms.

| | Definition | Examples |
|---|---|---|
| **Like terms** | Terms that contain the same variables raised to the same exponents | $2x$ and $-8x$<br>$6y^2$ and $-9y^2$<br>5 and 25 |
| **Unlike terms** | Terms that contain different variables, or contain the same variables raised to different exponents | $2xy$ and $3y$<br>32 and $5a$<br>$4x$ and $4x^2$ |

# Example 4

## Collecting Like Terms

Add or subtract like terms.

**a)** $3x + 2x + 2 - 3$

**b)** $4x^2 - 8x + 2 - 7x^2 + 4x + 3$

## Solution

**a)**
$$3x + 2x + 2 - 3$$
$$= 5x - 1 \quad \text{Add or subtract like terms.}$$

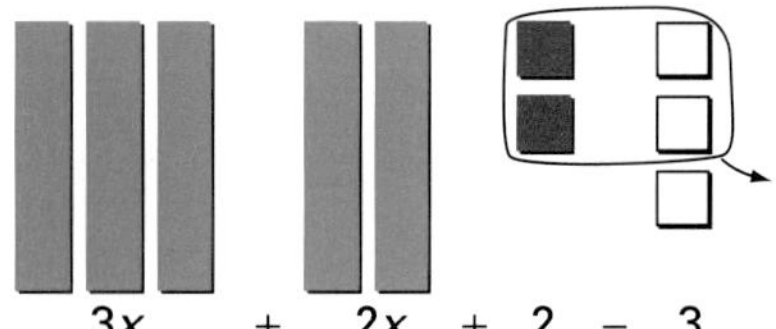


**b)**
$$4x^2 - 8x + 2 - 7x^2 + 4x + 3$$
$$= 4x^2 - 7x^2 - 8x + 4x + 2 + 3 \quad \text{Rearrange the terms, keeping the sign or operation with the term.}$$
$$= -3x^2 - 4x + 5 \quad \text{Add or subtract like terms.}$$

## Key Concepts

- A polynomial is made up of terms. Terms are separated by addition or subtraction.
  - A monomial has one term.
  - A binomial has two terms.
  - A trinomial has three terms.
- The coefficient of a term is the number that is multiplied by the variable.
- Like terms have exactly the same variables raised to the same exponents. Like terms can be added or subtracted.

## Discuss the Concepts

1. a) Describe two situations that could be represented by the expression $c - 3$.
   b) Describe two situations that could be represented by the expression $5m$.
2. Describe, in your own words, what is meant by "like terms."
3. Explain why $n$ and $n^2$ are not like terms.

## Practise

***For help with question 1, refer to Example 1.***

1. Copy and complete the table. Which polynomial is a trinomial?

| | Polynomial | Number of Terms |
|---|---|---|
| a) | $5h$ | |
| b) | $-9k + 6$ | |
| c) | $77b - 55$ | |
| d) | $2y^2 + 6y + 8$ | |
| e) | $6x^4 + 5x^3 - 8x^2 + 2x + 9$ | |

2. Identify the coefficient of each term.
   a) $10d^2$ b) $-3x$ c) $y$ d) $-y$

***For help with questions 3 and 4, refer to Example 2.***

3. Evaluate each polynomial for $a = 2$.
   a) $4a + 1$ b) $5 - a$ c) $7a - 18$ d) $6 - 10a$

4. Evaluate $5k^2 - 2k + 10$ for each value of $k$.

a) 1 b) 2 c) 0
d) −2 e) −5

***For help with question 5, refer to Example 4.***

5. Add or subtract like terms. Write your answers with the exponents in descending order.

a) $2x + 3x + 8 + 7$
b) $4p - p - 6 + 2$
c) $5y + 9 + 2y - 5$
d) $3x^2 + 7x - 7 - 8x^2 + 5x + 3$
e) $m^2 - 4m + 1 + 6m^2 - 7m - 10$
f) $5v^3 - v + 6 - 12v^3 - v - 6$

## Apply the Concepts

6. Write an expression for the area of each rectangle.

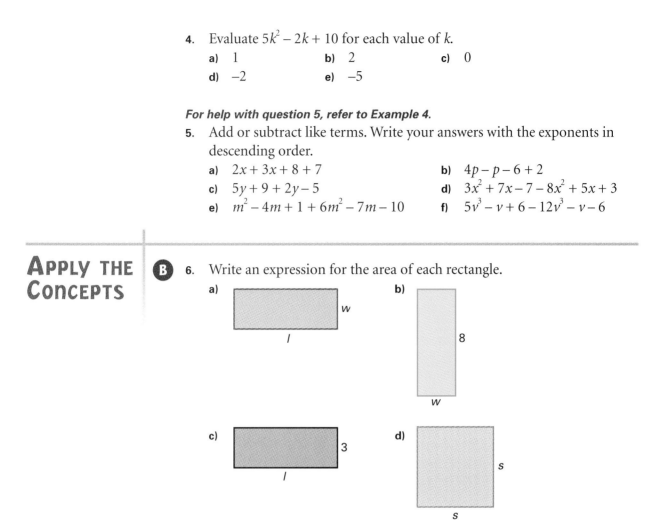

a)

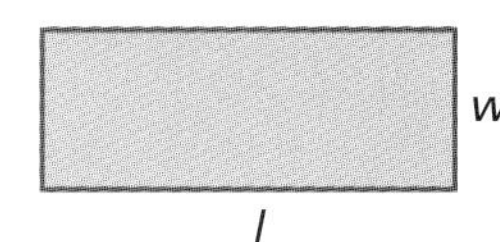


b)

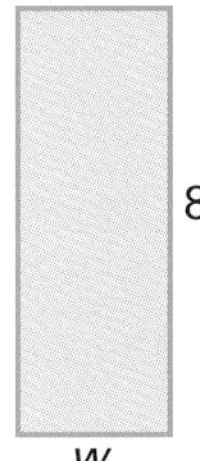


c)

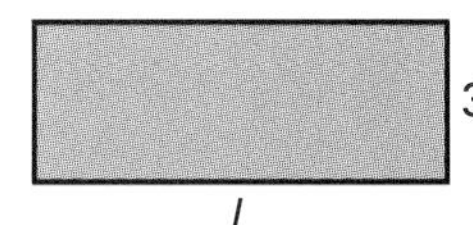


d)

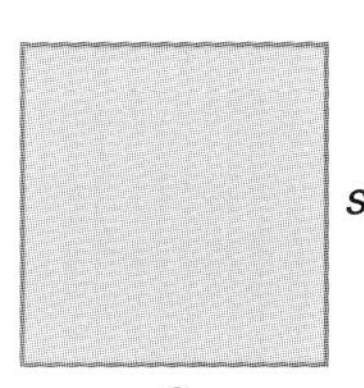


***For help with question 7, refer to Example 3.***

7. Write a polynomial to represent each phrase. Remember to define your choice for the variable first.

a) five more than Andy's height
b) triple the cost of the chocolate bar
c) the square of the length
d) three dollars off the cost of the phone call
e) four dollars more than twice the cost of the CD
f) Mae's earnings at ten dollars per hour

Did You Know?

The metric abbreviation for seconds is s. Two seconds is written as 2 s.

8. **Application** The formula $h = -5t^2 + 10t + 1$ gives the height, in metres, of a ball above the ground $t$ seconds after it is tossed into the air. Determine the height of the ball after

   **a)** 0 s  **b)** 1 s  **c)** 2 s

9. **Thinking/Inquiry/Problem Solving** The cost of renting a computer game is $3 for the first day and $2 per day after that.

   **a)** Copy and complete the table showing the cost to rent one game.

| Number of Days | 1 | 2 | 3 | 4 | 5 |
|---|---|---|---|---|---|
| Total Cost ($) | | | | | |

   **b)** Write a polynomial for the cost of renting a computer game for $n$ days.

   **c)** Use your polynomial to determine the cost of a 7-day rental.

   **d)** How much would it cost to rent the game for two weeks?

C 10. Write the next three terms in each pattern.
Write a polynomial to represent the value of term number $n$.
Then, use your polynomial to determine the value of term number 10.

   **a)** 2, 4, 6, 8, 10, …

   **b)** 3, 5, 7, 9, 11, …

   **c)** 1, 4, 9, 16, 25, …

11. Use trial and error to determine what integer value(s) of $x$ will give a value of zero for each polynomial.

   **a)** $2x - 4$  **b)** $x^2 + 5x - 6$  **c)** $3x^2 + 4x - 4$

# 9.2 Adding and Subtracting Polynomials

To simplify expressions or to solve equations, you may need to add or subtract terms or polynomials. These skills can be applied to areas such as measurement and business.

## DISCOVER

### Adding Polynomials

1. Describe how to find the perimeter of any triangle if you know the lengths of all three sides.

2. Determine the perimeter of each triangle below.

a)

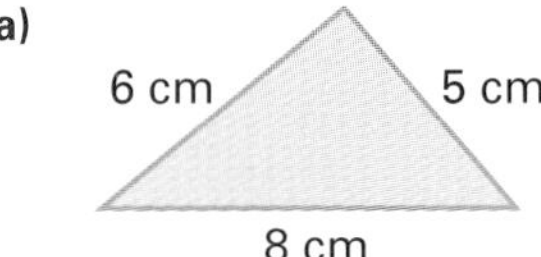


b)

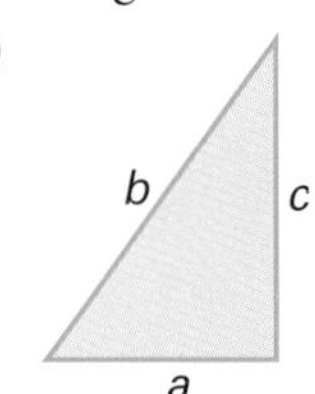


c)

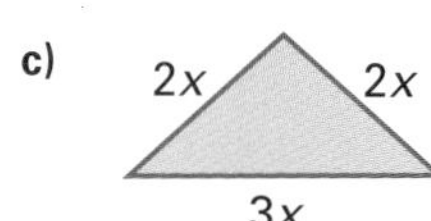


d)

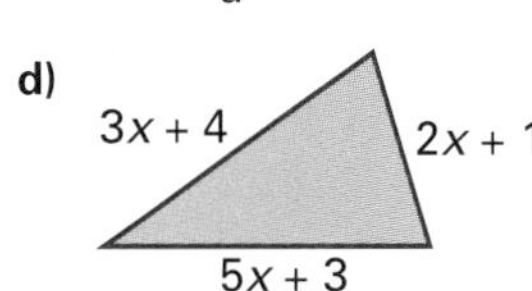


3. Use algebra tiles to model the sums in parts c) and d) of step 2.

4. State a rule for adding polynomials.

## EXAMPLE 1

### Adding Polynomials

Add by collecting like terms.

**a)** $(x + 3) + (2x - 1)$

**b)** $(6x^2 - 7x + 8) + (-4x^2 - 6x - 3)$

### Solution

**a)** $(x + 3) + (2x - 1)$

$= x + 3 + 2x - 1$ — **Remove the brackets.**

$= x + 2x + 3 - 1$ — **Collect like terms.**

$= 3x + 2$ — **Add or subtract like terms.**

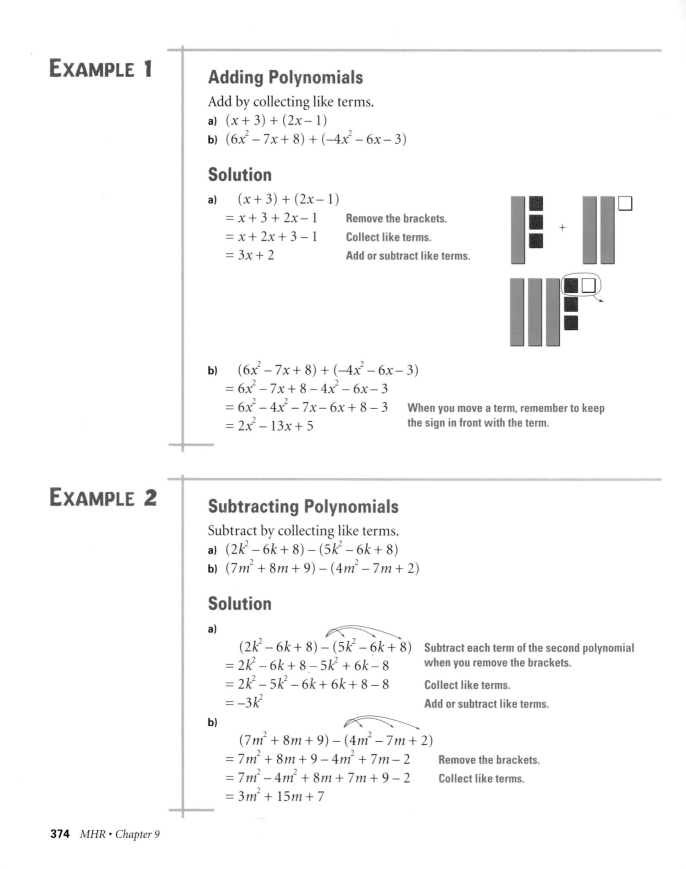

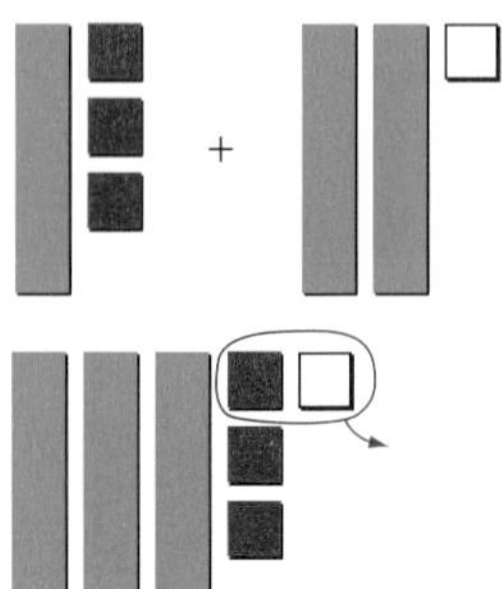


**b)** $(6x^2 - 7x + 8) + (-4x^2 - 6x - 3)$

$= 6x^2 - 7x + 8 - 4x^2 - 6x - 3$

$= 6x^2 - 4x^2 - 7x - 6x + 8 - 3$ — **When you move a term, remember to keep the sign in front with the term.**

$= 2x^2 - 13x + 5$

## EXAMPLE 2

### Subtracting Polynomials

Subtract by collecting like terms.

**a)** $(2k^2 - 6k + 8) - (5k^2 - 6k + 8)$

**b)** $(7m^2 + 8m + 9) - (4m^2 - 7m + 2)$

### Solution

**a)**

$(2k^2 - 6k + 8) - (5k^2 - 6k + 8)$ — **Subtract each term of the second polynomial when you remove the brackets.**

$= 2k^2 - 6k + 8 - 5k^2 + 6k - 8$

$= 2k^2 - 5k^2 - 6k + 6k + 8 - 8$ — **Collect like terms.**

$= -3k^2$ — **Add or subtract like terms.**

**b)**

$(7m^2 + 8m + 9) - (4m^2 - 7m + 2)$

$= 7m^2 + 8m + 9 - 4m^2 + 7m - 2$ — **Remove the brackets.**

$= 7m^2 - 4m^2 + 8m + 7m + 9 - 2$ — **Collect like terms.**

$= 3m^2 + 15m + 7$

## Example 3

### Subtracting Expressions in a Perimeter Context

The perimeter of the triangle is $18x + 15$. Determine the length of the third side.

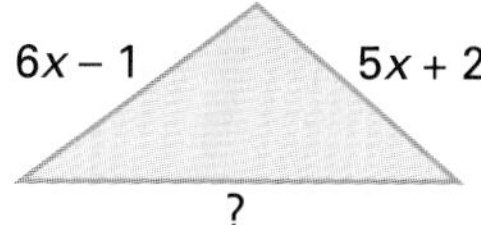


### Solution

Subtract each of the two given side lengths from the perimeter.

$$\begin{aligned} &(18x + 15) - (5x + 2) - (6x - 1) \\ &= 18x + 15 - 5x - 2 - 6x + 1 \\ &= 18x - 5x - 6x + 15 - 2 + 1 \\ &= 7x + 14 \end{aligned}$$

The third side has length $7x + 14$.

## Example 4

### Adding Expressions in an Application

The cost, in dollars, to print $n$ copies of a book is $9n + 1000$. The cost, in dollars, to ship $n$ copies is $2n + 100$.

a) How much would it cost to print and ship $n$ copies of the book?

b) How much would it cost to print and ship 1000 copies of the book?

### Solution

a) $$\begin{aligned} \text{Total cost} &= \text{printing cost} + \text{shipping cost} \\ &= (9n + 1000) + (2n + 100) \\ &= 9n + 1000 + 2n + 100 \\ &= 9n + 2n + 1000 + 100 \\ &= 11n + 1100 \end{aligned}$$

The cost, in dollars, to print and ship $n$ copies of the book is $11n + 1100$.

b) $$\begin{aligned} \text{Total cost} &= 11n + 1100 \\ &= 11(1000) + 1100 \\ &= 11\,000 + 1100 \\ &= 12\,100 \end{aligned}$$

**Substitute 1000 for *n*.**

The cost to print and ship 1000 copies of the book is \$12 100.

## Key Concepts

- To add two polynomials, remove the brackets. Then, collect and add or subtract like terms.
- To subtract two polynomials, remove the brackets by subtracting each term in the second polynomial, which changes the sign of each term. Then, collect and add or subtract like terms.

## Discuss the Concepts

1. What sum is modelled by these algebra tiles? What is the result? Explain.

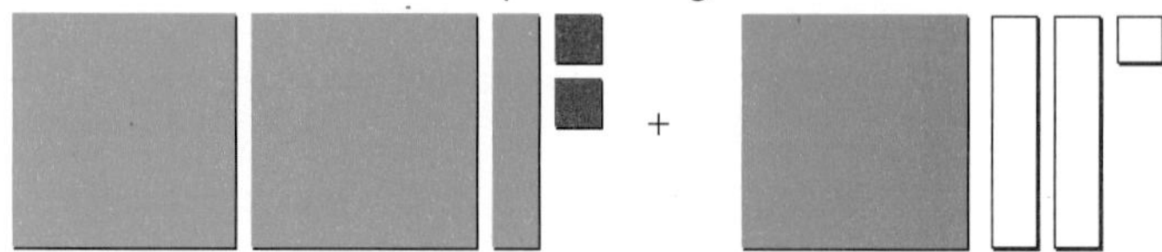

2. When removing the brackets from a subtracted polynomial, you change all signs. Why?

## Practise

**A**

***For help with questions 1 and 2, refer to Example 1.***

1. Identify the like terms.
   a) $5x^2, 7x, 8xy, 54x, 67, -8y^2, 9x$
   b) $6k, -10, 8k^3, 7k, -9k^2, 12, k^3$

2. Add.
   a) $(2x + 5) + (3x + 7)$
   b) $(6y + 8) + (7y - 12)$
   c) $(5n^2 + 12n - 6) + (8n^2 - 7n - 9)$
   d) $(4c^2 - 3c + 1) + (-5c^2 - 6c - 7)$
   e) $(g^2 + 6g - 2) + (g^2 + g - 4)$
   f) $(3m^2 - 5) + (5m - 8m^2)$
   g) $(3x^3 + 5x^2 - 7x - 8) + (5x^3 - 9x^2 + 2x + 7)$

***For help with question 3, refer to Example 2.***

3. Subtract.
   a) $(6x + 8) - (4x + 1)$
   b) $(7b + 3) - (9b - 6)$
   c) $(2d^2 + 9d + 5) - (7d^2 - 4d - 9)$
   d) $(3p^2 - 5p + 6) - (-2p^2 - 6p - 1)$
   e) $(y^2 - 7y - 3) - (y^2 + 2y - 4)$
   f) $(4y^2 - 2) - (2y - 9y^2)$
   g) $(5w^3 + 6w^2 - 3w + 2) - (6w^3 - 4w^2 + w + 5)$

4. Simplify.
   a) $(4c + 5) + (2c - 6)$
   b) $(12x - 8) - (9x - 3)$
   c) $(5y^2 + 7y - 2) + (-8y^2 - 9y + 4)$
   d) $(k^2 - 6k + 5) - (3k^2 + 7k - 5)$
   e) $(2x + 5) + (3x - 8) + (4x - 7)$

## Apply the Concepts

5. **Communication**

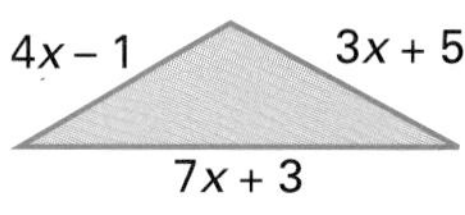


   a) For the triangle shown, substitute 5 for $x$ and find the length of each side. Use your results to find the perimeter of the triangle.
   b) Add the polynomials to find an expression for the perimeter of the triangle. Simplify the expression. Then, substitute 5 for $x$ to find the perimeter. What do you notice?
   c) Which method is easier? Why?
   d) In what circumstances would the other method be better?

6. The perimeter of the triangle shown is $6x^2 + 7x + 12$. Find a polynomial representing the length of the third side.

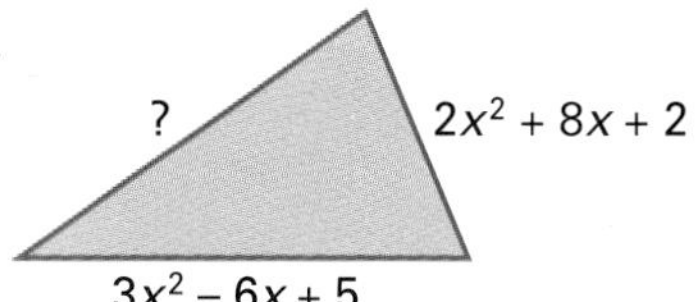


7. **Application** Pappy's Pizza estimates its profit for each of its stores $x$ months after the chain of stores opens.

| Store | Profit ($) |
|---|---|
| Diagonal St. | $5000x - 6500$ |
| Main St. | $3800x - 4000$ |
| Front St. | $6200x - 5000$ |
| Elm St. | $5700x - 4000$ |

   a) Write a polynomial representing the total estimated profit for the whole chain after $x$ months. Simplify the polynomial.
   b) Calculate the total profit (or loss) after 1 month.
   c) Calculate the total profit (or loss) after 1 year.

**Chapter Problem**

8. A small company manufactures stereo speakers. The revenue, in dollars, from selling $n$ speakers is given by $-n^2 + 4000n$. The cost, in dollars, to make $n$ speakers is given by $-5n^2 + 8000n + 90\ 000$. If the revenue minus the cost is positive, the company makes a profit. If the revenue minus the cost is negative, the company suffers a loss.
   a) Write a polynomial representing revenue minus cost. Simplify the polynomial.
   b) Determine whether there is a profit or a loss if the company sells 500 speakers. How much is the profit or loss?
   c) Repeat part b) for sales of 1000 speakers.

9. **Thinking/Inquiry/Problem Solving** When you substitute any positive integer values of $x$ into the expression $(7x + 11) - (3x + 5)$, will the result always be a prime number, always be a composite number, or sometimes be prime and sometimes be composite? Justify your answer.

**Use the Glossary at the back of this text if you are unsure of the meaning of terms such as prime and composite numbers.**

# 9.3 Multiplying a Monomial and a Polynomial

You may need to develop, and then simplify, formulas using multiplication to solve a problem. In this section, you will learn how to multiply a polynomial by a monomial. You will apply the process to some business applications.

## DISCOVER

### Multiplying Polynomials Using Area Models

1. Find an expression for the area of each large rectangle.

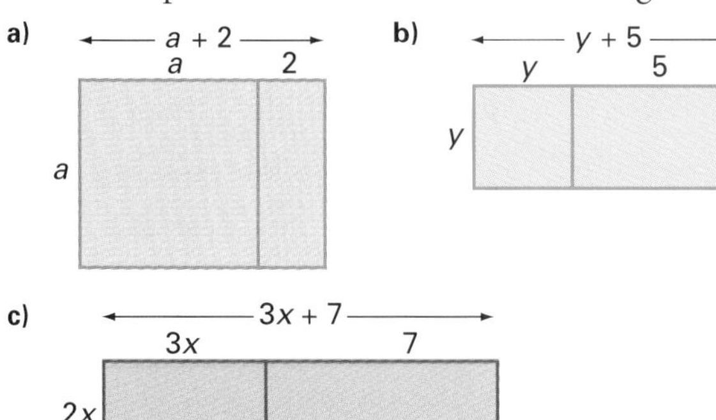


2. Find expressions for the areas of the two smaller parts of each rectangle in step 1. Then, add the expressions together for each rectangle.

3. For each rectangle, compare your answers in steps 1 and 2. What can you do to your answers in step 1 to get the same answers as in step 2?

4. Use your results to write a rule for multiplying a monomial and a polynomial.

5. Multiply using your rule from step 3.

a) $a(2a + 3)$

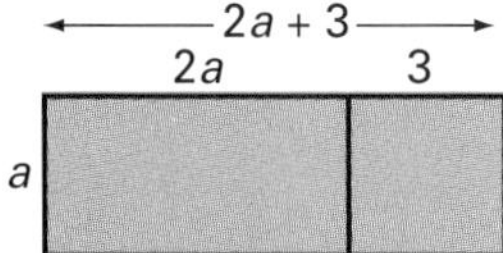


b) $2x(5x - 4)$

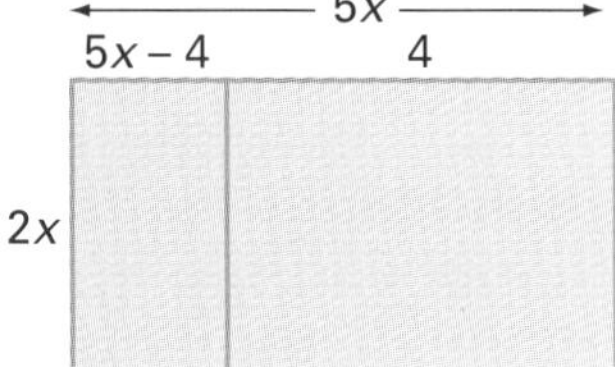

To multiply a monomial by a polynomial, multiply each term inside the brackets by the monomial outside the brackets. If the monomial is negative, change the sign on each term of the polynomial.

## EXAMPLE 1

### Multiplying by a Monomial

Expand.

a) $3(4x^2 - 5x + 8)$   b) $5y(7y - 1)$   c) $-2k^2(6k^2 + 4k - 2)$

### Solution

a) $3(4x^2 - 5x + 8)$
$= 12x^2 - 15x + 24$

**Multiply each term in the brackets by 3.**

b) $5y(7y - 1)$
$= 35y^2 - 5y$

**Multiply each term in the brackets by 5*y*.**
**Use the exponent laws: $5y \times 7y = 35y^2$**

c) $-2k^2(6k^2 + 4k - 2)$
$= -12k^4 - 8k^3 + 4k^2$

**Multiply each term in the brackets by $-2k^2$.**
**Multiplying by a negative changes the sign.**

## EXAMPLE 2

### Multiplying to Find an Expression for Area

a) Find an expression, in expanded form, for the area of the rectangle.

b) Find the area of the rectangle when $x$ is 5 cm.

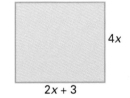

### Solution

a) Area = length × width
$= 4x(2x + 3)$
$= 8x^2 + 12x$

b) Substitute $x = 5$.
Area $= 8(5)^2 + 12(5)$
$= 8(25) + 60$
$= 200 + 60$
$= 260$
The area of the rectangle is 260 cm$^2$.

## Key Concepts

- When multiplying a monomial and a polynomial, multiply each term of the polynomial by the monomial.
- If the monomial is negative, change the sign on each term of the polynomial. For example, $-3(2k - 5) = -6k + 15$.

## Discuss the Concepts

1. Explain how you would expand each expression by multiplying.
   a) $2(x + 5)$ b) $4y(3y - 8)$
2. Explain how you would expand each expression by multiplying.
   a) $-2(x + 5)$ b) $-4y(3y - 8)$
3. Discuss the similarities and the differences between questions 1 and 2.

## Practise

**A** ***For help with questions 1–5, refer to Example 1.***

1. Expand.
   a) $3(x + 6)$ b) $7(k + 4)$ c) $4(d + 10)$
   d) $-2(y + 5)$ e) $-9(c + 3)$ f) $5(m - 4)$
   g) $2(w - 6)$ h) $-3(g - 5)$ i) $-5(y - 3)$
2. Expand.
   a) $x(x + 6)$ b) $c(c + 8)$ c) $m(m + 3)$
   d) $y(y - 5)$ e) $k(k - 4)$ f) $-x(x + 5)$
   g) $-a(a + 2)$ h) $-b(b - 3)$ i) $-x(x - 1)$
3. Expand.
   a) $2x(x + 3)$ b) $5y(y + 7)$ c) $3k(k + 8)$
   d) $4m(m - 6)$ e) $5w(w - 4)$ f) $-6p(p + 1)$
   g) $-5x(x + 5)$ h) $-3y(y - 9)$ i) $-2h(h - 8)$
4. Expand.
   a) $4y(2y + 5)$ b) $3c(7c + 8)$ c) $6m(2m + 4)$
   d) $-5a(8a - 3)$ e) $5h(7h - 1)$ f) $-4d(3d + 7)$
   g) $-2j(8j - 7)$ h) $0.1x(3x - 6)$ i) $-0.5x(2x + 8)$

**B**

5. Expand.
   a) $5(4x^2 + 3x - 2)$ b) $x(x^2 + 3x + 7)$ c) $y(4y^2 - 5y + 2)$
   d) $-m(m^2 + 2m - 4)$ e) $4k(k^2 + 7k + 3)$ f) $2w(3w^2 - 5w - 6)$

## Apply the Concepts

*For help with question 6, refer to Example 2.*

6. **Application** For each rectangle below
   - Write an expression for the area. Expand the expression.
   - Find the area, in square centimetres, when $x$ is 3 cm.

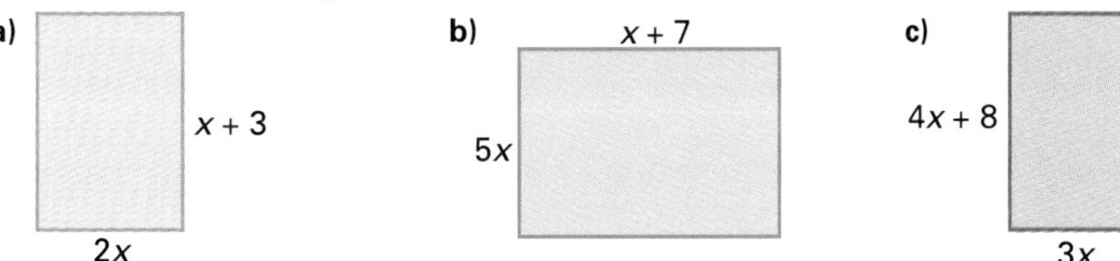


### Did You Know?

Canada is #1 for Internet use in the home. In 2001, 61% of homes had an Internet connection. This compares to a world average of about 5%.

7. **Communication** An Internet service provider has projected the number of customers to be $5m(20m + 30)$, where $m$ is the number of months after the business began.
   a) Expand the polynomial.
   b) Find the number of customers after 12 months, using the original expression. Check using the expanded version of the expression.
   c) Find the number of customers after 24 months, using both versions of the expression.
   d) Which version of the expression do you find easier to substitute into and evaluate? Explain why.

8. The dimensions, in centimetres, of each speaker in a pair of stereo speakers are shown.
   a) Write an expression for the area of each face of the speakers.
   b) Expand each expression.
   c) Find the area of each face when $x$ is 6 cm.
   d) Find the total surface area of wood required to build this set of speakers. There is no wood on the front of the speakers.

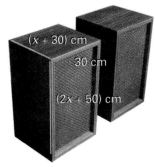

(x + 30) cm
30 cm
(2x + 50) cm

9. The distance, in metres, travelled by a train, $t$ seconds after the brakes are applied, is given by the expression $2t(20 - t)$.
   a) Expand the expression.
   b) Copy and complete the table using the two expressions.
   c) Which expression do you find easier to use? Explain.

| Time (s) | Distance Travelled by Train (m) | |
|---|---|---|
| | $2t(20 - t)$ | Expanded polynomial from part a) |
| 1 | | |
| 10 | | |
| 20 | | |

# 9.4 Expanding and Simplifying Polynomial Expressions

Many items, such as stereo components, require packaging. You need skills in measurement and algebra to design packages. This section extends the concepts to combining operations with polynomials.

**EXAMPLE 1**

## Expanding and Simplifying

Expand and simplify.

**a)** $2(x + 5) + 3(x - 4)$

**b)** $y(2y - 7) - 5(4y + 3)$

**c)** $4a(3a + 8) - 5(7a^2 - 3a + 1)$

## Solution

**a)**

$$\begin{aligned} & 2(x + 5) + 3(x - 4) \\ &= 2x + 10 + 3x - 12 \\ &= 2x + 3x + 10 - 12 \\ &= 5x - 2 \end{aligned}$$

**Multiply to remove the brackets.**

**Collect like terms.**

**b)**

$$\begin{aligned} & y(2y - 7) - 5(4y + 3) \\ &= 2y^2 - 7y - 20y - 15 \\ &= 2y^2 - 27y - 15 \end{aligned}$$

**Expand.**

**Collect like terms.**

**c)**

$$\begin{aligned} & 4a(3a + 8) - 5(7a^2 - 3a + 1) \\ &= 12a^2 + 32a - 35a^2 + 15a - 5 \\ &= 12a^2 - 35a^2 + 32a + 15a - 5 \\ &= -23a^2 + 47a - 5 \end{aligned}$$

**Expand.**

**Collect like terms.**

## Example 2

### Make Connections

You found the area of composite figures in section 2.4.

### Simplifying an Expression for Area

a) Determine an expression for the area of the composite figure shown.

b) Expand and simplify.

c) Determine the area, in square centimetres, when $x$ is 5 cm.

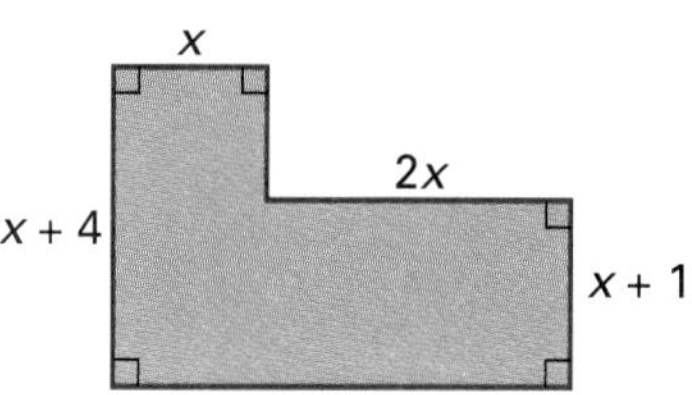


### Solution

a) Draw a vertical line segment to form two rectangles.
Add the areas of the two rectangles.
Area $= x(x + 4) + 2x(x + 1)$

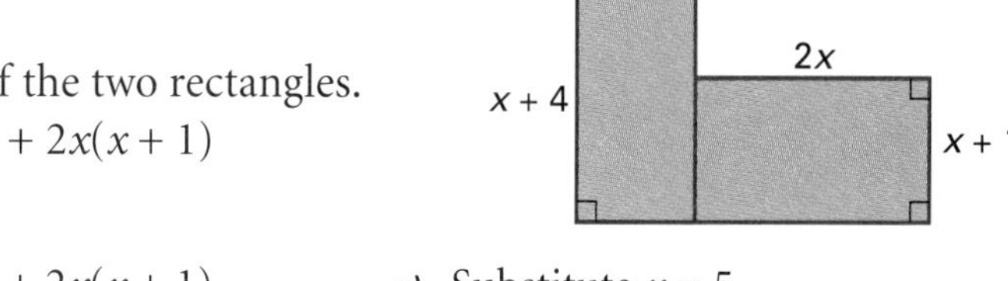


b) $$\begin{aligned}\text{Area} &= x(x + 4) + 2x(x + 1)\\ &= x^2 + 4x + 2x^2 + 2x\\ &= x^2 + 2x^2 + 4x + 2x\\ &= 3x^2 + 6x\end{aligned}$$

c) Substitute $x = 5$.
$$\begin{aligned}A &= 3(5)^2 + 6(5)\\ &= 3(25) + 30\\ &= 75 + 30\\ &= 105\end{aligned}$$
The area of the figure is 105 $\text{cm}^2$.

## Key Concepts

Polynomial expressions can be simplified by
- expanding brackets by multiplying
- rearranging to collect like terms
- adding or subtracting like terms

## Discuss the Concepts

1. To simplify an expression, Ghita drew arrows as shown.
$3x(2x + 5) - 7x(6x - 3)$
Explain how the arrows help her.

2. Describe how you would simplify the following. Tell the result of the first step in each case.
   a) $5(x - 4) + 2(6x + 7)$ b) $3x(6x - 1) - 4(7x + 5)$

## PRACTISE

**A** *For help with questions 1–6, refer to Example 1.*

1. Expand.
   a) $3(x + 4)$
   b) $-2(5y - 8)$
   c) $k(k + 3)$
   d) $3n(4n - 5)$
   e) $-x(4x - 7)$
   f) $-6y(-3y + 4)$

2. Expand and simplify.
   a) $5(x + 8) + 4(x + 3)$
   b) $6(y - 7) + 2(y - 1)$
   c) $-3(2m + 4) + 9(m + 2)$
   d) $4(g^2 + 5) - 6(3g^2 + 2)$
   e) $7(4y - 5) - 2(7y - 4)$
   f) $-2(8n + 3n^2) - 5(n^2 - 1)$

3. Expand and simplify.
   a) $y(y + 5) + y(y - 6)$
   b) $b(b - 3) + b(b - 4)$
   c) $-x(x + 6) + x(x + 1)$
   d) $c(c - 9) - c(c + 5)$
   e) $f(f + 3) - f(f - 7)$
   f) $p(4 - p^2) - p(p^2 + 5)$

4. Expand and simplify.
   a) $x(2x + 4) + x(5x + 2)$
   b) $c(3c + 5) - c(4c - 2)$
   c) $y(5y + 1) - y(5y + 6)$
   d) $2x(x + 4) + 3x(x + 7)$
   e) $3k(k + 5) + 2k(1 - k)$
   f) $4a(6 - a) - 3a(2 - a)$

**B**

5. Expand and simplify.
   a) $2x(2x + 5) + 3x(4x + 3)$
   b) $7y(3y - 10) + 5y(2y + 6)$
   c) $5m(3m + 4) - 3m(4m + 1)$
   d) $-g(2g - 3) + 4g(5g + 2)$
   e) $4a(2a + 1) - 3a(2a - 2)$
   f) $8(7k - 3) - 3k(2 + 6k)$

6. Expand and simplify.
   a) $3(x^2 + 5x - 2) + x(2x + 4)$
   b) $y(y^2 - 4y + 1) - y(y^2 + 5y - 2)$
   c) $2x(6x^2 + 4x + 3) - 3x(2x^2 - 5x + 2)$

## APPLY THE CONCEPTS

*For help with questions 7 and 8, refer to Example 2.*

7. **Communication** Consider the shape in Example 2 again.

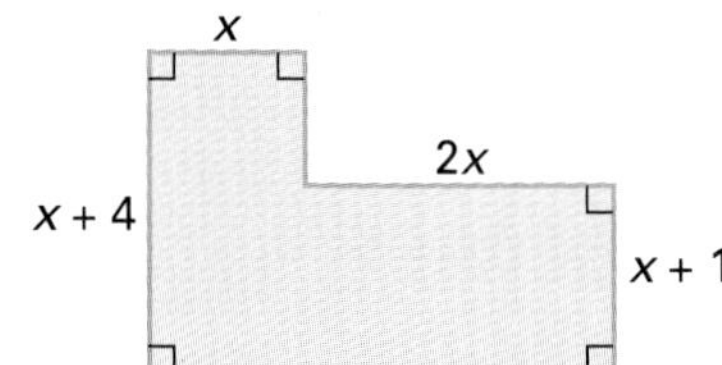


   a) Describe another way you could divide the composite figure to find its area.
   b) Describe how you could subtract polynomials to find the area.
   c) Show that all three methods simplify to give the same expression for the area.

8. **Application** For each figure, find an expression for the area by writing, expanding, and simplifying a polynomial. Then, find the area when $x$ is 2 cm.

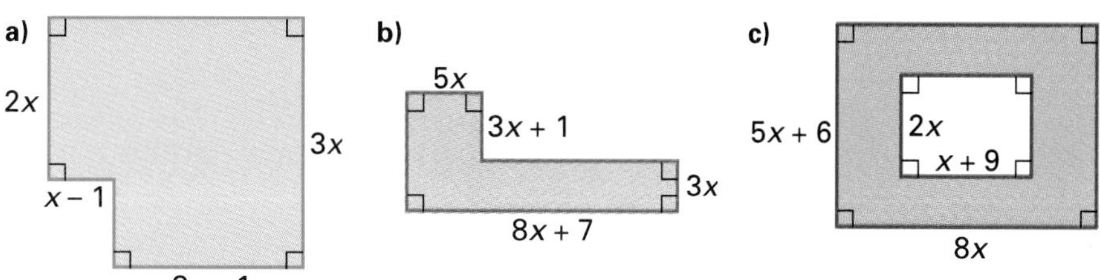


**Chapter Problem**

9. The dimensions of the carton for a mini-stereo, in centimetres, are $y$, $3y$, and $2y + 5$.

a) Write and expand an expression for the area of the front of the carton.

b) Write and expand an expression for the area of the top of the carton.

c) Write and expand an expression for the area of each end of the carton.

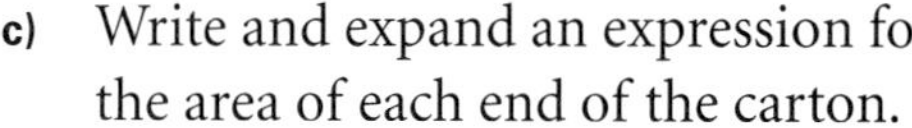

d) Write and simplify an expression for the total surface area of the carton.

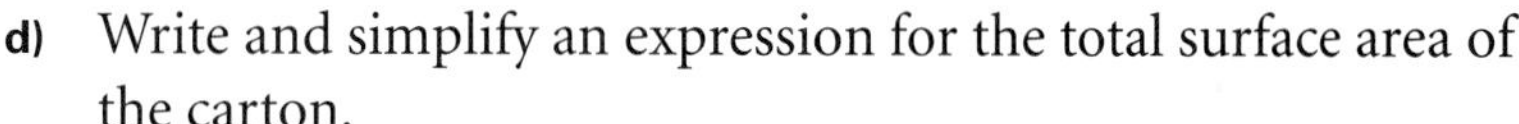

e) Find the total surface area of the carton when $y$ is 8 cm.

10. **Thinking/Inquiry/Problem Solving** A student invents a game using a spinner. Players have to spin the spinner five times and add the polynomials selected.

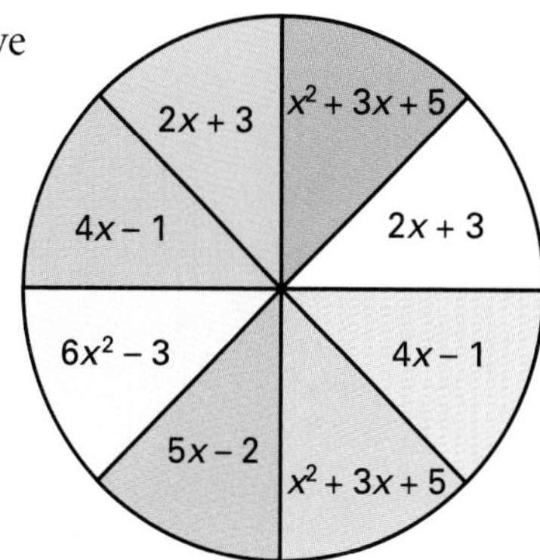


a) Find the results for each person's turn.
**Ahmed:** green, yellow, orange, white, red
**Briana:** pink five times in a row
**Chi:** two blue, two white, one red
**Dawn:** three pink, two purple

b) What are the results in part a) if the white and purple sections are subtracted instead of added?

c) How could a player obtain the result $10x + 1$?

# Review

## 9.1 Introduction to Polynomials, pages 366–372

1. Give the number of terms in each polynomial. Which polynomial is a trinomial?
   a) $2x - 3$
   b) $6n$
   c) $2y^5 - 9y^3 + 5y^2 + 6y$
   d) $k^2 + 3k - 7$
   e) $-8y^2$
   f) $8q + 5$

2. Simplify by adding or subtracting like terms.
   a) $4a + 2a + 9 + 2$
   b) $13x - 5x + 7 + 12$
   c) $2y - 6 + 5y + 1$
   d) $8n^2 + 3n + 5 - 2n^2 + 4n + 2$
   e) $2x^2 + 3x - 4 + x^2 - x + 7$
   f) $3w^2 + 2w + 5 - 3w^2 - 4w - 6$

3. The approximate height of a diver, in metres, above the water $t$ seconds after diving from a 10-m platform, is given by the polynomial $-5t^2 + 6t + 10$.
   a) What is the diver's approximate height after 1 s?
   b) What is the diver's approximate height after 2 s?
   c) What occurs after approximately 2.14 s? Explain.

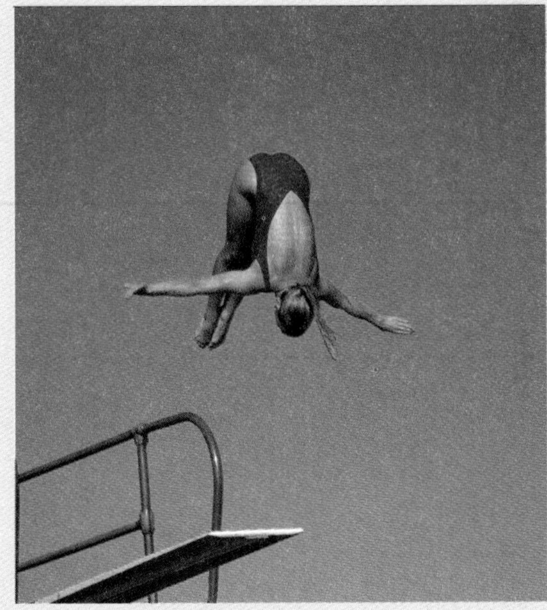

## 9.2 Adding and Subtracting Polynomials, pages 373–377

4. Add or subtract as indicated.
   a) $(3x + 4) + (2x + 9)$
   b) $(12y + 4) - (5y - 3)$
   c) $(k^2 + 5k - 1) + (2k^2 + k - 5)$
   d) $(7a^2 - 2a + 4) - (2a^2 - 5a - 4)$
   e) $(6x^2 + 5) - (2x - 7x^2)$
   f) $(4y^2 - 5y + 1) + (3y^2 + 2y + 7) - (6y^2 - 3y + 2)$

5. The perimeter of the triangle shown is $10x^2 + 8x + 2$.
   a) Find a polynomial for the length of the third side.
   b) Find the length of each side when $x$ is 5 cm.

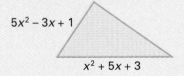

$5x^2 - 3x + 1$

$x^2 + 5x + 3$

## 9.3 Multiplying a Monomial and a Polynomial, pages 378–381

**6.** **Communication** Describe how you would expand and simplify each expression.

**a)** $2(x + 5)$ **b)** $-3x(6x^2 - 4x)$

**7.** Expand.

**a)** $3(x + 4)$ **b)** $2(x - 5)$ **c)** $y(y + 5)$
**d)** $y(y - 1)$ **e)** $7c(c - 3)$ **f)** $-5a(a + 2)$
**g)** $8w(2w + 3)$ **h)** $-4n(5n + 2)$ **i)** $-3v(7v - 6)$

**8.** Expand.

**a)** $3(x^2 + 5x - 1)$ **b)** $x(2x^2 + 4x + 3)$ **c)** $g(7g^2 - 3g + 5)$
**d)** $-y(y^2 + 5y - 2)$ **e)** $3a(a^2 + 3a + 4)$ **f)** $5m(2m^2 - 3m - 5)$

**9.** Copy and complete the table.

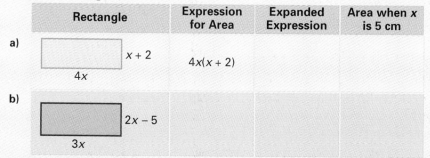

| | Rectangle | Expression for Area | Expanded Expression | Area when $x$ is 5 cm |
|---|---|---|---|---|
| a) | Rectangle $4x$ by $x + 2$ | $4x(x + 2)$ | | |
| b) | Rectangle $3x$ by $2x - 5$ | | | |

## 9.4 Expanding and Simplifying Polynomial Expressions, pages 382–385

**10.** Expand and simplify.

**a)** $3(x + 1) + 5(x + 2)$ **b)** $4(x - 8) + 3(x - 5)$
**c)** $y(y + 9) + y(y + 3)$ **d)** $d(d - 4) - d(d - 2)$
**e)** $5a(a - 6) + 2a(a + 8)$ **f)** $3k(k - 5) - 4k(k + 7)$
**g)** $6k(3 - k) + 2(5 + 3k)$ **h)** $7(8n - 4) - 5n(2 + 9n)$
**i)** $5(x^2 + 3x - 1) + x(5x + 7)$ **j)** $4y(2y^2 + y + 7) - 6y(3y^2 - 2y + 1)$

**11. a)** Find expressions for the area of the figure in two different ways. Use addition for one way and subtraction for the other.

**b)** Expand and simplify each expression.

**c)** Calculate the area when $x$ is 3 cm.

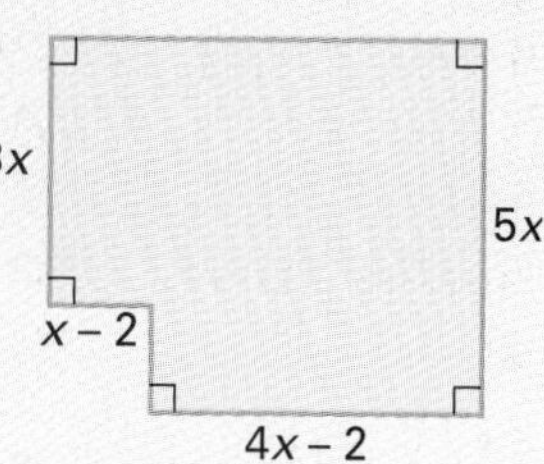

# Practice Test

## Multiple Choice

***For questions 1 to 4, select the correct answer.***

**1.** The polynomial $4x^2 - 5x + 3$ can be classified as a

**A** monomial **B** binomial **C** trinomial **D** none of these

**2.** In the polynomial $4x^2 + 3x - 5x^2 + 6 + 8x + 2$, the like terms are

**A** $4x^2$ and $5x^2$ **B** $3x$ and $8x$ **C** 6 and 2

**D** all of the pairs in A, B, and C

**3.** Which expansion does *not* equal $6x^3 - 12x^2$?

**A** $3x(2x^2 - 4x)$ **B** $2x(3x^2 - 2x)$ **C** $3(2x^3 - 4x^2)$ **D** $-3(-2x^3 + 4x^2)$

**4.** When simplified, $(x^2 - 4x + 2) - (5x^2 + 3x - 7)$ equals

**A** $-3x^2 - x - 5$ **B** $-5x^2 - 7x + 9$ **C** $-4x^2 - 7x - 5$ **D** $-4x^2 - 7x + 9$

## Short Answer

**5.** **a)** Describe how you would expand $3(x - 7)$.

**b)** How is the expansion of $-3(x - 7)$ similar? How is it different?

**6.** Write a polynomial to represent each phrase. Remember to define your variables.

**a)** 6 cm less than Tim's height **b)** double Asumi's age

**c)** \$10 in addition to the original cost **d)** half the number of people

**7.** Expand.

**a)** $5(x - 3)$ **b)** $-4(3y + 6)$ **c)** $2a(3a - 4)$

**d)** $-5k(4k - 2)$ **e)** $6(n^2 + 3n - 4)$ **f)** $-2(5c^2 + 6c - 2)$

**8.** Expand and simplify.

**a)** $(3x + 8) + (5x - 4)$ **b)** $(8y^2 - 7y + 2) - (3y^2 + 5y - 3)$

**c)** $3(x + 2) + 7(x + 1)$ **d)** $h(h + 3) + h(h - 2)$

**e)** $x(2x + 3) - x(3x - 5)$ **f)** $8(c^2 + 2c - 3) + c(3c + 5)$

9. Determine expressions for the perimeter and, then, the area of each figure.

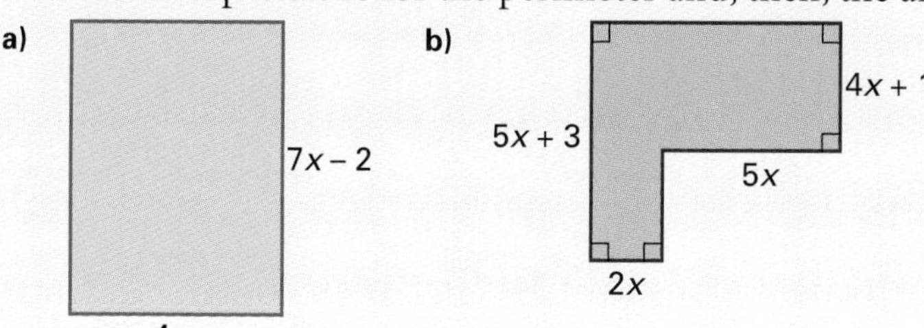


10. Calculate the perimeter and the area of each figure in question 9 when $x$ is 4 cm.

## Extended Response

11. **Thinking/Inquiry/Problem Solving** The perimeter of a rectangular field is given as $4x + 6$. Sketch four possible diagrams for the field, showing the length and the width. Write the four polynomials representing the area of each field.

**ACHIEVEMENT CHECK** Knowledge/Understanding Thinking/Inquiry/Problem Solving Communication Application

12. The dimensions of a shoe box, in centimetres, are 15, $3x - 1$, and $4x$. Determine polynomials, in simplified form, that represent each of the following

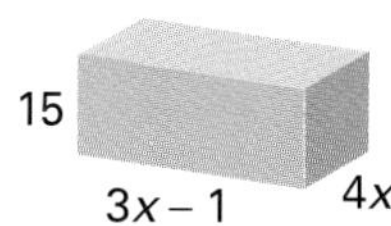


   a) the volume, $V$, of the box
   b) the surface area of the face of the box, $S_1$, which has the first two given dimensions
   c) the total surface area, $S$, of the box
   d) If each of the dimensions is doubled, what are the new expressions for the volume and the total surface area?

←A
C-FMEQ
↑ CB 16↑

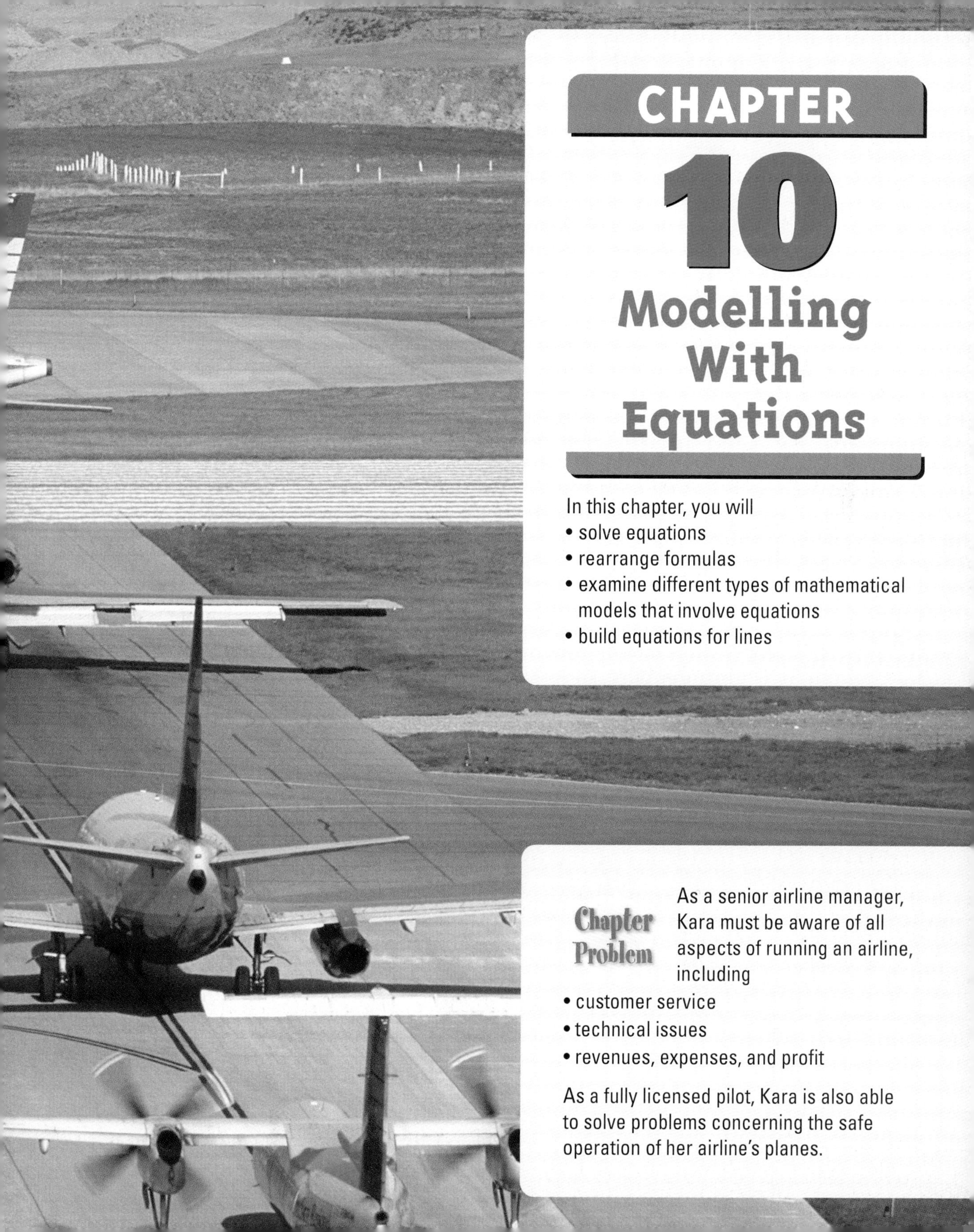

# CHAPTER 10
# Modelling With Equations

In this chapter, you will

- solve equations
- rearrange formulas
- examine different types of mathematical models that involve equations
- build equations for lines

**Chapter Problem**

As a senior airline manager, Kara must be aware of all aspects of running an airline, including

- customer service
- technical issues
- revenues, expenses, and profit

As a fully licensed pilot, Kara is also able to solve problems concerning the safe operation of her airline's planes.

# Get Ready

## Collecting Like Terms

Simplify by collecting like terms.

$$\begin{aligned} &2x + 3 + 5x + 8 \\ &= 2x + 5x + 3 + 8 \\ &= 7x + 11 \end{aligned} \qquad \begin{aligned} &3m - 4 + 6 - 7m + m \\ &= 3m - 7m + m - 4 + 6 \\ &= -3m + 2 \end{aligned}$$

1. Simplify by collecting like terms.
   a) $2x + 6 + 5x + 1$ b) $3y + 4 - y - 5$
   c) $7 - 2c + 5c - 11 + c$ d) $-d + 6 - 8 + 4d + 2$

## Multiplying a Binomial by a Constant

Expand.

$$\begin{aligned} &5(2y + 3) \\ &= 10y + 15 \end{aligned} \qquad \begin{aligned} &-2(x - 3) \\ &= -2x + 6 \end{aligned}$$

2. Expand.
   a) $3(x - 8)$ b) $4(2k + 5)$ c) $-2(3f + 1)$ d) $-9(3h - 7)$

## Modelling Equations With Algebra Tiles

Algebra tiles have the following values.

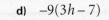

Each equation is represented using algebra tiles as shown.

$2x - 2 = 3$ $x + 3 = -4$

3. Match each tile equation to the correct algebraic equation.
   a) 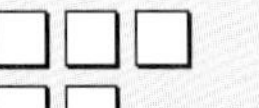
   b) 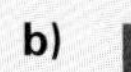  
   c) 
   d)

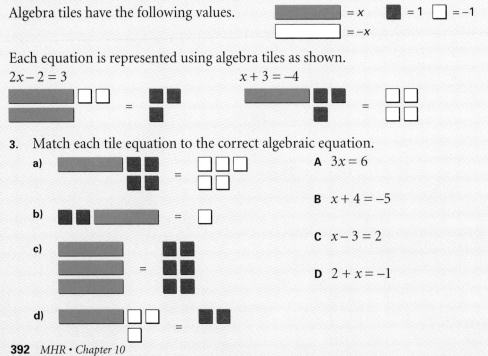

   A $3x = 6$
   B $x + 4 = -5$
   C $x - 3 = 2$
   D $2 + x = -1$

## Finding Slope

Find the slope of the line segment joining each pair of points.

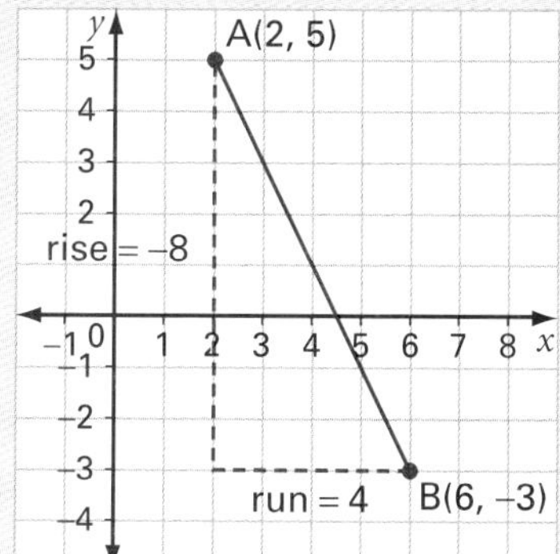


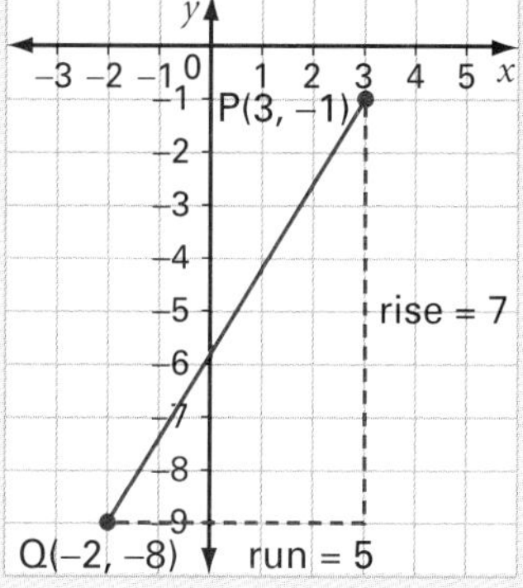

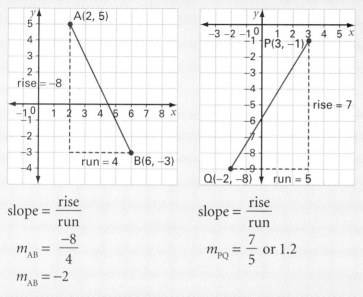

$$\text{slope} = \frac{\text{rise}}{\text{run}}$$
$$m_{AB} = \frac{-8}{4}$$
$$m_{AB} = -2$$

$$\text{slope} = \frac{\text{rise}}{\text{run}}$$
$$m_{PQ} = \frac{7}{5} \text{ or } 1.2$$

4. Find the slope of the line segment joining each pair of points.
   a) A(1, 4) and B(5, 0)
   b) P(–2, 5) and Q(2, –3)
   c) U(–4, 5) and V(–2, –1)
   d) R(0, –3) and S(2, 0)

## Equation of a Line: $y = mx + b$

Write the equation of the line in the form $y = mx + b$, where $m$ is the slope and $b$ is the $y$-intercept.

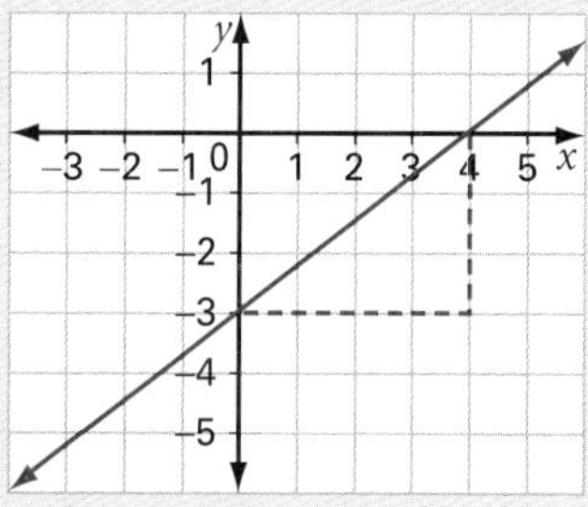

From the graph, the $y$-intercept is –3. Thus, $b = -3$.
Determine the slope.

$$m = \frac{\text{rise}}{\text{run}}$$
$$m = \frac{3}{4}$$
$$y = mx + b$$
$$y = \frac{3}{4}x - 3$$

5. Write the equation of each line in the form $y = mx + b$.
   a)
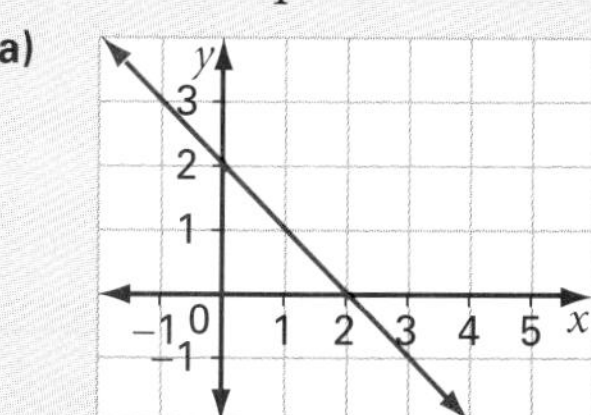
   b)
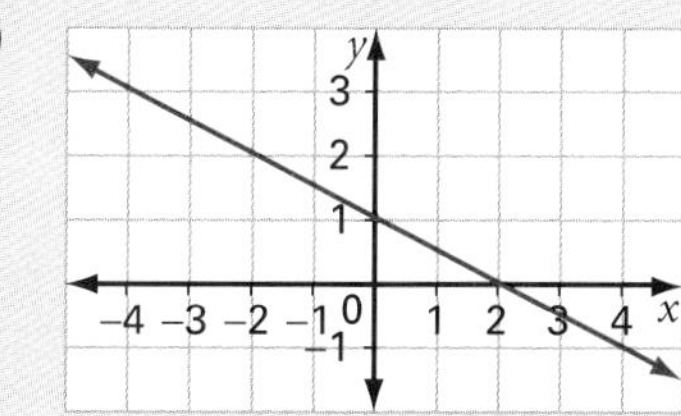

# 10.1 Solving One- and Two-Step Equations

To solve an equation means to find the value of the variable that makes the equation true.

Which of these equations can you solve mentally? What value of $x$ makes that equation true?

- $x + 2 = 5$
- $-4x + 5 = -7$

Some simple equations can be solved by **inspection** (just looking at them). For more complicated equations, an algebraic approach is usually better.

## DISCOVER

### Working With an Equation

Glen is renting a hall to host a meeting. The cost for the hall is \$140 plus \$0.75 per person. The equation for this partial variation is $C = 0.75n + 140$, where $n$ is the number of people attending and $C$ is the cost, in dollars. Glen has a budget of \$350 for this meeting.

**Make Connections**

Recall that you worked with partial variation in Section 6.2.

1. Use the equation to determine the cost if
   a) 100 people attend  b) 500 people attend
2. Graph the equation.
3. a) Use the graph to find out how many people can attend the meeting on Glen's budget. Explain.
   b) Describe any difficulty you had using the graph to answer this question.

Another way to find the number of people that can attend is to substitute $C = 350$ into the equation and solve for $n$:

$350 = 0.75n + 140$

4. Solve for the value of $n$. Describe your method.
5. Describe any advantages and disadvantages of using
   a) the graphing model  b) the algebraic model (equation)

## EXAMPLE 1

### Solving One-Step Equations by Adding or Subtracting

Solve each equation.

**a)** $x + 3 = -2$ **b)** $x - 2 = 5$

### Solution

**a)** $x + 3 = -2$

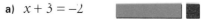

To solve for $x$, isolate it on one side of the equation by performing the opposite operation.

$x + 3 - 3 = -2 - 3$ **Subtract 3 from both sides.**

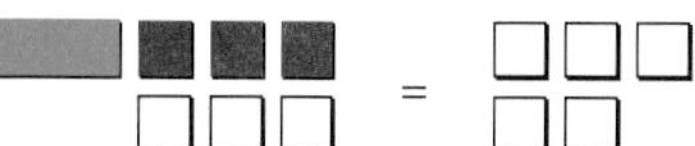

$x = -5$ **+3 – 3 = 0.**

**b)** $x - 2 = 5$

$x - 2 + 2 = 5 + 2$ **Add 2 to both sides.**

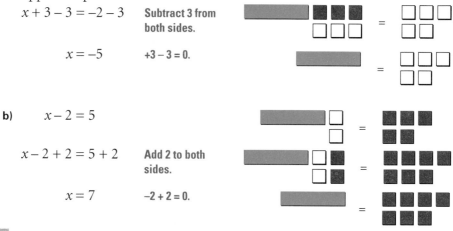

$x = 7$ **–2 + 2 = 0.**

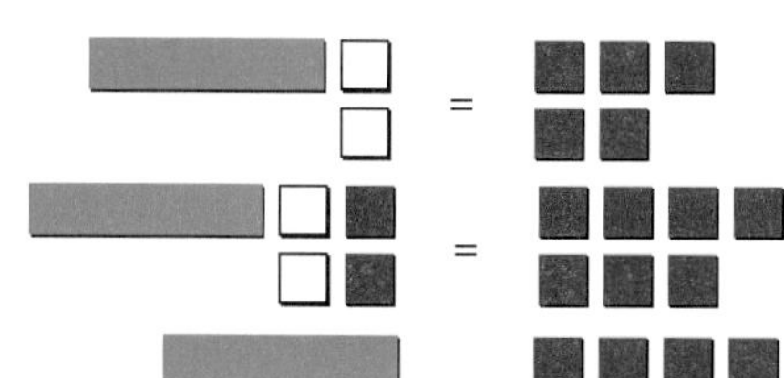

## EXAMPLE 2

### Solving One-Step Equations by Multiplying or Dividing

Solve each equation.

**a)** $4x = 20$ **b)** $\frac{b}{4} = 3$ **c)** $-k = 11$

### Solution

**a)**
$$4x = 20$$
$$\frac{4x}{4} = \frac{20}{4}$$ **Divide both sides by 4.**
$$x = 5$$

**b)**
$$\frac{b}{4} = 3$$
$$4 \times \frac{b}{4} = 4 \times 3$$ **Multiply both sides by 4.**
$$b = 12$$

**c)**
$$-k = 11$$ **$-k$ is the same as $-1k$. Divide both sides by –1.**
$$\frac{-k}{-1} = \frac{11}{-1}$$
$$k = -11$$

When there is more than one term on one side of the equation, isolate the variable term first by adding or subtracting.

**Note that, when isolating a variable, you are performing the order of operations backwards.**

## Example 3

### Solving Two-Step Equations

Solve each equation.

**a)** $2x + 3 = 5$ **b)** $-3y - 7 = 8$

### Solution

**a)**

$$2x + 3 = 5$$

$$2x + 3 - 3 = 5 - 3$$ **Subtract 3 from both sides to isolate the term containing *x*.**

$$2x = 2$$

$$\frac{2x}{2} = \frac{2}{2}$$ **Divide both sides by 2 to isolate *x*.**

$$x = 1$$

**b)**

$$-3y - 7 = 8$$

$$-3y - 7 + 7 = 8 + 7$$ **Add 7 to both sides to isolate the term containing *y*.**

$$-3y = 15$$

$$\frac{-3y}{-3} = \frac{15}{-3}$$ **Divide both sides by –3 to isolate *y*.**

$$y = -5$$

One way to check if the solution to an equation is correct is to substitute the answer into the original equation. Both sides of the equation must be equal.

For example, check that the solution to **Example 3b)** is $y = -5$.

Substitute $y = -5$ into the left side (L.S.) and right side (R.S.) of the equation $-3y - 7 = 8$ to check that it is the solution.

**L.S.** $= -3y - 7$ **R.S.** $= 8$

$= -3(-5) - 7$

$= 15 - 7$

$= 8$

**L.S. = R.S.**

The solution $y = -5$ is correct.

## Key Concepts

- To solve an equation means to find the value of the variable that makes the equation true.
- To solve a one-step equation, isolate the variable by performing the opposite operation.
- In a two-step equation, there is more than one term on one side, so isolate the variable term first by adding or subtracting.
- Check a solution to an equation by substituting it into the left side and the right side of the equation. Both sides must be equal.

## Discuss the Concepts

1. Describe the first step you would take to solve each equation.
   a) $x - 4 = -7$  b) $-3u = 15$  c) $2p + 5 = 9$
2. $a = 3$ is the solution to one of the following equations. Which one? Explain how you can tell.
   a) $a + 3 = -3$  b) $2a + 1 = 7$  c) $3a - 2 = 4$

## Practise

**A** ***For help with question 1, refer to Example 1.***

1. Solve each equation by adding or subtracting.
   a) $x + 4 = 9$  b) $y + 3 = 12$  c) $m - 6 = 2$
   d) $k - 5 = 0$  e) $n - 2 = -3$  f) $p + 4 = -8$

***For help with question 2, refer to Example 2.***

2. Solve each equation by multiplying or dividing.
   a) $3x = 21$  b) $2p = 18$  c) $\frac{m}{4} = 1$
   d) $\frac{w}{5} = 4$  e) $6h = 9$  f) $\frac{y}{2} = 8$

***For help with questions 3 and 4, refer to Example 3.***

3. Substitute to check whether $x = 3$ is the solution to each equation.
   a) $x + 4 = 7$  b) $-2x = 6$

4. Solve each equation.
   a) $3x - 5 = 13$  b) $2j + 9 = 11$
   c) $6k + 3 = 21$  d) $4w - 5 = 15$

**B** 5. Solve each equation.

a) $m - 3 = 19$
b) $-v = 6$
c) $-8t = 24$
d) $9z - 4 = 14$
e) $\frac{q}{5} = -3$
f) $\frac{c}{-4} = -7$

6. Solve each equation. Check your solutions.

a) $-5w = -35$
b) $8y + 3 = -5$
c) $-2h + 1 = -5$
d) $3 - p = 11$
e) $4 + 8r = 4$
f) $5a - 5 = 10$

## APPLY THE CONCEPTS

7. **Application** The budget for Glen's meeting is raised to \$500. Recall from the **Discover** that the cost, $C$, for a meeting with $n$ people is given by $C = 0.75n + 140$.

a) Estimate how many people can go to the meeting by using a graph.
b) Determine how many people can go to the meeting by using algebra.
c) Which method gives a more accurate solution?

8. **Communication** One of your classmates missed this lesson. He phones you for help with solving the equation $6 - 2x = 8$. Write down what you would say to explain

a) the steps to solve the equation
b) how to check the solution

**Chapter Problem**

9. Kara makes sure that customer service agents can solve simple equations related to flight times. The distance travelled, $d$, is given by $d = st$, where $s$ is the average speed and $t$ is the time. Toronto is 4500 km from Vancouver. If a plane travels at an average speed of 1000 km/h, how long will the flight take?

**C** 10. **Thinking/Inquiry/Problem Solving** Jacques is enclosing a rectangular swimming pool deck with 144 m of fencing.

a) What is the width of the rectangle if the length is 40 m?
b) Explain how you solved this problem.

# 10.2 Solving Multi-Step Equations

In the previous chapter, you learned how to simplify algebraic expressions. You can apply these skills to solve complicated equations.

## Discover

### Modelling a Garden Design With an Equation

Mateo is building a garden in the shape of an isosceles triangle. He wants each of the equal sides to be double the length of the base. He plans to use all of the 25 m of decorative border that he has.

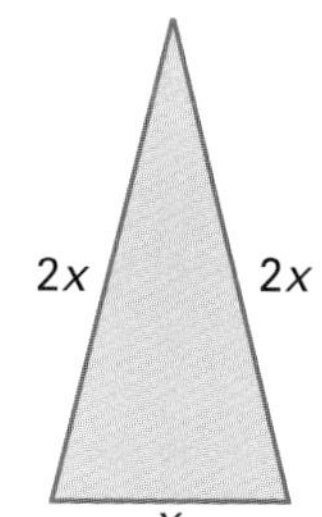


1. a) Determine the dimensions of Mateo's garden. You may use technology, such as *The Geometer's Sketchpad*® or a graphing calculator, or paper and pencil.
   b) Explain how you solved this problem.

2. Suppose Mateo buys more border. He now has 32 m.
   a) Determine the new dimensions of the garden.
   b) Explain how you solved this problem.

3. The formula for the perimeter, $P$, of a triangle with side lengths $a$, $b$, and $c$ is $P = a + b + c$.
   a) Look at the diagram for Mateo's garden. Substitute the side lengths and the perimeter, 25 m, into the formula.
   b) Add the three like terms on the right side of the equation.
   c) Solve the equation for $x$.
   d) Compare this answer to the one you found in step 1. What does this value of $x$ mean?
   e) Determine the dimensions of the garden.

4. Repeat step 3 for $P = 32$ and compare your answer to the one in step 2.

The equation in the **Discover** contained multiple (more than two) terms. To solve equations involving multiple terms,

- collect variable terms on one side of the equation
- collect constant terms on the other side
- simplify and solve

## EXAMPLE 1

### Solving Equations by Collecting Variable and Constant Terms

Solve each equation.

**a)** $5x - 1 = 3x + 6$ **b)** $4y - 11 = 8y - 3$

### Solution

**a)**

$$5x - 1 = 3x + 6$$

$$5x - 1 - 3x = 3x + 6 - 3x$$

**Collect variable terms on one side. Subtract 3*x* from both sides.**

$$5x - 3x - 1 + 1 = 6 + 1$$

**Collect constant terms on the other side. Add 1 to both sides.**

$$2x = 7$$

**Simplify by adding or subtracting like terms.**

$$\frac{2x}{2} = \frac{7}{2}$$

**Divide both sides by 2.**

$$x = 3.5$$

**b)**

$$4y - 11 = 8y - 3$$

**You can collect variable and constant terms in the same step.**

$$4y - 11 + 11 - 8y = 8y - 3 + 11 - 8y$$

**Subtract 8y from, and add 11 to, both sides.**

$$4y - 8y = -3 + 11$$

$$-4y = 8$$

$$\frac{-4y}{-4} = \frac{8}{-4}$$

**Divide both sides by –4.**

$$y = -2$$

It is a good idea to check your solutions by substituting into the original equation. For instance, in **Example 1b)**, check that $y = -2$ is correct.

| | |
|---|---|
| **L.S.** $= 4y - 11$ | **R.S.** $= 8y - 3$ |
| $= 4(-2) - 11$ | $= 8(-2) - 3$ |
| $= -19$ | $= -19$ |

**L.S. = R.S.**

When solving an equation containing brackets, you may need to expand the brackets first. It does not matter which side you collect the variable terms on. Choose the easier method.

## Example 2

### Solving Equations Containing Brackets

Solve each equation.

**a)** $2(3m - 4) = -4(m + 6)$ **b)** $4 = 2k - (3k - 5)$

### Solution

**a)** Expand to remove brackets.

$$\begin{aligned} 2(3m - 4) &= -4(m + 6) \\ 6m - 8 &= -4m - 24 \\ 6m - 8 + 8 + 4m &= -4m + 4m - 24 + 8 \\ 6m + 4m &= -24 + 8 \\ 10m &= -16 \\ \frac{10m}{10} &= \frac{-16}{10} \\ m &= -1.6 \end{aligned}$$

**Take care with integer signs.**

The solution is $m = -1.6$.

Use a scientific calculator to check.

**L.S.:** C 2 × ( 3 × 1.6 +/− − 4 ) = −17.6

**R.S.:** C 4 +/− × ( 1.6 +/− + 6 ) = −17.6

**L.S. = R.S.**

**b)**

$$\begin{aligned} 4 &= 2k - (3k - 5) \\ 4 &= 2k - 3k + 5 \\ 4 &= -k + 5 \end{aligned}$$

**Subtract polynomials.**

**Simplify.**

In this case it is easier to collect variable terms on the *right* side and constant terms on the *left* side.

$$\begin{aligned} 4 - 5 &= -k + 5 - 5 \\ -1 &= -k \\ \frac{-1}{-1} &= \frac{-k}{-1} \\ 1 &= k \end{aligned}$$

**Divide both sides by −1.**

The solution is $k = 1$.

## Key Concepts

- To solve an equation involving multiple terms, collect variable terms on one side of the equation and constant terms on the other.
- To solve an equation involving brackets, you may need to expand the brackets first.
- Check a solution by substituting the value into the left and right sides of the original equation.

## Discuss the Concepts

1. Explain the first step you would take to solve each equation.
   a) $4x + 5 = 2x - 9$ b) $4y = 3 + 5y - 2$ c) $3 = 7p - 1 - p$
2. $n = 3$ is the correct solution to two of the following equations. Which equations? How can you tell?
   a) $3n + 5 = 14$ b) $2n - 1 = 2(n + 2)$ c) $3(n + 2) = n + 12$

## Practise

***For help with question 1, refer to Example 1.***

1. Solve each equation.
   a) $9x = 5x + 8$ b) $8y = -y + 18$ c) $7d + 2 = 5d - 3$
   d) $3k - 5 = k - 9$ e) $8u - 3 = 4u + 9$ f) $32 = 7e - 17$

***For help with questions 2 and 3, refer to Example 2.***

2. Solve. Then, check your solutions.
   a) $2(x - 3) = 15$ b) $3(r + 4) = 12$ c) $5(n + 4) = 35$
   d) $8(m - 7) = 16$ e) $-3(k + 1) = 9$ f) $-4(2y - 3) = 6$
3. a) Is $x = 2$ a solution to the equation $3x - 4 = 6 - 2x$? Check by substitution.
   b) Is $y = -1$ a solution to the equation $3(2y - 1) = 2(y - 4)$? How do you know?

**B**

4. Solve each equation.
   a) $16x - 8 = 27 + 9x$ b) $55 - 2b = 3b + 10$ c) $3 - 2w = 6 - 5w$
   d) $6 - y = -2y + 9$ e) $h - 3 = 3(h - 1)$ f) $2(p - 3) = 4(3p + 1)$
5. Solve each equation. Check your solutions.
   a) $-4(k - 1) = -3(k + 2)$ b) $6z - 9 - z = 7 - 3z + 4$
   c) $3b - 4 = 1 - (2b + 5)$ d) $5 - (v - 3) = 7 - 2v$
   e) $9 - 8(3a + 5) = -7(4a + 5)$ f) $12q - 6(q + 1) = 4(2q - 1) - 3$

## Apply the Concepts

6. **Communication** A solution is shown for the equation $3(2x-1) = 2(4x-5)$. Copy the solution. Then, write a short explanation beside each step.

| Step | Solution |
|---|---|
| | $3(2x-1) = 2(4x-5)$ |
| 1 | $6x - 3 = 8x - 10$ |
| 2 | $6x - 3 + 3 - 8x = 8x - 8x - 10 + 3$ |
| 3 | $6x - 8x = -10 + 3$ |
| 4 | $-2x = -7$ |
| 5 | $\frac{-2x}{-2} = \frac{-7}{-2}$ |
| 6 | $x = 3.5$ |

**Did You Know?**

Quilters believe that all your dreams will come true if you sleep under a new quilt.

7. **Application** In a quilt pattern, Krista is using a trapezoid shape in which one parallel side is twice as long as the other side. The height is 4 cm. The total area of the trapezoid is 30 cm$^2$.

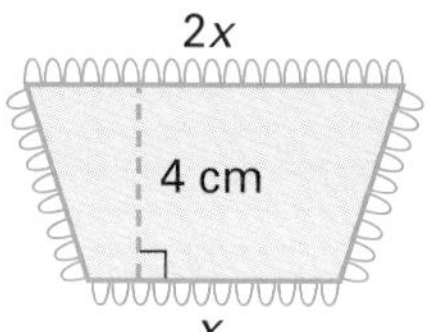


   a) Substitute the values $A = 30$, $h = 4$, $a = 2x$, and $b = x$ into the formula $A = \frac{h}{2}(a + b)$.

   b) Solve the equation for $x$.
   c) What does the value of $x$ mean?
   d) What are the lengths of the two parallel sides?

**Chapter Problem**

8 On one flight, the airline sold twice as many economy class tickets as business class tickets. Economy class costs \$400 and business class costs \$900. Five of the economy class ticket holders redeemed a voucher and did not have to pay. The total revenue for the flight was \$49 000.
   a) Solve the equation $900n + 400(2n - 5) = 49\,000$ for $n$, the number of business-class travellers.
   b) How many travelled economy class?

C 9. **Application** Andy has \$500 in a savings account that pays 3% per year simple interest.
   a) Solve the following equation to determine the number of years, $n$, that it will take for the account to reach an amount of \$800:
   $800 = 500 + (0.03 \times 500)n$
   b) Solve this problem another way, without using the given equation.
   c) Describe the method you used in part b).
   d) Compare the two solutions. Did you get the same answer? Which method do you prefer? Explain why.

# 10.3 Modelling With Formulas

A **formula** describes a relationship between two or more variables. For example, you can solve for the volume, $V$, of a cylinder if you know its radius, $r$, and height, $h$, by using the formula $V = \pi r^2 h$.

In this section, you will learn to rearrange formulas to solve for an unknown value.

## DISCOVER

### Different Ways of Working With a Formula

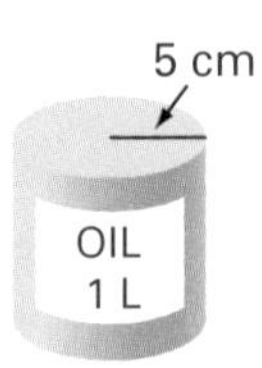


Suppose you are designing a cylindrical can to hold 1000 cm$^3$ (1 L) of oil. The radius must be 5 cm so that the can is easy to hold. You must find the height of the can.

*Algebraic Model I: Substitute, Then Solve*

1. a) Substitute $V = 1000$ and $r = 5$ into the formula $V = \pi r^2 h$.
   b) Find the height of the can by solving the equation for $h$.

You can use 3.14 for $\pi$, or use the (π) key on your scientific calculator.

2. Repeat this process for a can with the same radius, and the following volumes:
   a) 1500 cm$^3$ b) 2000 cm$^3$

*Algebraic Model II: Rearrange, Then Substitute*

If you divide both sides of the formula $V = \pi r^2 h$ by $\pi r^2$, you get a formula for $h$: $h = \dfrac{V}{\pi r^2}$.

3. a) Substitute $V = 1000$ and $r = 5$ into this formula and solve for $h$.
   b) Compare this answer with the one in step 1.

4. Repeat this process for a can with the same radius, and the following volumes:
   a) 1500 cm$^3$ b) 2000 cm$^3$

*Graphical Model*

5. **a)** Substitute $r = 5$ into the formula $V = \pi r^2 h$.
   **b)** Expand $\pi(5)^2$. Round to one decimal place.
   **c)** Construct a table of values. Then, graph $V$ versus $h$. Is this graph linear or non-linear? Explain.
   **d)** Use the graph to estimate the value of $h$ that will give a volume of 1000 $cm^3$.
   **e)** Compare your answer with the ones in steps 1 and 3.

6. Use the graph to estimate the value of $h$ that will give a volume of
   **a)** 1500 $cm^3$ **b)** 2000 $cm^3$

*Comparing the Models*

7. Describe at least one advantage and one disadvantage of each of the three models used.

You can rearrange simple formulas by performing opposite operations in a similar way as you would solve an equation. Isolate the unknown variable.

## EXAMPLE 1

### Rearranging a Formula Using One Step

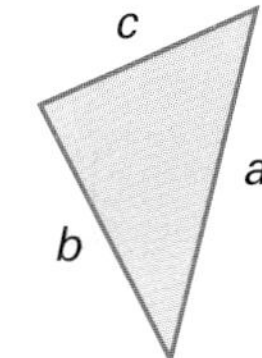


**a)** The formula $P = a + b + c$ relates the perimeter of a triangle to its three side lengths. Rearrange this formula to isolate $a$.

**b)** The formula $C = 2\pi r$ relates the circumference of a circle to its radius. Rearrange $C = 2\pi r$ to isolate $r$.

### Solution

**a)**

$$P = a + b + c$$

$$P - b - c = a + b + c - b - c \quad \text{Subtract } b \text{ and } c \text{ from both sides.}$$

$$P - b - c = a$$

or $$a = P - b - c$$

**b)**

$$C = 2\pi r$$

$$\frac{C}{2\pi} = \frac{2\pi r}{2\pi} \quad \text{To isolate } r\text{, divide both sides by } 2\pi.$$

$$\frac{C}{2\pi} = r$$

or $$r = \frac{C}{2\pi}$$

To rearrange a formula to isolate an unknown variable,
• isolate the term that contains the unknown variable
• isolate the unknown variable

## Example 2

### Rearranging a Formula Using Multiple Steps

a) The formula for the perimeter of a rectangle is $P = 2l + 2w$. Rearrange the formula to isolate $w$.

b) Determine the width of a rectangular park with length 0.8 km and perimeter 2.8 km.

### Solution

a) $P = 2l + 2w$

Isolate the term containing $w$.

$P - 2l = 2l + 2w - 2l$ **Subtract $2l$ from both sides.**

$P - 2l = 2w$

or

$2w = P - 2l$

$\frac{2w}{2} = \frac{P - 2l}{2}$ **Divide both sides by 2.**

$w = \frac{P - 2l}{2}$

b) To determine the width of the park, substitute $l = 0.8$ and $P = 2.8$ into the rearranged formula.

$w = \frac{2.8 - 2(0.8)}{2}$

$w = \frac{2.8 - 1.6}{2}$

$w = \frac{1.2}{2}$

$w = 0.6$

The width of the park is 0.6 km.

When you apply a formula, you can solve for any unknown variable if you know the values of the other variables.

It is useful to rearrange a formula before solving for an unknown variable, if you will be determining several values.

## Example 3

### Rearranging a Formula

The formula for the volume, $V$, of a box with length $l$, width $w$, and height $h$ is $V = lwh$. What is the height of a box with volume 450 cm$^3$, length 6 cm, and width 6 cm?

**a)** Solve by substituting first and then solving.

**b)** Solve by rearranging the formula first, and then substituting.

**c)** Compare the two solutions.

**d)** Which method would you use if you had to complete the table? Explain.

| $h$ | $V$ | $l$ | $w$ |
|---|---|---|---|
| | 500 | 5 | 10 |
| | 600 | 6 | 8 |
| | 1000 | 10 | 4 |
| | 3600 | 9 | 90 |

### Solution

**a)** In $V = lwh$ substitute $V = 450$, $l = 6$, and $w = 6$.

$450 = (6)(6)h$

Simplify and solve.

$$450 = 36h$$

$$\frac{450}{36} = \frac{36h}{36}$$ **Divide both sides by 36.**

$$12.5 = h$$

The box has a height of 12.5 cm.

**b)** $$V = lwh$$

$$\frac{V}{lw} = \frac{lwh}{lw}$$ **Divide both sides by *lw*.**

$$\frac{V}{lw} = h$$

In $h = \frac{V}{lw}$ substitute $V = 450$, $l = 6$, and $w = 6$.

$$h = \frac{450}{(6)(6)}$$

$$h = \frac{450}{36}$$

$$h = 12.5$$

The box has a height of 12.5 cm.

**c)** Both methods give the same answer.

**d)** To complete the table you need to perform repeated calculations, so, rearranging the formula first would be the better method.

## Key Concepts

- Formulas can be rearranged to isolate variables.
- To rearrange a formula to isolate an unknown variable:
  - isolate the term containing the unknown variable
  - isolate the unknown variable

## Discuss the Concepts

1. Describe the first step you would take to isolate the variable indicated for each equation.
   a) $E = P + K$ for $P$
   b) $P = 4s$ for $s$
   c) $a = \frac{v}{t}$ for $v$
2. Explain when it might be better to rearrange a formula first before substituting values.

## Practise

**A** *For help with questions 1 and 2, refer to Examples 1 to 3.*

1. Rearrange each formula to isolate the variable indicated.
   a) $A = lw$ for $w$
   b) $A = P + I$ for $I$
   c) $s = \frac{d}{t}$ for $d$
   d) $C = \pi d$ for $d$
   e) $A = bh$ for $b$
   f) $V = lwh$ for $w$
   g) $y = mx + b$ for $b$
   h) $P = 2l + 2w$ for $l$
   i) $P = I^2R$ for $R$

2. The formula for the surface area, $S$, of a cylinder with radius $r$ and height $h$ is $S = 2\pi r^2 + 2\pi rh$. Rearrange the formula so that you can find the height if you know the surface area and the radius.

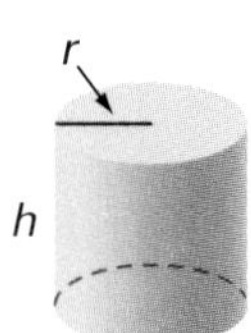


## Apply the Concepts

**B**

3. **Application** The formula for the final amount, $A$, in an investment with principal $P$ and interest $I$ is $A = P + I$.
   a) Rearrange this formula so that you can find the principal if you know the final amount and the interest.
   b) Determine the principal if $A$ is \$6000 and $I$ is \$750.

The short forms for the units in this question are shown in the table.

| Unit | Short Form |
|---|---|
| volt | V |
| ampere | A |
| ohm | Ω |

4. **Ohm's Law** The formula for the voltage, $V$, in volts, in an electric circuit with current $I$, in amperes, and resistance $R$, in ohms, is $V = IR$.
   a) Rearrange this formula so that you can find the current if you know the voltage and the resistance. Determine the current when $V$ is 12 V and $R$ is 4 Ω.
   b) Rearrange this formula so that you can find the resistance if you know the voltage and the current. Determine the resistance when $V$ is 9 V and $I$ is 0.25 A.

5. **Communication** The formula for the volume, $V$, of a cylinder with radius $r$ and height $h$ is $V = \pi r^2 h$. The following steps show how the formula can be rearranged to isolate $r$. Copy the steps into your notebook, and provide a short explanation beside each step.

| **Step** | **Explanation** |
|---|---|
| $V = \pi r^2 h$ | Start with the original formula. |
| $\frac{V}{\pi h} = \frac{\pi r^2 h}{\pi h}$ | |
| $\frac{V}{\pi h} = r^2$ | |
| $\sqrt{\frac{V}{\pi h}} = \sqrt{r^2}$ | |
| $\sqrt{\frac{V}{\pi h}} = r$ | |
| $r = \sqrt{\frac{V}{\pi h}}$ | |

6. Suppose that the radius of a cylinder is fixed at 8 cm. Determine the height required to hold a volume of 340 cm$^3$ using each method.
   a) Substitute into the formula $V = \pi r^2 h$, and then solve for $h$.
   b) Rearrange the formula to isolate $h$, and then substitute.
   c) Substitute $r = 8$ into the formula $V = \pi r^2 h$. Then, graph $V$ versus $h$ and estimate the value of $h$ when $V = 340$.
   d) Which of these three methods do you prefer? Explain why.

7. A line has $y$-intercept 3 and passes through the point (4, 5). Find the slope of this line using each method.
   a) Substitute $x = 4$, $y = 5$, and $b = 3$ into $y = mx + b$. Then, solve for $m$.
   b) Rearrange $y = mx + b$ to isolate $m$. Then, substitute the values of $x$, $y$, and $b$ and solve for $m$.
   c) Plot (4, 5) on a coordinate grid. Plot the $y$-intercept. Join the points and determine $m$.
   d) Compare the results of each method. Describe at least one advantage of each method.

Make Connections

Hooke's Law is an example of a direct variation.

8. **Hooke's Law** The formula for the force, $F$, required to stretch a spring a distance of $x$ is $F = kx$, where $k$ is called the spring constant.
   a) Rearrange $F = kx$ so that you can find the distance if you know the force and the spring constant.
   b) Use your result from part a). Determine $x$ if $F = 10$ and $k = 2$.

**Chapter Problem**

9. One of Kara's engineers is designing a fuel tank for a light aircraft. The fuel tank will be built into the wing. Its cross section is oval. The volume of the tank is given by the formula $V = \pi abL$.
   a) Rearrange the formula so that you can find $L$ if you know $V$, $a$, and $b$.
   b) How long must the tank be to hold 0.11 $m^3$ of fuel? The dimension $a$ is 0.30 m and the dimension $b$ is 0.10 m.

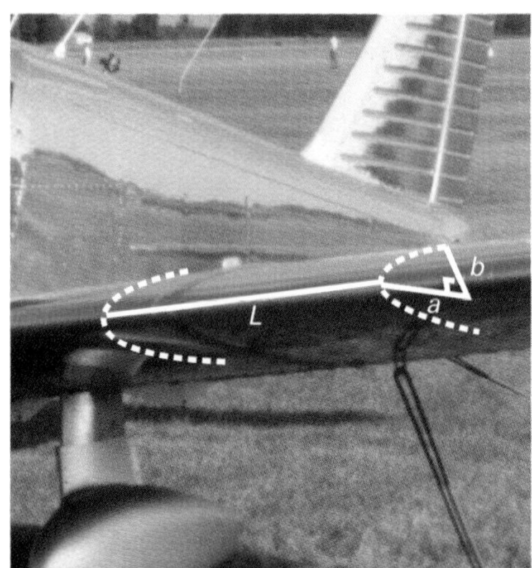


C

10. **Thinking/Inquiry/Problem Solving**
Light travels at a constant speed of 300 000 km/s. The Sun is 150 000 000 km from Earth.
   a) Rearrange the formula $d = st$ to express time in terms of distance and speed (isolate $t$).
   b) Use this formula to determine how long it takes for a particle of light (called a photon) to travel from the Sun to Earth.
   c) Light takes time to travel from its source to our eyes. So, if you look through a telescope at something far away, you are seeing what happened in the past!
   In 1987, scientists saw a star called Sanduleak 69° 202 explode. This star was located $1.6 \times 10^{18}$ km from Earth. Use the formula in part a) to determine how long before the observation the explosion actually happened.

Did You Know?

Supernova 1987A was observed by Ian Shelton, a Canadian astronomer. It was the explosion of Sanduleak 69°202, a star located in the Greater Magellanic Cloud.

# 10.4 Modelling With Algebra

Algebra is an efficient way to express mathematical ideas. Algebraic modelling is one of many ways to solve a problem. The choice of which strategy to use often depends on the problem and the problem solver.

## DISCOVER

### It's Magic! (or Is It?)

1. a) Choose any number from 1 to 100. Write it down.
   b) Add 50.
   c) Double the result.
   d) Now subtract 16.
   e) Subtract twice the value of your original number.
   f) Add 5. Use this result in the next step.

2. Turn to the page in this textbook matching your result in step 1f). Read the second word in the first sentence. This word is found at the bottom of this page in purple.

3. Explain how you think this trick works.

4. a) Pick a new number and repeat steps 1 and 2.
   b) What do you notice?
   c) Compare your results with some classmates. What do you notice?
   d) How can you explain these results?

5. a) Simplify the expression $2(n + 50) - 16 - 2n + 5$.
   b) How is this expression related to the "magic trick" above?

volume

If you want to amaze your family and friends, use this variation to make the trick from the **Discover** more dramatic:

Pick a book from home and look up the second word on page 89. Then, when you do the trick, pretend to pick the book at random from a shelf.

- The first surprise will be when you announce the page number. **Oooh!**
- The second surprise will be when you announce the word. **Aaah!**

You can only use this trick once with any audience. To repeat the trick, you will need to create your own "magic expression" that will give a different final result.

The "magic trick" you just did is an application of **algebraic modelling**, which is using algebra to solve problems. Algebraic modelling can be used for much more than just magic tricks.

## EXAMPLE 1

### Applying Algebraic Modelling to a Number Problem

Noreen is twice as old as her niece, Jessica. The sum of their ages is 54. How old are they?

### Solution

Let $J$ be Jessica's age. Noreen's age is twice Jessica's, or $2J$. The sum of their ages is 54. Translate this into an equation:

| Jessica's age | plus | Noreen's age | is 54 | ⇐ in words |
|---|---|---|---|---|
| $J$ | $+$ | $2J$ | $= 54$ | ⇐ in algebra |

Solve for the unknown, $J$.

$$J + 2J = 54$$
$$3J = 54$$
$$\frac{3J}{3} = \frac{54}{3} \quad \text{Divide both sides by 3.}$$
$$J = 18$$

Jessica is 18 years old.

Noreen's age is twice Jessica's, so, Noreen is 36.

When using a formula with several variables, you can sometimes use known relationships to simplify the equation.

## EXAMPLE 2

### Applying Algebraic Modelling to a Measurement Problem

The length of a rectangular picture frame is double its width. The perimeter is 3.6 m. Determine the length and width of the frame.

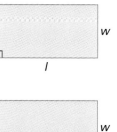

### Solution

The length is double the width.

$l = 2w$

The formula for the perimeter of a rectangle is

$P = 2l + 2w$

$(3.6) = 2(2w) + 2w$ **Substitute $P = 3.6$ and $l = 2w$ into the formula.**

Solve for $w$.

$3.6 = 4w + 2w$

$3.6 = 6w$

$\frac{3.6}{6} = \frac{6w}{6}$ **Divide both sides by 6.**

$0.6 = w$

The width is 0.6 m.

$l = 2w$

$l = 2(0.6)$

$l = 1.2$

The length of the frame is 1.2 m and its width is 0.6 m.

Algebraic modelling is one of several strategies that can be used to solve problems. You could have used *The Geometer's Sketchpad*® to solve the problem posed in Example 2. The next example shows three possible ways of solving a problem. You may find that you prefer different methods for different problems.

## Example 3

### Comparing Algebraic Modelling With Other Strategies

A landscape architect wants to double the area of a circular pool. Determine the radius required to double the existing area using

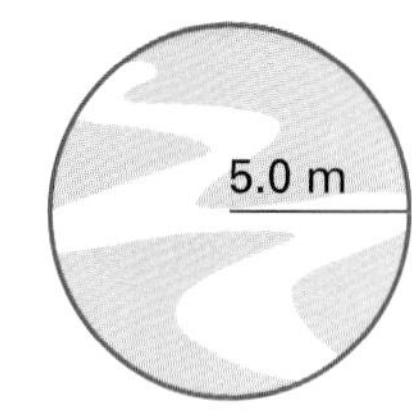


a) guess and test

b) an algebraic model

c) a graphical model

### Solution

a) **Guess and Test** Determine the area of the existing pool.

$A = \pi r^2$

$A = \pi(5)^2$ C π × 5 $x^2$ =

$A \doteq 78.5$

The area of the pool is 78.5 m$^2$.

Double this to get the new area:

$78.5 \times 2 = 157$ m$^2$

Try different values for $r$ until you find one that gives the correct area. Use the results from one trial to try to get closer on your next trial. Organize the results in a table.

| Radius (m) | Area (m$^2$) | |
|---|---|---|
| 8 | 201 | too high |
| 6 | 113 | too low |
| 7 | 154 | close—try for greater accuracy |
| 7.2 | 163 | too high |
| 7.1 | 158 | very close |

The radius of the pool must increase to approximately 7.1 m to double the area.

b) **Algebraic Model** Work as in part a) to find that the new area will be 157 m$^2$. Then, substitute the new area into the formula and solve for $r$.

$$A = \pi r^2$$
$$157 = \pi r^2$$
$$\frac{157}{\pi} = \frac{\pi r^2}{\pi}$$
$$\frac{157}{\pi} = r^2$$

C 157 ÷ π =

$$r^2 \doteq 50.0$$
$$\sqrt{r^2} = \sqrt{50.0}$$
$$r \doteq 7.1$$

The radius of the pool must increase to approximately 7.1 m to double the area.

**c)** **Graphical Model** Work as in part a) to find that the new area will be 157 m$^2$. Turn on a graphing calculator and press [Y=].

- Clear all equations and make sure all **PLOT**s are turned off.

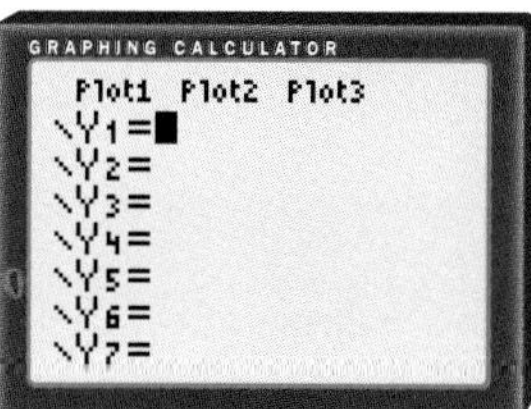

- Input the equation $A = \pi r^2$ as Y1. Let X represent $r$.

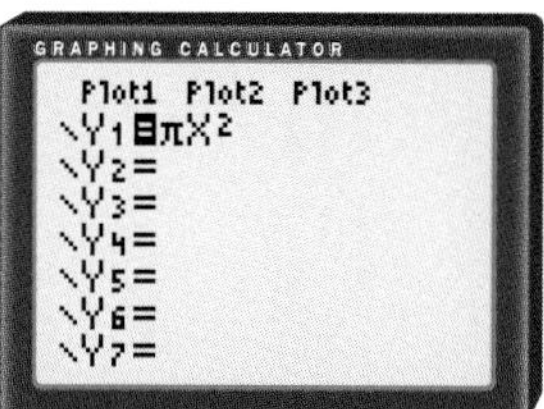


Refer to the Technology Appendix for help with **Setting Window Variables**, and **Using Zoom**.

- Press [WINDOW] and set the window variables as shown.

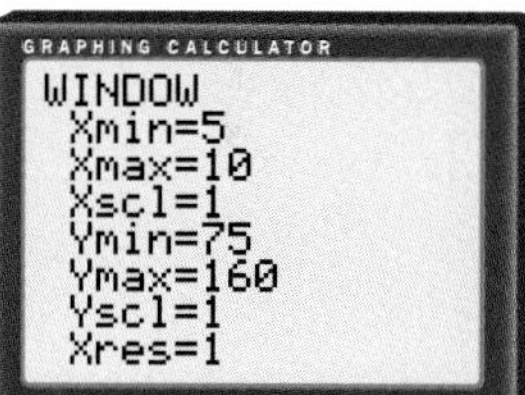


- Press [GRAPH].
- Press [TRACE].
- Use the left and right arrow keys to move the cursor near Y1 = 157. Zoom in, if necessary.

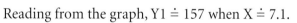

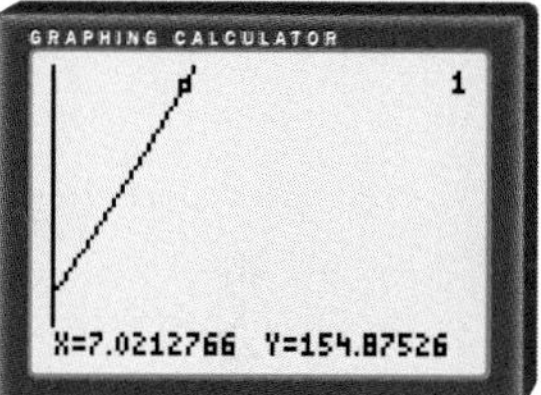


Reading from the graph, Y1 ≐ 157 when X ≐ 7.1.
The radius of the pool must increase to approximately 7.1 m to double the area.

## Key Concepts

- Algebraic modelling is one method that can be used to solve problems.
- Many problems can be solved using more than one method.

## Discuss the Concepts

1. a) What is algebraic modelling?
   b) What is the difference between algebraic modelling and graphical modelling?
2. Describe the process of guess and test.
3. Identify one advantage and one disadvantage of each type of problem solving strategy:
   a) writing and solving an equation
   b) guess and test
   c) using a graph, drawn by hand or with a graphing calculator

## Practise

***For help with questions 1–4, refer to Example 1.***

1. Write an algebraic expression to represent each description.
   a) four times a number
   b) a number decreased by three
   c) double a number plus nine

2. Write an equation to represent each sentence.
   a) Five times a number is 30.
   b) A length decreased by 10 is 2.
   c) Double a number plus 3 is 25.

## Apply the Concepts

3. Donna is three times as old as her daughter, Sophie. The sum of their ages is 52. How old are Donna and Sophie?

4. André is four years older than Luke. Their ages total 32. How old are the boys?

B ***For help with questions 5 and 6, refer to Examples 2 and 3.***

5. The perimeter of a rectangular field is 640 m. The length of the field is triple the width.

a) Find the dimensions of the field using algebraic modelling.
b) Determine the dimensions of the field using another strategy. Describe your method of solution.
c) Compare your answer and method with those of your classmates.

6. **Thinking/Inquiry/Problem Solving** The length of the second side of a triangle is twice the length of the first side. The length of the third side is four times the length of the first side. The perimeter is 280 cm.
   a) Determine the lengths of the three sides using the method of your choice.
   b) Describe your method.
   c) Compare your answers and method with those of your classmates.

7. **Thinking/Inquiry/Problem Solving** A quilt pattern uses a right triangle with area 27 $cm^2$. The base is twice as long as the height.
   a) Determine the base and the height of the triangle.
   b) Determine the perimeter of the triangle.

8. Kara has twice as many hours of flight time as her younger brother, Steve. Together they have 966 h.
   a) How many hours has Kara logged?
   b) How many hours has Steve logged?

9. **Thinking/Inquiry/Problem Solving** Three consecutive numbers total 87. What are the numbers?

10. **Thinking/Inquiry/Problem Solving**
   a) Create your own magic expression like the one in the **Discover**.
   b) Create a magic trick based on your magic expression. Try the trick out on a friend, family member, or classmate. Discuss whether the trick worked and why.

C

11. **Thinking/Inquiry/Problem Solving** A gardener is designing a rose bed in the shape of a right triangle. The two shorter sides will have lengths in the ratio 2:1. The perimeter will be 25 m.

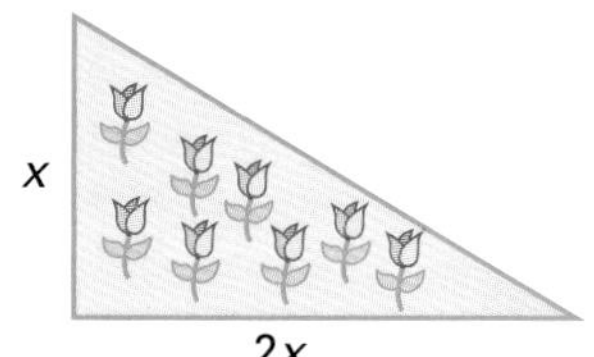


   a) Determine the dimensions of the rose bed. Use any method you choose.
   b) Describe how you solved this problem.
   c) Compare your methods and answers with those of some of your classmates.

# 10.5 Equation of a Line, Given the Slope and a Point

In Chapter 7, you learned that $y = mx + b$ is the slope-intercept form for the equation of a line, where

- $m$ is the slope
- $b$ is the $y$-intercept

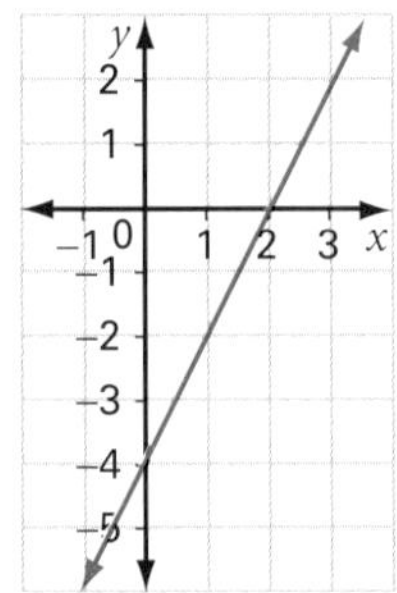

You can write the equation of a line if you know its slope and $y$-intercept. For example, the line shown has slope 2 and $y$-intercept $-4$, so its equation is $y = 2x - 4$.

## DISCOVER

### Creating a Linear Model From the Slope and a Point

While on a car trip to visit relatives in St. Thomas, Nina sees a highway sign.

At this point, Nina's family has been driving for two and a half hours at a fairly constant speed of 80 km/h. She is wondering

- how much longer is the trip?
- have they reached the halfway point yet?
- how far and how long is the total trip?

1. Set up a distance-time graph, as shown. $d = mt + b$ is the form for the equation of a linear distance-time graph.

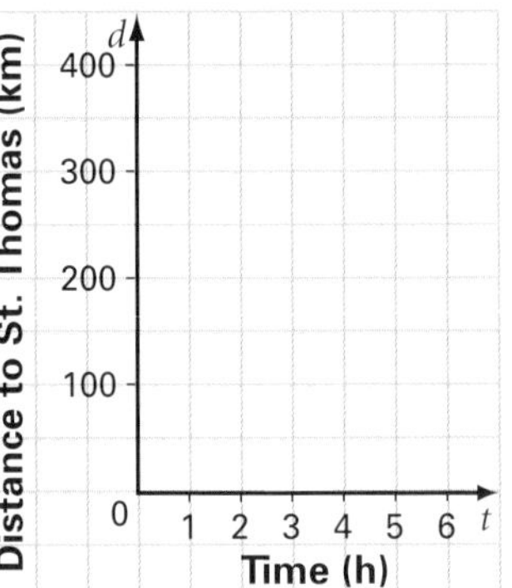


2. (2.5, 180) is on the line. Plot the point (2.5, 180). What does this point mean?

3. The slope of the line representing the distance-time graph is –80. What does this number represent? Why is it negative?

4. You could find additional points on the line by "rising" –80 and "running" 1, from the point (2.5, 180). Why might this method not produce an accurate line?

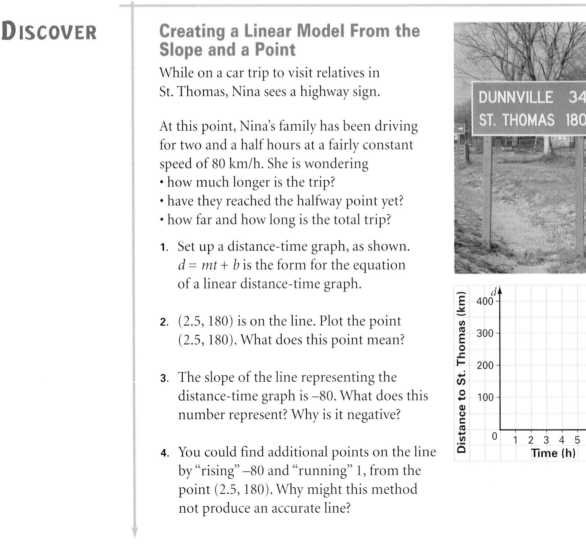

5. You can find the equation accurately by using the following method.
   a) Substitute the known values into the equation $d = mt + b$:
      $m = -80 \quad t = 2.5 \quad d = 180$
   b) Solve the equation for $b$.
   c) Substitute the values for $m$ and $b$ only into $d = mt + b$. This is the equation relating distance and time.
   d) Plot the value of $b$ on the $d$-axis. Draw a line through the two points. Label the line with the equation.

6. a) Use the equation or graph to answer Nina's questions.
      • How much longer is the trip?
      • Have they reached the halfway point yet?
      • How far and how long is the total trip?
   b) Explain how you found the answers to these questions.

You can find the equation of a line if you know
• the slope, $m$
• the coordinates of one point on the line

**EXAMPLE 1**

## Finding the Equation of a Line, Given the Slope and a Point

A line passing through (3, 5) has slope –2.

a) Graph the line. b) Determine the equation of the line.

### Solution

a) Mark the given point (3, 5).
Use the slope to move to another point.

$$\frac{\text{rise}}{\text{run}} = -2$$

$$\frac{\text{rise}}{\text{run}} = \frac{-2}{1}$$

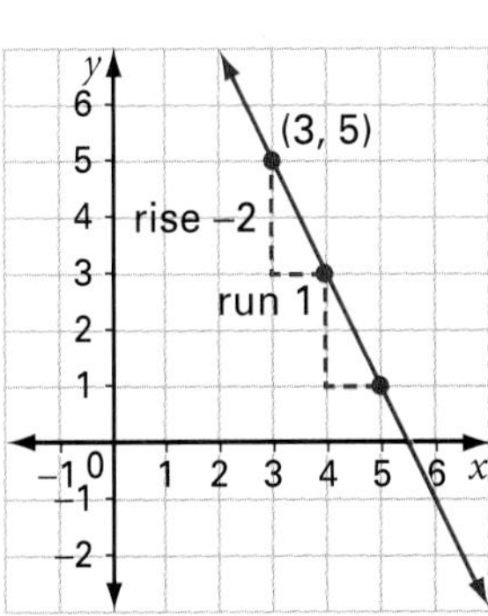


b) Substitute the known values into $y = mx + b$.
$m = -2$ and, when $x = 3$, $y = 5$.

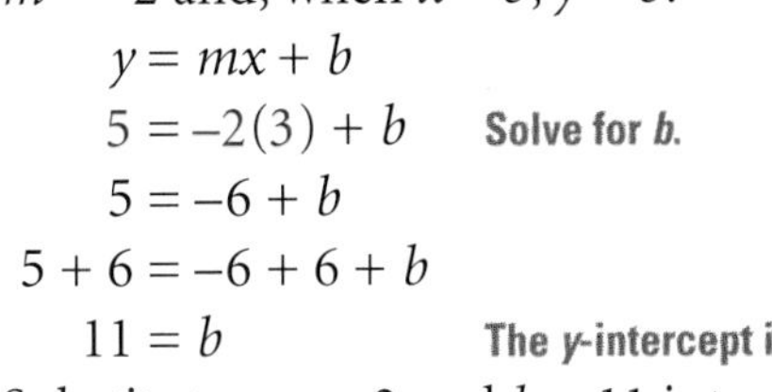

$$y = mx + b$$

$$5 = -2(3) + b \quad \text{Solve for } b.$$

$$5 = -6 + b$$

$$5 + 6 = -6 + 6 + b$$

$$11 = b \quad \text{The } y\text{-intercept is 11.}$$

Substitute $m = -2$ and $b = 11$ into $y = mx + b$.
The equation of the line is $y = -2x + 11$.

# EXAMPLE 2

## Finding the Equation of a Partial Variation, Given the Slope and a Point

Rachel needs to rent a snow-blower. Rachel's friend tells her of a company that charges \$5 per hour plus a fixed amount that she cannot remember. She does recall that she rented the snow-blower for 4 h and was charged \$50.

**a)** Describe the variation. What is the variable amount? What is the fixed amount?

**b)** Construct a linear model to relate cost to number of hours.

**c)** Graph the line.

**d)** Determine the cost to rent the snow-blower for 6 h.

### Solution

**a)** This is a partial variation. The variable amount is $5t$, where $t$ is the number of hours. The fixed amount is unknown.

In a partial variation, the *fixed part* is the *y-intercept* of a line. The *coefficient of the variable part* is the *slope*.

**b)** The equation relating cost, $C$, to number of hours, $t$, is $C = 5t + b$.
This is also the form for the equation of a line.
The cost for 4 h is \$50. Substitute $t = 4$ and $C = 50$.

$$C = 5t + b$$
$$50 = 5(4) + b \qquad \text{Solve for } b\text{, the fixed cost.}$$
$$50 = 20 + b$$
$$50 - 20 = 20 - 20 + b$$
$$30 = b$$

The fixed cost is \$30. Substitute $b$ into the equation to construct the linear model.
The equation relating cost to number of hours is $C = 5t + 30$.

**c)** Mark the $C$-intercept 30 and the point (4, 50). Draw the line and label it.

**d)** Substitute $t = 6$ to determine the cost of a 6-h rental.

$$C = 5t + 30$$
$$C = 5(6) + 30$$
$$C = 30 + 30$$
$$C = 60$$

It will cost \$60 to rent the snow-blower for 6 h.
Alternatively, you can read the graph to determine this cost. While reading from a graph can be faster, an equation can give greater accuracy.

## Key Concepts

You can find the equation of a line of the form $y = mx + b$ if you know the slope and one point on the line. To find the equation,

- substitute $m$ and the coordinates of the point into $y = mx + b$
- solve for $b$
- substitute the values of $m$ and $b$ into $y = mx + b$

## Discuss the Concepts

1. a) What are two pieces of information that you need in order to write the equation of a line?
   b) Explain how to use the slope and a point to find the equation of a line.
2. A line has slope 2 and $y$-intercept –3. What is the equation of the line?
3. The point (0, 4) is on a line that has a slope of –1.
   a) What is the $y$-intercept?  b) What is the equation of the line?

## Practise

***For help with questions 1–7 , refer to Example 1.***

1. Solve each equation for $b$.
   a) $9 = 4(2) + b$  b) $7 = -5(-3) + b$  c) $-2 = \frac{1}{2}(6) + b$
2. The point (0, 0) is on a line that has a slope of 2.
   a) What is the $y$-intercept?  b) What is the equation?
3. Substitute the given values for slope and $y$-intercept to write the equation of each line.
   a) $m = 2, b = -3$  b) $m = -3, b = 5$  c) $m = \frac{2}{3}, b = -1$
   d) $m = -\frac{1}{2}, b = -9$  e) $m = -6, b = 0$  f) $m = 0, b = -2$
4. What is the equation of a line that intersects the $y$-axis at the origin and has slope $\frac{2}{3}$?
5. Find the equation of the line with the given slope passing through the given point.
   a) $P(4, 5), m = 2$  b) $P(-4, 2), m = 3$  c) $P(5, 0), m = -1$
   d) $P(-3, 0), m = 1$  e) $P(-3, -2), m = 5$  f) $P(-1, 1), m = -2$

**B** 6. Find the equation of the line with the given slope passing through the given point.

a) $P(2, -3), m = \frac{1}{2}$ b) $P(-2, -5), m = -\frac{1}{4}$ c) $P(0, -4), m = -\frac{3}{5}$

## Apply the Concepts

7. A line that passes through (–2, 0) has $y$-intercept 3.

a) What is the slope of this line? b) What is the equation of this line?

***For help with questions 8–11, refer to Example 2.***

8. **Application** The cost of making T-shirts is a partial variation of the form $C = mn + b$, where $n$ is the number of T-shirts and $C$ is the cost in dollars. The cost of making 100 T-shirts is $1000. It is known that the variable cost is $\$8n$.

a) Find the value of $b$. What does this represent?

b) Write the equation relating cost and number.

c) Graph this relation.

d) How much would it cost to make 500 T-shirts?

e) The break-even point is the number of T-shirts that must be sold so that revenues equal expenses. If the break-even point is known to be $5480, find how many T-shirts must be sold in order to break even
- using the graph
- using the equation

Which method do you think is better in this case? Explain why.

9. **Communication** In Niagara-on-the-Lake, you can ride a rickshaw for a fixed price plus a variable amount that depends on the length of the trip. Suppose that you know the following
- the variable cost is $10/km
- a 2.5-km trip costs $40

a) Determine the equation relating cost, $C$, and distance, $d$.

b) Graph this relation.

c) Use the equation to determine the cost of a 5.5-km ride.

d) Use the graph to determine the cost of a 5.5-km ride.

e) A classmate suggests an alternative solution, using a table. Explain this method.

| Distance (km) | Cost ($) |
|---|---|
| 2.5 | 40 |
| 3.5 | 50 |
| 4.5 | 60 |
| 5.5 | 70 |

f) Use each of the three methods (equation, graph, table) to determine how far you could go for $100.

g) Use each method to determine the cost of a 4.2-km ride.

h) Describe at least one advantage and one disadvantage of each method of solution.

**Chapter Problem**

10. After cruising at a steady altitude (height above sea level), Kara's plane begins to climb at a rate of 50 m/s. After 8 s of climbing, the altitude is 1900 m. The equation relating the height of Kara's plane to time is of the form $A = mt + b$, where
    - $t$ is the time of the climb, in seconds
    - $A$ is the altitude, in metres
    - $m$ is the rate of climb, in metres per second

    **a)** The point (8, 1900) satisfies this linear relation. What does this point mean?
    **b)** Substitute the point (8, 1900) and $m = 50$ into $A = mt + b$ and solve for $b$.
    **c)** Write the equation that relates altitude and time.
    **d)** At what altitude did Kara start the plane's climb?
    **e)** How long will it take to reach an altitude of 3000 m?

11. **Communication** Piers has been driving at a fairly constant speed of 90 km/h for 2 h, when he sees the following sign.

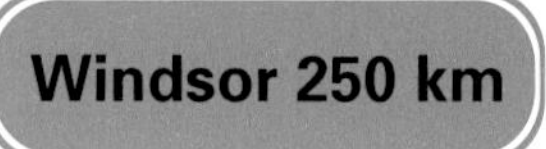


The equation relating distance and time is of the form $d = mt + b$.
**a)** What does the ordered pair (2, 250) mean?
**b)** The slope is $m = -90$. What does this value represent? Why is it negative?
**c)** Determine the value of $b$.
**d)** Write the equation relating distance and time.
**e)** Graph the relation. What is the meaning of the $d$-intercept?
**f)** How long will the trip to Windsor take, in total?
**g)** Has Piers reached the halfway point of his trip yet? Explain.

**C** 12. **Thinking/Inquiry/Problem Solving** Refer to the previous question. Suppose that, when Piers sees the sign, he increases his driving speed to 100 km/h.
**a)** Construct a graph to model Piers' trip.
**b)** How would your answers to parts f) and g) change?
**c)** Explain how you solved this problem.

# 10.6 Equation of a Line, Given Two Points

In the previous section, you found that you can build the equation of a line in the form $y = mx + b$ if you know

- the slope
- any point on the line

In this section, you will learn how to build the equation when you know any two points on the line.

## DISCOVER

### Creating a Linear Model From Two Points

Jenna gets a new job 5 km from home. She plans to take a taxi to work. To estimate the cost, she asks her siblings what it costs them for taxi rides. They usually use Red Line Taxis.

Manuel: "I work 9 km away. I normally get charged \$21.50."

Hanna: "It usually costs me \$10.50 for the 3.5-km ride to college."

Jenna knows that Red Line charges a fixed amount plus a variable amount that depends on the trip distance.

1. Based on the information given, estimate the cost for Jenna's taxi to work.

2. On grid paper, set up a graph of cost versus distance. Choose appropriate scales. The equation $C = md + b$ relates cost, $C$, and distance, $d$, for this relation. Explain why the points (9, 21.5) and (3.5, 10.5) are known to be on the line.

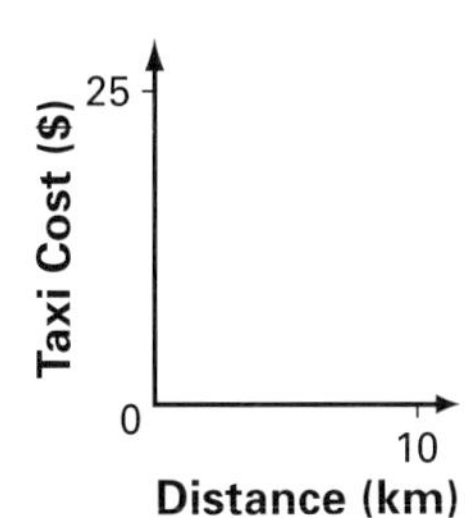


3. a) Plot the two points (9, 21.5) and (3.5, 10.5).
   b) Use these points to draw the line.
   c) Determine the slope, $m$, of the line using the two points.

4. a) Substitute the value of $m$ and the coordinates of *one* of the given points into the equation $C = md + b$.
   b) Solve the equation for $b$.
   c) Substitute the values of $m$ and $b$ only into $C = md + b$ to give the equation of the line.

5. a) Use the equation to determine the cost for Jenna's taxi ride to work.
   b) Compare this value to your estimate in step 1. How close were you?
   c) How much will it cost Jenna to take a taxi from home to her friend's home, 1.5 km away?

## Example 1

### Finding the Equation of a Line, Given Two Points

A line passes through (–6, 5) and (4, –2).

a) Graph the line. b) Determine the equation of the line.

### Solution

a)

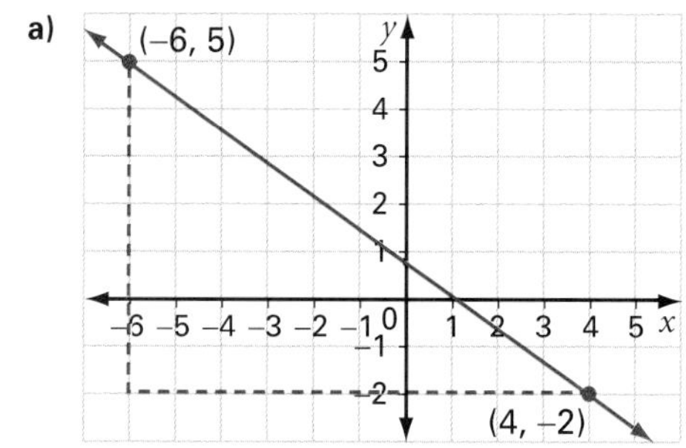


b) *Step 1*: Find the value for $m$, the slope.

From the graph:

$$\text{slope} = \frac{\text{rise}}{\text{run}}$$

$$m = \frac{-7}{10}$$

$$m = -\frac{7}{10} \text{ or } -0.7$$

Using the formula:

$$m = \frac{y_B - y_A}{x_B - x_A}$$

$$m = \frac{-2 - 5}{4 - (-6)}$$ Substitute integers carefully.

$$m = \frac{-7}{10}$$ Take care with integer calculations.

$$m = -\frac{7}{10} \text{ or } -0.7$$

*Step 2*: Find the value for $b$, the $y$-intercept.

Substitute $m = -0.7$ and the coordinates of *one* of the given points into $y = mx + b$. Use (–6, 5). Substitute $x = -6$ and $y = 5$.

$$y = mx + b$$

$$5 = -0.7(-6) + b$$ Solve for *b*.

$$5 = 4.2 + b$$

$$b = 0.8$$

*Step 3*: Write the equation of the line. Substitute the values of $m$ and $b$ into $y = mx + b$.

The equation of the line is $y = -0.7x + 0.8$.

# EXAMPLE 2

## Finding the Equation of a Distance-Time Linear Relation, Given Two Points

The graphing calculator screens show the distance-time graphs of a person walking in front of a motion sensor.

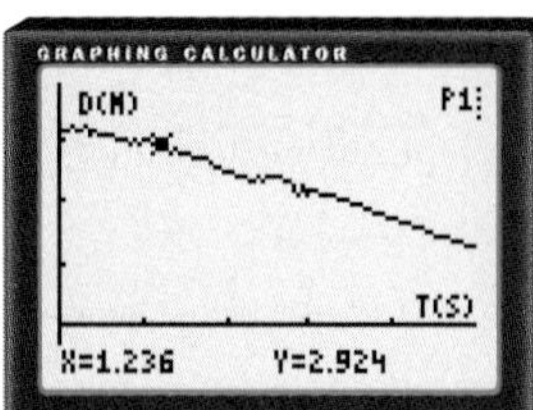


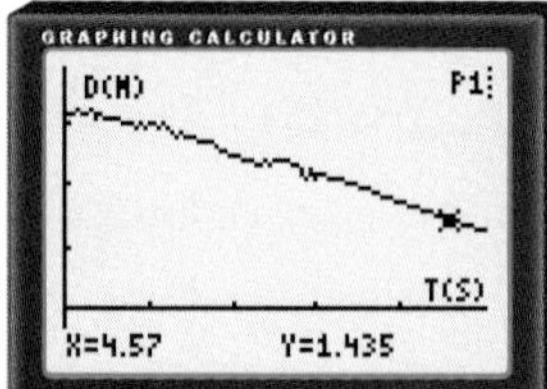


a) Determine the equation of the line relating distance and time.

b) Use the equation to find the location of the walker after 1 s.

### Solution

a) The distance-time graph is approximately a straight line. The points (1.2, 2.9) and (4.6, 1.4) are on the line. Note: the coordinates are rounded to one decimal place for ease of calculation.

*Step 1*: Find the slope.

$m = \dfrac{\text{rise}}{\text{run}}$ or $\dfrac{d_B - d_A}{t_B - t_A}$

$m = \dfrac{1.4 - 2.9}{4.6 - 1.2}$

$m = \dfrac{-1.5}{3.4}$

$m \doteq -0.44$

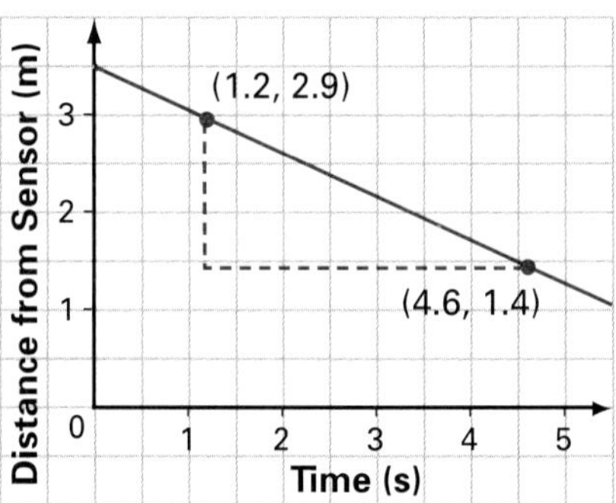


This slope value means that the person was walking at a speed of 0.44 m/s toward the sensor.

*Step 2*: Substitute $m = -0.44$ and the coordinates of one of the given points into $d = mt + b$. Use (1.2, 2.9).

$d = mt + b$

$1.2 = (-0.44)(2.9) + b$

$1.2 = -1.3 + b$ **Solve for *b*.**

$1.2 + 1.3 = b$

$2.5 = b$

This $b$-value is the $y$-intercept. It means that, at time zero, the walker started 2.5 m away from the motion sensor.

*Step 3*: Substitute $m = -0.44$ and $b = 2.5$ into $d = mt + b$.

The equation relating distance and time is $d = -0.44t + 2.5$.

**Make Connections**

You analysed the connection between the slope of a distance-time graph and the speed and direction of a walker in **Section 7.1 Motion Sensors and Distance-Time Graphs** and **Section 7.2 Slope**.

b) Substitute $t = 1$.

$d = -0.44t + 2.5$

$d = -0.44(1) + 2.5$

$d = -0.44 + 2.5$

$d \doteq 2.1$

After 1 s, the walker was approximately 2.1 m from the sensor.

## Key Concepts

You can find the equation of a line of the form $y = mx + b$ if you know the coordinates of any two points on the line. To find the equation,

- use the two points to find the slope, $m$
- substitute $m$ and the coordinates of *one* point into $y = mx + b$
- solve for $b$
- substitute the values of $m$ and $b$ into $y = mx + b$

## Discuss the Concepts

1. Explain how to use two points to find the equation of a line.
2. Does it matter which point you use when substituting the known slope and a point to find the value of $b$? Explain.
3. a) Can you determine the equation of a line if you know one point on the line and the $y$-intercept?
   b) If yes, explain how. If no, explain why not.

## Practise

***For help with questions 1–7, refer to Example 1.***

1. Find the slope of the line passing through each pair of points.

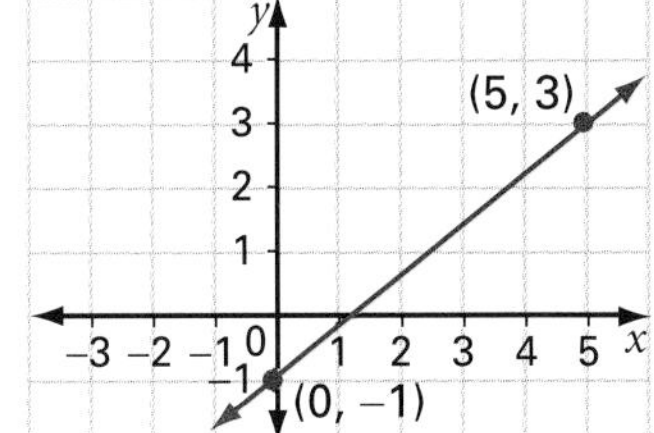

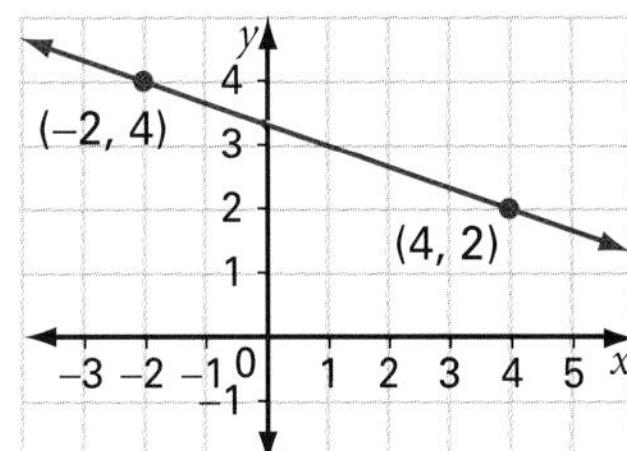

2. Determine the slope of the line passing through each pair of points.
   a) P(9, 1) and Q(–1, 0)
   b) R(–5, 0) and S(5, –5)
   c) T(0, 6) and V(–3, 0)
   d) W(–2, –3) and X(3, 2)

3. Find the value of $b$ in the equation $y = mx + b$ for a line passing through the given point with the given slope.
   a) P(3, 6), $m = -4$
   b) Q(2, 7), $m = 3$
   c) A(0, –4), $m = 1$

4. Substitute the given values for slope and $y$-intercept to write the equation of a line in the form $y = mx + b$.
   a) $m = -1$, $b = 4$
   b) $m = 5$, $b = -1.5$
   c) $m = \frac{3}{4}$, $b = -2$

5. Determine the equation of the line passing through each pair of points.
   a) A(3, 5) and B(1, 1)
   b) P(8, 1) and Q(4, 3)
   c) U(2, –2) and V(4, 0)
   d) X(–3, –2) and Y(3, –4)
   e) G(–6, –2) and H(2, 0)
   f) J(–2, 3) and K(1, –6)

6. a) Find the equation of the line whose $x$-intercept is 5 and $y$-intercept is –3.
   b) Find the equation of the line whose $x$- and $y$-intercepts are both –4.

## APPLY THE CONCEPTS

7. **Application** Workers at a grocery store get a constant raise each year. Kathy, who has been working at the store for 5 years, earns $16.25/h. Juan, who has been working at the store for 2 years, earns $11.75/h. The equation relating wage and number of years worked is of the form $w = mn + b$, where $w$ is the hourly wage and $n$ is the number of years worked.
   a) (5, 16.25) and (2, 11.75) are two points on the line. Explain why.
   b) Find the slope of this linear relation.
   c) Find the $y$-intercept.
   d) Write the equation of the line.
   e) Leo has been working at the store for 7 years. Use the equation to determine Leo's wage.
   f) What wage does this linear model predict for a worker who has been with the store for 25 years? Does this seem reasonable? Explain. How might the store modify the raise policy?

*For help with question 8, refer to Example 2.*

8. **Thinking/Inquiry/Problem Solving** A walker makes three movements in front of a motion sensor, each at a constant speed. The beginning and end points are given for each movement:
   - start at 1 m and walk to the 3-m mark in 2 s
   - from the 3-m mark take 4 s to walk to the 5-m mark
   - from the 5-m mark take 3 s to walk to the 1-m mark

   **a)** Sketch a distance-time graph for this series of movements.

   **b)** Find the equation for each of the three line segments (time: 0–2 s, 2–6s, 6–9 s) in the form $d = mt + b$.

9. While flying from Halifax to Calgary, the pilot of one of Kara's airplanes announces, after 2 h in the air, that the plane is 3000 km from Calgary. After 3.5 h in the air, he announces that the plane is 1500 km from Calgary. Assume that the plane flies at a constant speed. The distance is related to the time by an equation of the form $d = mt + b$, where
   - $t$ is the elapsed time in the air, in hours
   - $d$ is the distance from Calgary, in kilometres
   - $m$ is the flying speed, in kilometres per hour

   **a)** Set up a graph of distance versus time and plot the points (2, 3000) and (3.5, 1500). These points are on the distance-time line. Explain what these points mean.

   **b)** Draw the line. Calculate the slope of the graph. What does this value mean? Why is it negative?

   **c)** Substitute one of the points and the value of $m$ into $d = mt + b$. Solve for $b$.

   **d)** Write the equation for this relation.

   **e)** How far apart are Halifax and Calgary?

   **f)** How long will the trip take?

# Review

## 10.1 Solving One- and Two-Step Equations, pages 394–398

1. Solve and check.
   a) $3 + x = 8$
   b) $y - 5 = -1$
   c) $4m = -24$
   d) $\frac{k}{3} = -6$

2. Solve and check.
   a) $4n + 3 = 11$
   b) $6p - 7 = 2$
   c) $-3v - 5 = 16$
   d) $9 - 7r = -5$

3. A taxi charges \$3.00 plus \$1.25/km. The equation relating cost, $C$, and distance, $d$, is $C = 1.25d + 3.00$. How far is a trip that costs \$16.75?

## 10.2 Solving Multi-Step Equations, pages 399–403

4. Solve.
   a) $6x - 5 = 4x + 9$
   b) $3w + 8 = -10 - 6w$
   c) $3(2d - 1) = 7d$
   d) $5(4 - 2f) = 3 - (2f - 1)$

5. A hockey team earns two points for each win and one point for each regulation tie. The Montréal Canadiens won twice as many home games as away games. They had nine regulation ties. Their point total for the season is 99. If $a$ represents their number of away wins, then $99 = 2(a + 2a) + 9$.
   a) Solve the equation for $a$.
   b) How many home wins did the Canadiens have?
   c) How many games did the Canadiens win, in total?

## 10.3 Modelling With Formulas, pages 404–410

6. Rearrange each formula to isolate the variable indicated.
   a) $A = lw$ for $w$
   b) $A = \pi r^2$ for $r$
   c) $P = 2b + 2h$ for $h$
   d) $E = kx - P$ for $k$

7. The formula for the volume of a pyramid is $V = \frac{1}{3}b^2h$, where $b$ is the base side length and $h$ is the vertical height.
   a) The great pyramid of Cheops in Egypt has a base side length of 230 m and a volume of 2 600 000 m$^3$. What is the height of this pyramid?
   b) Describe how you solved this problem.

## 10.4 Modelling With Algebra, pages 411–417

**8.** Write an equation to represent each sentence.

**a)** Six times a number gives 48.

**b)** One third of a number is 7.

**c)** A number is increased by eight and the result is 22.

**9.** The two equal sides of an isosceles triangle are twice as long as the third side.

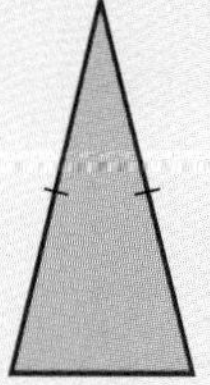

**a)** The perimeter of the triangle is 210 cm. How long is each side?

**b)** Explain how you solved this problem.

**10.** The length of a locker room is 4 times its width. The perimeter is 25 m.

**a)** Determine the length and width of the room.

**b)** Explain how you solved this problem.

## 10.5 Equation of a Line, Given the Slope and a Point, pages 418–423

**11.** Find the equation of the line passing through (5, 6) with a slope of –3.

**12.** A taxi charges \$2.20/km plus an unknown fixed charge. An 8-km trip costs \$21.10.

**a)** How much is the fixed charge?

**b)** Write an equation relating cost, $C$, to distance, $d$.

**c)** Find the cost of a 12-km trip.

## 10.6 Equation of a Line, Given Two Points, pages 424–429

**13.** Find the equation of the line passing through (1, 5) and (5, –3).

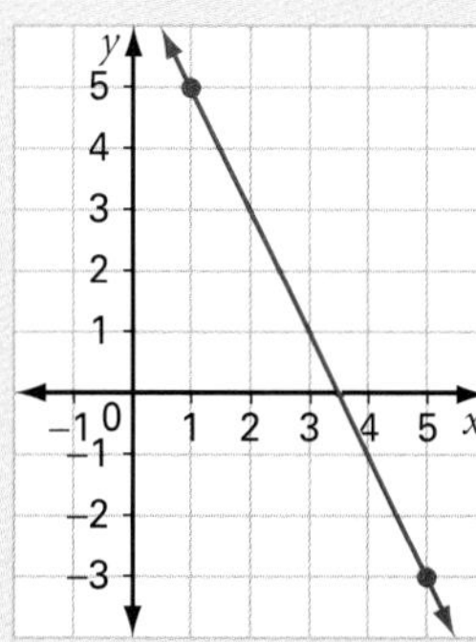


**14.** Gina starts at a distance of 4 m and walks at a constant speed toward a motion sensor. After 2 s, she is 1.5 m from the sensor.

**a)** How fast is Gina walking?

**b)** Write the equation that relates distance and time, in the form $d = mt + b$.

**c)** How far from the sensor was Gina after 0.8 s?

# Practice Test

## Multiple Choice

***For questions 1 to 7, select the best answer.***

**1.** Which is the solution to $5x - 3 = 17$?

**A** $x = 3$ **B** $x = 4$ **C** $x = 5$ **D** $x = 6$

**2.** Which is the solution to $14 = -2(k + 8)$?

**A** $k = -15$ **B** $k = -11$ **C** $k = -3$ **D** $k = 11$

**3.** When the formula $P = 2l + 2w$ is rearranged to isolate $w$, you obtain

**A** $w = P - 2l$ **B** $l = \dfrac{P - 2w}{2}$ **C** $w = \dfrac{P - 2l}{2}$ **D** $w = P - \dfrac{l}{2}$

**4.** When the formula $V = \pi r^2 h$ is rearranged to isolate $r$, you obtain

**A** $h = \dfrac{V}{\pi r^2}$ **B** $r = \dfrac{V}{\pi h}$ **C** $r = \left(\dfrac{V}{\pi h}\right)^2$ **D** $r = \sqrt{\dfrac{V}{\pi h}}$

**5.** Which algebraic expression means "three less than a number"?

**A** $n + 3$ **B** $n - 3$ **C** $3 - n$ **D** $3n$

**6.** What is the $y$-intercept of a line passing through $(-4, 0)$ with a slope of 2?

**A** $-4$ **B** 0 **C** 2 **D** 8

**7.** Which is the equation for the line shown?

**A** $d = -5t$ **B** $d = t + 5$

**C** $d = -t + 5$ **D** $t = d + 5$

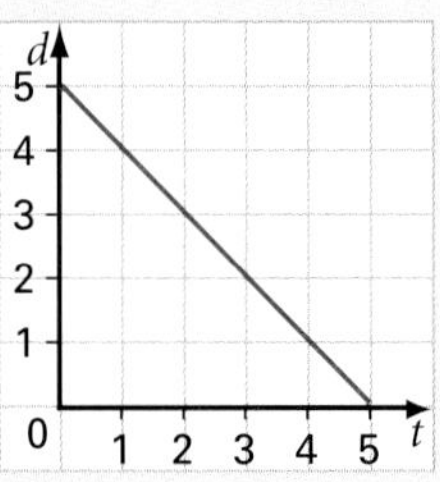


## Short Answer

**8.** **a)** Solve the equation $3(2m + 4) = -2(m - 4)$.

**b)** Check your answer.

**9.** A farmer is building a rectangular pen using 58 m of fencing. How wide should the pen be if the length is 18 m?

10. Determine the equation of the line passing through $(2, -3)$ and $(6, 1)$.

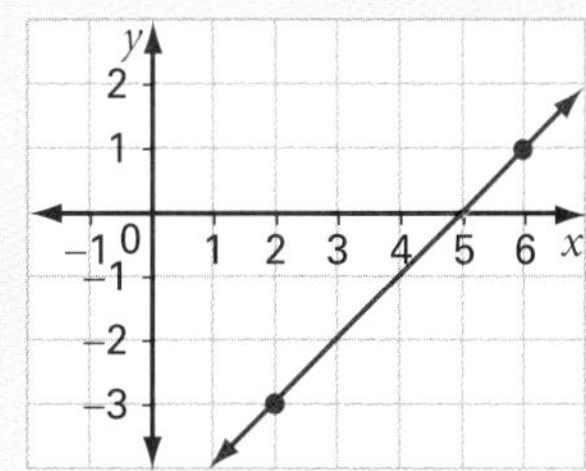

## Extended Response

11. **Thinking/Inquiry/Problem Solving** Chuck is walking at a constant speed in front of a motion sensor. After 2 s, Chuck is 4 m away from the sensor. After 4 s, he is 1 m away.
    - a) How fast is Chuck walking?
    - b) Is Chuck walking toward or away from the sensor? Explain how you can tell.
    - c) Write the equation that relates distance and time, in the form $d = mt + b$, for this relation.
    - d) Graph this distance-time relation.
    - e) How far was Chuck from the sensor when he started walking, at $t = 0$?
    - f) At what point in time was Chuck 2.5 m from the sensor?

**ACHIEVEMENT CHECK** Knowledge/Understanding Thinking/Inquiry/Problem Solving Communication Application

12. Luisa found the following formula in a fitness book. It relates a person's age, $a$, to the maximum safe heart rate, $M$, they should have when completing vigorous exercise.

    $M = 0.7(295 - a)$

    Luisa wonders if the formula applies to her family. Luisa is 14 and her Mom is 40. Luisa measured her own and her mother's heart rates immediately after they had finished jogging together. The rates were188 and 172 respectively.
    - a) Use the given formula to calculate the maximum safe heart rate for a 14-year-old and also for a 40-year-old. Are Luisa and her mother within the safe limits?
    - b) Luisa has a friend who boasts that she has a heart rate of 220 after playing a game for the girls' hockey team. Is this reasonable? What age should her friend be for this heart rate to be safe?
    - c) Luisa decides to create a new formula, just for the members of her family. Use the data she collected for herself and her mother to create a linear equation that relates their ages and maximum heart rates. Using this formula, what is the maximum heart rate for Luisa's 43-year-old father?

# Cumulative Review

## Chapters 8 to 10

**1.** Evaluate, using the method of your choice.

**a)** $\left(\frac{1}{3}\right)^2$ **b)** $\left(\frac{5}{2}\right)^4$ **c)** $\left(\frac{2}{5}\right)^4$ **d)** $\left(\frac{5}{3}\right)^2$

**2.** **Thinking/Inquiry/Problem Solving** Find the value of the unknown exponent.

**a)** $3^4 \times 3^6 = 3^w$ **b)** $\frac{2^x}{2^5} = 2^7$ **c)** $(2^6)^3 = 2^y$ **d)** $(8^y)^3 = 8^{12}$

**3.** Evaluate each power. Check your answers by using a calculator.

**a)** $5^{-2}$ **b)** $8^4$ **c)** $2^{-7}$ **d)** $7^0$

**4.** **Radioactive decay** Carbon-14 decays to $\frac{1}{2}$ of its original mass after 6000 years. A Cro-Magnon bone tool is about 18 000 years old. What fraction of the original mass of carbon-14 remains? Hint: How many times has the mass halved?

**5.** Express each measure in scientific notation.

**a)** 32 700 kg **b)** 7 120 357 $m^2$

**c)** 0.000 2 s **d)** 0.000 000 000 405 g

**6.** **Scientific measures** Write in standard form.

**a)** The diameter of an electron is $5.63588 \times 10^{-15}$ m.

**b)** Canadians dispose of about $1.15 \times 10^{10}$ beverage cans per year.

**c)** The diameter of a red blood cell is $2.0 \times 10^{-5}$ m.

**7.** **Diamonds** Diamond masses are measured in carats. One carat is equal to $2 \times 10^{-4}$ kg. Five equal-sized diamonds, with a total mass of $1.5 \times 10^{-4}$ kg, are mounted onto a ring.

**a)** What is the mass of each diamond, in kilograms, expressed in scientific notation?

**b)** How large is each diamond, in carats, expressed as a decimal?

**8.** Simplify.

**a)** $(5n + 8) + (n + 1)$ **b)** $(n + 5) - (4n + 1)$

**c)** $(3h^2 - 5h - 7) + (h^2 - 3h - 2)$

9. Expand and simplify.

a) $6(2t + 5)$

b) $-2a(a + 3)$

c) $3(m - 1) + 2(m + 5)$

d) $n(5n - 3) - 2n(n + 1)$

e) $3(x^2 + 4x - 7) + 5x(x - 8)$

10. Find an expression in simplified form for

a) the perimeter of the figure

b) the area of the figure

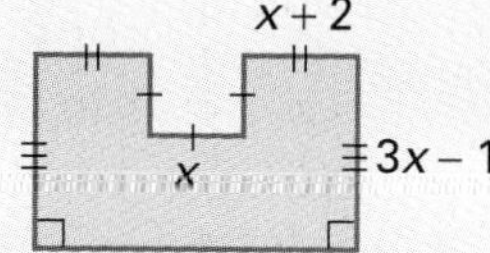


11. Solve each equation.

a) $n - 5 = 8$

b) $4t = 36$

c) $3p + 1 = 10$

d) $6k + 10 = 15 + 9k$

e) $2(3y - 5) = 4(y + 3)$

12. To convert photographs to digital images, a store charges \$10 plus \$0.75 per image.

a) Write an equation relating cost, $C$, and number of images, $n$.

b) If Frank was charged \$21.25, how many digital images did he get?

13. Rearrange each formula to solve for the variable indicated.

a) $d = st$ for $t$

b) $E = mc^2$ for $c$

c) $A = P + Prt$ for $t$

14. A line passes through (0, 1) and (2, 4). Find the equation of the line.

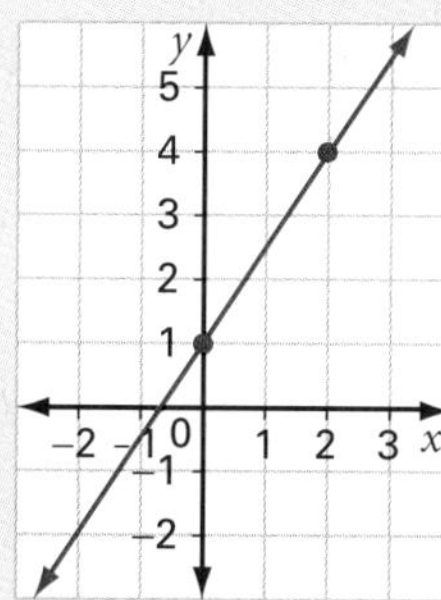

# CHAPTER 11

# Exploring Geometric Relationships

In this chapter, you will investigate geometric relationships
- in triangles
- in quadrilaterals
- with parallel lines

**Chapter Problem**

Cargo ships travelling the Great Lakes must pass through the Welland Canal joining Lake Ontario and Lake Erie, rising or dropping over 100 m through eight lift locks. The lock gates have a triangular design, to withstand the great pressure of the water behind them. Road and rail traffic passes over the Canal at specially engineered bridges. As you work through this chapter, you will investigate the geometry of structures such as these.

# Get Ready

## Classifying Triangles and Quadrilaterals

**1.** State the number of sides for each shape.

**a)** triangle **b)** pentagon **c)** quadrilateral

**2.** Classify each triangle as right, acute, or obtuse.

**a)**

**b)**
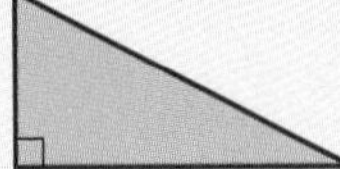
**c)**
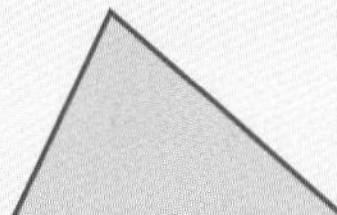

**3.** Classify each triangle as isosceles, equilateral, or scalene.

**a)**

**b)**
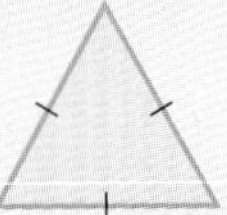
**c)**
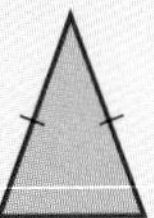

**4.** Classify each quadrilateral using names from this list: square, rectangle, rhombus, kite, trapezoid, parallelogram.

**a)**

**b)**
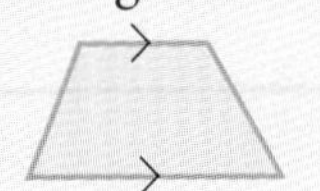
**c)**
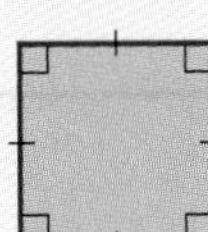
**d)**
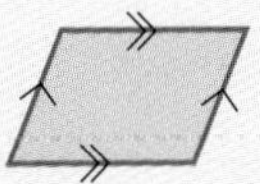
**e)**
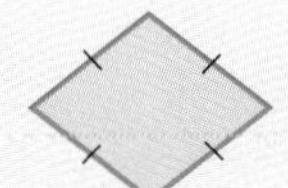
**f)**
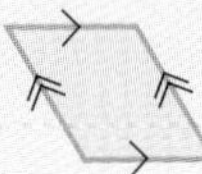

## Angle Properties

When two straight lines cross, the angles formed on either side are called **opposite angles**. Opposite angles are equal.

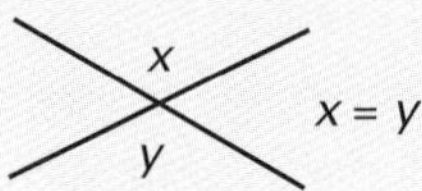


Angles along a straight line are called **supplementary angles**. Supplementary angles add to 180°.

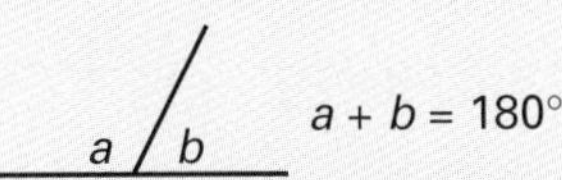


Angles dividing a right angle are called **complementary angles**. Complementary angles add to 90°.

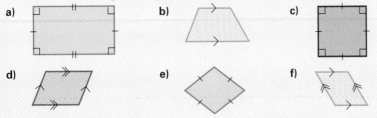

y x $x + y = 90°$

5. Measure each angle, and classify it as acute, right, or obtuse.

a)

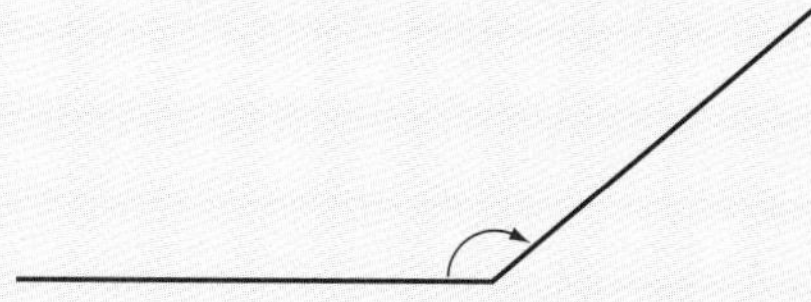

b)

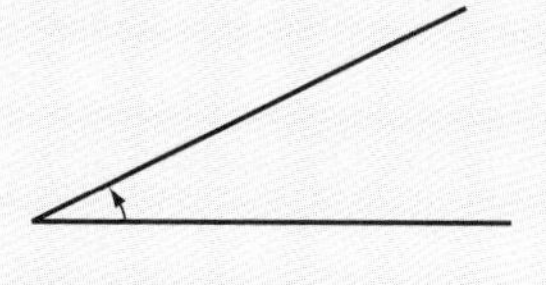

c)

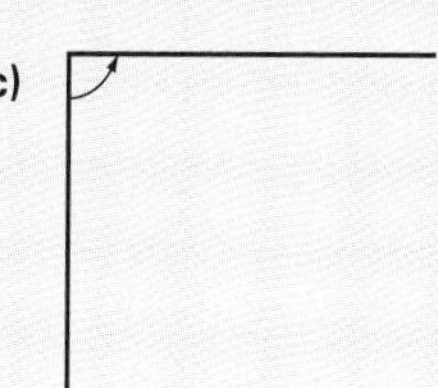

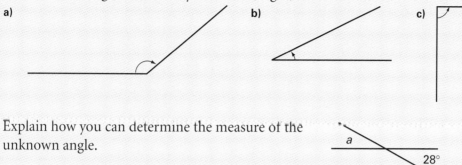

6. Explain how you can determine the measure of the unknown angle.

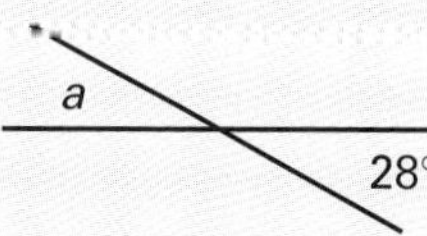


7. In each diagram, calculate the measure of the unknown angle.

a)

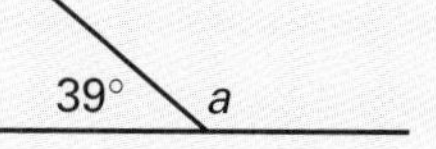


b)

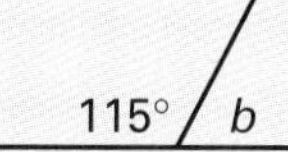


c)

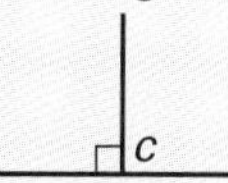


8. In each diagram, calculate the measure of the unknown angle.

a)

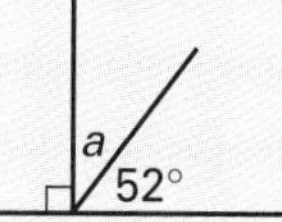


b)

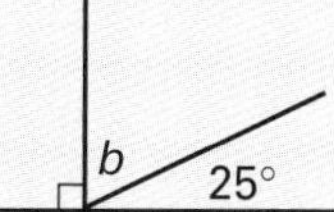


c)

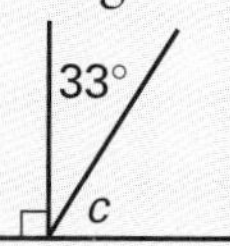


## Naming Angles and Sides

To identify angles in polygons or angles involving parallel lines, you may need to use three letters. The right angle is ∠ABC. The angle with the dot is ∠QPR.

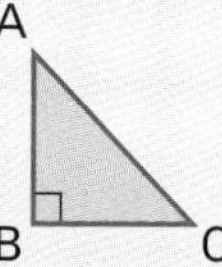


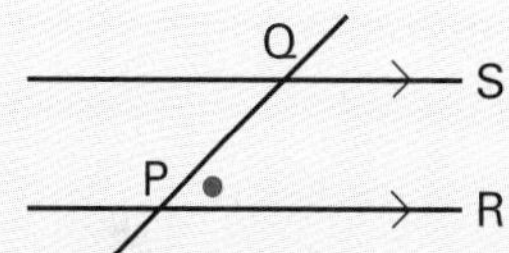


9. Use three letters to name the angle with the dot in each diagram.

a)

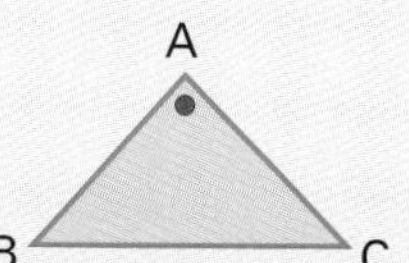


b)

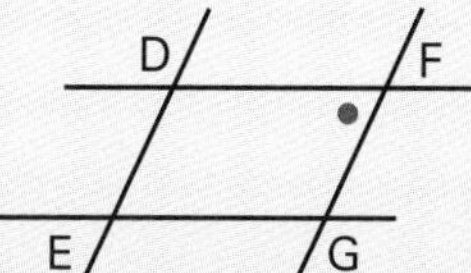

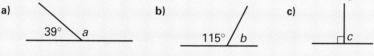

A side of a triangle or polygon can be identified by the two vertices on the ends of the line segment. For example, in the quadrilateral shown, the sides are AB, BC, CD, and AD. These sides can also be expressed as BA, CB, DC, and DA.

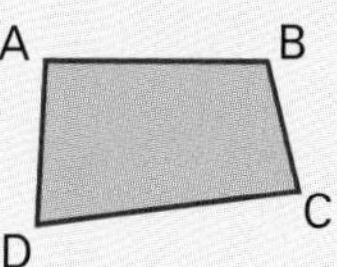


10. For each figure, use two letters to identify the side marked with the $x$.

a)

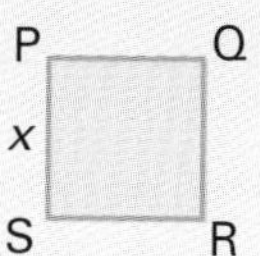


b)

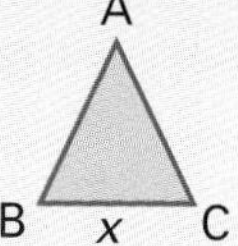

# 11.1 Investigating Angles of Triangles and Quadrilaterals

This bridge crosses the Welland Canal near St. Catharines, Ontario. It is a type of swing bridge, called a bascule bridge. A large counterweight block is mounted near the base of the bridge to balance it almost exactly on its pivot. This makes it much easier for the lifting motor to swing the bridge up and open. Triangular supports keep the counterweight block firmly in position. You can model this with a pencil. Balance the pencil horizontally on the end of your finger. Gently push one end down. The other end will rise very easily.

In this section, you will investigate
- relationships involving angles in triangles, such as the ones in the bascule bridge
- relationships involving angles in quadrilaterals

## Discover 1

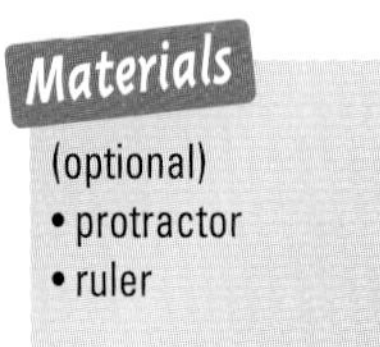


### Angle Relationships in a Triangle

***Using The Geometer's Sketchpad®, or ruler and protractor***

**Sum of Interior Angles of a Triangle**

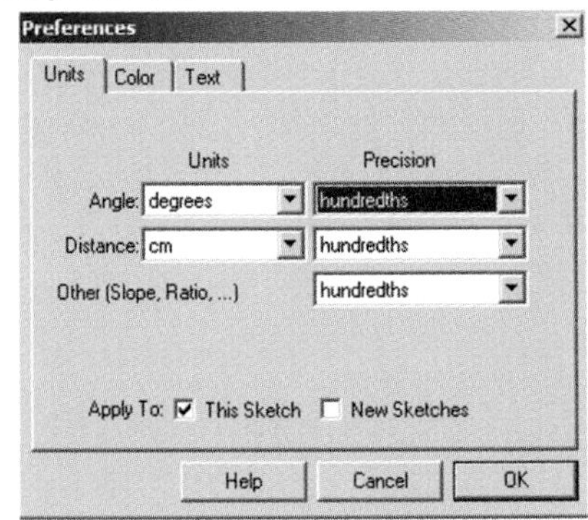


1. a) Open *The Geometer's Sketchpad®*.
   b) From the **Edit** menu, choose **Preferences....**
   c) In the **Units** panel, set all the **Precision** boxes to "**hundredths,**" as shown.
   d) Click on the **Text** tab in the **Preferences...** box. Check **For All New Points** and **As Objects Are Measured**. Click **OK** to close the box. All points that you create will now be labelled automatically, starting from A.

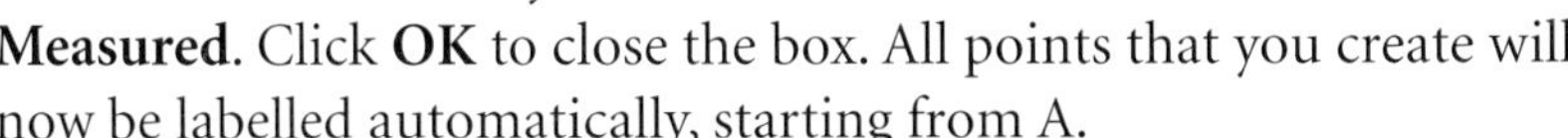

2. a) Place three points in the workspace, using the **Point Tool**. Do not place your points too close to each other.
   b) Click on the **Selector Tool**. Select all three points by clicking on each one.

**Did You Know?**

You can switch from the **Point Tool** to the **Selector Tool** by pressing the Esc key.

You can select points by dragging the **Selector Tool** to create a dashed box around the points.

c) To construct line segments to form a triangle, pull down the **Construct** menu and choose **Segments**. Then, click any blank area in the workspace to deselect the new segments.
*Ruler and protractor:* Draw a triangle, large enough to measure the angles with a protractor.

3. To measure each angle, use the **Selector Tool** to click on the points in these sequences:
   a) B, A, C; pull down **Measure** menu, **Angle**, then deselect the measure
   b) A, B, C; **Measure**, **Angle**; deselect
   c) A, C, B; **Measure**, **Angle**; deselect

   The angle inside a vertex is called an **interior angle**. The angle measures for each of the three interior angles should now be displayed in the upper left corner of your workspace.
   *Ruler and protractor:* Measure each interior angle using a protractor.

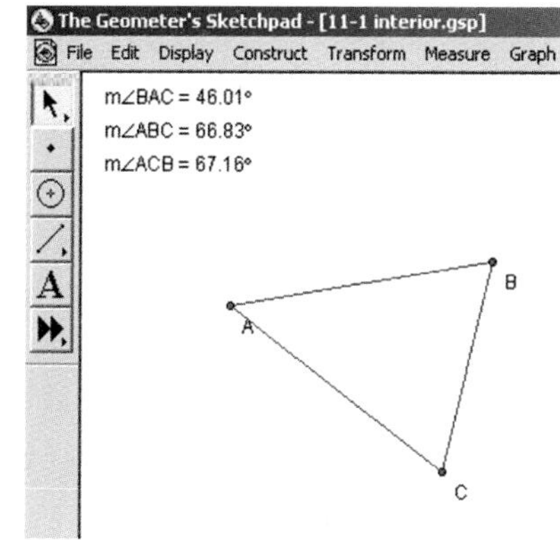


4. To find the sum of these interior angles, choose **Measure**, **Calculate**. You should see a calculator on your screen.
   Click on:
   • **m∠BAC** (in the upper left corner of the workspace)
   • + (on the calculator pad)
   • **m∠ABC**
   • +
   • **m∠ACB**
   • **OK** (on the calculator pad)

   The interior sum should now appear below the angle measures from step 3.
   *Ruler and protractor:* Find the sum of the angle measures from step 3.

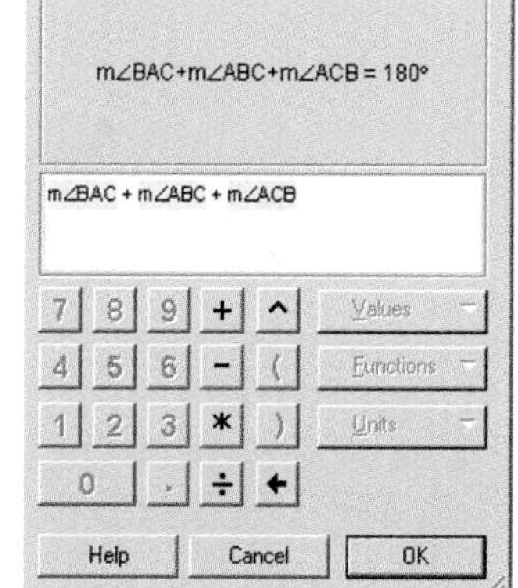


5. To change the shape of the triangle, click on any vertex, holding the left mouse button down, and drag the vertex. Notice how the angle measures change. Does the sum of the interior angles stay the same?
   *Ruler and protractor:* Draw another triangle, measure its interior angles, and find their sum. Is the sum of the interior angles the same as in step 4?

6. Write a statement about the relationship between the interior angles of a triangle. Include a diagram.

## Exterior Angles of a Triangle

7. Start a new sketch: Choose **File**, **New Sketch**.

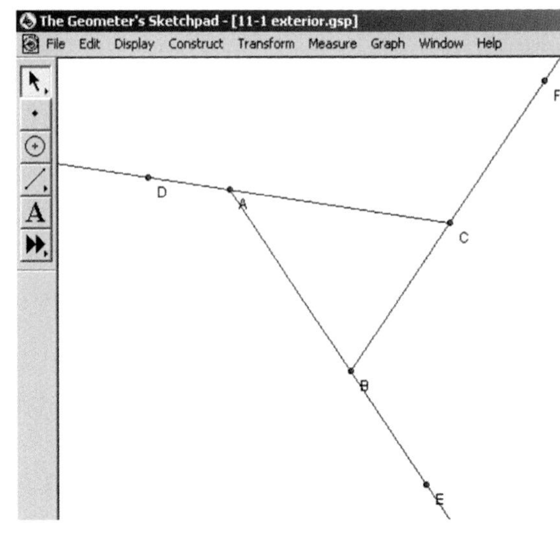


8. Construct a triangle that looks similar to the one shown:
   a) Place three points in the workspace.
   b) You need to make the sides of the triangle extend on one side of each vertex. These extensions are called **rays**. To construct rays, select all three points, choose **Construct**, **Rays**, and then deselect the rays.
   c) Choose the **Point Tool.** Add three more points, on the parts of the rays outside the triangle. Before you place each point, make sure the ray changes colour, showing that the **Point Tool** is positioned on it.

   *Ruler and protractor:* Draw a triangle ABC. Extend each side in a clockwise direction. These extensions are called **rays**. Add three more points, D, E, and F, on the exterior parts of the rays.

9. a) Make sure nothing is selected. Create measures for these angles:
      - D, A, B; **Measure**, **Angle**; deselect
      - E, B, C; **Measure**, **Angle**; deselect
      - F, C, A; **Measure**, **Angle**; deselect

      The angles you have measured are the **exterior angles** of the triangle.
   b) Use the on-screen calculator to find the sum of the three exterior angles.

   *Ruler and protractor:* Measure the angle formed by points D, A, and B, in that order. This is the **exterior angle** at A. Also measure the other two exterior angles, ∠EBC and ∠FCA. Find the sum of the three exterior angles.

Go to the Technology Appendix if you need help **Using the On-Screen Calculator**.

10. Write a statement about the relationship between the exterior angles of a triangle. Include a diagram.

11. a) Delete the angle measures and the calculation from step 9. Click on each measure or calculation in turn, and press the Del key.
    b) Create measures for ∠DAB, ∠ABC, and ∠ACB.
    c) To compare the exterior angle, ∠DAB, with the two opposite interior angles, ∠ABC and ∠ACB, use the on-screen calculator to enter this sequence: **m∠ABC**, +, **m∠ACB**, **OK**. The sum of the two interior angles should now be displayed in the workspace. What relationship do you notice?
    d) Click on and drag any vertex to change the shape of the triangle. Discuss how this affects the relationship in part c).

    *Ruler and protractor:* Measure the interior angles ∠ABC and ∠ACB, and find their sum. Compare with the exterior angle ∠DAB. What relationship do you notice?

12. Write a statement about the relationship between the exterior angle and the two interior angles opposite it. Include a diagram.

## DISCOVER 2

(optional)
- centimetre grid paper
- ruler
- protractor

Use the Technology Appendix for help with **Setting Preferences** or **Constructing Triangles and Polygons**.

## Angle Relationships in Quadrilaterals

***Using ruler and protractor, or The Geometer's Sketchpad®***

### Sum of Interior Angles of Quadrilaterals

1. Fold a sheet of centimetre grid paper into quarters. Use a ruler to draw a rectangle, a trapezoid, a rhombus, and a square. Draw one shape in each quarter of the paper.

   *The Geometer's Sketchpad®*: Place four points in a new sketch and select them, in clockwise order, to create a quadrilateral. Make sure, by dragging a vertex if necessary, that your quadrilateral does not have any reflex interior angles (greater than 180°).

2. a) Using a protractor or **Measure**, **Angle**, measure each interior angle. Record your results in a table like the one shown.

| ∠A | ∠B | ∠C | ∠D | ∠A + ∠B + ∠C + ∠D |
|---|---|---|---|---|
| | | | | |
| | | | | |

Go to the Technology Appendix if you need help **Using the On-Screen Calculator**.

b) Calculate the sum of the interior angles of each quadrilateral.
*The Geometer's Sketchpad®*: Drag vertices to change the angles and record three more sets of angle measures. Make sure your new quadrilaterals do not have any reflex interior angles.

c) What can you conclude about the sum of the interior angles of a quadrilateral?

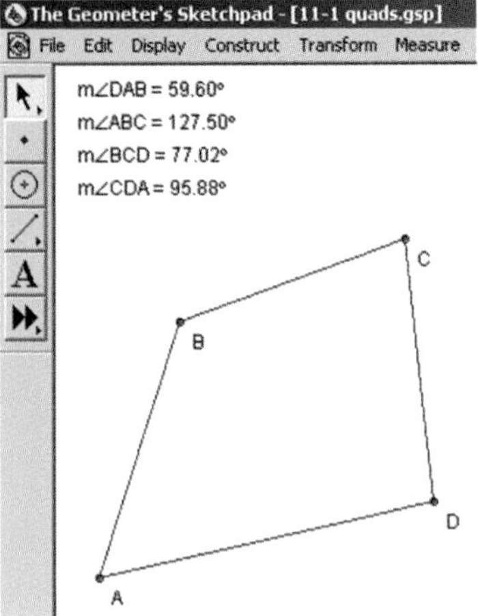


### Sum of Exterior Angles of Quadrilaterals

3. Draw clockwise extensions of each side of your first quadrilateral. Use these rays to mark the exterior angles.

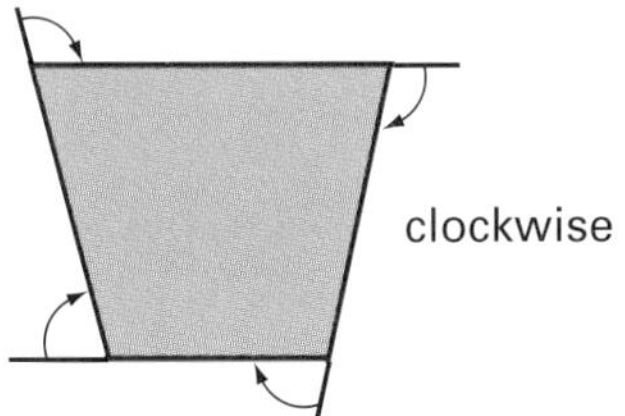


*The Geometer's Sketchpad®*: Create rays, as in **Discover 1**, step 8 (page 442). Add four extra points to the quadrilateral, one on each ray.

4. a) Measure each exterior angle of your quadrilateral. Record your results in a table similar to the one in step 2.
*The Geometer's Sketchpad®*: Use the new points on the rays to create measures for the exterior angles, as in **Discover 1**, step 9.
b) Calculate the sum of the exterior angles of your quadrilateral.

5. a) Repeat steps 3 and 4 for the other quadrilaterals you drew in step 1.
*The Geometer's Sketchpad®*: Drag vertices to change the angles and record three more sets of angle measures, making sure your new quadrilaterals do not have any reflex interior angles.
b) What can you conclude about the sum of the exterior angles of a quadrilateral?

6. Summarize all your findings about quadrilateral angle sums.

## EXAMPLE 1

### Using Angle Properties of Triangles and Quadrilaterals

Find each unknown angle measure. Give reasons.

**a)**

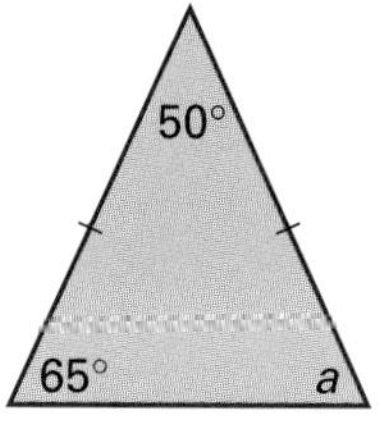


**b)**

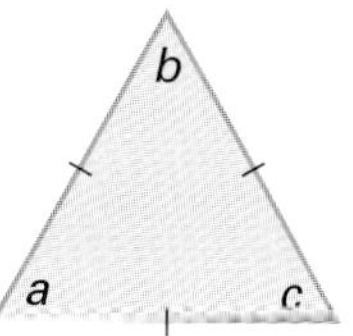


**c)**

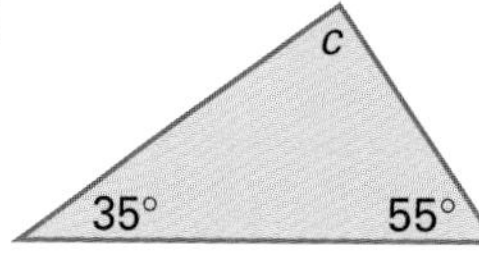


**d)**

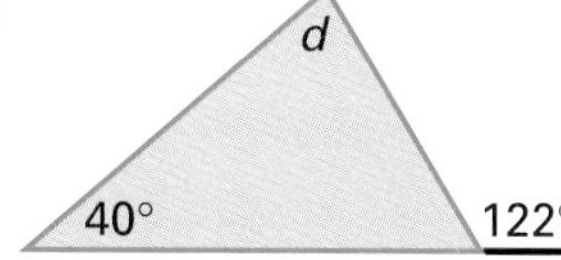


**e)**

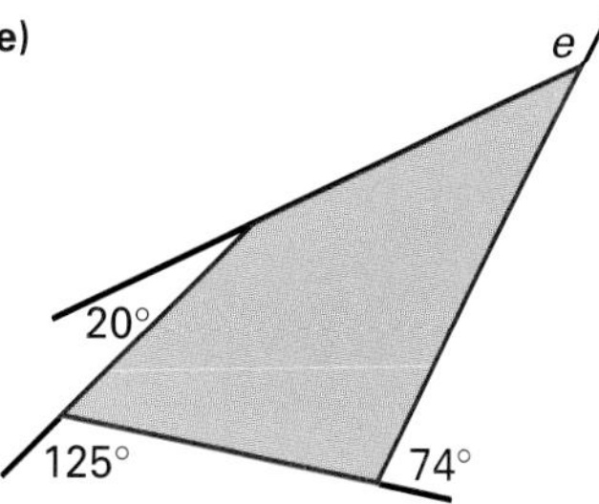


### Solution

**a)** $a = 65°$. Reason: The triangle is isosceles, so the two angles opposite the equal sides are the same.

**b)** $a = b = c = 60°$. Reason: The triangle is equilateral.

**c)**
$$
\begin{aligned}
35° + 55° + c &= 180° \\
90° + c &= 180° \\
c &= 90°
\end{aligned}
$$
Reason: The sum of the interior angles of a triangle is 180°.

**d)**
$$
\begin{aligned}
40° + d &= 122° \\
d &= 82°
\end{aligned}
$$
Reason: An exterior angle of a triangle is equal to the sum of the two opposite interior angles.

**e)**
$$
\begin{aligned}
20° + 125° + 74° + e &= 360° \\
209° + e &= 360° \\
e &= 141°
\end{aligned}
$$
Reason: The sum of the exterior angles of a quadrilateral is 360°.

## EXAMPLE 2

**Chapter Problem**

### Applying Triangle Properties

The bascule bridge near St. Catharines has triangular support structures. The angle measures for one triangle are shown in the diagram. Where the bridge meets the counterweight, a right angle is formed. Determine the measures of the angles *a*, *b*, and *c*.

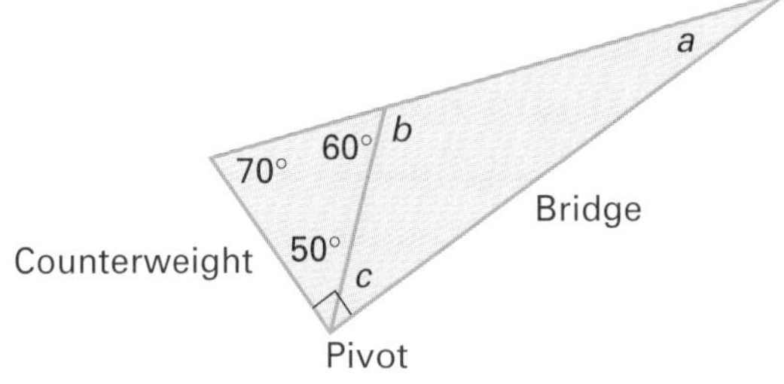


### Solution

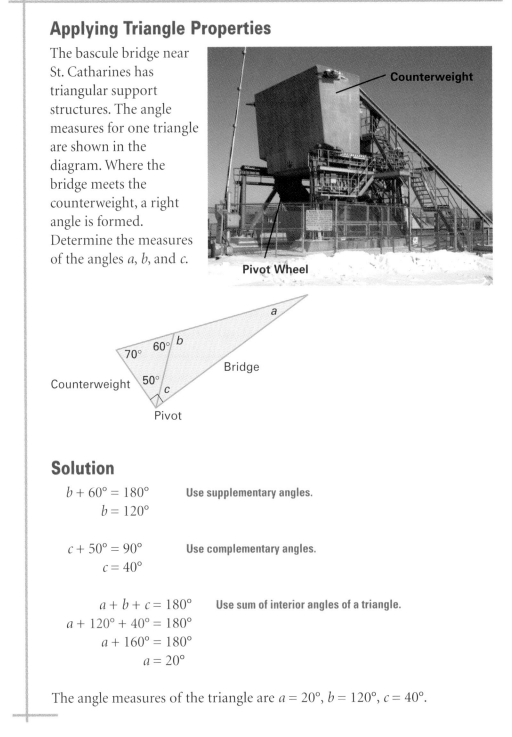

$b + 60° = 180°$ **Use supplementary angles.**

$b = 120°$

$c + 50° = 90°$ **Use complementary angles.**

$c = 40°$

$a + b + c = 180°$ **Use sum of interior angles of a triangle.**

$a + 120° + 40° = 180°$

$a + 160° = 180°$

$a = 20°$

The angle measures of the triangle are $a = 20°$, $b = 120°$, $c = 40°$.

## Key Concepts

**Angle properties of triangles**

- The sum of the interior angles of a triangle is 180°.
- An exterior angle of a triangle is equal to the sum of the two opposite interior angles.

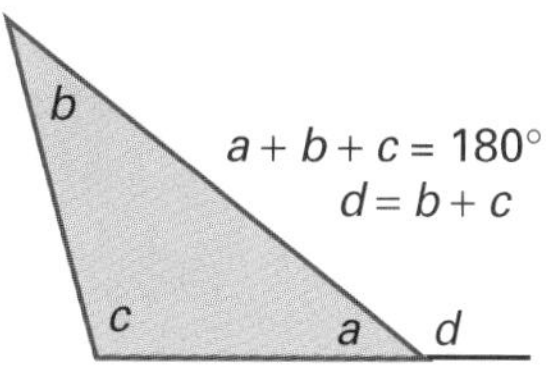


- The sum of the exterior angles of a triangle is 360°.

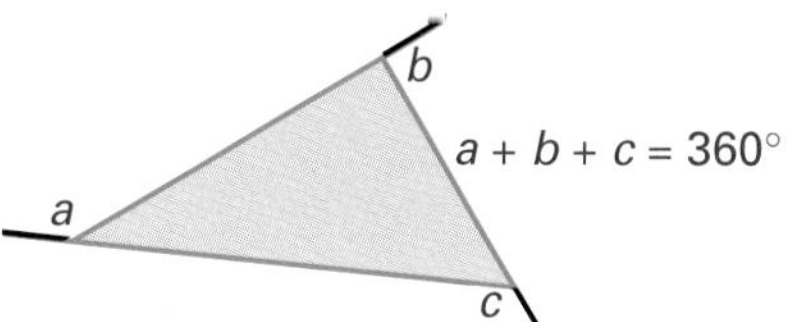


**Angle properties of quadrilaterals**

- The sum of the interior angles of a quadrilateral is 360°.

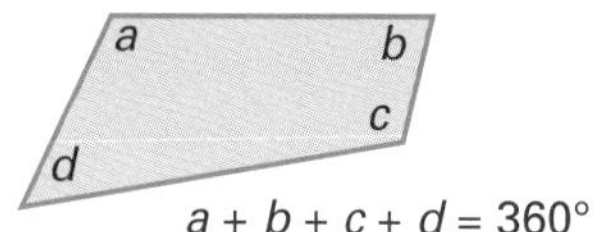


- The sum of the exterior angles of a quadrilateral is 360°.

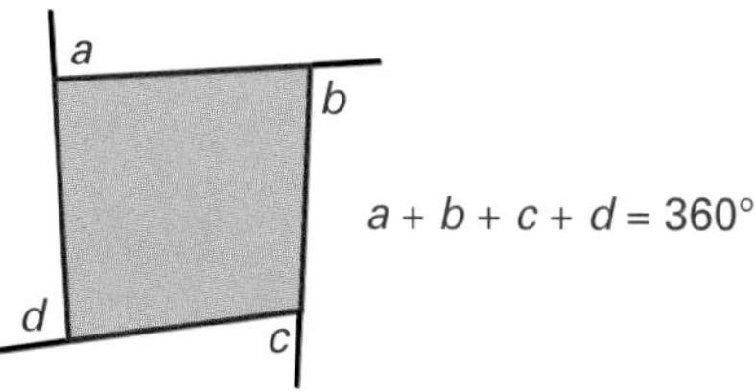


## Discuss the Concepts

1. Sometimes the order in which you solve unknown angles is important. Discuss which angle you would find first in the triangle shown.

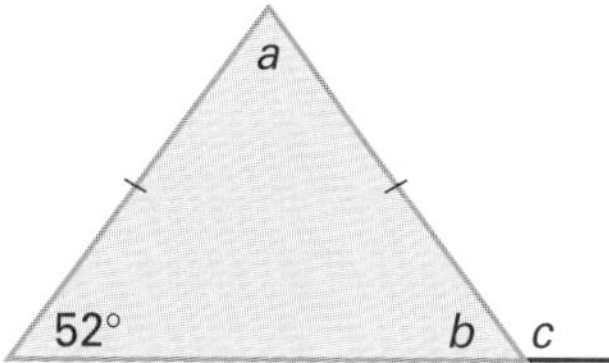


2. If you completed the **Discovers** in this section by hand, you measured angles using a protractor. Discuss why this method may not always produce accurate answers.
3. If you completed the **Discovers** in this section using *The Geometer's Sketchpad*®: Suppose you try to construct a line segment, but you pull down the **Construct** menu and the **Segment** option is not available ("greyed out"). What can you do to fix this problem?

## PRACTISE

*For help with questions 1 to 6, refer to Examples 1 and 2.*

1. In each triangle, calculate the measure of each unknown angle.

a) 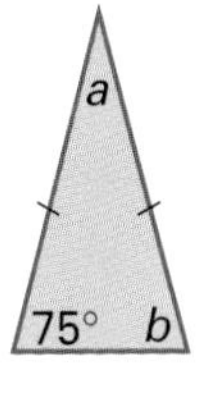


b) 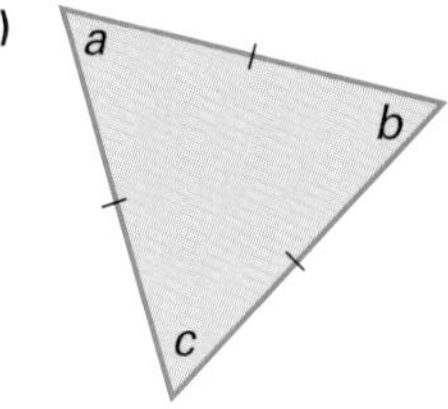


c) 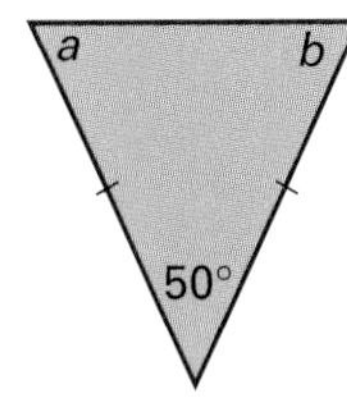


d) 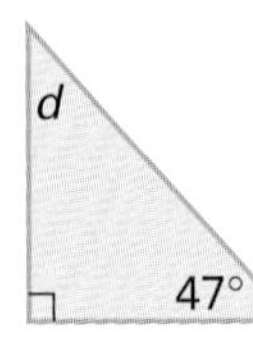


e) 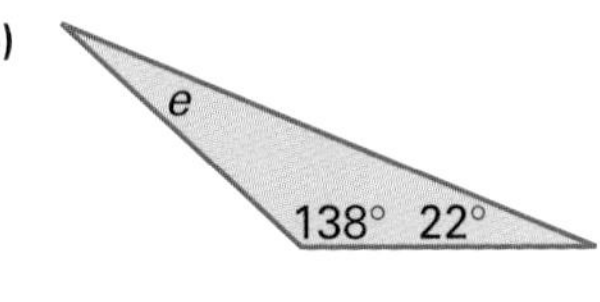


f) 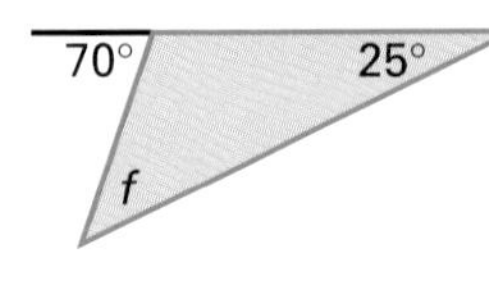

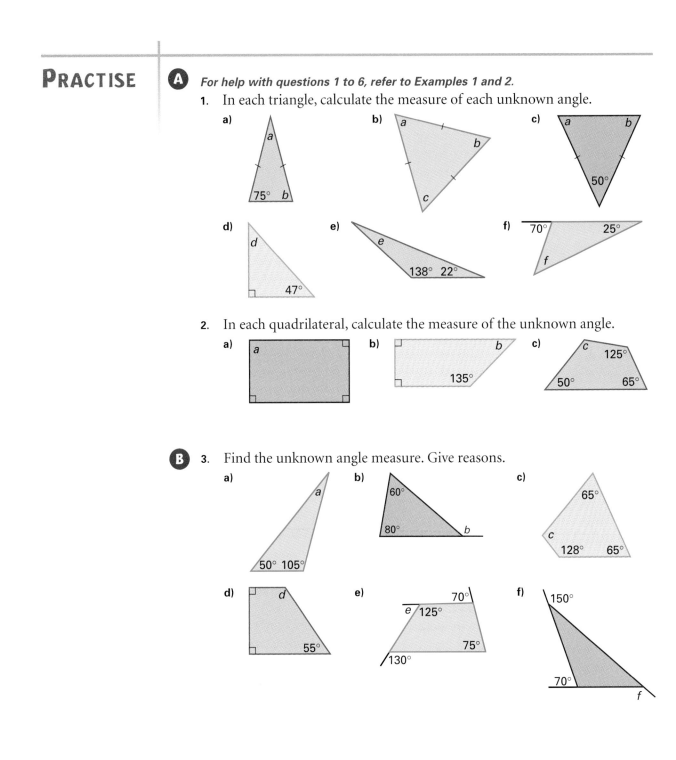

2. In each quadrilateral, calculate the measure of the unknown angle.

a) 

b) 

c) 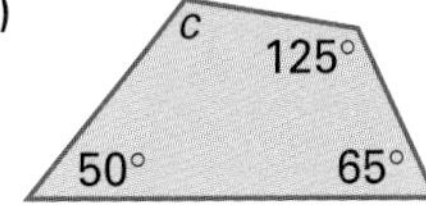


**B**

3. Find the unknown angle measure. Give reasons.

a) 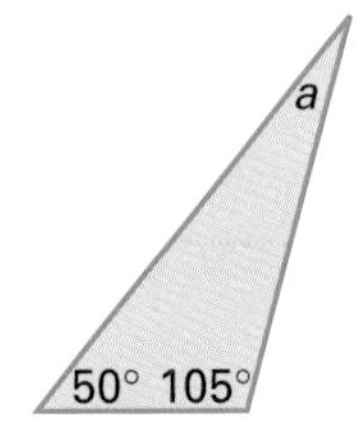


b) 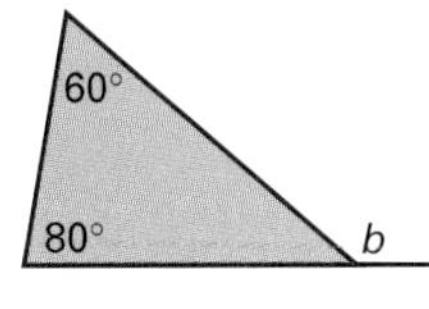


c) 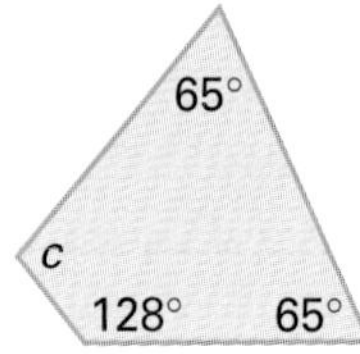


d) 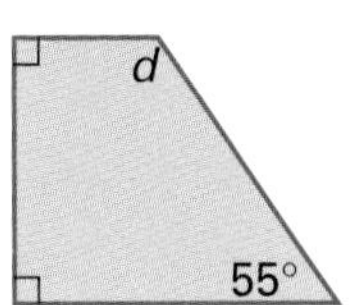


e) 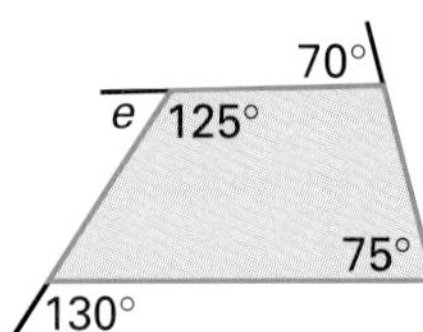


f) 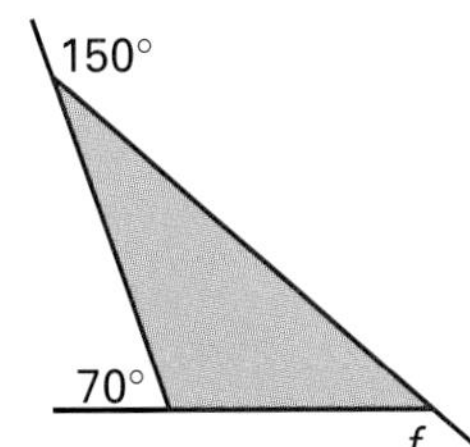

## Apply the Concepts

4. **Communication** A student was asked to draw the exterior angles for a triangle. The student drew the diagram shown.
   a) Explain what is wrong with the student's diagram.
   b) Redraw the diagram with the correct exterior angles.

**Did You Know?**

The Canadian Snowbirds fly at up to 600 km/h, and are only 1.2 m apart in some formations!

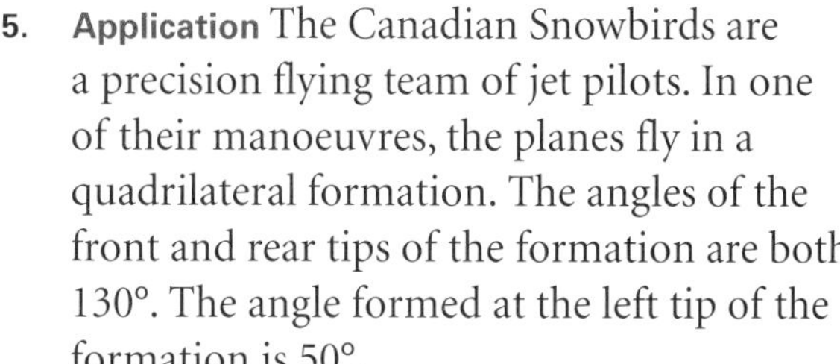

5. **Application** The Canadian Snowbirds are a precision flying team of jet pilots. In one of their manoeuvres, the planes fly in a quadrilateral formation. The angles of the front and rear tips of the formation are both 130°. The angle formed at the left tip of the formation is 50°.
   a) Make a sketch of this quadrilateral.
   b) Calculate the angle formed at the right tip.

**Chapter Problem**

6. This bridge links the cities of Ottawa, Ontario and Hull, Québec.

   a) The quadrilateral highlighted contains two 90° angles and a 100° angle. Calculate the measure of the fourth angle. Give reasons.
   b) The triangle formed at the end of the bridge is a right triangle. The angle at the base is 55°. Calculate the measure of the other angle. Give reasons.
   c) Suggest reasons why these shapes are used in the bridge.

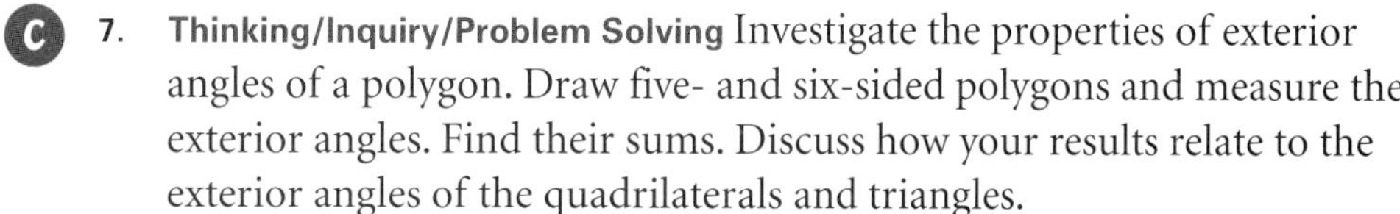

**C** 7. **Thinking/Inquiry/Problem Solving** Investigate the properties of exterior angles of a polygon. Draw five- and six-sided polygons and measure the exterior angles. Find their sums. Discuss how your results relate to the exterior angles of the quadrilaterals and triangles.

# 11.2 Investigating Angles and Parallel Lines

The sides of the Welland Canal are parallel. Just beside the canal, secure posts or bollards allow ships to tie up against the side. One ship is tied up at bollard A, forming a 65° angle with the side of the canal and the bollard on the opposite side. You can use the properties of parallel lines to determine the angle at the bollard on the other side of the canal.

In this section, you will explore the properties of angles related to parallel lines.

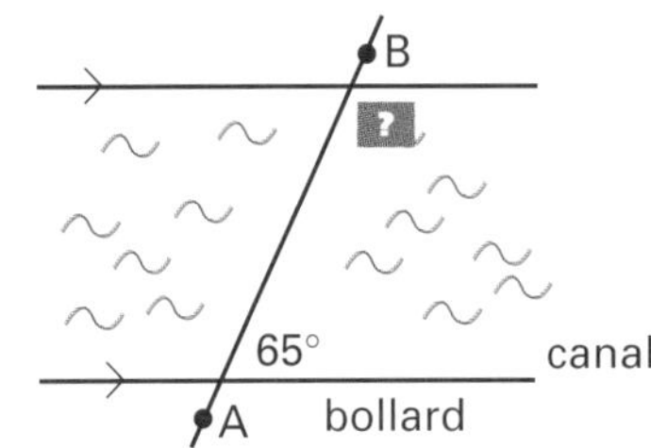


## DISCOVER 1A

### Parallel Lines

***Using The Geometer's Sketchpad®***

1. Create a new sketch. Use **Edit**, **Preferences…** to check that automatic labelling is turned on.

For help with **Setting Preferences**, refer to the Technology Appendix.

2. Using the **Point Tool**, add two points, A and B, to your workspace. Create a line through these points:
   • Select both points.
   • Choose **Construct**, **Line.**
   • Deselect by clicking in a blank part of the workspace.

3. Add another point, C, above the line. To cancel the point tool, click on the **Selector Tool**, or press the Esc key.

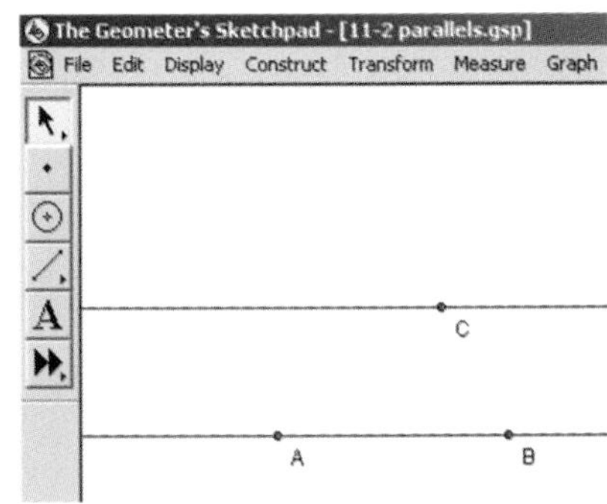


4. Create a line parallel to your first line:
   • Select point C and the first line (click on each of these objects).
   • Choose **Construct**, **Parallel Line.**

5. A **transversal** is a line that cuts through (intersects) a pair of parallel lines. Add a transversal through points A and C:
   • Select points A and C.
   • Choose **Construct**, **Line**.

6. a) To help with identifying angles, add the points exactly as shown in the diagram. Be careful that these points lie exactly on the lines.

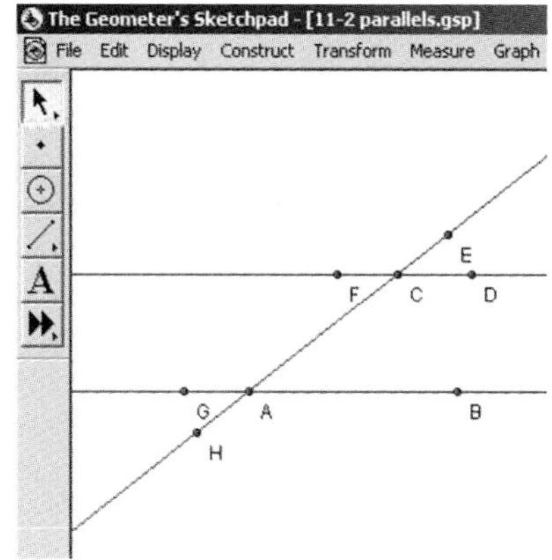


   b) You can change the label name, if it does not correspond to the label in the diagram, by placing the **Selector Tool** over the label. The pointer will change to a hand pointer. Double-click to open the label window. Change the name and click **OK**. Then, deselect the point.

7. a) Measure these pairs of angles, using **Measure**, **Angle**:
   • ∠DCA and ∠CAG
   • ∠FCA and ∠CAB

   **For each angle, make sure nothing is selected, then select the three points in order.**

   These pairs of angles are called **alternate angles**. In each pair, the angles are positioned on either (alternate) side of the transversal, between the parallel lines.
   b) Drag point A, B, or C around, and look for any relationship in each pair of angles.
   c) Describe the relationship between a pair of alternate angles.

8. a) Delete the angle measures from step 7. Measure these pairs of angles:
   • ∠ECD and ∠CAB
   • ∠ECF and ∠CAG
   • ∠FCA and ∠GAH
   • ∠DCA and ∠BAH

   These pairs of angles are called **corresponding angles** because they are in corresponding positions: either above a parallel line or below it, and either right of the transversal or left of it.
   b) Drag point A, B, or C around, and look for any relationships.
   c) Describe the relationship between a pair of corresponding angles.

9. a) Delete the angle measures from step 8. Measure these pairs of angles:
   - ∠DCA and ∠BAC
   - ∠FCA and ∠GAC

   These pairs of angles are called **co-interior angles** because both angles are in the same interior region formed by the parallel lines and the transversal.

   b) Choose **Measure**, **Calculate**, and use the on-screen calculator to find the sum of each pair of angles in part a). Drag point A, B, or C around. Do the sums of the angle pairs change?

   c) Describe the relationship between a pair of co-interior angles.

Go to the Technology Appendix if you need help **Using the On-Screen Calculator**.

10. a) Find and measure a pair of opposite angles in your sketch.

    b) Explain the relationship between a pair of opposite angles.

## DISCOVER 1B

**Materials**

- ruler
- protractor

## Parallel Lines

***Using ruler and protractor***

1. Keeping your ruler still, draw a line on either side of the ruler, about 6 cm long. These will be your parallel lines. To indicate the lines are parallel, place a single arrow mark (>) on each line.

2. A **transversal** is a line that cuts through (intersects) a pair of parallel lines. Draw a transversal across your parallel lines. Use any angle as long as both parallel lines are intersected.

3. Add labels to the eight angles formed by your diagram, using *the same order of letters* as in the diagram shown.

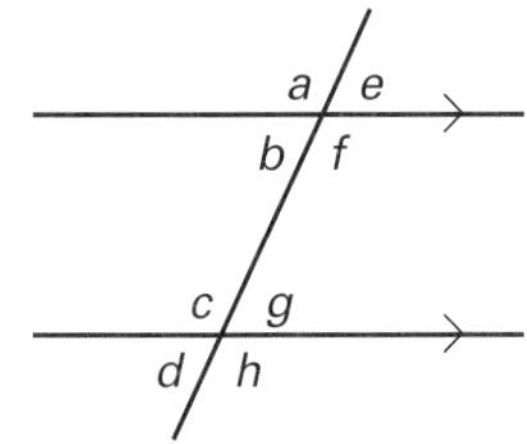


4. a) Using a protractor, measure these pairs of angles: *b* and *g*, *c* and *f*. Record the measures.

   b) Compare your results with those of a classmate.

   c) These pairs of angles are called **alternate angles**. In each pair, the angles are positioned on either (alternate) side of the transversal, between the parallel lines. Describe the relationship between a pair of alternate angles.

5. a) Using a protractor, measure these pairs of angles: $a$ and $c$, $b$ and $d$, $e$ and $g$, $f$ and $h$. Record the measures.
   b) Compare your results with those of a classmate.
   c) These pairs of angles are called **corresponding angles** because they are in corresponding positions: either above a parallel line or below it, and either right of the transversal or left of it. Describe the relationship between a pair of corresponding angles.

6. a) Calculate the sum of these pairs of angles: $b$ and $c$, $f$ and $g$.
   b) Compare your results with those of a classmate.
   c) These pairs of angles are called **co-interior angles** because both angles are in the same interior region formed by the parallel lines and the transversal. Describe the relationship between a pair of co-interior angles.

7. a) Find and measure a pair of opposite angles in your sketch.
   b) Describe the relationship between a pair of opposite angles.

## EXAMPLE 1

### Calculating Angles With Parallel Lines

Find the indicated angle measures.
Give reasons for your answers.

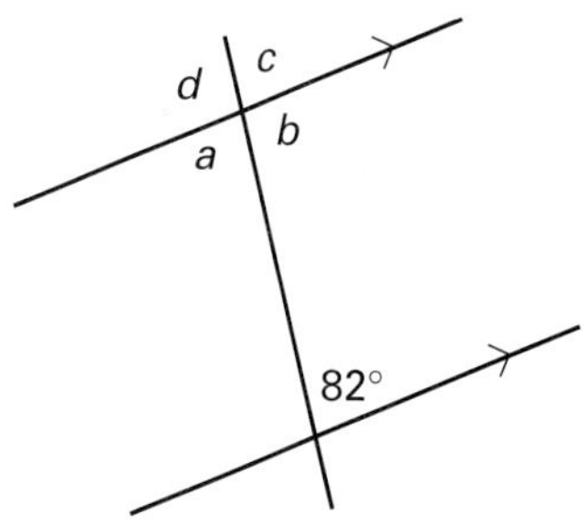


### Solution

$a = 82°$. Reason: alternate angles

$82° + b = 180°$

$b = 98°$

Reason: co-interior angles

$c = 82°$. Reason: corresponding angles

$d = 98°$. Reason: opposite angle to $b$

## EXAMPLE 2

### Applying Angle Properties of Parallel Lines

Find the indicated angle measures in each shape. Give reasons for your answers.

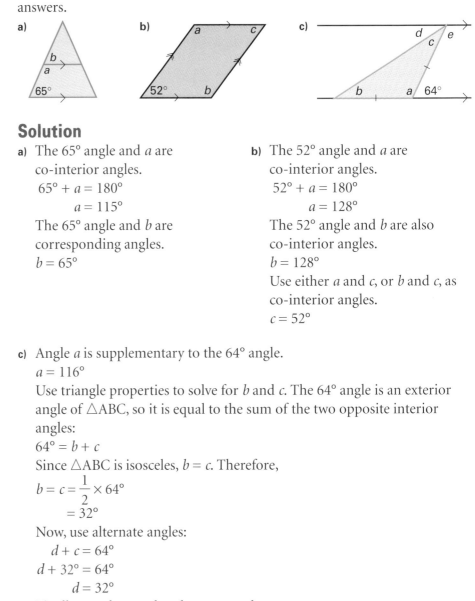

a) 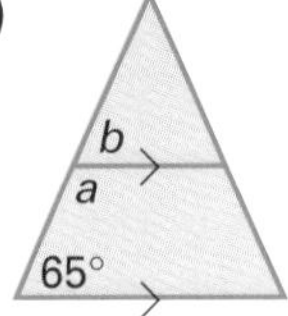


b) 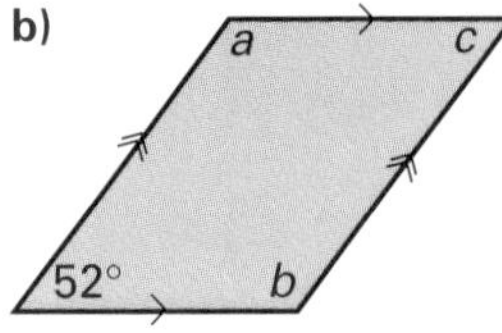


c) 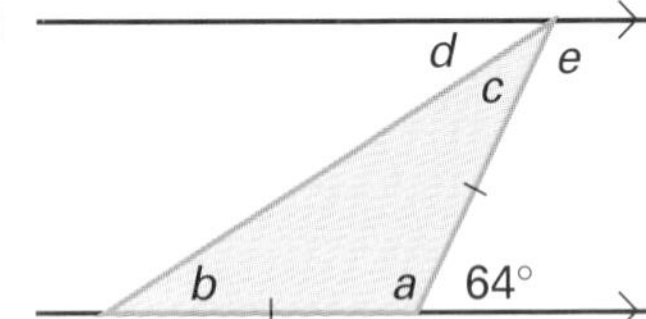


### Solution

a) The 65° angle and $a$ are co-interior angles.

$65° + a = 180°$
$a = 115°$

The 65° angle and $b$ are corresponding angles.

$b = 65°$

b) The 52° angle and $a$ are co-interior angles.

$52° + a = 180°$
$a = 128°$

The 52° angle and $b$ are also co-interior angles.

$b = 128°$

Use either $a$ and $c$, or $b$ and $c$, as co-interior angles.

$c = 52°$

c) Angle $a$ is supplementary to the 64° angle.

$a = 116°$

Use triangle properties to solve for $b$ and $c$. The 64° angle is an exterior angle of △ABC, so it is equal to the sum of the two opposite interior angles:

$64° = b + c$

Since △ABC is isosceles, $b = c$. Therefore,

$$b = c = \frac{1}{2} \times 64°$$
$$= 32°$$

Now, use alternate angles:

$d + c = 64°$
$d + 32° = 64°$
$d = 32°$

Finally, $e$ and $a$ are also alternate angles, so

$e = 116°$

**Check: $c + d + e = 180°$**

## Key Concepts

- Parallel lines are identified by single or double arrow markers pointing in the same direction. Parallel lines do not intersect.
- Pairs of alternate angles are positioned on either side of the transversal, between the parallel lines. Alternate angles are equal. In the diagram, $b$ and $g$ are alternate angles, and so are $c$ and $f$.

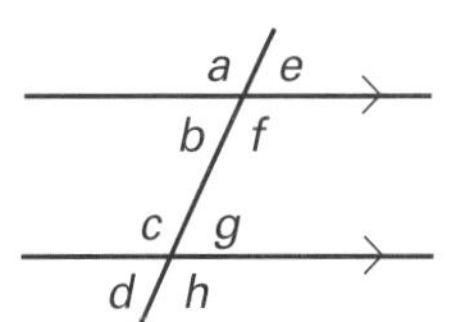


- Pairs of corresponding angles are located in corresponding positions, relative to the transversal and each parallel line. Corresponding angles are equal. In the diagram, corresponding angle pairs are:
  $a$ and $c$ $b$ and $d$ $e$ and $g$ $f$ and $h$
- Pairs of co-interior angles are in the same interior region formed by the parallel lines and the transversal. Co-interior angles add to 180°. In the diagram, $b + c = 180°$, and $f + g = 180°$.

## Discuss the Concepts

1. Describe some real situations where a transversal crosses parallel lines.
2. If two lines appear to be parallel but are not marked with parallel arrows, discuss whether you can apply any of the properties that you investigated in this section.

## Math Tip

### Letter Names for Angle Pairs

You can use letter names to think about alternate, corresponding, co-interior, and opposite angle pairs.

Z-angles are alternate angles.

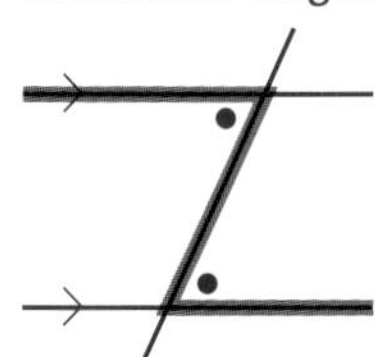

F-angles are corresponding angles.

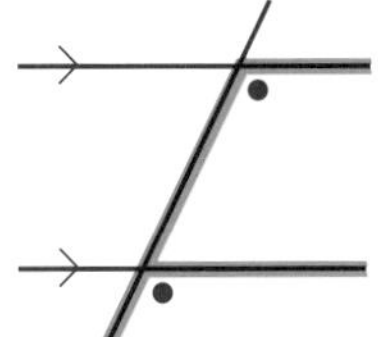

C-angles are co-interior angles.

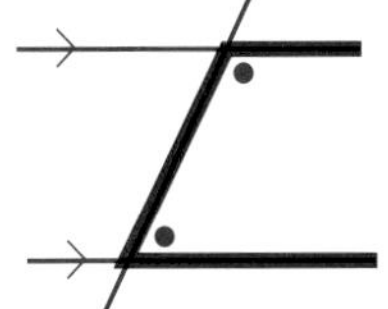

X-angles are opposite angles

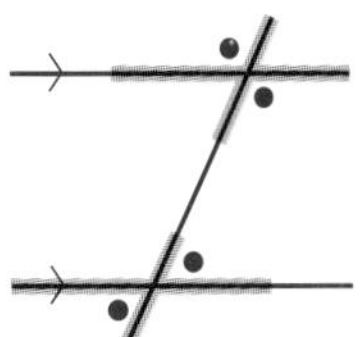

## PRACTISE

1. Refer to the diagram to answer these questions.
   a) Identify two pairs of corresponding angles.
   b) Describe the relationship between angles $p$ and $s$.
   c) List four pairs of opposite angles.
   d) How many pairs of alternate angles do two parallel lines and one transversal have?

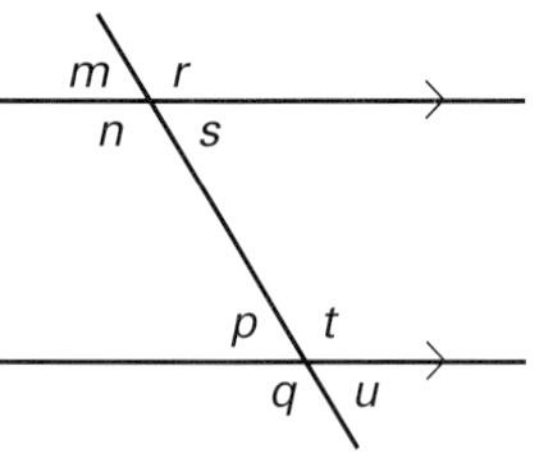


***For help with question 2, refer to Example 1.***

2. Determine the measures of the unknown angles. Give reasons.

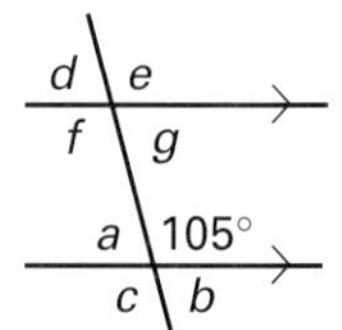

***For help with question 3, refer to Example 2.***

3. Find the measures of the unknown angles. Give reasons.

a)

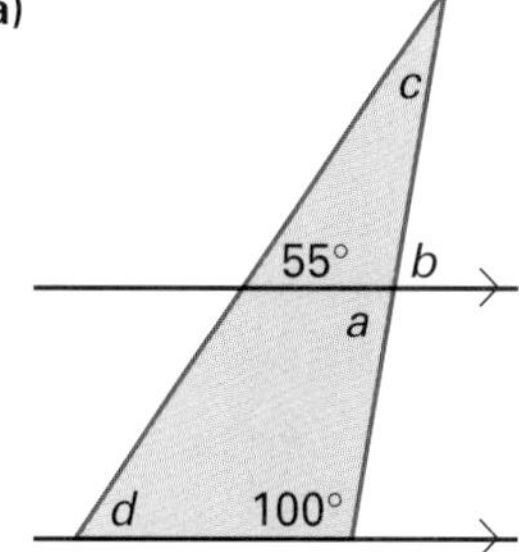


b)

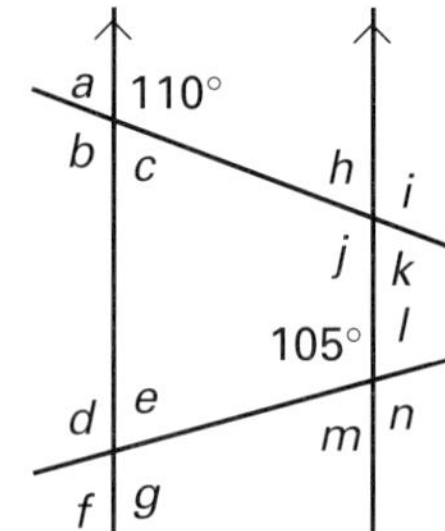


c)

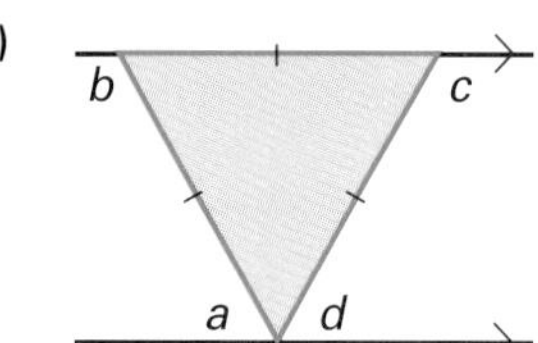


d)

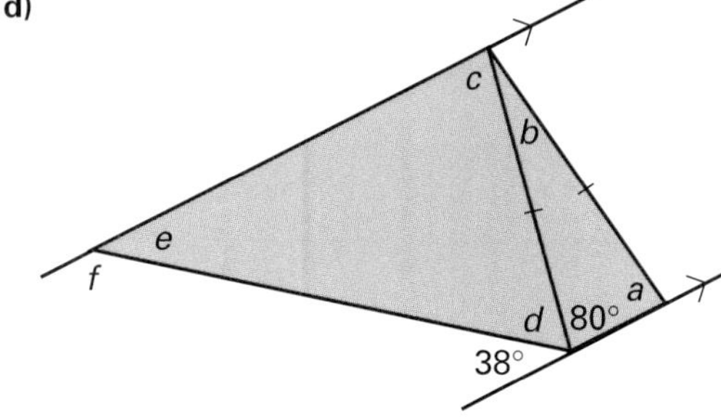


## APPLY THE CONCEPTS

4. a) **Communication** Draw a pair of parallel lines with a transversal. Label a pair of alternate angles on your diagram.
   b) Using different colours, label a pair of corresponding angles and a pair of co-interior angles on your diagram.

5. **Communication** Make a sketch of two parallel lines and one transversal. Insert an estimated value for any one angle measure. Explain how to estimate the measures of all other angles in your sketch.

**Chapter Problem**

6. Along the Welland Canal, bollards A and B form an angle of 65°, as shown. Determine the angle marked ?. Explain your reasoning.

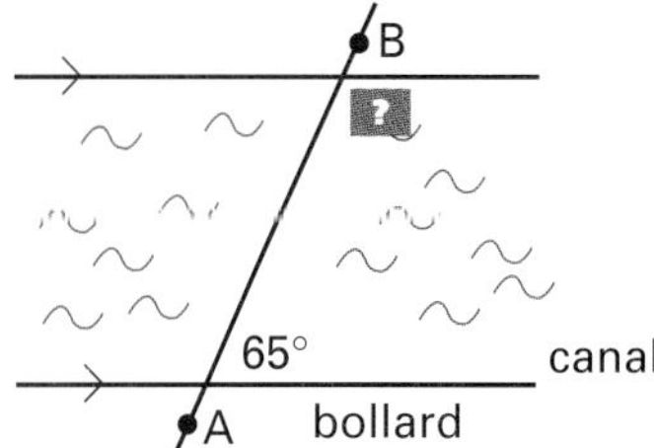


**Did You Know?**

Ocean-going ships use standard navigational bearings. Due North is 000, due East is 090, and due West is 270. Navigation officers must know how to work with bearings quickly and accurately, to minimize any risk of collision.

7. **Airport runways** The Hamilton airport has two parallel runways that are crossed by a third runway. Determine the measures of ∠A and ∠B. Explain your reasoning.

**C**

8. A parallelogram is formed by two sets of intersecting parallel lines.

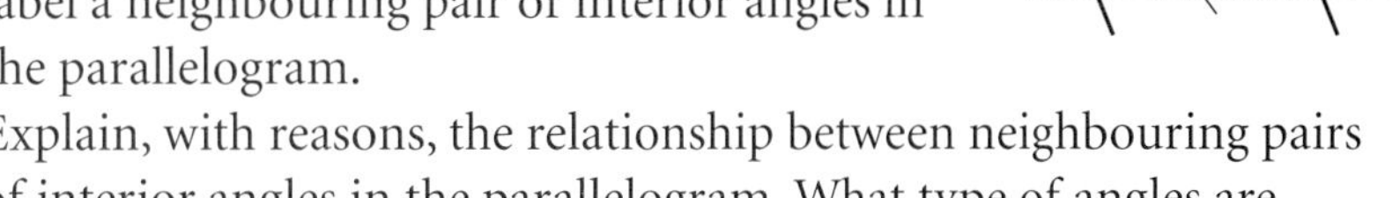

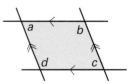

   a) Copy the diagram carefully. On your diagram, label a neighbouring pair of interior angles in the parallelogram.
   b) Explain, with reasons, the relationship between neighbouring pairs of interior angles in the parallelogram. What type of angles are these, in terms of parallel lines?
   c) Explain, with reasons, the relationship between opposite interior angles in the parallelogram. On your diagram, label any angles you need for your explanation.

# 11.3 Investigating Angle Bisectors, Medians, and Altitudes of Triangles

On landing approach, an airplane's flight path should **bisect** (divide exactly in half) the 4° angle shown (distorted by perspective) in the photograph. In this section, you will

- investigate some new constructions for triangles
- discover some properties related to these constructions

## Discover 1A

### Materials

- card
- ruler
- scissors
- pin
- clamp
- string
- washer

### Medians of a Triangle

***Using card, string, and mass***

1. Using a ruler, draw a large triangle on a piece of card, and cut it out carefully. Write vertex labels A, B, and C on your triangle.

2. a) Use a pin to poke a hole through one corner of the triangle, as close to vertex A as possible without tearing the edges of the triangle.
   b) Clamp the pin with the triangle mounted on it at vertex A.
   c) Fasten the washer to the string, and tie the other end of the string to the pin. Let the string hang straight down.
   d) On side BC of your triangle, mark the place where the string crosses the edge of the triangle. Label this mark M1. Remove your triangle from the clamp.

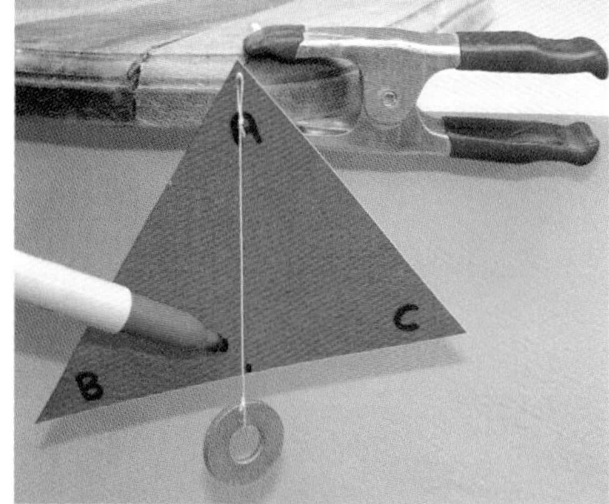


3. Repeat step 2 for vertices B and C, labelling the crossing points on the triangle as M2 and M3.

4. a) Measure the distances from B to M1 and from M1 to C. Record these lengths. How close is M1 to being the exact midpoint of side BC?
   b) Draw a line from vertex A down to M1. This is a median of $\triangle$ABC. A **median** of a triangle is the line extending from one vertex to the midpoint of the opposite side.

5. a) Draw medians from vertices B and C to the other midpoints, M2 and M3. The medians should meet at a single point. This is called the **centroid**. Label the centroid as point G.
   b) If your medians did not meet exactly, suggest a reason why. Mark the centroid, G, as close as you can to all three medians.

6. a) Measure the lengths AG and GM1. Make a hypothesis about the relationship between these lengths. Hint: Try division.
   b) Test your hypothesis by comparing the lengths of BG and GM2, and of CG and GM3.
   c) Describe the relationship between
      - the distance from a vertex to the centroid of a triangle, and
      - the distance from the centroid to the midpoint of the opposite side

      Draw a diagram to illustrate your response.

7. a) Measure and record the height of the triangle, from side BC to vertex A. Make sure your ruler crosses side BC at a right angle. Use this height measurement and the length of BM1 from step 4a) to calculate the area of $\triangle$ABM1.

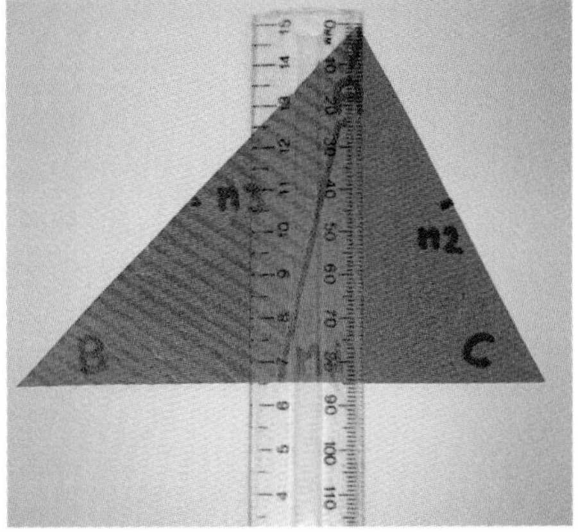


   b) Use your height measurement from step 7a) and the length M1C from step 4a) to calculate the area of $\triangle$AM1C. Compare this area to the area you calculated in step 7a). What do you notice?

8. Summarize the properties of triangle medians and centroids that you have discovered.

9. Pin the triangle to the clamp again, exactly through the centroid at point G. Rotate the triangle around the pin. What do you notice?

# DISCOVER 1B

## Medians of a Triangle

*Using The Geometer's Sketchpad®*

1. a) Open a new sketch. Construct a triangle, ABC.
   b) Mark the midpoint of one side of the triangle:
      - Select side BC only.
      - Choose **Construct**, **Midpoint.**
      - Change the label of the midpoint: double-click on the label, and type M1.

Use the Technology Appendix for help with **Setting Preferences** or **Constructing Triangles and Polygons**.

2. a) Construct a line segment from vertex A to midpoint M1. This is a median of △ABC. A **median** of a triangle is the line extending from one vertex to the midpoint of the opposite side.
   b) Repeat step 1 to mark the midpoints on the other sides of the triangle. Change the labels of these midpoints to M2 and M3.
   c) Construct a median to each new midpoint.

3. The medians all intersect at one point. This is called the **centroid.** Add a point, G, at this point of intersection.

4. a) Measure the distance from vertex A to the centroid G:
      - Select points A and G.
      - Choose **Measure**, **Distance.**
      - Deselect.
   b) Measure the distance from G to the midpoint M1.
   c) Investigate the relationship between the vertex-to-centroid and centroid-to-midpoint distances. (Hint: Use the calculator to divide these two numbers.) Check the relationship by dragging one of the vertices A, B, or C.

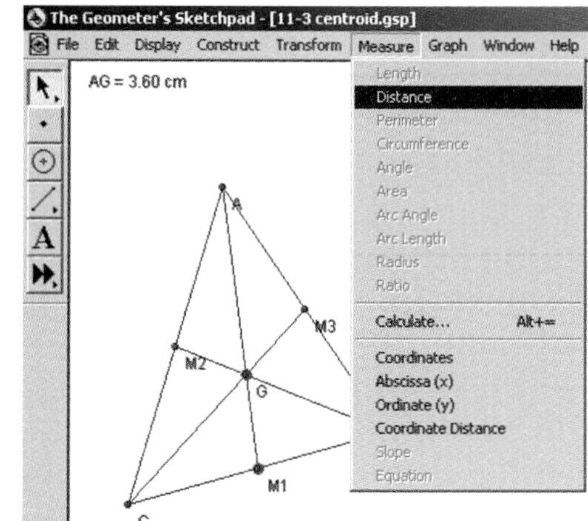


Go to the Technology Appendix if you need help **Using the On-Screen Calculator**.

5. a) Repeat step 4 for the other two medians. Does the relationship appear to hold true for any median of any triangle?
   b) Describe the relationship between
      - the distance from a vertex to the centroid of a triangle, and
      - the distance from the centroid to the midpoint of the opposite side

6. a) Measure the area of one part of $\triangle ABC$:
   - Select points A, B, and M1.
   - Choose **Construct**, **Triangle Interior.**

   The triangle ABM1 will change colour. You can tell that it is selected because it is patterned with a grid.
   - Choose **Measure**, **Area.**
   - Deselect the area measure.

   b) Repeat part a) to calculate the area of the other part of $\triangle ABC$, selecting points A, C, and M1.

   c) Describe the relationship between a median of a triangle and its area.

   d) Move any vertex and notice how the areas of the half-triangles change. Does your relationship hold true for any triangle?

# DISCOVER 2

(optional)
- paper
- pencil
- ruler

## Altitudes of a Triangle

***Using The Geometer's Sketchpad®, or ruler and paper***

1. Open a new sketch, and construct a triangle. Drag vertices, if necessary, to make sure your triangle is acute (all angles are less than 90°).
   *Ruler and paper:* Draw a triangle on a sheet of paper. Make sure your triangle is acute (all angles are less than 90°). Label the vertices A, B, and C.

2. An **altitude** of a triangle is the line drawn from a vertex to the opposite side, forming a right angle with the opposite side. An altitude is the height of a triangle. To construct an altitude:
   - Select a vertex and the opposite side of the triangle.
   - Choose **Construct**, **Perpendicular Line**.
   - Deselect.

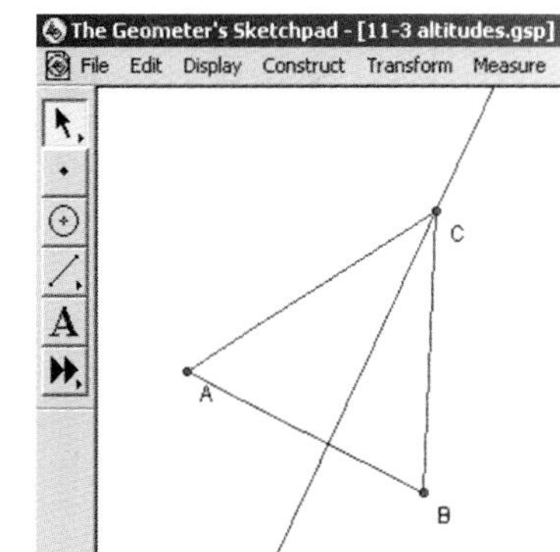


   *Ruler and paper:*
   - Fold the paper carefully through point C, so that the two parts of side AB line up on top of each other.
   - Draw over the triangle again if you cannot see both parts of AB clearly through the paper.
   - Unfold the paper, and draw over the crease from vertex C to side AB.

For reminders of the meanings of the terms in this section, refer to the **Glossary** at the back of this book.

3. a) Repeat step 2 to construct altitudes for the other two sides.
   b) The point where the altitudes meet is called the **orthocentre**. Add a point where the altitudes intersect. Change the label of the point to O.

4. a) Choose **Edit**, **Preferences...**, and in the **Units** box, change the angle precision to "**Units.**" Then, click **OK**.
   b) Create an angle measure for ∠ACB.
   c) Click and slowly drag a vertex to change your triangle into a right triangle. ∠ACB should be equal to 90°.

   *Ruler and paper:* Draw a right triangle. Label the triangle so the right angle is at vertex C. Construct the altitude through vertex C. Try to construct the altitudes through the other vertices. What do you notice?

5. How has the position of the orthocentre changed?

6. Click and slowly drag a vertex to change the triangle into an obtuse triangle. ∠ACB should be greater than 90°.

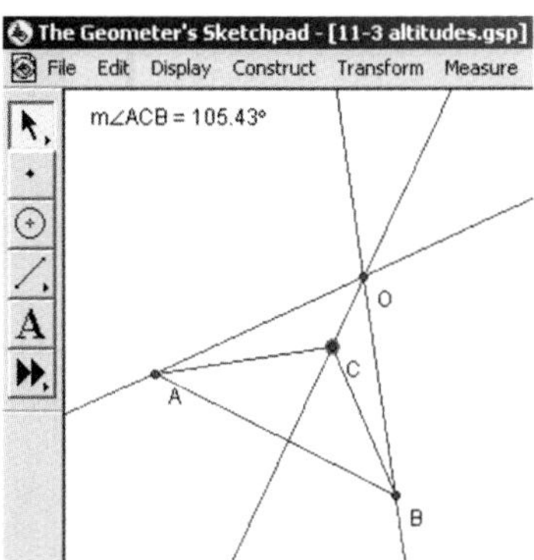


   *Ruler and paper:* Draw an obtuse triangle. Label the triangle so the obtuse angle is at vertex C. Construct the altitude through vertex C. Extend both sides through vertex C. Construct the altitudes through the other vertices. What do you notice?

7. Compare the position of the orthocentre in an obtuse triangle with its positions in acute and right triangles.

8. Describe how the orthocentre's position depends on the type of triangle. Draw diagrams to illustrate your response.

## DISCOVER 3

(optional)
- ruler
- paper
- compasses

The Technology Appendix has help sections on **Constructing Parallel and Perpendicular Lines** and **Constructing a Circle**.

## Angle Bisectors of a Triangle

***Using The Geometer's Sketchpad®, or ruler and compasses***

1. Open a new sketch, and construct a triangle.
   *Ruler and compasses:* Draw a triangle. Label the vertices A, B, and C.

2. An **angle bisector** is a line drawn from a vertex through the middle of the angle. To construct an angle bisector:
   - Select ∠ABC.
   - Choose **Construct**, **Angle Bisector.**
   - Deselect.

   *Ruler and compasses:* Fold your paper until the two sides meeting at vertex A are exactly on top of each other. Make a crease. Unfold, and mark the angle bisector with your pencil.

3. Construct an angle bisector for the other two angles.

4. Mark the point where the angle bisectors intersect. This point is called the **incentre**. Relabel the incentre as point I.

5. a) Select point I and segment AB. Construct a perpendicular line through I. Where this line meets segment AB, add a point, E.
   b) Choose the **Compass Tool**. Place the centre of a circle at point I. Drag the edge-point of the circle until it meets E, and click to complete the circle.
   c) To hide the perpendicular line through I and E:
      - Switch to the **Selector Tool** and deselect all objects.
      - Select the perpendicular line.
      - Choose **Display, Hide Perpendicular Line**.

   d) Click and slowly drag a vertex of your triangle around.

   *Ruler and compasses:* Centre your compasses on the incentre of your triangle. Draw the largest circle you can, that lies just inside the triangle.

6. a) What do you notice about the circle? Compare your observations with your classmates' observations.
   b) The circle you have created inside the triangle is called the **incircle** of the triangle. Write a statement relating the incentre and the incircle of a triangle. Your statement should include what you noticed in part a).

**Medians**

- A median is drawn from a vertex to the midpoint of the opposite side.

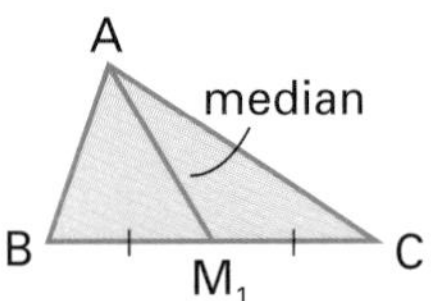


- The point at which the three medians of a triangle meet is called the centroid.
- The distances from a vertex to the centroid, and from the centroid to the opposite midpoint, are in the ratio of 2:1.

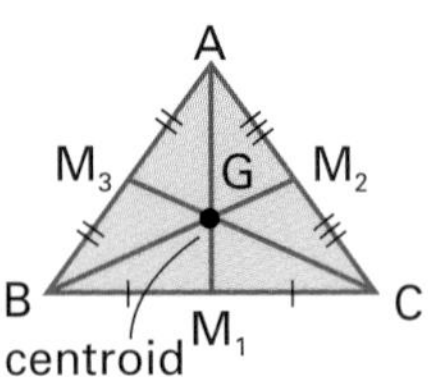


- A median divides the area of the triangle in half.

**Altitudes**

- An altitude is drawn from a vertex to the opposite side, forming a right angle.
- The point where the three altitudes of a triangle intersect is called the orthocentre.

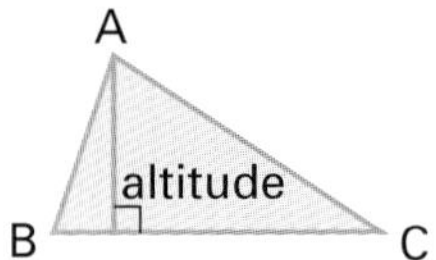


**Bisectors**

- An angle bisector is a ray drawn from the vertex of an angle, exactly through the middle of the angle.
- The point where the three angle bisectors of a triangle meet is called the incentre.
- The incircle of a triangle is centred at the incentre of the triangle, and just touches all three sides.

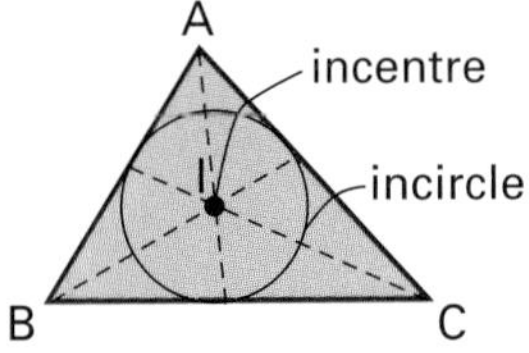

1. Identify each line drawn from the vertex as a median, an altitude, or an angle bisector. Discuss the reasons in each case.

a)
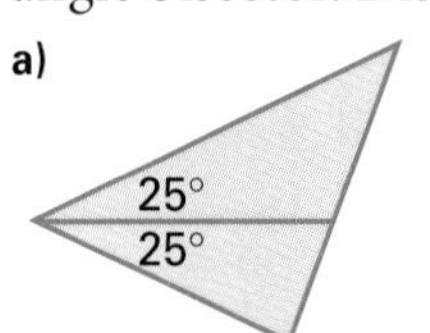


b)
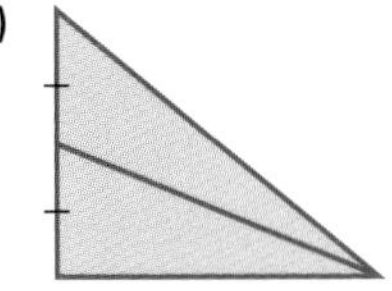

c)
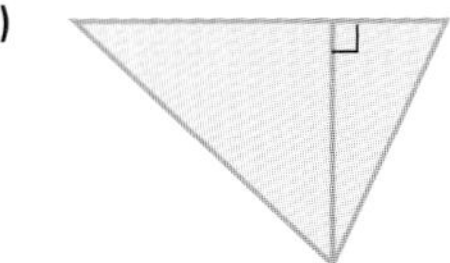

## PRACTISE

1. To describe each expression, choose the correct term from this list: altitude, centroid, orthocentre, incentre.
   a) the height of a triangle
   b) the point where the medians intersect
   c) the point where the altitudes intersect
   d) the point where the angle bisectors intersect

2. Identify each line drawn from the vertex as a median, altitude, or angle bisector.

a) 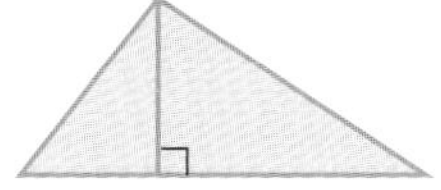

b) 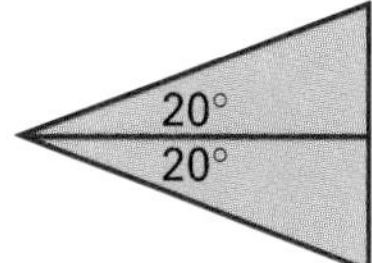


c) 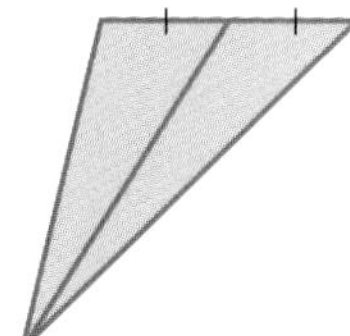

## APPLY THE CONCEPTS

3. Prepare a poster to show how the position of the orthocentre is related to the type of triangle.
   a) Make a sketch of a right, an acute, and an obtuse triangle. Include a label for each.
   b) Using a ruler, accurately draw and label the altitudes.
   c) Label the orthocentres in each triangle.

4. Prepare a poster to show the properties of a median.
   a) Draw a large triangle with the medians constructed. Label the centroid.
   b) Show that the distances from each vertex to the centroid, and from the centroid to the opposite midpoint, are in the ratio 2:1.
   c) Include calculations showing that a median divides the area of a triangle in half.

5. If the distance from a vertex to a centroid is 10 cm, what is the distance from the centroid to the midpoint of the opposite side of the triangle? Give reasons.

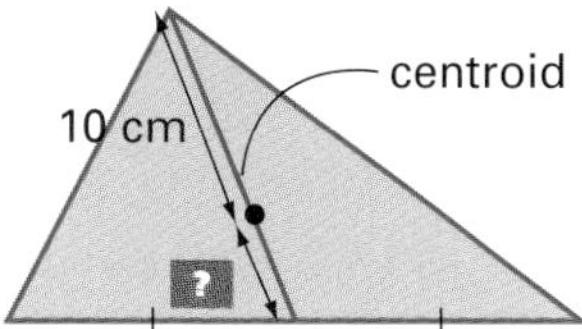

**Did You Know?**

In hang-gliding contests, pilots have stayed in the air for total distances of over 600 km! They do this by circling in rising air currents, called thermals.

6. **Thinking/Inquiry/Problem Solving, Communication** Hang gliders are usually triangle-shaped kites that are large enough to lift and carry a human pilot. Investigate where the pilot should be positioned under a triangular hang-glider to maintain balance. Support your answer with well-labelled drawings and/or scale models.

7. **Window design** You are to create an unusual window design, using a circle within a triangle. The triangle must have side lengths 40 cm, 65 cm, and 70 cm.
   a) Explain how to construct the incentre of the triangle in your design.
   b) How could you use the incentre in your design?
   c) Construct a window design, based on your responses to parts a) and b). Use *The Geometer's Sketchpad®* or ruler and compasses.

C 8. ***The Geometer's Sketchpad®***
   a) Open your sketch from **Discover 2**, or follow steps 1 to 3 of **Discover 2** to create a triangle with three altitudes and the orthocentre constructed.
   b) Create measures for the sides of the triangle.
   c) Create measures for the altitudes or heights. For each height, make sure nothing is selected, then select a vertex and the opposite line segment; choose **Measure, Distance**; deselect. For example, **Distance A to $\overline{\text{BC}}$** measures the length of the altitude from vertex A to side BC.
   d) Use the calculator to discover a relationship between each altitude length, or height, and the opposite side length. Hint: Use the on-screen calculator to try combinations of these two measures, and compare with the same combinations for one of the other altitude-side pairs. Then, use the third altitude-side pair as a check.
   e) Suggest a reason for this relationship.

# 11.4 Investigating Sides and Diagonals of Quadrilaterals

This bridge, in Fort Erie, Ontario, is in the shape of a trapezoid. There are several other types of quadrilaterals. This section will explore types of quadrilaterals and their properties.

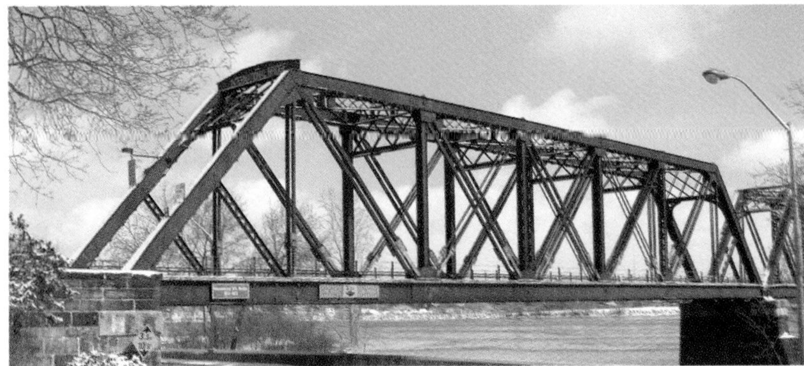

## DISCOVER 1

### Constructing Quadrilaterals

***Using The Geometer's Sketchpad®***

*The Geometer's Sketchpad®* can be used to construct any type of quadrilateral. You will need these constructions to complete **Discover 2A**, where you will investigate quadrilateral properties.

Use the Technology Appendix for help with **Setting Preferences** or **Constructing Line Segments**.

**Part A: Construct a Square**

1. a) Start a new sketch.
   b) Use the **Compass Tool** to place a circle, with radius approximately 3 cm, on your workspace.
   c) Point A should be the centre of your circle and point B should be on the circle's edge. Construct a line segment joining points A and B.

2. a) Construct two lines perpendicular to AB:
   • Check that line segment AB is selected.
   • Select both endpoints, A and B.
   • Choose **Construct**, **Perpendicular Lines.**
   • Deselect.
   b) Use the **Point Tool** to place a point, C, where the perpendicular line through A intersects the edge of the circle. Switch back to the **Selector Tool**.
   c) Construct a line perpendicular to the line through A and C:
   • Select the line though A and C.
   • Check that point C is selected.
   • Choose **Construct**, **Perpendicular Lines.**
   • Deselect.

d) Place a point, D, where the two perpendicular lines intersect outside the circle. Switch back to the **Selector Tool**.

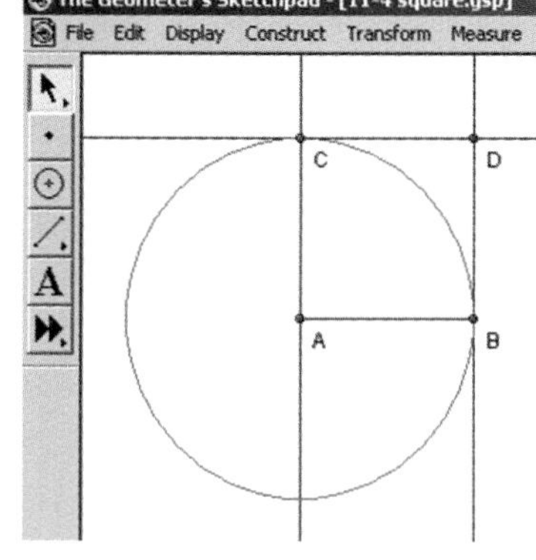


3. a) To hide the lines and circle: Select all three lines and the circle, and choose **Display**, **Hide Path Objects**.
   b) Select the points A, B, D, and C, *in that order*, and choose **Construct**, **Line Segments**. You have now constructed a square ABDC.
   c) Click on and drag any vertex to confirm your square remains a square as it moves and changes size.

**Part B: Construct a Rectangle**

4. a) Start a new sketch.
   b) Use the **Straightedge** tool to construct a roughly horizontal line segment, AB.

5. Construct lines through A and B, perpendicular to the line segment AB:
   • Select points A and B.
   • Check that line segment AB is selected.
   • Choose **Construct**, **Perpendicular Lines**.
   • Deselect.

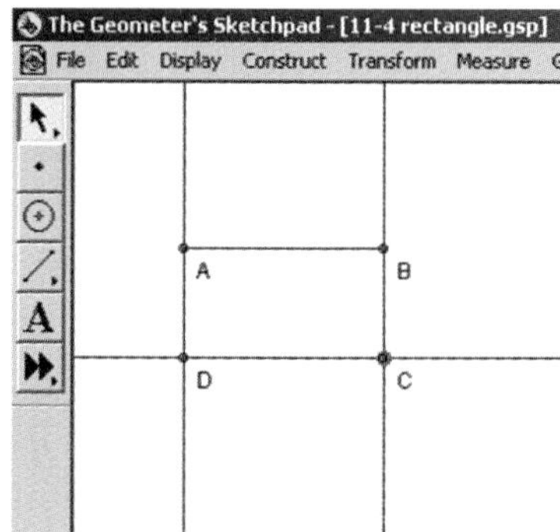


6. a) Place a point, C, on the vertical line below B. Switch to the **Selector Tool.**
   b) Draw a line through C, parallel to AB:
      • Check that point C is selected.
      • Select line segment AB.
      • Choose **Construct**, **Parallel Line.**
      • Deselect.
   c) Add a point, D, at the intersection of the lines through A and C.

7. a) To hide the lines: select all three lines, and choose **Display**, **Hide Lines**.
   b) Select the points A, B, C, and D, and choose **Construct**, **Line Segments**.
   c) Click on and drag any vertex to confirm your rectangle remains rectangular as it moves and changes size.

## Part C: Construct a Parallelogram

In a parallelogram, both pairs of opposite sides are parallel.

**8. a)** Start a new sketch.

**b)** Use the **Straightedge** tool to construct a roughly horizontal line segment, AB.

**9. a)** Use the **Point Tool** to place a third point, C, below and to the right of B.

**b)** Construct a line through C, parallel to AB:
- Check that point C is selected.
- Select line segment AB.
- Choose **Construct**, **Parallel Line**.
- Deselect.

**c)** Construct the line segment BC.

**10. a)** Construct a line through A, parallel to BC:
- Select point A.
- Check that line segment BC is selected.
- Choose **Construct**, **Parallel Line**.
- Deselect.

**b)** Add a point, D, at the intersection of the lines through A and C. Your parallelogram should be similar to the example shown.

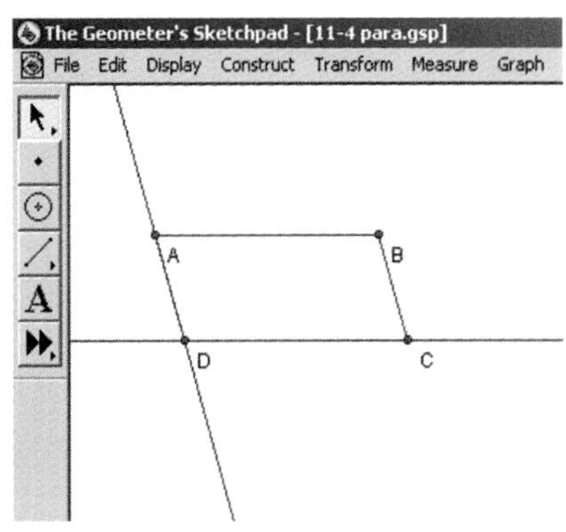


**11. a)** To hide the lines: select both lines, choose **Display**, **Hide Parallel Lines**.

**b)** Construct the line segments CD and AD.

**c)** Click on and drag any vertex to confirm your parallelogram moves according the definition of a parallelogram.

## Part D: Construct a Trapezoid

In a trapezoid, only one pair of opposite sides are parallel.

**12.** Start a new sketch. Use the **Straightedge** tool to construct a roughly horizontal line segment, AB.

13. a) Use the **Point Tool** to place a third point, C, above the line segment.
   b) Construct a line through C, parallel to AB:
      • Check that point C is selected.
      • Select line segment AB.
      • Choose **Construct**, **Parallel Line**.
      • Deselect.
   c) Construct the line segment BC.

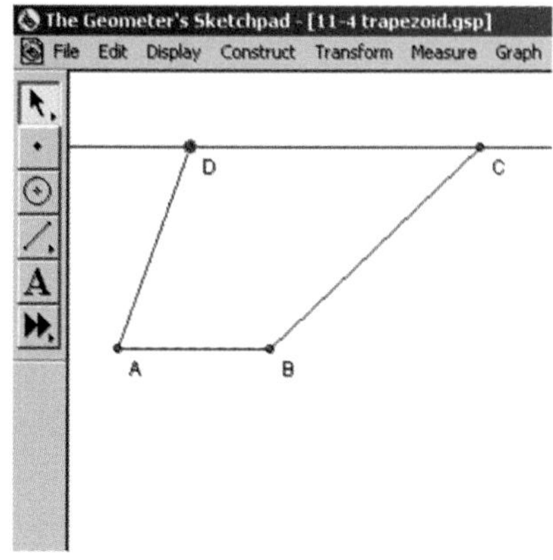


14. a) Place a fourth point, D, on the parallel line above AB.
   b) Construct the line segment AD.

15. a) To hide the line: select the line, choose **Display**, **Hide Parallel Line**.
   b) Construct the line segment CD.
   c) Click on and drag any vertex to confirm your trapezoid moves according to the definition of a trapezoid.

**Part E: Construct a Kite**

In a kite, the two pairs of adjacent sides are equal in length.

16. Start a new sketch. Construct a triangle ABC.

17. A mirror image of this triangle will create a kite.
   a) Make sure nothing is selected. Then, select the line segment AC. To identify AC as the mirror line, select **Transform**, **Mark Mirror** (a brief animation will appear).
   b) To reflect the triangle in the mirror: Select point B and line segments AB and BC, and choose **Transform**, **Reflect**.
   c) Relabel the new point B′ as point D, and deselect it.

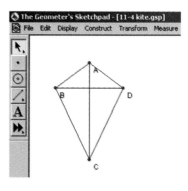

18. Drag any vertex to confirm the kite remains a kite as it moves.

## Part F: Construct a Rhombus

In a rhombus, both pairs of opposite sides are parallel and all sides are equal in length.

**19. a)** Start a new sketch. Place a circle, with radius approximately 3 cm, on your workspace.

**b)** Point A should be the centre of your circle and point B should be on the circle's edge. Place another point, C, on the edge of the circle.

**c)** Construct the line segments AB, AC, and BC.

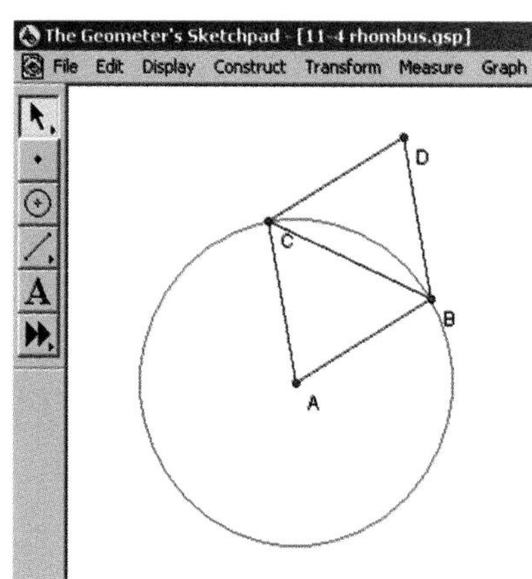


**20.** You have just constructed an isosceles triangle. If the isosceles triangle is reflected in the line segment BC, it will create a rhombus.

**a)** Make sure nothing is selected. Then, select the line segment BC. To identify BC as the mirror line, choose **Transform**, **Mark Mirror** (a brief animation will appear).

**b)** To reflect the isosceles triangle in the mirror: Select point A and line segments AC and AB, and choose **Transform**, **Reflect**.

**c)** Relabel the new point A′ as point D, and deselect it.

**21. a)** Hide the circle: select the circle, and choose **Display**, **Hide Circle**

**b)** Drag any vertex to confirm the rhombus moves according to the definition of a rhombus.

# DISCOVER 2A

• recording table

Refer to the Technology Appendix for help with **Constructing Line Segments, Constructing Measures,** or **Using the On-Screen Calculator**.

## Sides and Diagonals of Quadrilaterals

***Using The Geometer's Sketchpad®***

You will investigate some properties of different types of quadrilaterals. Your teacher may provide you with a recording table for this investigation.

**1. a)** Use the square you constructed in **Discover 1**, Part A. Create measures for the four side lengths of the square. Record them in your table.

**b)** Describe any relationships involving the side lengths.

**2. a)** A diagonal is a line segment drawn between opposite vertices of a quadrilateral. Construct the two diagonals in your square.

**b)** Measure and record the lengths of both diagonals.

**c)** Describe any relationships involving the diagonal lengths.

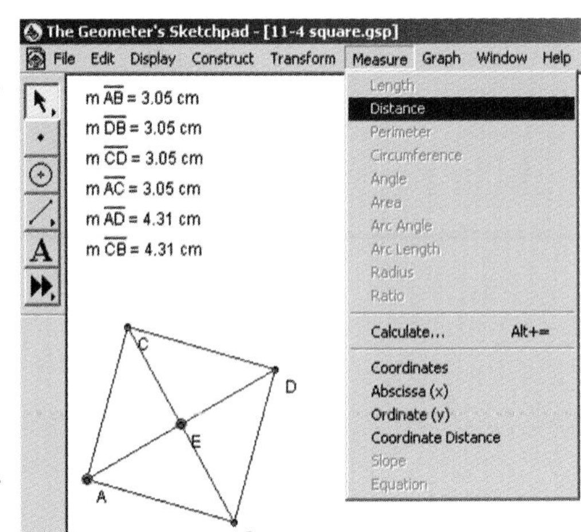


**3. a)** Place a point, E, where the diagonals intersect. Measure the distance from each vertex to point E:

- Select points A and E.
- Choose **Measure, Distance**.
- Deselect.

Repeat for vertices B, C, and D. Record these measurements in your table.

**b)** To **bisect** a line segment means to cut it into two equal parts. Describe any relationships involving the distances you determined in part a). Use the term bisect, if appropriate.

**4. a)** Create measures for the angles where the diagonals intersect. Record these measures in your table.

**b)** Describe any relationships involving the angles where the diagonals intersect. Use the on-screen calculator to check your findings.

**5.** Repeat steps 1 to 4 for each of the other quadrilaterals constructed in **Discover 1**. Note: Some quadrilaterals may not have any relationships. For example, each side length of a trapezoid can be different.

# DISCOVER 2B

- ruler
- protractor
- rocording tablo

## Sides and Diagonals of Quadrilaterals

***Using ruler and protractor***

You will investigate some properties of these quadrilaterals. Your teacher may provide you with a recording table for this investigation.

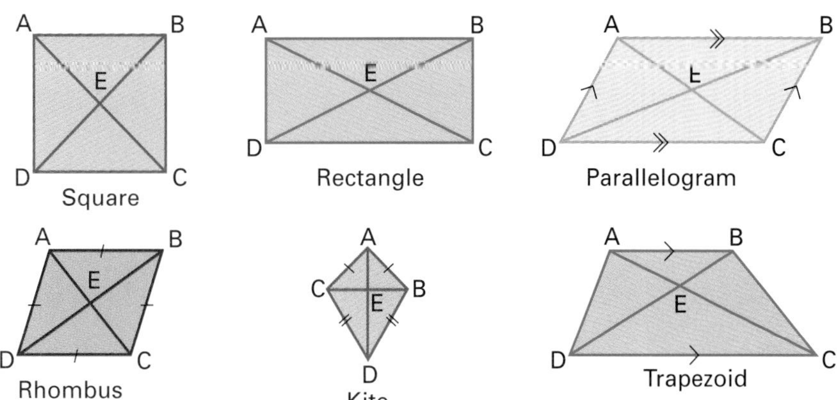


1. **a)** Measure the side lengths of the square. Record them in your table.
   **b)** Describe any relationships involving the side lengths.

2. **a)** A diagonal is a line segment drawn from one vertex of the quadrilateral to the opposite vertex. Measure and record the lengths of both diagonals.
   **b)** Describe any relationships involving the diagonal lengths.

3. **a)** Mark the point E where the diagonals intersect. Measure the distance from each vertex to point E. Record these measurements in your table.
   **b)** To **bisect** a line segment means to cut it into two equal parts. Describe any relationships involving the distances you determined in part a). Use the term bisect, if appropriate.

4. **a)** Using a protractor, measure the angles where the diagonals intersect. Record these measures in your table.
   **b)** Describe any relationships involving the angles where the diagonals intersect.

5. Repeat steps 1 to 4 for each of the other quadrilaterals in the diagrams. Note: Some quadrilaterals may not have any relationships. For example, each side length of a trapezoid can be different.

# Review

## 11.1 Investigating Angles of Triangles and Quadrilaterals, pages 440–449

1. Write these values:
   a) the sum of the interior angles of a triangle
   b) the sum of the interior angles of a quadrilateral
   c) the sum of the exterior angles of a triangle
   d) the sum of the exterior angles of a quadrilateral

2. **Communication** Draw a triangle showing the relationship between an exterior angle of a triangle and the two opposite interior angles. Express this relationship in words.

3. Find each unknown angle measure. Give reasons.

a)

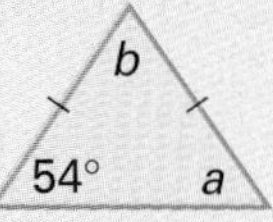


b)

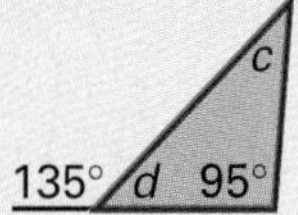


c)

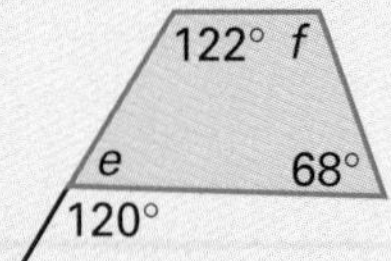


4. **Canadarm 2** The Canadarm 2, attached to the International Space Station, can move at the elbow from about 20° through to 180° (a straight extension). While conducting repairs, the Canadarm 2 had a 100° angle at the elbow and an angle of 42° at its base. Make a drawing of the Canadarm 2, showing these angles. Use a protractor.

**Did You Know?**

In April 2001, Canadian astronaut Chris Hadfield helped to mount the Canadarm 2 onto the International Space Station. It measures 17.6 m at full stretch, and has a mass of 1640 kg.

## 11.2 Investigating Angles and Parallel Lines, pages 450–457

5. a) Explain the difference between corresponding and alternate angles. Include a diagram to support your answer.
   b) Draw a diagram to explain the relationship of co-interior angles.

6. Find each unknown angle measure. State your reasoning.

a)

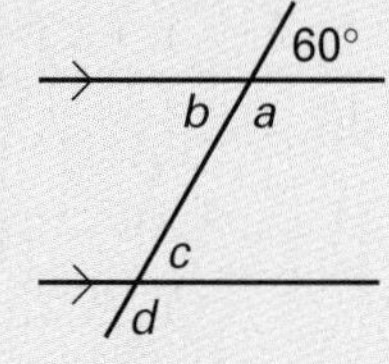


b)

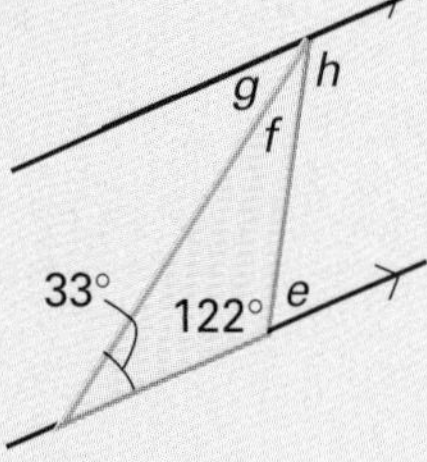

## 11.3 Investigating Angle Bisectors, Medians, and Altitudes of Triangles, pages 458–466

7. The orthocentre of a triangle can be inside the triangle, outside the triangle, or neither. For each triangle type, state the position of the orthocentre.
   a) acute  b) obtuse  c) right triangle

8. If the distance from one vertex of a triangle to its centroid is 4 cm, what is the distance, along the median, from the centroid to the opposite side of the triangle? Explain your answer.

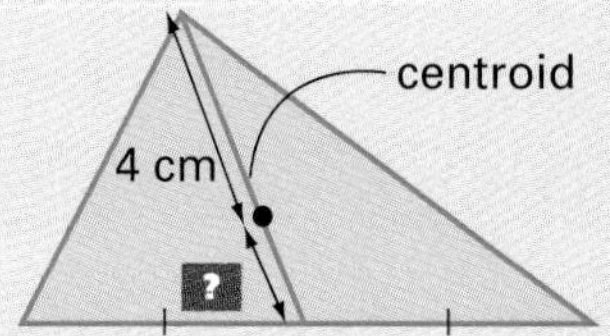


9. ***The Geometer's Sketchpad®*** Imagine you have constructed a triangle using *The Geometer's Sketchpad®*.
   a) Describe how to construct an angle bisector of the triangle.
   b) Describe how to find the incentre of the triangle.
   c) How could you construct the incircle of the triangle?

## 11.4 Investigating Sides and Diagonals of Quadrilaterals, pages 467–473

10. Copy the table shown. (Your teacher may provide you with a copy.) Use it to summarize the properties of the sides and diagonals of quadrilaterals. The first quadrilateral has been done for you.

| Quadrilateral | Side Lengths | Diagonal Lengths | Diagonal Length (vertex to intersection of diagonals) | Angles at Intersection of Diagonals |
|---|---|---|---|---|
| Square | all the same | both the same | all the same (the diagonals bisect each other) | all 90° |
| Rectangle | | | | |
| Parallelogram | | | | |
| Rhombus | | | | |
| Kite | | | | |
| Trapezoid | | | | |

11. Use each clue to identify a quadrilateral type. Some clues may refer to more than one quadrilateral type.
    a) bisectors intersect at right angles
    b) two pairs of equal sides
    c) two pairs of parallel sides and the diagonals bisect each other
    d) diagonals bisect at right angles
    e) diagonals are equal in length

# Practice Test

## Multiple Choice

***For questions 1 to 9, select the best answer.***

1. The sum of the interior angles of a triangle is
   - **A** 360°
   - **B** 180°
   - **C** 90°
   - **D** all of the above, depending on the shape of the triangle

2. The sums of the exterior angles of a quadrilateral, and of a triangle, are
   - **A** the same
   - **B** 360°
   - **C** different
   - **D** all answers except C

3. If a triangle is equilateral,
   - **A** you need two angles to determine the value of the third
   - **B** the sum of the exterior angles is 180°
   - **C** each angle measures 60°
   - **D** the sum of the interior angles is 360°

4. In an isosceles triangle,
   - **A** the sum of the interior angles is 180°
   - **B** the angles opposite the equal sides have the same measure
   - **C** if you know the value of one angle, you can determine the value of the other two
   - **D** all of the above

5. Identify the measure of $a$, and the correct explanation.
   - **A** 120°, supplementary angles
   - **B** 60°, corresponding angles
   - **C** 60°, alternate angles
   - **D** 120°, co-interior angles

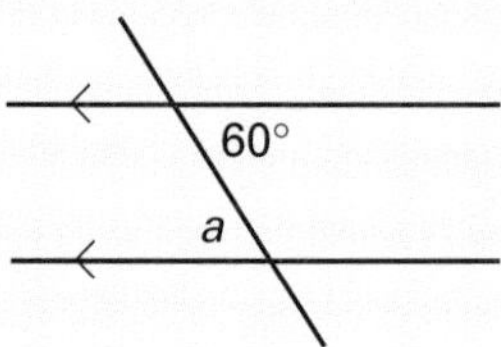


6. In a triangle, the point where the angle bisectors intersect is called the
   - **A** orthocentre
   - **B** centroid
   - **C** incentre
   - **D** median

7. The line segments AD and AE are, *in order*,
   - **A** the median and altitude
   - **B** the median and bisector
   - **C** the bisector and median
   - **D** the bisector and altitude

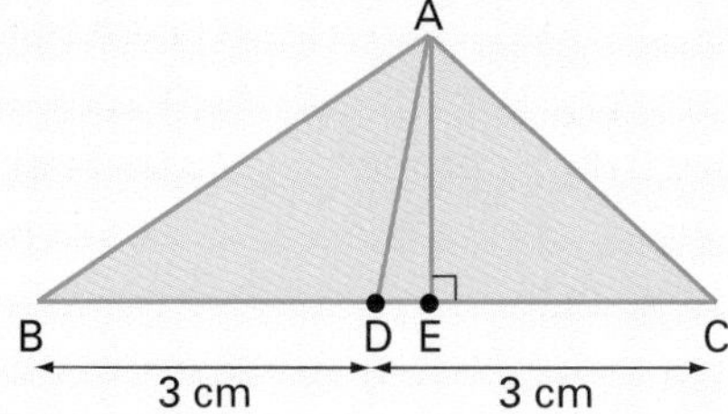

8. Identify the quadrilaterals in which the diagonals bisect each other.

**A** trapezoid **B** kite **C** parallelogram **D** all of these

9. A parallelogram can also be

**A** a rectangle **B** a square **C** a rhombus **D** all of these

## Short Answer

10. Find the measures of the unknown angles. Give reasons.

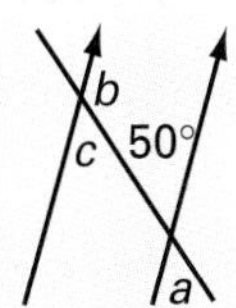


11. A student drew the following exterior angles in a triangle. Explain what the student did wrong.

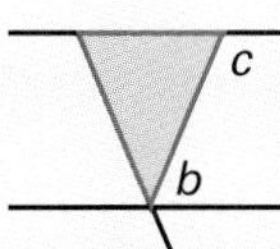


12. Find the measure of each unknown angle. Give reasons.

a)

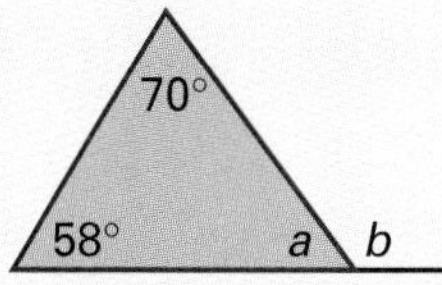


b)

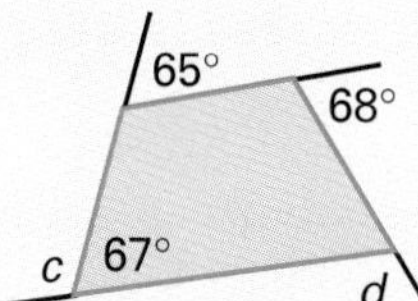


c)

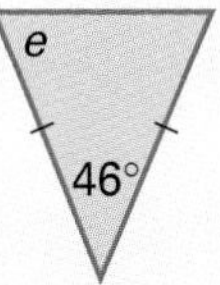


## Extended Response

13. Draw a diagram and write an explanation of each type of angle pair in parallel lines.

**a)** alternate angles **b)** corresponding angles **c)** co-interior angles

**ACHIEVEMENT CHECK** Knowledge/Understanding Thinking/Inquiry/Problem Solving Communication Application

14. Examine the quadrilateral.

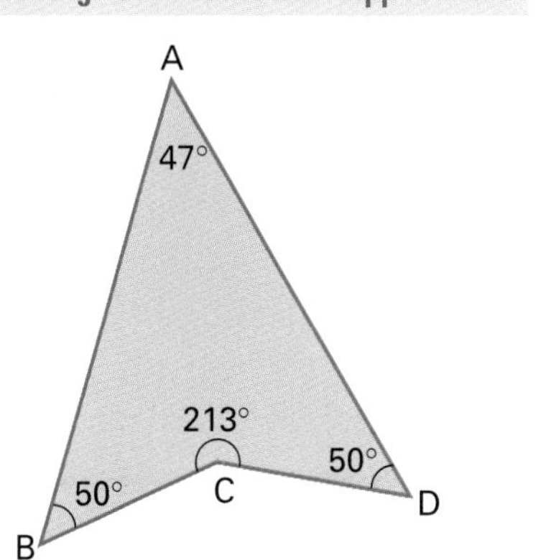


**a)** Determine the sum of the interior angles of this quadrilateral.

**b)** Determine the sum of the exterior angles of this quadrilateral. Hint: The exterior angle at the reflex vertex, C, must be negative.

**c)** Determine any properties of the sides of this quadrilateral

**d)** Determine any properties of the diagonals of this quadrilateral.

# Course Review

## Chapters 1 to 11

1. Sandra is buying trim for a window with an unusual shape. While in the hardware store, she realizes she forgot to measure the sloping sides, marked $a$ and $b$ in the diagram.
   **a)** Calculate the lengths of the sloping sides.
   **b)** How much trim does Sandra need to buy to go around the outer edge of the window?

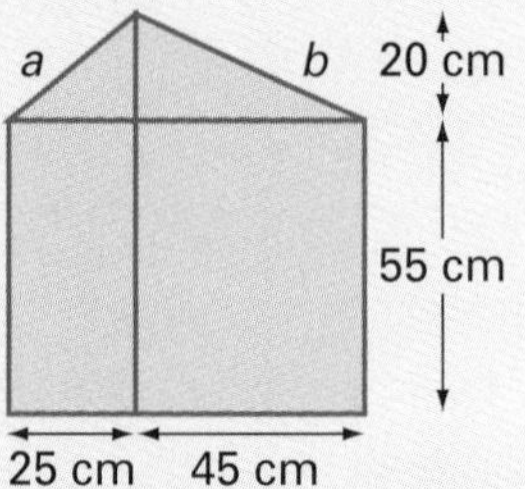


2. **Communication** Vassily wants to create a rectangular run for his pet rabbits in his backyard. He must decide whether to make a free-standing run, or use the side of the house. He has 6.0 m of fencing to work with.
   **a)** If Vassily wants to give his rabbits the maximum area, which plan should he choose?
   **b)** Draw a plan of the maximum-area run.

3. **Sculpture** As part of an abstract sculpture, a solid cylinder is to be painted blue. The cylinder is 0.95 m long and has a diameter of 0.32 m.
   **a)** What is the surface area of the whole cylinder, including top and bottom?
   **b)** Each can of paint covers 0.8 $m^2$. How many cans will be needed to paint the cylinder?

4. **Application** The diagram shows the net of a package in the shape of a triangular prism.
   **a)** Sketch the package when the net is folded up.

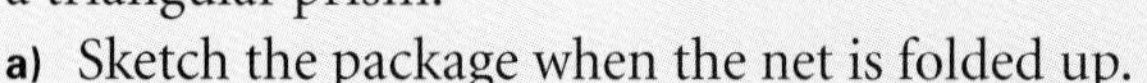

   **b)** Calculate the height of each triangular end.
   **c)** Calculate the area of one end.
   **d)** Calculate the volume of the package.

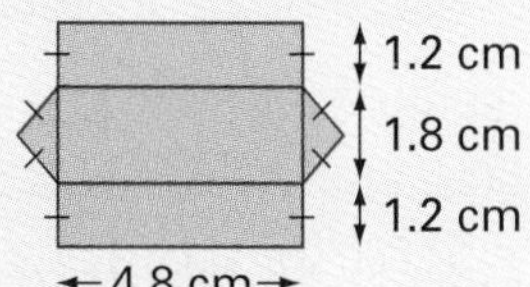


5. Consider this question: "What percent of students take regular swim classes?"
   **a)** State a hypothesis for this question.
   **b)** Would you use primary or secondary data to answer this question? Give reasons for your answer.
   **c)** If a survey is used to answer the question, what sampling technique should be used, and why?

**6.** **Application** Cho bought some supplies for school, at the prices shown in the table.

| Item | Cost |
|---|---|
| Set of pencils | \$0.39 |
| Hole punch | \$1.85 |
| Side Alley Souls lunch box | \$8.50 |
| Set of binders | \$1.49 |
| Yellow highlighter pen | \$0.99 |
| Pencil case | \$3.50 |
| Compasses set | \$3.50 |

**a)** How much money did Cho spend in total?

**b)** Calculate the mean, median, and mode for this data set.

**c)** Which measure of central tendency would be most reduced, if Cho had not bought the lunch box? Explain.

**7.** **Enrolment levels** Carver Creek is a rural community. The table shows grade 9 enrolments at Carver Creek High over a ten-year period.

| Year | 1993 | 1994 | 1995 | 1996 | 1997 | 1998 | 1999 | 2000 | 2001 | 2002 |
|---|---|---|---|---|---|---|---|---|---|---|
| Enrolment | 119 | 115 | 104 | 109 | 101 | 96 | 97 | 93 | 90 | 88 |

**a)** Plot a broken-line graph of the data.

**b)** Describe any trend in the data.

**c)** Suggest a hypothesis to explain the trend. How could you test this hypothesis?

**8.** Calculate.

**a)** $\frac{3}{4} \times \frac{1}{2}$ **b)** $\frac{4}{5} \times \frac{3}{2}$ **c)** $\frac{3}{7} + \frac{2}{7}$ **d)** $\frac{5}{3} - \frac{1}{3}$

**e)** $\frac{3}{8} + \frac{3}{4}$ **f)** $-\frac{3}{8} + \frac{3}{4}$ **g)** $\frac{7}{8} + \left(-\frac{1}{12}\right)$ **h)** $-4\frac{1}{2} - 1\frac{3}{8}$

**9.** An egg-packing machine can fill 45 dozen-packs of eggs in 5 min.

**a)** What is the unit rate for this process, in packs per minute?

**b)** How many eggs are packed by the machine in an hour?

**10.** **Sound system** A dance club is planning to rent a sound system. The club has budgeted \$2400 for the rental. The rental rates are:

- \$1200 for the first night, plus
- \$350 for each extra night

**a)** Set up a table of values, from 0 to 4 extra nights, and graph this relation.

**b)** How many extra nights can the club afford?

**11.** **Application, Communication** The height $h$, in metres, of a diver, $t$ seconds after she jumps, is given by the relation $h = 9.5 + 6.7t - 4.9t^2$

**a)** Copy and complete the table of values for this relation.

**b)** Graph the relation from the table of values. Is the relation linear or non-linear? Explain.

**c)** Describe another way you could decide whether the relation is linear or non-linear.

| *t* (s) | *h* (m) |
|---|---|
| 0 | 9.5 |
| 0.5 | |
| 1.0 | |
| 1.5 | |
| 2.0 | |

**12.** These data were collected for six grade 9 students:

| Student | Height (cm) | Thumb Length (mm) |
|---|---|---|
| Robert | 149 | 78 |
| Marie | 160 | 89 |
| Arturo | 177 | 96 |
| Deepak | 168 | 97 |
| Leigh-Anne | 143 | 71 |
| Christiana | 155 | 75 |

**a)** Create a scatter plot of the data. You may use technology if you wish.

**b)** Create a line of best fit for the data.

**c)** Write an equation for your line of best fit.

**13.** **Thinking/Inquiry/Problem Solving** Suppose that, on average, an airport security gate processes 45 people every hour.

**a)** How many people go through a security gate in 24 h, on average? Express your answer in scientific notation.

**b)** A survey of regional and international airports in North America counted $1.7 \times 10^3$ security gates. How many people clear security in all the airports surveyed, in a single day? Express your answer in scientific notation.

**14.** Simplify.

**a)** $(2x + 3) + (7x - 4)$

**b)** $(7x^2 - 12x + 3) + (5x - 4)$

**c)** $(2x^2 - 7) - (3x + 2)$

**d)** $5x(7x^2 - 12x + 3)$

**e)** $\left(\frac{2}{3}x^2 - 7x + 1\right) - \left(2 - \frac{1}{3}x^2\right)$

**f)** $x(7x^2 - 12x + 3) + 2(4 - x^2)$

15. a) Find an expression, in simplified form, for the perimeter of this shape.
b) Find an expression, in simplified form, for the area of the shape.
c) Match the expressions in parts a) and b) with terms from this list: trinomial, monomial, binomial.
d) The value of $x$ is to be between 2 cm and 5 cm. What is the minimum length of the perimeter? What is the maximum?

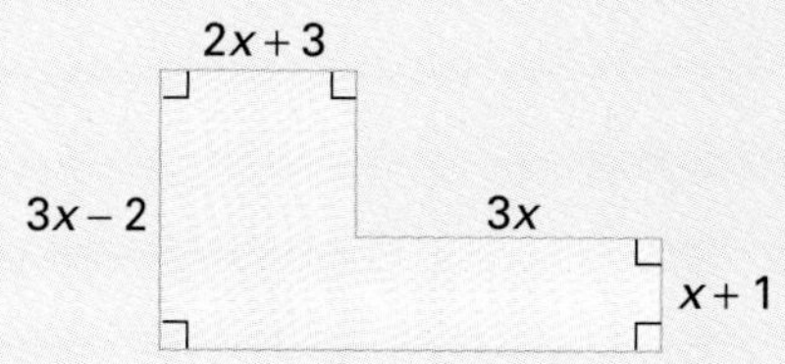


16. **Savings** Pierre has invested $1000 in a savings account that pays 2% per year simple interest. Solve the following equation to determine the number of years, $n$, that it will take for Pierre's savings to reach $1800:
$1800 = 1000 + (0.02 \times 1000)n$

17. a) Find the equation of the line with slope 3, passing through the point $(2, -1)$. Explain your method.
b) Find the equation of the line that passes through the points $(2, 3)$ and $(4, -5)$. Explain your method.

18. **Street Plan**
a) Identify a pair of alternate angles involving Simcoe Avenue, Macdonald Street, and Cartier Street. Use the letter labels on the street plan.
b) Identify a pair of co-interior angles.
c) The city hall is built on a block with a 73° angle at Simcoe and Cartier. What angle do the grounds of Borealis Stadium make at Simcoe and Macdonald? Explain your answer.

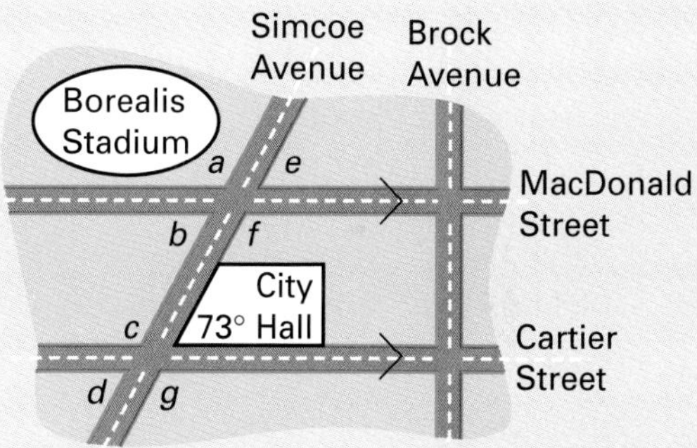

# Tasks

## CD Racks

A company builds CD racks. The width is 15 cm. The depth is 16 cm. The height is $2x + 1$, where $x$ is the number of slots for the CDs. The CD racks are made of wood on all sides except the front.

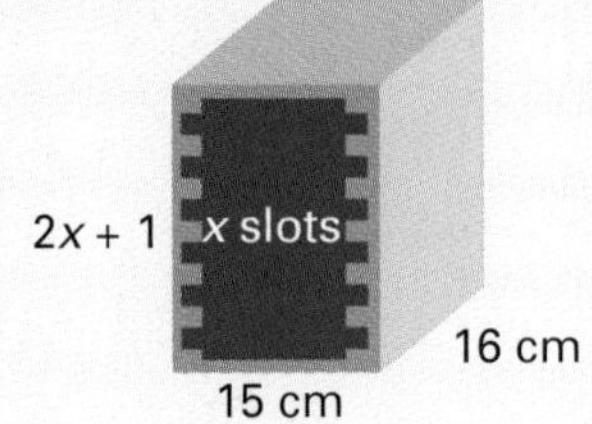


**a)** Write a polynomial expression for the outside surface area of the CD rack, not including the front.

**b)** Simplify the expression.

**c)** Determine the surface area of wood needed for a 10-slot CD rack.

**d)** Determine the surface area of wood required for a 50-slot CD rack.

**e)** The company has decided to offer a double-stack CD rack, which would add an extra 14 cm to the width. Write a polynomial expression for the surface area of the double-stack CD rack, not including the front, where $x$ is the number of slots. Use $x + 1$ for the height.

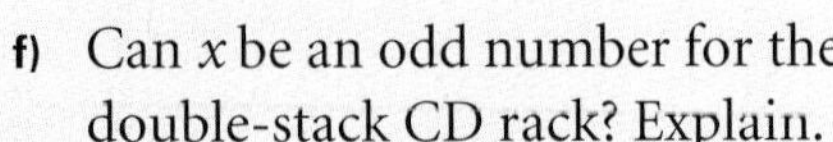

**f)** Can $x$ be an odd number for the double-stack CD rack? Explain.

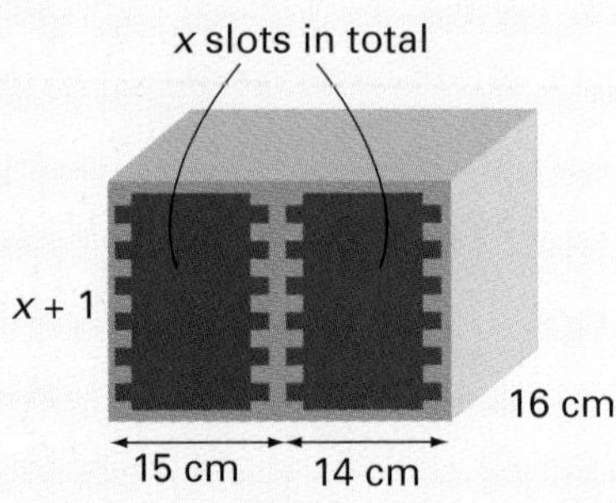


**g)** Determine the surface area of wood required for a 10-slot double-stack CD rack.

**h)** Determine the surface area of wood required for a 50-slot double-stack CD rack.

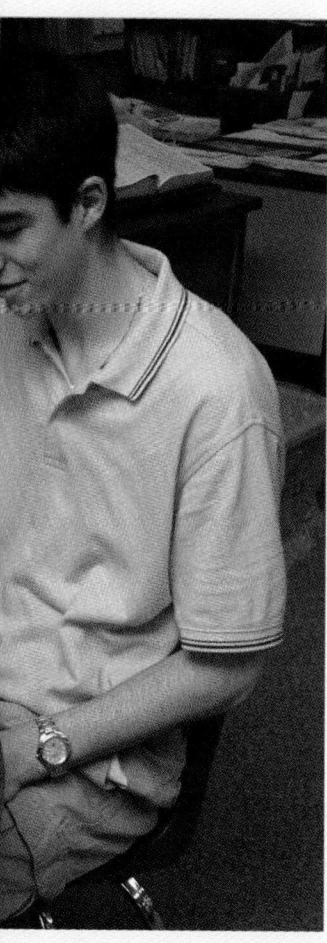

## Hexagon Trains

John is making some "train" patterns with hexagonal coasters. Each coaster has side length 1 unit. He wants to know about the relationship between the number of coasters, $n$, and the perimeter of the train, $P$.

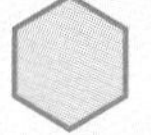 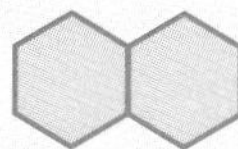 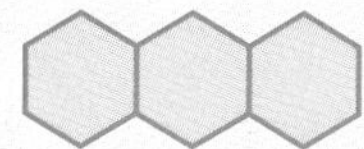

**a)** Make a table showing the values of $n$ and $P$ for the first five trains. Make a scatter plot of your results. Is the relationship linear or non-linear?

**b)** Create an equation of the form $P = mn + b$ to model this relationship.

**c)** Describe the meaning of $m$ and $b$ in terms of the coasters.

**d)** John also has some square coasters that also have side length 1 unit. If he makes trains using the square coasters, how will the equation in part b) change?

**e)** John then cuts one of the hexagonal coasters in half and places it at the front of each train, as shown. What is the equation that models this new relationship? Hint: the diameter of the coaster is twice the length of one side.

 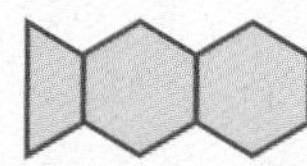 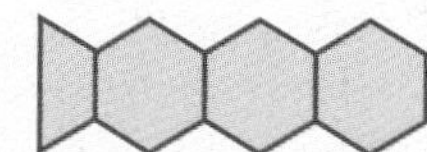

## Consecutive Sums

**a)** Choose five consecutive numbers; find their sum. Choose a different set of five consecutive numbers; find their sum. What do you notice about these sets of numbers and their sums? List as many properties as you can.

**b)** If the first consecutive number is $n$, what is the second number? the third? the fourth? the fifth? Find, and simplify, an expression for the sum of these five numbers. Is your result divisible by 5? Explain.

**c)** Examine what happens with six consecutive numbers. What conclusion can you make?

# Technology Appendix

## Contents

### The Geometer's Sketchpad® Geometry Software



### TI-83 and TI-83 Plus Graphing Calculators



### CBR™ (Calculator-Based Ranger)

# THE GEOMETER'S SKETCHPAD® BASICS

## Menu Bar:

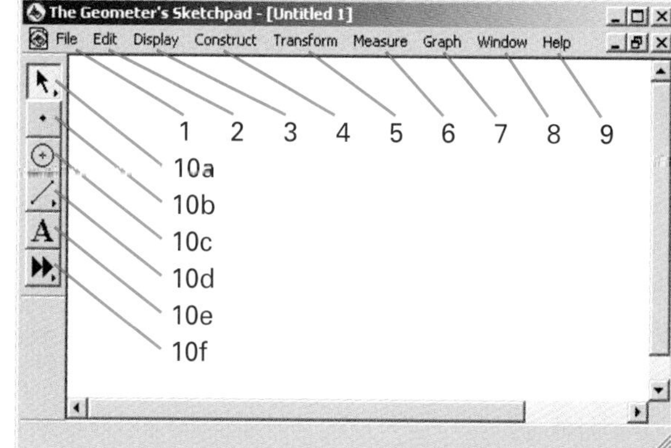


1 **File** menu—open/save/print sketches

2 **Edit** menu—undo/redo actions, set preferences

3 **Display** menu—control appearance of objects in sketch

4 **Construct** menu—construct new geometric objects based on objects in sketch

5 **Transform** menu—apply geometric transformations to selected objects

6 **Measure** menu—make various measurements on objects in sketch

7 **Graph** menu—create axes and plot measurements and points

8 **Window** menu—manipulate windows

9 **Help** menu—to use help system; this is an excellent reference guide

10 **Toolbox**—tools for selecting and creating points, circles, and straight objects (segments, lines, and rays), also includes text and custom tools.

- 10a **Selection Arrow Tool** (Arrow)—to select and transform objects
- 10b **Point Tool** (Dot)—to draw points
- 10c **Compass Tool** (Circle)—to draw circles
- 10d **Straightedge Tool**—to draw line segments, rays, and lines
- 10e **Text Tool** (Letter A)—to label points and to write text
- 10f **Custom Tool** (Double Arrow)—to create or use special "custom" tools

## Creating a Sketch

- Under the **File** menu, choose **New Sketch** to start with a new work area.

## Opening an Existing Sketch

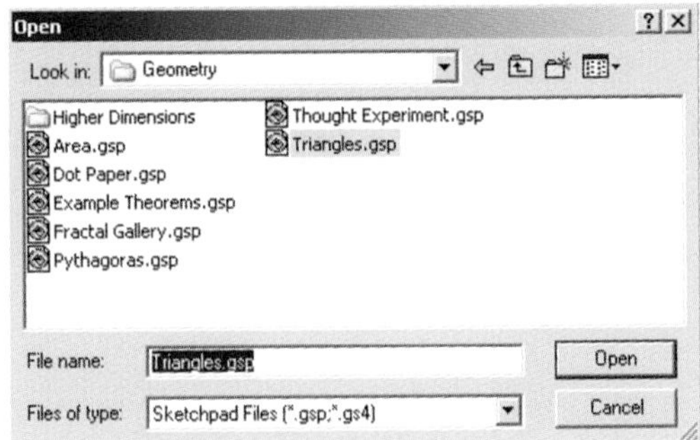


- Under the **File** menu, choose **Open….** The dialog box shown will appear.
- Choose the sketch you wish to work on. Then, choose **OK**.

OR

- Type in the name of the sketch in the **File name:** entry box.

## Saving a Sketch

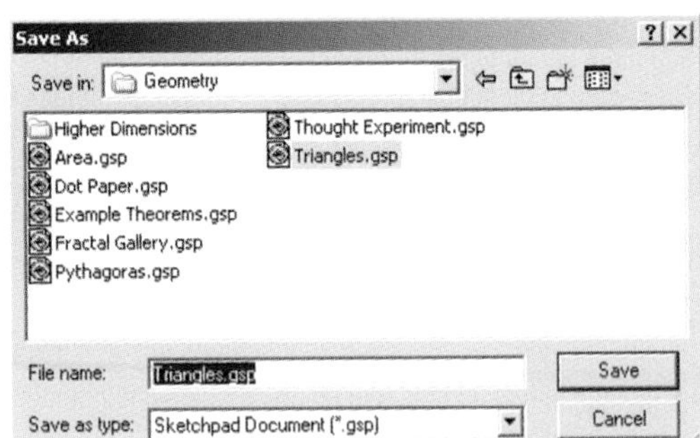


If you are saving for the first time in a new sketch:

- Under the **File** menu, choose **Save As**. The dialog box shown will appear.
- You can save the sketch with the name assigned by *The Geometer's Sketchpad®*.

OR

- Press the Backspace or Del key to clear the name.
- Type in whatever you wish to name the sketch/file.

If you have already given your file a name:

- Select **Save** from under the **File** menu.

## Closing a Sketch Without Exiting *The Geometer's Sketchpad®*

- Under the **File** menu, choose **Close**.

## Exiting *The Geometer's Sketchpad®*

- Under the **File** menu, choose **Exit**.

## Setting Preferences

- Choose **Preferences…** from the **Edit** menu.
- Click on the **Units** tab.
- Set the units and precision for angles, distances, and calculated values like slopes or ratios.

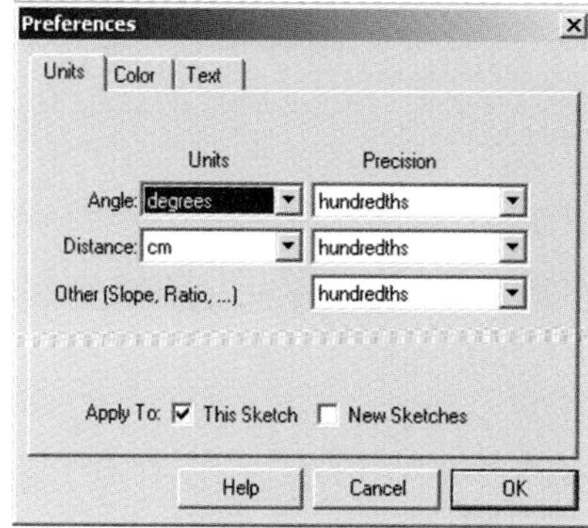


- Press the **Text** tab.
- If you check the auto-label box **For All New Points**, then *The Geometer's Sketchpad®* will label points as you create them.
- If you check the auto-label box **As Objects Are Measured**, then *The Geometer's Sketchpad®* will label any measurements that you define.

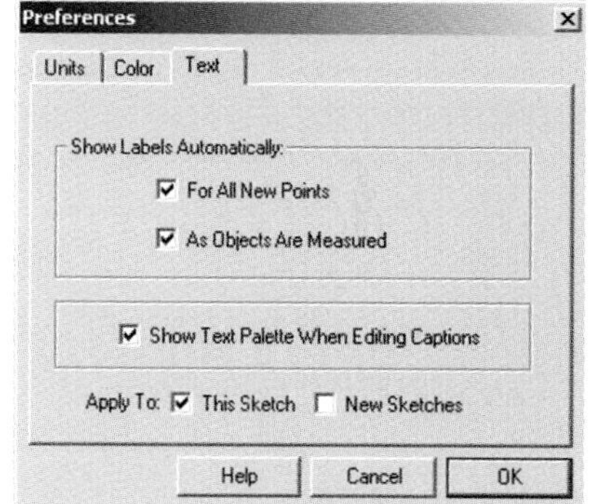


You can also choose whether the auto-labelling functions will apply only to the current sketch, or also to any new sketches that you create.

## Selecting Points and Objects

- Choose the **Selection Arrow Tool**. The mouse cursor appears as an arrow.

To select a single point:

- Select the point by moving the cursor to the point and clicking on the point. The selected point will now appear as a darker point, similar to a *bull's eye* ⊙.

To select an object such as a line segment or a circle:

- Move the cursor to a point on the object until it becomes a horizontal arrow.
- Click on the object. The object will change appearance to show it is selected.

To select a number of points or objects:

- Select each object in turn, by moving the cursor to the object and clicking on it.

To deselect a point or an object:

- Move the cursor over it, and click the left mouse button.
- To deselect all selected objects, click in an open area of the workspace.

## Constructing Line Segments

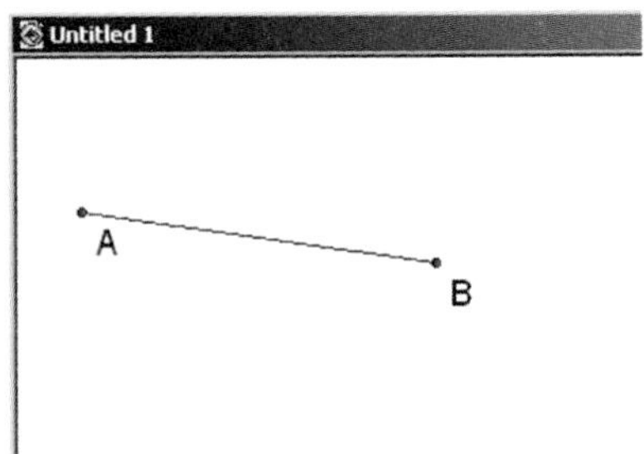


- Choose the **Point Tool**. Create two points in the workspace.
- Choose the **Selection Arrow Tool**, and select both points.
- From the **Construct** menu, choose **Line Segment**.

You can also use the **Straightedge Tool**:
- Choose this tool.
- Move the cursor to the workspace.
- Click and hold the left mouse button.
- Drag the cursor to form the line segment.
- Release the mouse button.

## Constructing Triangles and Polygons

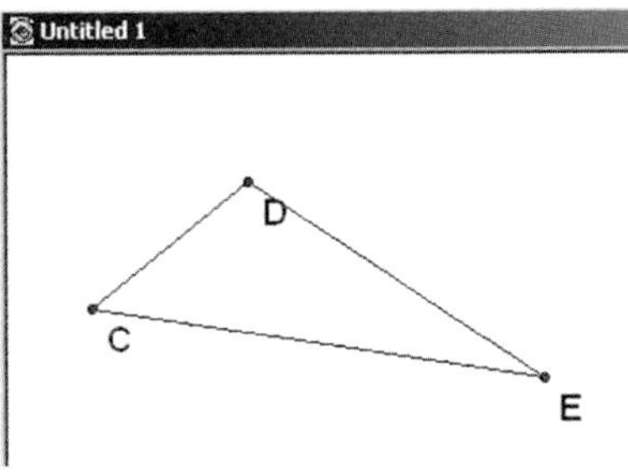


To construct a triangle:
- Choose the **Point Tool**. Draw three points in the workspace.
- Select the points.
- From the **Construct** menu, choose **Line Segments**.

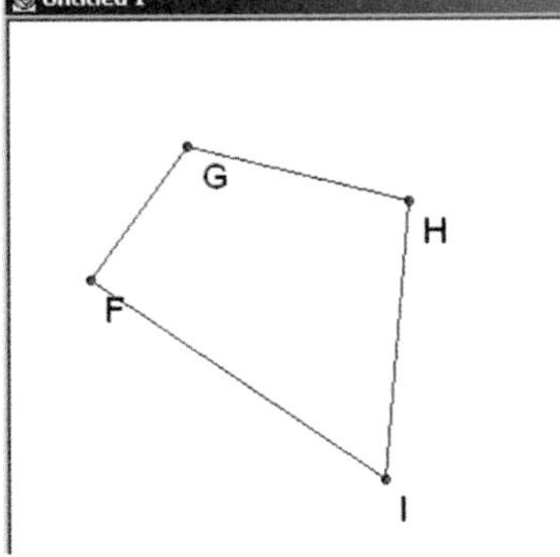


You can construct a polygon with any number of sides.
To construct a quadrilateral:
- Draw four points.
- Deselect all points.
- Select the points in either clockwise or counterclockwise order.
- From the **Construct** menu, choose **Line Segments**.

## Constructing a Circle

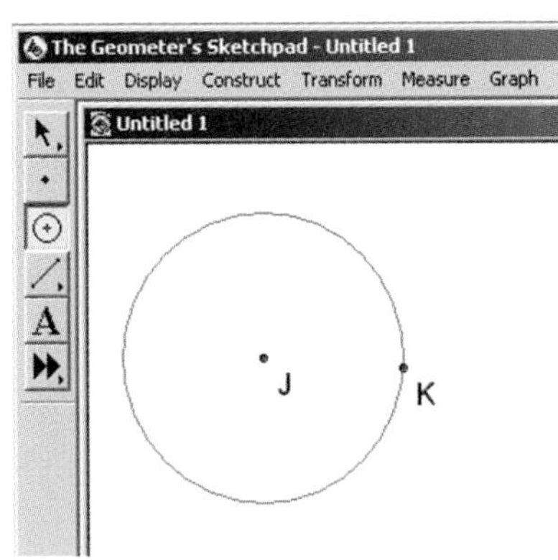


- Select the **Compass Tool**.
- Move the cursor to the point where you want the centre of the circle.
- Click and hold the left mouse button. Drag the cursor to the desired radius.
- Release the mouse button.

## Constructing Parallel and Perpendicular Lines

To construct a line parallel to LM, passing through N:

- Select the line segment LM (but not the end points), and the point N.
- Choose **Parallel Line** from the **Construct** menu.

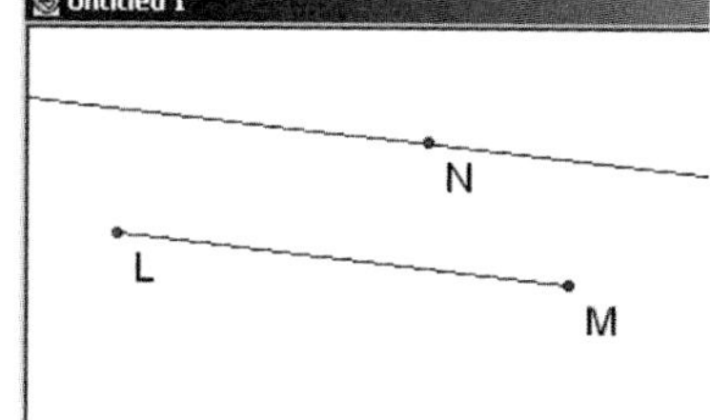


To construct a line perpendicular to LM, passing through N:

- Select the line segment LM (but not the end points), and the point N.
- Choose **Perpendicular Line** from the **Construct** menu.

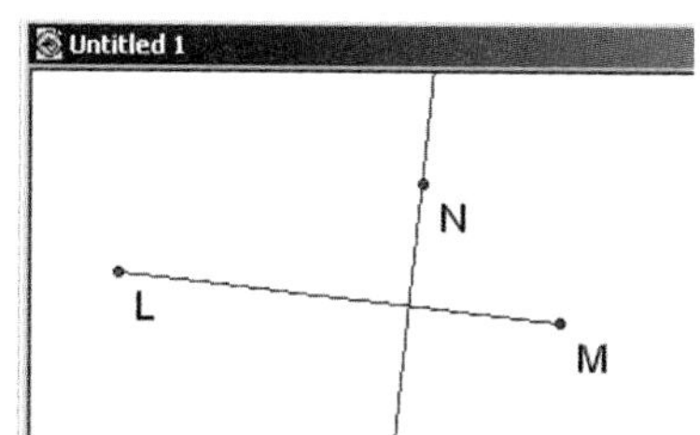


## Constructing Measures

To measure the distance between two points:

- Ensure nothing is selected.
- Select the two points.
- Choose **Distance** from the **Measure** menu.

*The Geometer's Sketchpad®* will display the distance between the points, using the units and accuracy selected in **Preferences…** under the **Edit** menu.

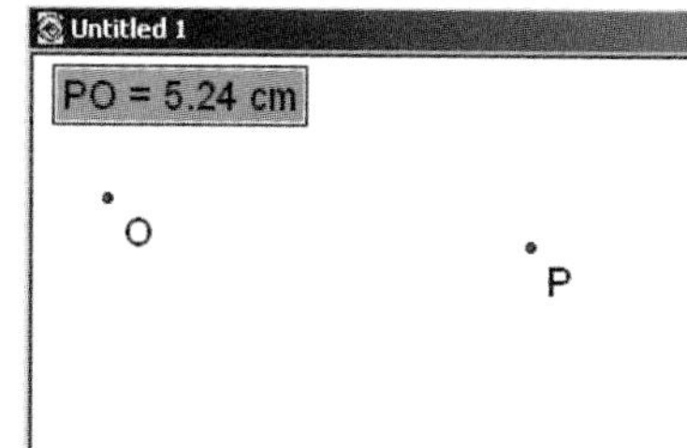


To measure the length of a line segment:

- Ensure nothing is selected.
- Select the line segment (but not the endpoints).
- Choose **Length** from the **Measure** menu.

To measure an angle:

- Ensure nothing is selected.
- Select the three points that define the angle, in the order Q, R, S. The second point selected is the vertex of the angle.
- Choose **Angle** from the **Measure** menu.

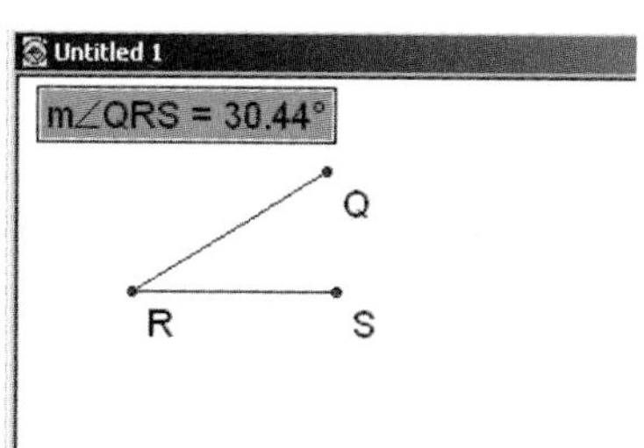

## Constructing and Measuring Polygon Interiors

*The Geometer's Sketchpad®* will measure the perimeter and the area of a polygon. However, you must first construct the interior of the polygon.

To construct the interior of this quadrilateral:

- Choose the four points of the quadrilateral, in either clockwise or counterclockwise order.
- Choose **Quadrilateral Interior** from the **Construct** menu. The interior of the quadrilateral will change colour.

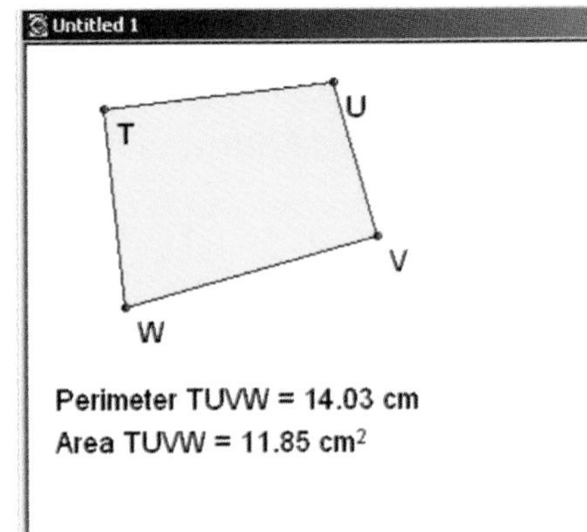


To measure the perimeter:

- Select the interior of the polygon. It will have a cross-hatched appearance when selected.
- Choose **Perimeter** from the **Measure** menu.

*The Geometer's Sketchpad®* will display the perimeter of the polygon, using the units and accuracy selected in **Preferences...** under the **Edit** menu.

To measure the area:

- Select the interior of the polygon.
- Choose **Area** from the **Measure** menu.

## Using the On-Screen Calculator

You can use the on-screen calculator to do calculations involving measurements, constants, functions, or other mathematical operations.

To add two distances:

- Choose **Calculate** from the **Measure** menu. The on-screen calculator will appear.
- From the workspace, click on the first measure.
- From the keyboard, click on +.
- From the workspace, click on the second measure.
- Click on **OK**.

The sum of the measures will appear in the workspace.

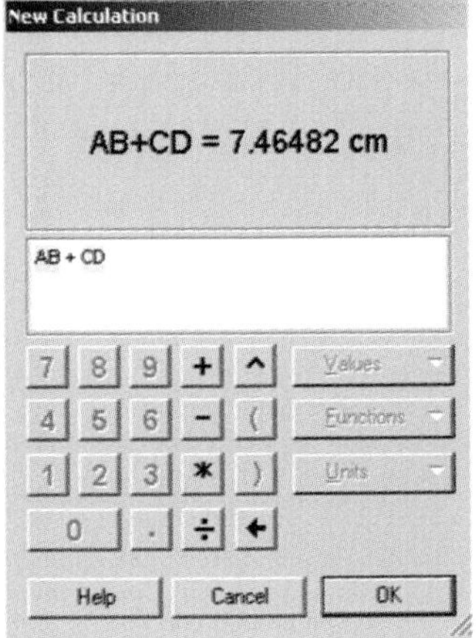

## Loading Custom Tools

Before you can use the **Custom Tool** in *The Geometer's Sketchpad®*, you must either create your own custom tools, or transfer the sample tools included with the program to the **Tool Folder**. Ask your teacher for guidance.

To transfer a sample custom tool:

- Open **Windows Explorer**, and navigate to the **Sketchpad** directory, or whatever directory was used to install *The Geometer's Sketchpad®*.
- Choose **Samples**, then **Custom Tools**. You will see a list of the custom tools provided with the program.
- Select the sets of tools you want to use. Then, select **Copy** from the **Edit** menu.
- Move back up two directory levels to the **Sketchpad** directory, and select **Tool Folder**. Select **Paste** from the **Edit** menu.
- Open *The Geometer's Sketchpad®*, and choose the **Custom Tool**.

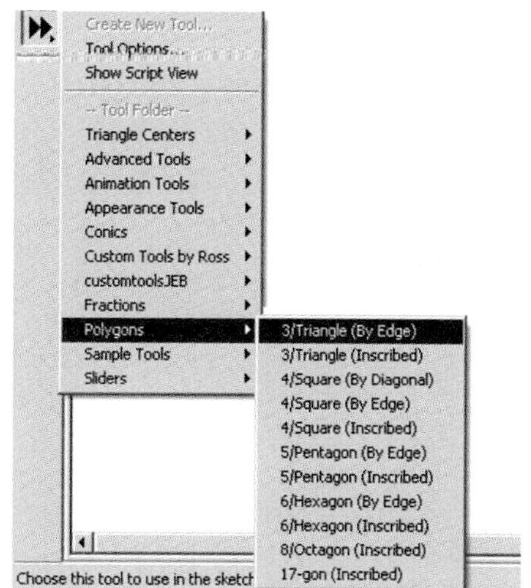


You will see the custom tool sets that you copied. Select one of the tool sets, say **Polygons**. You will see a list of the individual tools available.

# TI-83 AND TI-83 PLUS BASICS

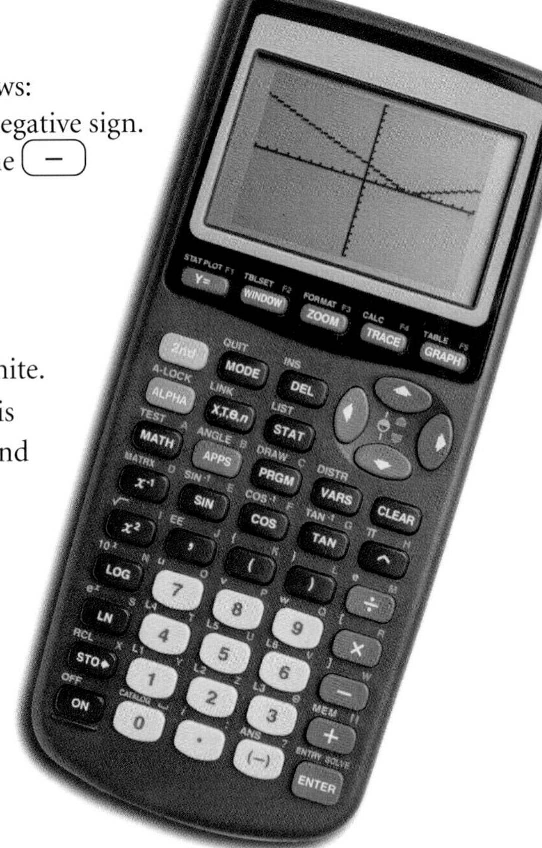


The keys on the TI-83 or TI-83 Plus are colour-coded, as follows:

- The grey keys include the number keys, decimal point, and negative sign. When entering negative values, use the (−) grey key, not the − blue key.
- The blue keys on the right side are the math operations.
- The blue keys with arrows move the cursor around.
- The blue keys across the top are used when graphing.
- The primary function of each key is printed on the key, in white.
- The secondary function of each key is printed in yellow and is activated by pressing the yellow 2nd key. For example, to find the square root of a number, press 2nd $x^2$.
- The alpha function of each key is printed in green and is activated by pressing the green ALPHA key.

## Working With Fractions

To display a decimal as a fraction:

- Key in a decimal.
- Press MATH, and select **1:Frac.** Press ENTER.

The decimal will be displayed as a fraction.

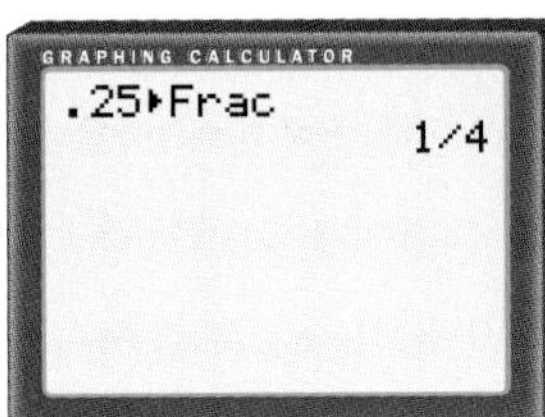


To enter fractions in calculations:

- Use the division key ÷ to create fractions as you key them in.
- If you want the result displayed as a fraction, press MATH, and select **1:Frac.**
- Press ENTER.

For example, calculate $\frac{3}{4} - \frac{2}{3}$ by pressing

**3** ÷ **4** − **2** ÷ **3** MATH **1:Frac** ENTER.

The result will be displayed as a fraction.

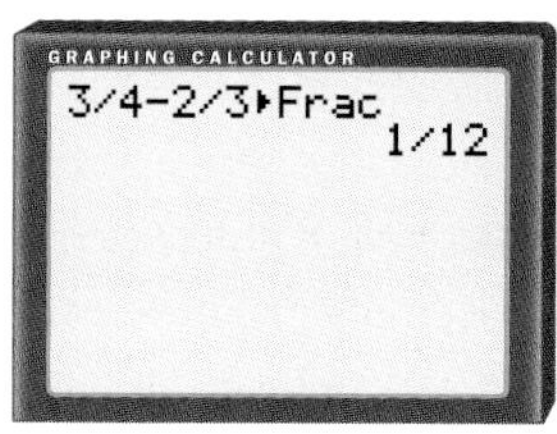


To calculate with mixed numbers:

- Use the + and ÷ keys to enter mixed numbers.
- If you want the result displayed as a fraction, press MATH, and select **1:Frac.**
- Press ENTER.

For example, calculate $2\frac{3}{8} + 1\frac{3}{4}$ by pressing

**2** + **3** ÷ **8** + **1** + **3** ÷ **4** MATH **1:Frac** ENTER.

The result will be displayed as a fraction.

## Graphing Relations and Equations

- Press Y=. Enter the equation.
- To display the graph, press GRAPH.

For example, enter $y = \frac{3}{5}x - 2$ by pressing

Y= ( **3** ÷ **5** ) X,T,θ,*n* − **2.**

Press GRAPH.

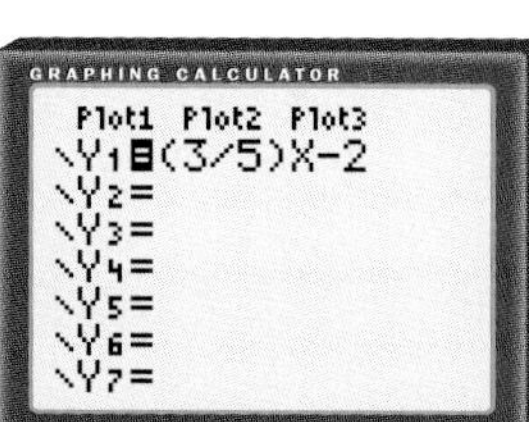


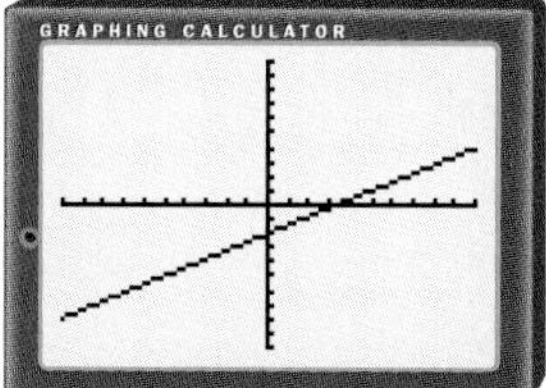


## Setting Window Variables

The WINDOW key defines the appearance of the graph. The standard (default) window settings are shown.

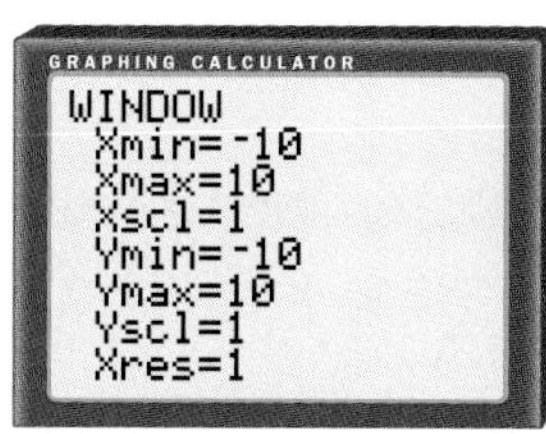


To change the window settings:

- Press WINDOW. Enter the desired window settings.

In the example shown,

- the minimum *x*-value is –47
- the maximum *x*-value is 47
- the scale of the *x*-axis is 10
- the minimum *y*-value is –31
- the maximum *y*-value is 31
- the scale of the *y*-axis is also 10
- the resolution is 1, so equations are graphed at each horizontal pixel

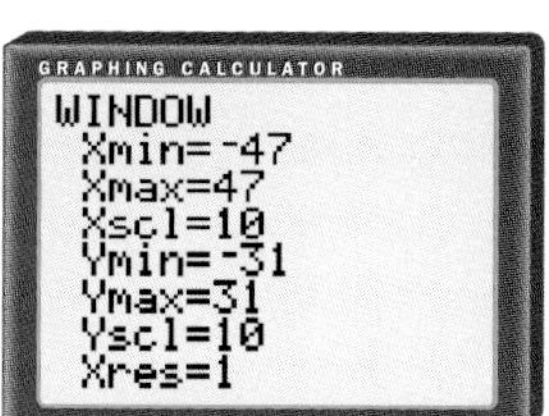

## Changing Line Style

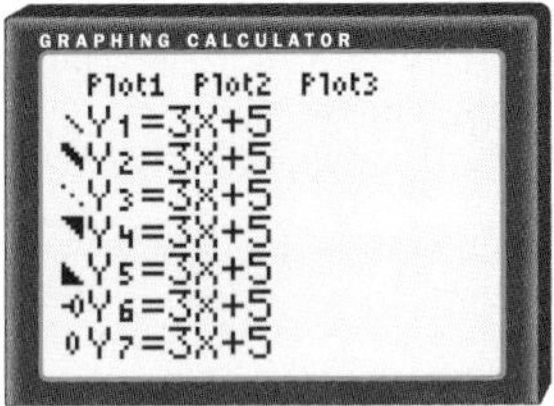


The default line appearance, or graph style, of the TI-83 Plus, is a thin, solid line. There are:

- three different line styles (thin ⧅, thick ⧅, and dot ⧅)
- two shading styles (shading either above ◥ or below ◣ the line)
- two circular styles (one tracing the graph ⧅ and the other animating it ⧅ — such as, the path of a bouncing ball)

- Press Y=.
- Using the ◀ key, cursor over to the slanted line just before the function **Y1** you are working on.
- Press ENTER repeatedly to go through the line styles.
- When you have come to the style you want, use the ▶ key to take you back to the function, or just press GRAPH to graph the function.

For example, the equation $y = 3x + 5$ is shown in the three line styles.

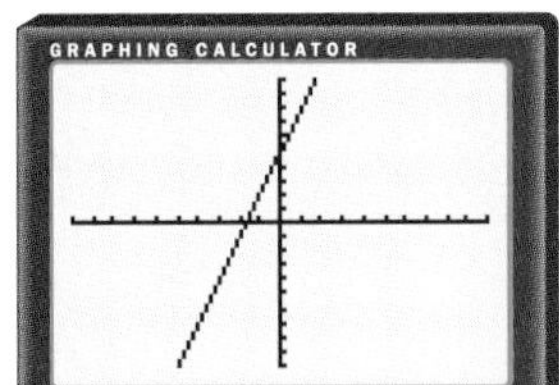


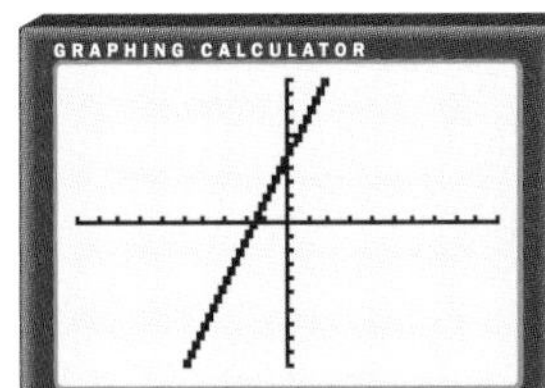


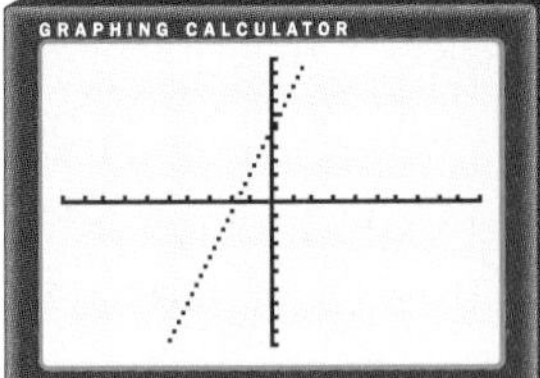


## Tracing a Graph

- Enter a function using Y=.
- Press TRACE.
- Press ◀ and ▶ to move along the graph.
  The $x$- and $y$-values are displayed at the bottom of the screen.

## Setting the Format

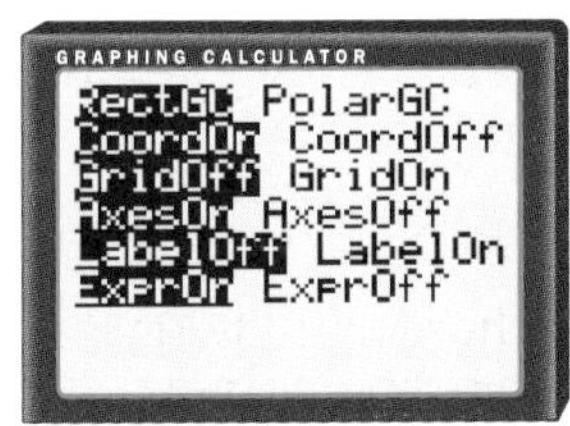


To define a graph's appearance:

- Press 2nd ZOOM for [**FORMAT**] to view the choices available.

The **Default Settings**, shown here, have all the features on the left "turned on."

To use Grid Off/Grid On:

- Select [**FORMAT**] by pressing 2nd ZOOM. Cursor down and right to **GridOn**. Press ENTER.
- Press 2nd MODE for [**QUIT**].

## Using Zoom

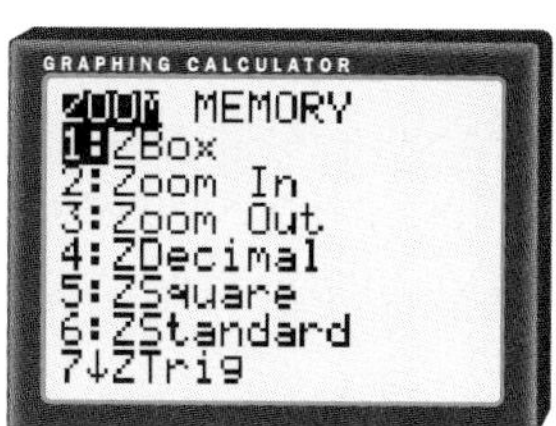


The (ZOOM) key is used to change the area of the graph that is displayed in the graphing window.

To set the size of the area you want to zoom in on:
- Press (ZOOM). Select **1:Zbox**. The graph screen will be displayed, and the cursor will be flashing.
- If you cannot see the cursor, use the (◄), (►), (▲), and (▼) keys to move the cursor until you see it.
- Move the cursor to an area on the perimeter of where you would like a closer view. Press (ENTER) to mark that point as a starting point.
- Press the (◄), (►), (▲), and (▼) keys as needed to move the sides of the box to enclose the area you want to look at.
- Press (ENTER) when you are finished. The area will now appear larger.

To zoom in on an area without identifying a boxed-in area:
- Press (ZOOM). Select **2:Zoom In**.

To zoom out of an area:
- Press (ZOOM). Select **3:Zoom Out**.

To display the viewing area where the origin appears in the centre and the *x*- and *y*-axes intervals are equally spaced:
- Press (ZOOM). Select **4:ZDecimal**.

To reset the axes range on your calculator:
- Press (ZOOM). Select **6:ZStandard**.

## Plotting Points

- Press the (ZOOM) key, and select **4:ZDecimal**.
- Press (2nd)(PRGM) to access the **DRAW** menu.
- Press (►) once to select [**POINTS**]. Press (ENTER).
- Use the (▲), (▼), (►), and (◄) keys to move the cursor to your chosen point. Press (ENTER).

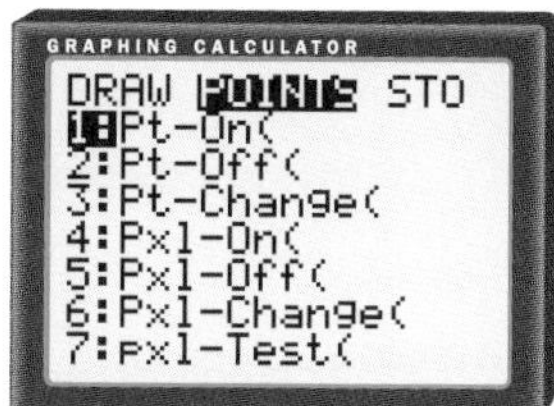


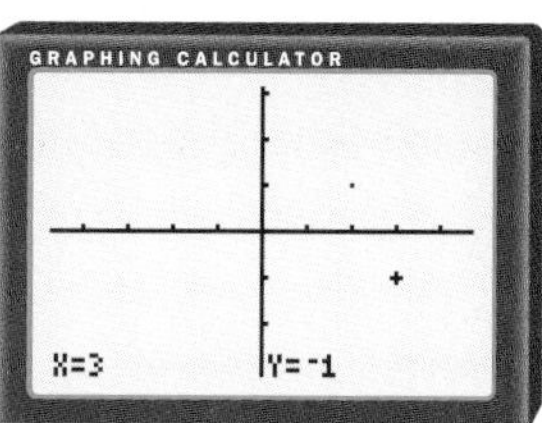

## Entering Data Into Lists

To enter data:

- Press (STAT). The cursor will highlight the **EDIT** menu.
- Press **1** or (ENTER) to select **Edit…** mode.
  This allows you to enter new data, or edit existing data, in lists **L1** to **L6**.

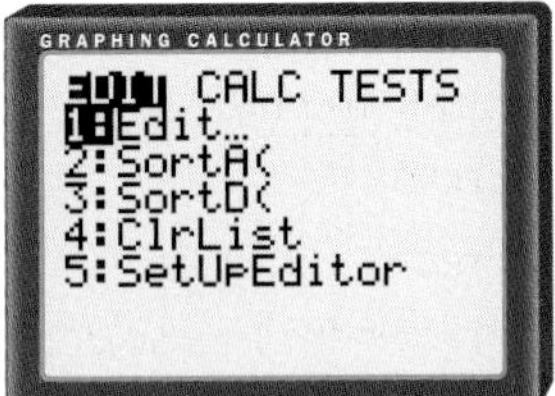


For example, press (STAT) **1** or (STAT) (ENTER), and enter six test scores in **L1**.

- Use the cursor to move around the editor screen.
- Complete each data entry by pressing (ENTER).
- Press (2nd) (MODE) for [**QUIT**] to exit the list editor when the data are entered.

You may need to clear a list before you enter data into it. For example, to clear list **L1**:

- Press (STAT) **4** to select **ClrList**.
- Press (2nd) **1** for [**L1**], and press (ENTER).

## 1-Variable Statistics

To obtain statistics for a data set, for example the values 9, 10, 18, 14, 13, 10, 14, 10, 17, 5:

- Enter the data set in a list, for example **L1.**
- Press (STAT) and cursor across to select the **CALC** menu.
- Press **1** or (ENTER) to select **1-Var Stats.**
- Press (2nd) **1** for [**L1**], then (ENTER).

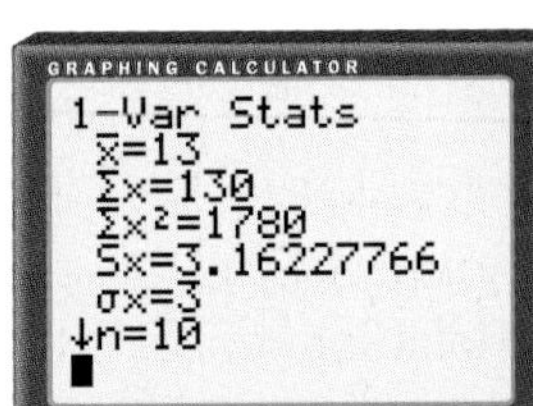


A set of statistics are displayed.

- The first line, "$\overline{x}$=," gives the mean.
- The final line on the first screen, "n=," gives the number of data.

You can cursor down for more statistics.

- "minX=" gives the minimum value in the data set.
- "Med=" gives the median of the data set.
- "maxX=" gives the maximum value.

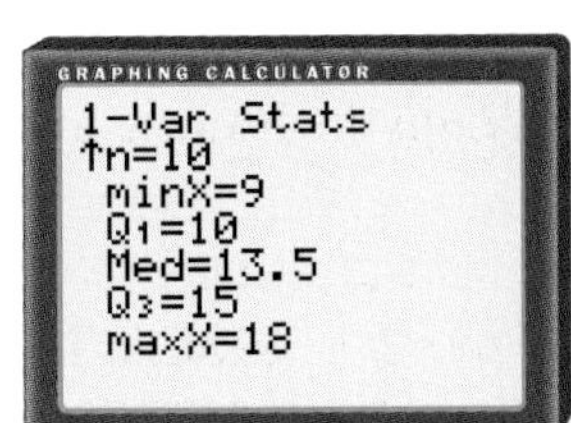

### Creating a Scatter Plot

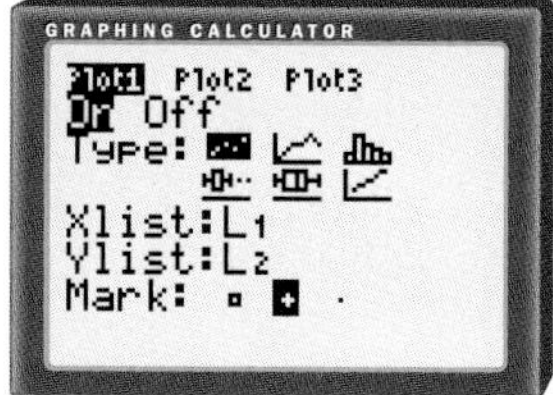


To create a scatter plot:

- Enter the two data sets in lists **L1** and **L2**.
- Press (2nd)(Y=) for [**STAT PLOT**].
- Press **1** or (ENTER) for **Plot 1…**
- Press (ENTER) to select **On**.
- Cursor down, then (ENTER) to select the top left graphing option, a scatter plot.
- Cursor down and press (2nd) **1** for [**L1**].
- Cursor down and press (2nd) **2** for [**L2**].
- Cursor down and select a mark style by pressing (ENTER).
- Press (2nd)(MODE) for [**QUIT**] to exit the stat plot editor.

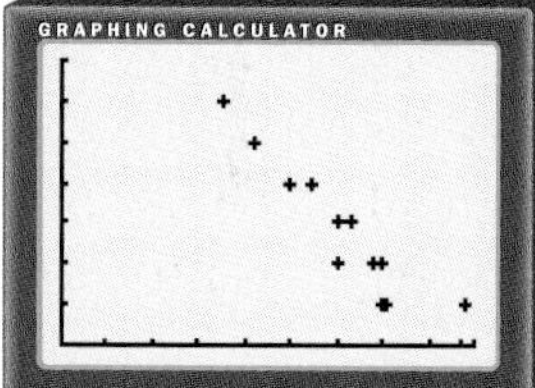


To display the scatter plot:

- Press (Y=) and use (CLEAR) to remove any graphed equations.
- Press (2nd)(MODE) for [**QUIT**] to exit the **Y=** editor.
- Press (ZOOM) **9:ZoomStat** to display the scatter plot.

# CBR™ (Calculator-Based Ranger)

### Using the CBR™ With the TI-83 Plus Graphing Calculator

To access the CBR™ through the TI-83 Plus:

- Connect CBR™ to the TI-83 Plus with the calculator-to-CBR cable. Make sure both ends of the cable are firmly in place.
- Press (APPS). Select **2:CBL/CBR**.
- When the CBL/CBR menu is presented, press (ENTER).
- To access the programs available, select **3:Ranger**.
- When the **Ranger** menu is presented press (ENTER).

To set the units:

- Press **3:APPLICATIONS**. Then, select **1:METERS**. The **APPLICATIONS** menu will appear with a choice of programs.

# Answers

## Chapter 1

### Get Ready, pages 2–3

**1. a)** 45 **b)** 210 **c)** 45 **d)** 79 **e)** 169 **f)** 103 **g)** 133 **h)** 198 **i)** 530
**2. a)** 43 **b)** 45 **c)** 1807 **d)** 420 **e)** 44 **f)** 0
**3. a)** 12 **b)** 16 **c)** 100 **d)** 5467
**4. a)** 25.3 **b)** 176.1 **c)** 0.1 **d)** 0.2
**5. a)** 1300 **b)** 54 300 **c)** 1 993 600 **d)** 100
**6. a)** 12 000 cm **b)** 15 000 m **c)** 41 mm **d)** 0.65 m **e)** 0.8 km **f)** 1340 mg **g)** 4.2 g **h)** 1020 mL **i)** 7.5 L
**7.** Answers may vary.

### 1.1 Connecting Perimeter With Whole Numbers and Decimals, pages 7–9

**1. a)** 21.6 **b)** 302.86 **c)** 65.6 **d)** 141.736 **e)** 10.58 **f)** 2388.1 **g)** 112.1 **h)** 16.2
**2. a)** 56 cm **b)** 179.4 cm **c)** 352.8 mm
**3. a)** 94.9 cm **b)** 21.4 m
**4. a)** 8.4 cm; 13.7 cm; 76.4 cm **b)** 6.5 m; 37.4 m
**5. a)** 13.7 m **b)** $25.35
**6. a)** A square has four equal sides. To find the length of one side, divide the perimeter by 4. **b)** 0.3 m
**7.** 1.5 cm
**8.** 283 cm
**9.** 19 m
**10.** The vertical supports can be cut from a 4.0 m board (1.8 m × 2). The waste would be 4.0 m – 3.6 m, or 0.4 m. The shelves can be cut from two 3.0 m boards and one 2.0 m board, leaving a waste of 8.0 m – 7.5 m, or 0.5 m. Total waste would be 0.9 m.

### 1.2 Estimation, pages 13–15

**1. a)** $139 **b)** 30 km **c)** 570 mm **d)** 7¢ **e)** 2101 L **f)** 35 m
**2. a)** 13 500 km **b)** 100 cm **c)** $200 **d)** 100 years **e)** 600 m **f)** 100 L
**3. a)** 1.5 kg **b)** 12.3 mm **c)** 612.8 L **d)** 53.0 cm **e)** 6.1 mL **f)** 1.0 km
**4. a)** A **b)** I **c)** H **d)** C **e)** J **f)** B **g)** D **h)** G **i)** K **j)** E
**5. a)** 70 **b)** 80 **c)** 30 **d)** 10
**6. a)** no **b)** yes **c)** no **d)** no
**7. a)** $1, $2, $5, $5, $3, $4, $6, $9 **b)** $35 **c)** $5
**8. a)** $1.27 **b)** $2.32 **c)** $0.68 **d)** $2.93
**9. a)** $1.90 **b)** $1.25 **c)** $8.50 **d)** $5.67
**10.** Answers may vary.
**11.** 6 km/h
**12. a)** $36 **b)** $17 **c)** 55 L
**13.** 172.8 L
**14.** Answers may vary.

### 1.3 Exponents and the Order of Operations, pages 20–21

**1. a)** $6^4$ **b)** $9^4$ **c)** $12^1$ **d)** $15^2$ **e)** $8^5$ **f)** $5^7$
**2. a)** 2 **b)** 3 **c)** 10 **d)** 7 **e)** 1 **f)** 12
**3. a)** 16 807 **b)** 6561 **c)** 20 736 **d)** 7776 **e)** 1.96 **f)** 185.193
**4. a)** The base is 3 and the exponent increases by 1; $3^1$, $3^2$, $3^3$, $3^4$, $3^5$ **b)** The base increases by 1 and the exponent is always 2; $1^2$, $2^2$, $3^2$, $4^2$, $5^2$, $6^2$, $7^2$ **c)** The base is 10 and the exponent starts at 0 and increases by 1; $10^0$, $10^1$, $10^2$, $10^3$, $10^4$ **d)** The base is 2 and the exponent starts at 0 and increases by 1; $2^0$, $2^1$, $2^2$, $2^3$, $2^4$, $2^5$ **e)** The base increases by 1 and the exponent is always 3; $1^3$, $2^3$, $3^3$, $4^3$ **f)** The numerator is always 1. The denominator is the base of 4 with an exponent starting at 0 and increasing by 1; $\frac{1}{4^0}, \frac{1}{4^1}, \frac{1}{4^2}, \frac{1}{4^3}, \frac{1}{4^4}$
**5. a)** 900 **b)** 52 **c)** 100 **d)** 12 **e)** 8 **f)** 143 **g)** 192 **h)** 9.4 **i)** −28.46 **j)** 1 **k)** 180 **l)** 10
**6. a)** $3 + 2 \times (15 - 7) = 19$ **b)** $(4^2 - 7)^2 = 81$ **c)** $10 \div (2.3 + 7.7) = 1$ **d)** $(3^2 - 1) \div 5 = 1.6$
**7. a)** 4000 **b)** 16 000 **c)** 16 384 000
**8.** B
**9. a)** 8 **b)** 16 **c)** 1024
**10. a)** 5, 0.5 **b)** 6, 0.6 **c)** 9, 0.9 **d)** 2, 0.2
**11. a)** $0.25 \times 1572 + 72.95 \times 8 + 2.50 \times 8$ **b)** $8 \times (72.95 + 2.50) + (0.25 \times 1572)$ **c)** $996.60

### 1.4 Working with Area and Other Formulas, pages 24–27

**1. a)** 16 $cm^2$ **b)** 240 $mm^2$ **c)** 90 $m^2$ **d)** 22.7 $cm^2$ **e)** 120.8 $m^2$ **f)** 63.6 $mm^2$
**2. a)** 20 **b)** 31.4 **c)** 160 **d)** 34 **e)** 30 **f)** 10 **g)** 4.2 **h)** 13.9

**3. a)** 283.5 mm$^2$ **b)** 3.1 cm$^2$ **c)** 254.5 mm$^2$ **d)** 4.5 cm$^2$ **e)** 5.3 cm$^2$ **f)** 6.2 cm$^2$
**4. a)** 105 cm$^2$ **b)** 2500 **c)** 4200 cm$^2$ **d)** 10 500 000 cm$^2$
**5. a)** 15 m **b)** 20 m **c)** 18.75 m **d)** 0 m **e)** From zero to two seconds, the stone is moving higher in the air. At two seconds, it has reached its highest point. From two to four seconds, the stone is falling in the air. At four seconds it has hit the ground.
**6. a)** 14 cm$^2$ **b)** 25 cm$^2$ **c)** 18 cm$^2$
**7. a)** 0.2 km/h **b)** 0.4 km/h **c)** 0.7 km/h
**8. a)** 208 **b)** 194 **c)** 158 **d)** Answers may vary.
**9. a)** 1560 L **b)** 3620 L
**10. a)** \$600 **b)** \$1140
**11.** 294°

## Review, pages 28–29

**1. a)** 50 cm **b)** 52.8 cm **c)** 79.2 cm **d)** 26 cm
**2.** 9 m
**3. a)** yes **b)** no **c)** no
**4. a)** 127 cm **b)** 10.5 cm
**5. a)** $8^6$ **b)** $17^3$ **c)** $9^1$
**6. a)** 6 **b)** 10 **c)** 7
**7. a)** 121 **b)** 1 **c)** 10 **d)** 14 **e)** 8
**8. a)** 81 **b)** 729 **c)** $3^{20}$
**9.** 28.7 cm$^2$
**10.** 5226 mm$^2$
**11.** 113.1 cm$^2$
**12.** 70 cm$^2$

## Practice Test, pages 30–31

**1.** A **2.** C **3.** D **4.** B **5.** C
**6.** To find the area, you multiply two lengths, which results in cm × cm. This can be expressed as cm$^2$.
**7.** The digit in the tenths column is 4. The digit to the right of it is a 7, which is greater than 5, so you round up. So, you get 23.5 cm.
**8. a)** base **b)** exponent **c)** standard form
**9.** perimeter 4.2 m; area 0.9 m$^2$
**10.** Answers may vary.
**11.** Yes. The area of the first poster board is 2400 cm$^2$ and the area of the second poster board is 9600 cm$^2$. The second poster board has 4 times the area of the first, and is 4 times the price.
**12. a)** \$17 000 **b)** Yes, because for 1400 yearbooks the cost is \$19 000, but for 1500 yearbooks the cost is \$18 500.

# CHAPTER 2

## Get Ready, pages 34–35

**1. a)** 13 **b)** 17.4 **c)** −10 **d)** 16.3 **e)** 16
**2. a)** 18 **b)** 8 **c)** 26
**3. a)** 50 mm **b)** 10 cm **c)** 11.0 m
**4. a)** 30 m **b)** 20.4 cm **c)** 24 km
**5. a)** 12 m **b)** 24 cm **c)** 11.2 cm
**6. a)** 154 mm$^2$ **b)** 6.25 cm$^2$ **c)** 6 m$^2$
**7. a)** 30 m$^2$ **b)** 17.6 cm$^2$ **c)** 25 km

## 2.1 The Pythagorean Theorem, pages 40–41

**1. a)** $y$ **b)** $p$ **c)** $w$
**2. a)** 10 mm **b)** 5.3 cm **c)** 9 m
**3. a)** 5 m **b)** 12 mm **c)** 36 m
**4. a)** 16 m **b)** 8.0 cm **c)** 15 m
**5.** 50 km
**6.** 9″
**7. a)** Square the distance between both the bases and find the sum of the squares. Take the square root of the sum to find the distance from the home plate to second base. **b)** 38 m
**8.** 75 m

## 2.2 Perimeter and Area of Right Triangles, pages 45–47

**1. a)** 7.4 m **b)** 30 m **c)** 143 mm
**2. a)** 20 mm$^2$ **b)** 160 m$^2$ **c)** 13 cm$^2$
**3. a)** 11.0 cm **b)** 0.86 cm **c)** 23.6 m
**4. a)** 26.5 cm **b)** 2.03 cm **c)** 57.0 m
**5. a)** 27 cm$^2$ **b)** 0.16 cm$^2$ **c)** 139 m$^2$
**6. a)** 13.4 cm **b)** 53 km
**7. a)** 30 mm$^2$ **c)** 62.7 cm$^2$
**8. a)** Find the length from sprocket M to L using the Pythagorean theorem. Add the lengths from sprockets K to M, K to L, and L to M together. **b)** 133 cm
**9. a)** 6.6 m **b)** 23.4 m **c)** \$79.38
**10.** 5.8 km

## 2.4 Perimeter and Area of Composite Figures, pages 60–63

**1. a)** $a = 32$ m, $b = 19$ m; 132 m **b)** $a = 2$ cm, $b = 6$ cm, $c = 8$ cm; 32 cm **c)** $a = 4$ cm, $b = 12$ cm; 52 cm
**2. a)** 40 cm$^2$ **b)** 530 cm$^2$

**3. a)** two rectangles; 77 $cm^2$ **b)** two triangles, rectangle; 20 $m^2$ **c)** three rectangles; 400 $mm^2$
**4. a)** 22 cm **b)** 54 cm
**5.** The 1.8 m measurement should not to be included. The perimeter is 17.5 m.
**6.** 320 $cm^2$
**7. a)** 62 cm **b)** 230 $cm^2$
**8. a)** 401 m **b)** 464 m **c)** 63 m
**9. a)** 4000 $cm^2$ **b)** 3 cans **c)** $34.33
**12. a)** 480 $m^2$ **b)** 10 kg
**13. a)** large circle 11 mm, small circle 1.5 mm **b)** 380 $mm^2$ **c)** 7.1 $mm^2$ **d)** 48 $mm^2$ **e)** Half the area of the large circle, then, subtract the area of the small white circle. **f)** 180 $mm^2$

## 2.5 Maximizing the Area of a Rectangle, pages 70–71

**1. a)** 4 m by 4 m **b)** 7 cm by 7 cm **c)** 12 km by 12 km **d)** 250 m by 250 m
**2.** 36 $m^2$
**3. a)** 640 $m^2$ **b)** 1800 $m^2$
**4. a)**

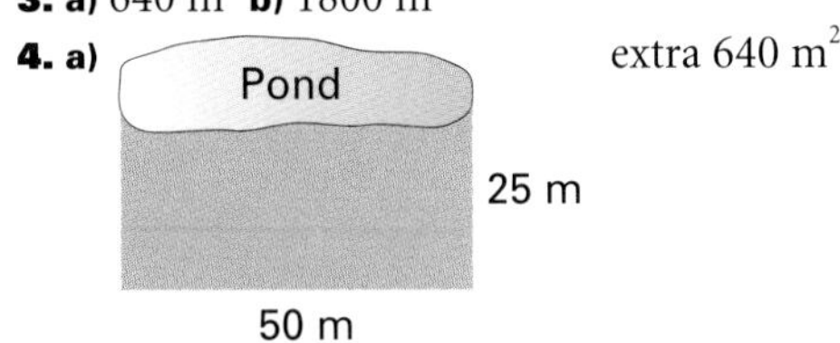


extra 640 $m^2$

**b)**

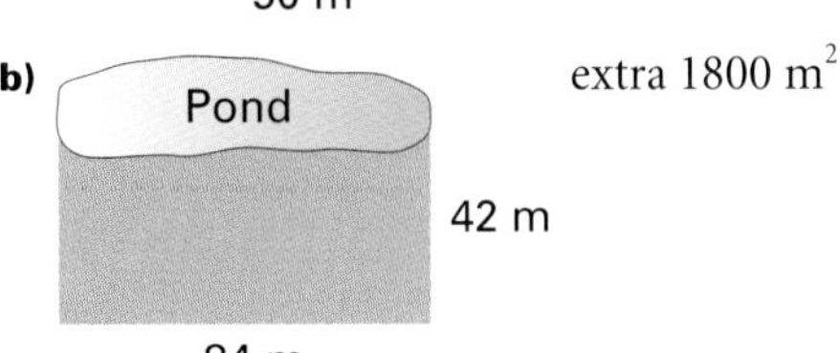


extra 1800 $m^2$

**5. a)** square **b)** Answers may vary.
**c)**

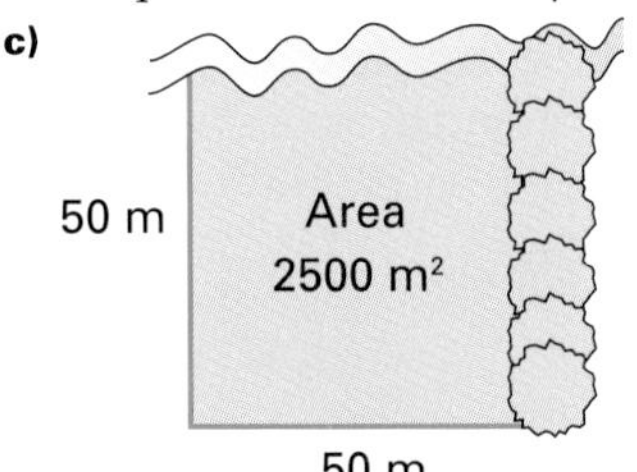


**d)** no borders: 25 m by 25 m, area 625 $m^2$; with two borders: 50 m by 50 m, area 2500 $m^2$
**e)** one border; 33 m by 67 m, area 2200 $m^2$
**6. a)** 22.5 m by 22.5 m **b)** Because 22.5 m cannot be created using 3 m barriers. **c)** Answers may vary.
**7.** Answers may vary.
**8. a)** 2.5 m by 2.5 m **b)** 6.25 $m^2$ **c)** Use a natural border like the border of the roof or use a circular window.
**9. b)** triangle 62 $m^2$, rectangle 81 $m^2$, hexagon 94 $m^2$, circle 100 $m^2$

## Review, pages 72–73

**1. a)** 8.6 cm **b)** 9 cm
**2.** 16 m
**3.** 1.9 km
**4.** 105 km
**5.** 117 $m^2$
**6. a)** 26 cm **b)** 16 cm
**7. a)** 120 $cm^2$ **b)** 74 $m^2$
**9. a)** 17 m by 17 m **b)** 17 m by 34 m **c)** 290 $m^2$

## Practice Test, pages 74–75

**1.** A **2.** B **3.** B **4.** C **5.** B
**6.** Estimate the diameter of the entire doughnut and find the area. Estimate the diameter of the hole in the doughnut and find the area. Subtract the area of the hole from the area of the doughnut.
**7. a)** Find the area of the rectangular part. Find the area of the semi-circular part. Add the area of the semi-circle to the area of the rectangle. **b)** 1.5 $m^2$
**8. a)** You need to divide the perimeter of the circle by two to find the perimeter of the semi-circle. You need to subtract the side of the rectangle that attaches to the semi-circle. **b)** 5.9 m
**9. a)** 7 m by 7 m **b)** 7 m by 14 m

# CHAPTER 3

## Get Ready, pages 78–79

**1. a)** 16 cm **b)** 383 mm **c)** 38 m
**2. a)** 20 cm$^2$ **b)** 11 700 mm$^2$ **c)** 110 m$^2$
**3. a)** 63 **b)** 180 **c)** 38 **d)** 59 **e)** 200 **f)** 110
**4. a)** 26 mm **b)** 3.2 cm **c)** 2.5 m

## 3.1 Volume: Prisms and Cylinders, pages 84–85

**1. a)** 10 m$^3$ **b)** 4000 mm$^3$ **c)** 95 cm$^3$
**2. a)** 35 m$^3$ **b)** 25 000 mm$^3$
**3. a)** 90 cm$^3$ **b)** 700 m$^3$ **c)** 12 000 cm$^3$
**4. a)**

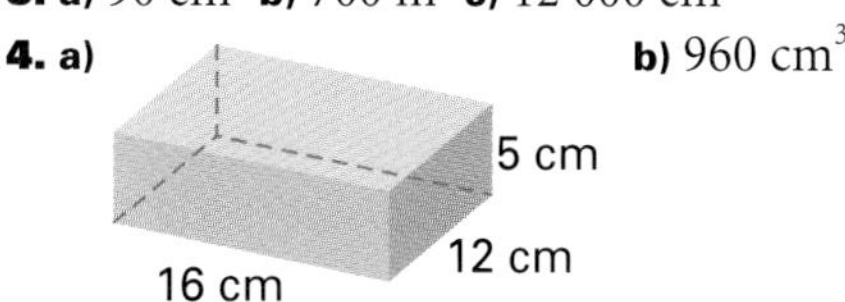


**b)** 960 cm$^3$
**5. a)** 6.3 m$^3$
**b)**

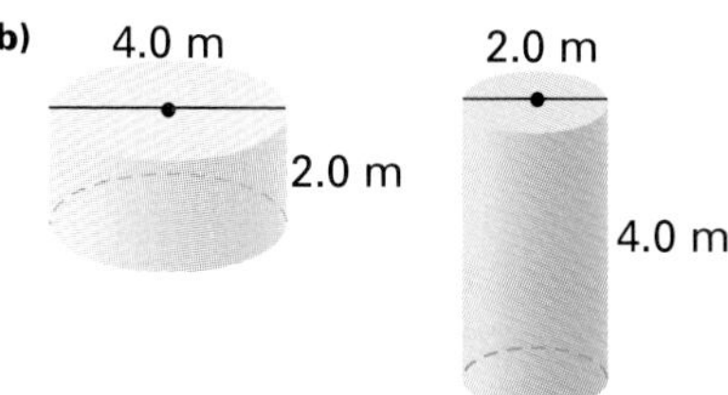


**c)** 25 m$^3$, 13 m$^3$
**7.** 1800 cm$^3$
**8. a)** 7600 cm$^3$

## 3.2 Volume: Cones and Spheres, pages 89–91

**1. a)** 3 cm$^3$ **b)** 150 cm$^3$ **c)** 2300 mm$^3$
**2. a)** 15 300 cm$^3$ **b)** 170 m$^3$ **c)** 27 mm$^3$
**3.** 1700 cm$^3$
**4. a)** 3.1 cm$^3$ **b)** 37 cm$^3$
**5. a)** 75 cm$^3$ **b)** 7 times
**6. a)** 14 cm$^3$ **b)** 36
**7. a)** Farouk **b)** Assume the height and radius are the same for both containers.
**8. a)** 1.7 cm$^3$
**b)**

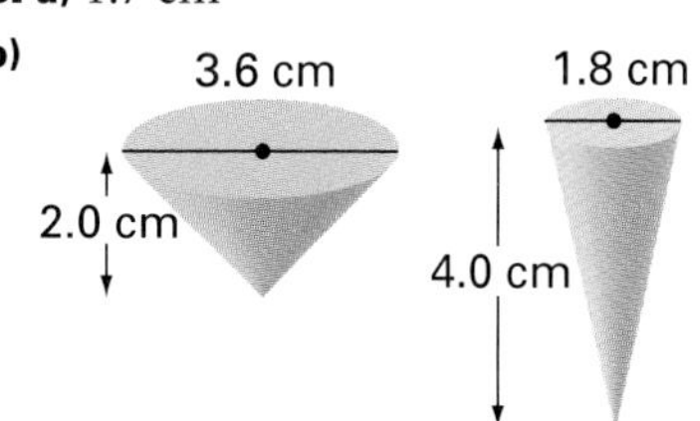


**c)** 6.8 cm$^3$, 3.4 cm$^3$
**9. a)** 34 cm$^3$ **b)** Answers may vary. **c)** 270 cm$^3$
**10. a)** 110 cm$^3$, 900 cm$^3$ **b)** When the radius is doubled, the volume increases by a factor of 8.
**11. a)** 24 cm$^3$ **b)** 3
**12.** $1.4 \times 10^{11}$ km$^3$
**13. a)** 48 cm$^3$ **b)** Find the volume of the outer sphere, 113.1 cm$^3$. Find the volume of the inside hollow sphere, 65.5 cm$^3$. Subtract the inside sphere from the outer sphere.
**14. a)** 1000 cm$^3$ **b)** First find the height of the cone, using the Pythagorean theorem.

## 3.3 Surface Area: Rectangular Prisms, pages 96–99

**1. a)** 59 m$^2$ **b)** 1400 mm$^2$
**2. a)**

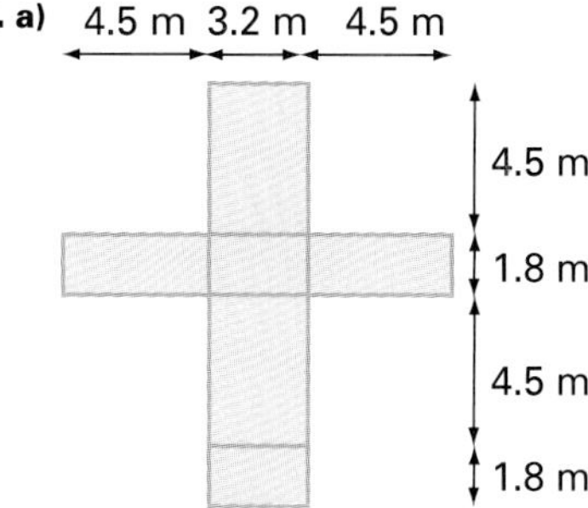


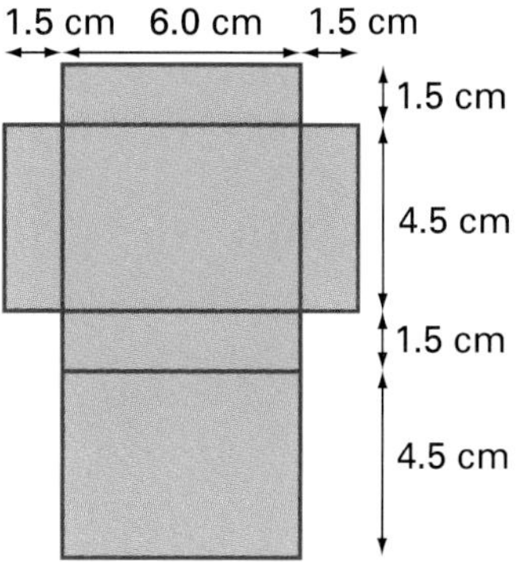


**3. a)** 57 m$^2$ **b)** 86 cm$^2$
**4.** 130 000 cm$^2$

**5. a)** 1200 cm$^2$ **b)** 1200 cm$^2$ **c)** The answers are the same. **d)** This formula works because all sides are the same.

**6. a)** 5 faces

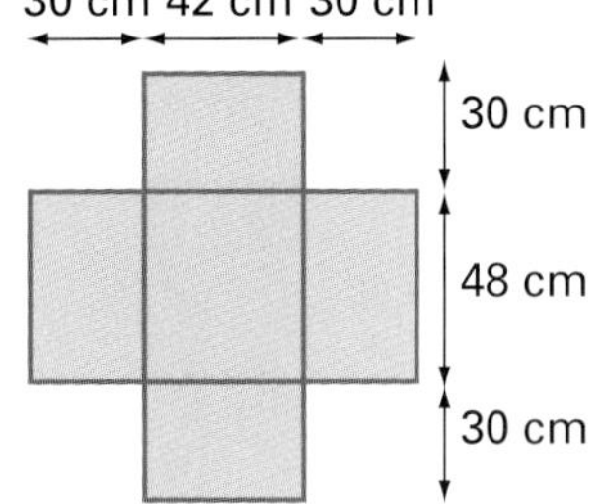


**b)** 7400 cm$^2$ **c)** 2000 cm$^2$

**7. a)** 18 cm by 18 cm by 15 cm; Answers may vary.

**b)**

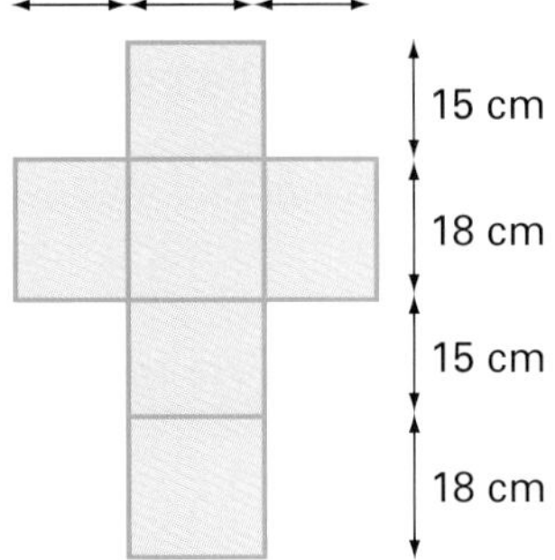


**c)** 1400 cm$^2$

**8. a)** Answers may vary. **b)** A 580 cm$^3$, B 580 cm$^3$, C 580 cm$^3$ . **c)** Answers may vary. **d)** A 420 cm$^2$, B 480 cm$^2$, C 610 cm$^2$ **e)** cube with sides 8.3 cm, 410 cm$^2$

**9. a)** 1.5 m$^2$ **b)** four times the area **c)** 6.0 m$^2$ **d)** 24 m$^2$, 96 m$^2$ **e)** nine times the area; 13.5 cm$^2$

**10. a)** 260 cm$^2$ **b)** 0.026 L

## 3.4 Surface Area: Cylinders and Prisms, pages 104–105

**1. a)** 3600 cm$^2$ **b)** 60 m$^2$ **c)** 570 mm$^2$

**2. a)** 320 m$^2$ **b)** 22 m$^2$

**3.** 3600 cm$^2$

**4. a)** Answers may vary. **b)** X: 300 cm$^2$, Y: 600 cm$^2$; Cylinder Y has double the surface area of Cylinder X. **c)** Answers may vary. **d)** X: 400 cm$^3$, Y: 800 cm$^3$; Cylinder Y has double the volume of Cylinder X

**5. a)** 1200 cm$^2$ **b)** 55 m$^2$

**6. a)**

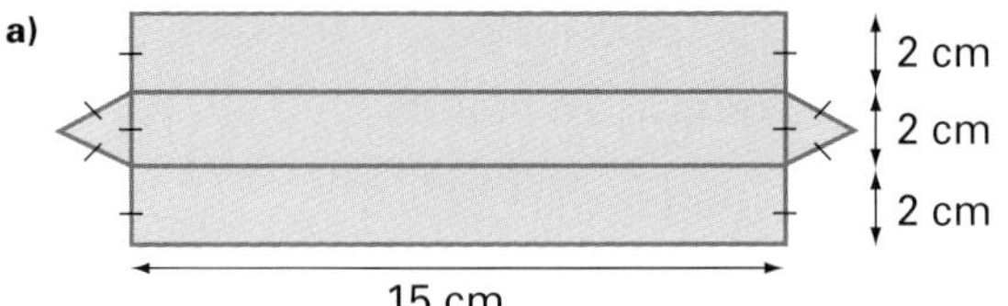


**b)** 93 cm$^2$

## 3.5 Minimizing Surface Area, pages 110–111

**1.** B, A, C

**2.** B, A, C

**3.** 10 cm by 10 cm by 10 cm

**4. a)** 12.6 cm by 12.6 cm by 12.6 cm **b)** 2 L converts to 2000 cm. The cube root of 2000 cm$^3$ is approximately 12.6 cm.

**5.** $r = 4.3$ cm, $h = 8.6$ cm

**6.** $r = 4.0$ cm, $h = 8.0$ cm

**7. a)** 46 cm by 46 cm by 46 cm **b)** 13 000 cm$^2$

## Review, pages 112–113

**1. a)** 30 cm$^3$ **b)** 130 mm$^3$

**2.** 15 m$^3$

**3. b)** 59 m$^3$

**4.** 8180 mm$^3$

**5. a)** 11 000 cm$^3$ **b)** 110 cm$^3$ **c)** 100. No, because there will be space wasted in between pucks.

**6. a)** Answers may vary. **b)** 600 cm$^3$ **c)** Answers may vary.

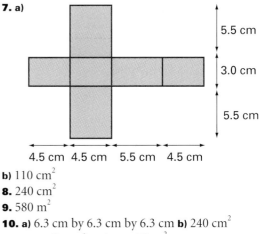

**7. a)**

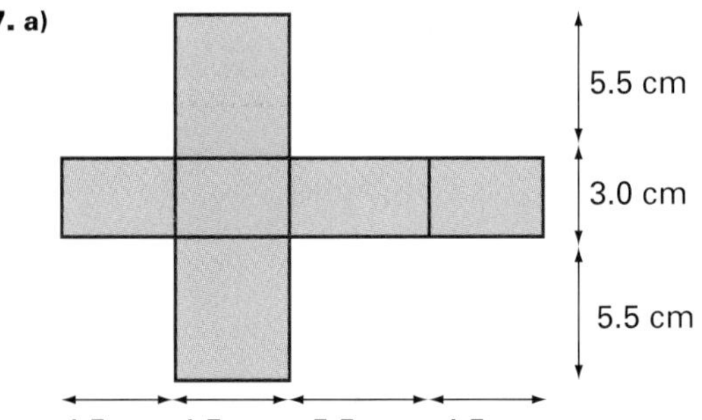


**b)** 110 cm$^2$

**8.** 240 cm$^2$

**9.** 580 m$^2$

**10. a)** 6.3 cm by 6.3 cm by 6.3 cm **b)** 240 cm$^2$

**11. a)** $r = 2$ m , $h = 4$ m **b)** 75 m$^2$

## Practice Test, pages 114–115

**1.** C **2.** D **3.** D **4.** C **5.** A **6.** A **7.** B

**8. a)**

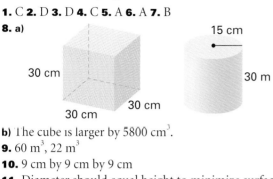

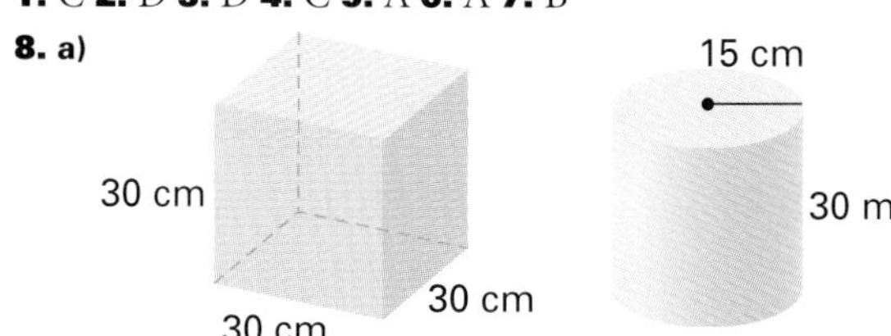


**b)** The cube is larger by 5800 $cm^3$.

**9.** 60 $m^3$, 22 $m^3$

**10.** 9 cm by 9 cm by 9 cm

**11.** Diameter should equal height to minimize surface area.

## Cumulative Review, pages 116–117

**1. a)** 22 cm **b)** 17.8 cm **c)** 4.7 m

**2. a)** 72 $cm^2$ **b)** 15 $m^2$

**3. a)** 13 **b)** 26 **c)** 7

**4. a)** 24 $cm^2$ **b)** 5400 $cm^2$ **c)** 13.5 $m^2$

**5. a)** 15 cm **b)** 7.0 m **c)** 8 mm

**6. a)** 23.2 m **b)** 21.4 m **c)** 25 $m^2$. The room is divided up into two rectangles. One measures 2.1 cm by 3.0 m, or 6.3 $m^2$. The second measures 3.8 m by 4.8 m, or 18 $m^2$.

**7.** 70 m by 140 m

**8. a)**

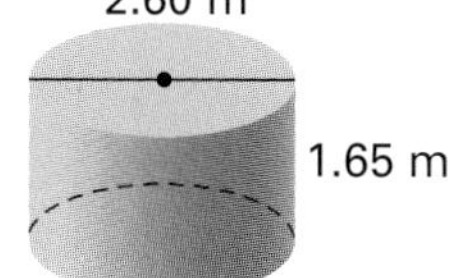


**b)** 8.76 $m^3$ **c)** 8760 L

**9.** 700

**10. a)**

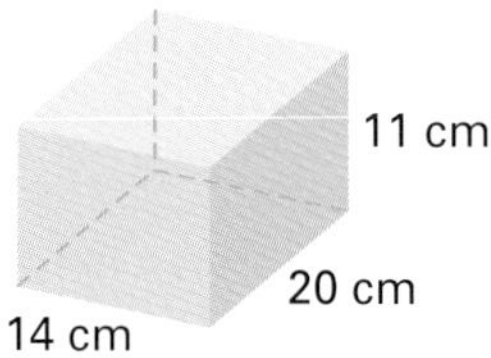


**b)**

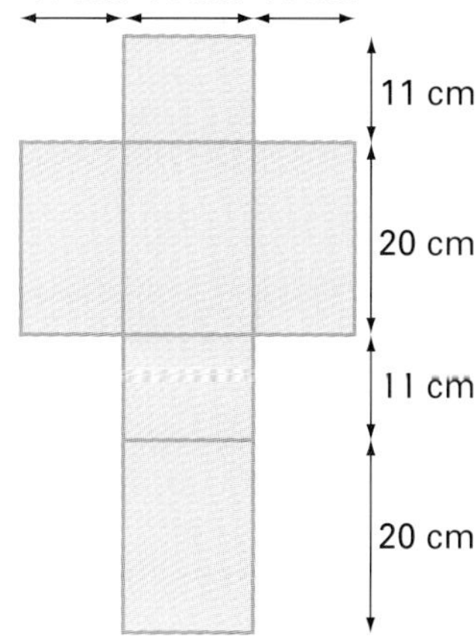


**c)** 1300 $cm^2$ **d)** Use the formula $S = 2(lw + wh + hl)$.

**11. a)** 671 $m^2$ **b)** 134 L

**12. a)** Diameter equals height.

**b)** 7.7 cm, 7.6 cm **c)** $r = 3.8$ cm, $h = 7.6$ cm

# CHAPTER 4

## Get Ready, pages 122–123

**1. a)** $0.88; \frac{22}{25}$ **b)** $0.16; \frac{4}{25}$ **c)** $0.36; \frac{9}{25}$ **d)** $0.75; \frac{3}{4}$
**e)** $0.66; \frac{33}{50}$ **f)** $0.15; \frac{3}{20}$ **g)** $0.125; \frac{1}{8}$ **h)** $0.0875; \frac{7}{80}$
**2. a)** 90.67% **b)** 92.86% **c)** 41.67% **d)** 66.67%
**3. a)** 4.8 **b)** $6.48 **c)** 16 m **d)** 537.5 **e)** 0.9 kg **d)** 27°
**4. a)** bar graph **b)** Saturday **c)** Monday
**d)-e)** Answers may vary.
**5. a)** circle graph **b)** weight training **c)** squash **d)** weight training 64, aerobics 42, jogging 32, swimming 28, tennis 18, squash 16
**6.**
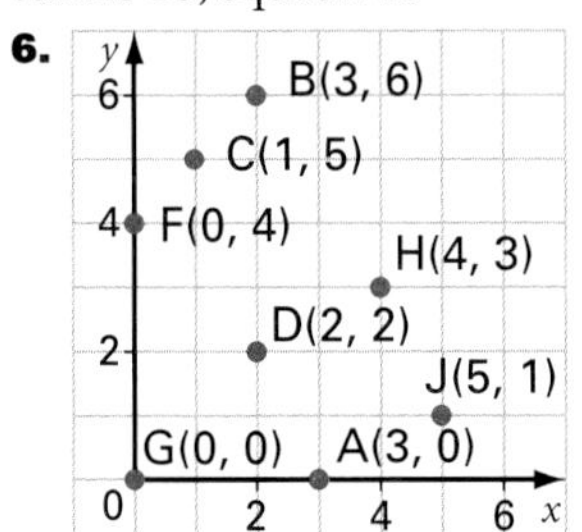


**7. a)**
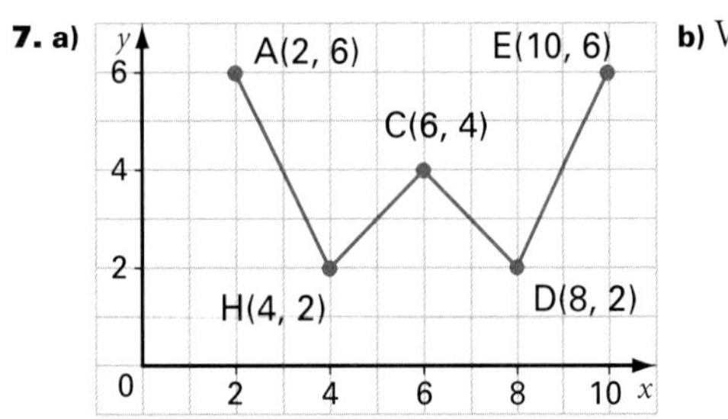

**b)** W

## 4.1 Formulating Hypotheses and Gathering Data, pages 127–129

**1. a)** secondary **b)** primary **c)** secondary **d)** primary **e)** primary
**2. a)** primary **b)** secondary **c)** secondary **d)** primary **e)** primary
**3. a)** Answers may vary.
**b)**

| Type | Tally | Frequency |
|---|---|---|
| Pop | 𝍸𝍸 \|\| | 12 |
| Juice | \|\|\| | 3 |
| Snacks | 𝍸 \|\| | 7 |
| Sandwiches | 𝍸 \|\|\|\| | 9 |
| Coffee | 𝍸 \|\|\|\| | 9 |

**c)** pop, sandwiches, coffee, snacks, juice **d)** primary **e)** yes
**f)** pop and sandwiches
**4. a)** More people use the Internet for e-mail than for any other single activity. **b)** secondary
**c)**
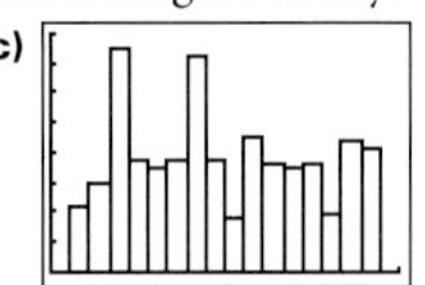
**d)** yes **e)** Answers may vary.
**5.-7.** Answers may vary.

## 4.2 Surveys and Sampling Principles, pages 134–135

**1. a)** systematic random sampling
**b)** non-random sampling **c)** stratified random sampling
**d)** simple random sampling **e)** non-random sampling
**f)** simple random sampling
**2. a)** people who use the Internet
**b)** people who read the Toronto Star **c)** all teenagers
**d)** Canadian population **e)** people who used the drug
**f)** campers at parks
**3.** Select randomly from each grade level, proportional to the number of students in each grade.
**4.** Put all the names of the figure skaters into a hat and draw names.
**5.** Take the speed of every tenth car.
**6.** Divide the residents by region and select randomly from within each region, proportional to each region's population.
**7.–8.** Answers may vary.

## 4.3 Organizing Data Using the TI-83 Graphing Calculator, pages 140–142

**1. a)** time it takes to get to school **b)** frequency that a digit occurs **c)** average high temperature during a month
**d)** number of times for number of goals scored
**2. a)** broken-line graph **b)** bar graph **c)** broken-line graph
**d)** bar graph
**3. a)** day 2 **b)** day 5 **c)** two-variable relationship
**4. b)**
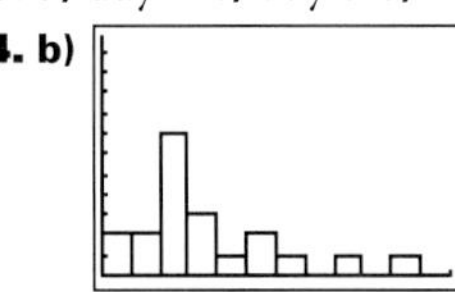
**d)** The graph shows how many students purchased each number of CDs.

**5. b)** 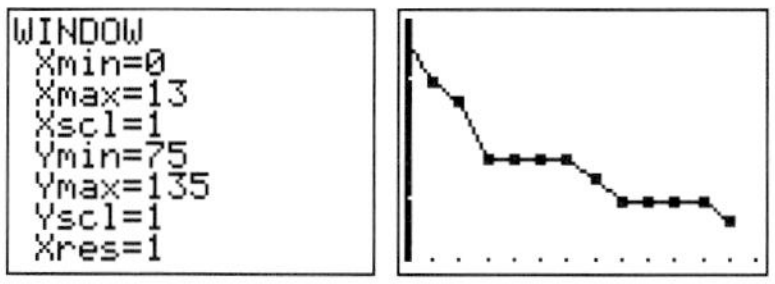


**d)** The graph shows how the average heart rate changes as you age.

**6. a)** 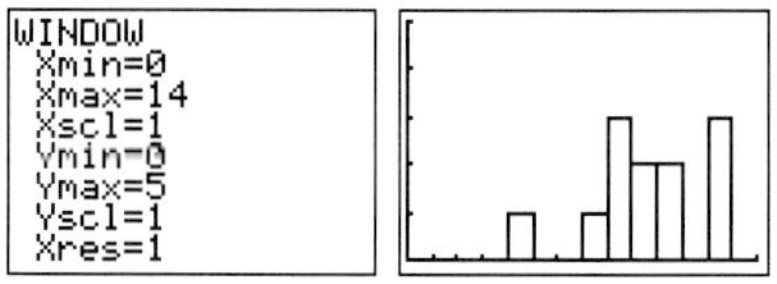


**b)** 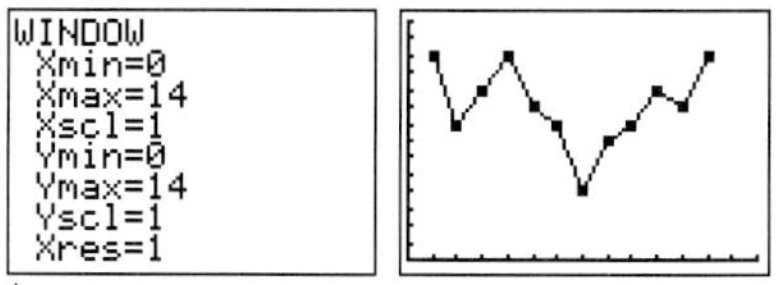


**c)** Answers may vary.

**8. b)** 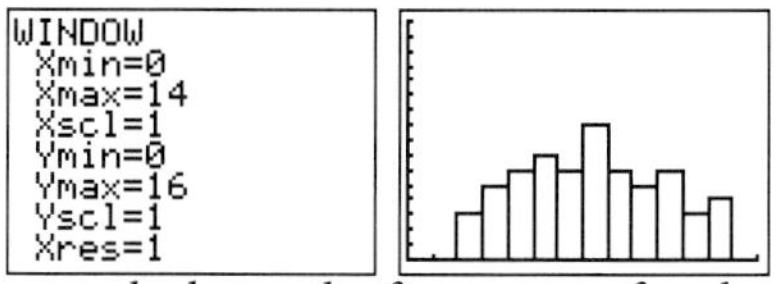


**c)** The graph shows the frequency of each sum when two dice were rolled 50 times.

## 4.4 Measures of Central Tendency, pages 147–148

**1. a)** mean 14.1, median 13, mode 20, outlier 34
**b)** mean 20.5, median 18, mode 13, outliers 48 and 56
**2. a)** mean 69.6, median 71, mode 71
**b)** mean 71.4, median 72, mode 88
**3. a)** mean 67, median 66, mode 53
**b)** mean 79, median 76, mode 70
**4. a)** mean **b)** mode **c)** median **d)** mean **e)** mode
**5. a)** mean 18.2°C, median 18°C, mode 21°C
**6.** Answers will vary.
**7. a)** mean 137 350 km, median 130 500 km, mode 125 000 km **b)** 44 000 km **c)** mean 141 650 km, median 130 500 km, mode 125 000 km **d)** The outlier lowered the mean. **e)** The mean including the outlier.
**f)** The mean including the outlier.
**8.** 100%

## 4.5 Data Analysis; Trends and Relationships, pages 152–155

**1. a)** independent – height; dependent – mark **b)** E, A, C **c)** B – height of 144 cm and a mark of 43%; D – height of 168 cm and a mark of 68% **d)** There is no relationship.
**2. a)** As variable 1 increases, variable 2 increases.
**b)** no relationship **c)** As variable 1 decreases, variable 2 decreases. **d)** As variable 1 increases, variable 2 increases.
**3. a)** no outliers **b)** no outliers **c)** One outlier has a high variable 2 value. **d)** One outlier has a low variable 2 value.
**4. a)** number of days absent because the mark depends on it

**b)** 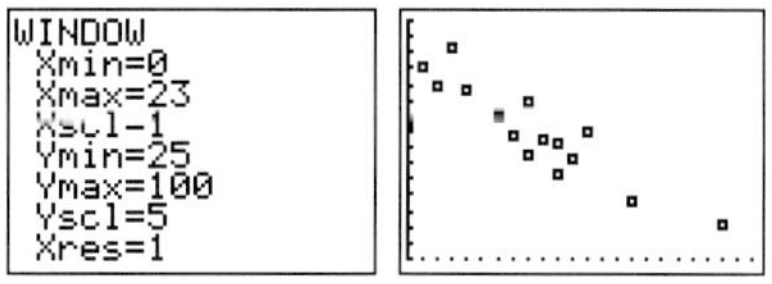


**c)** As the number of days absent increases, the mark decreases.
**5. a)** average mass, because lifespan depends on it

**b)** 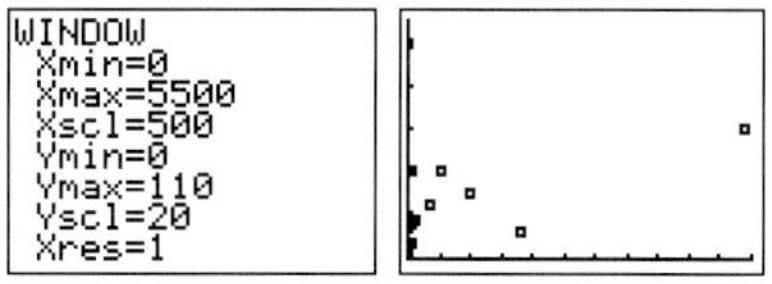


**c)** no relationship
**6.** Answers will vary.

## Review, pages 160–163

**1. a)** secondary **b)** secondary **c)** primary **d)** primary
**2. a)** secondary **b)** primary **c)** primary **d)** secondary
**3.** Answers may vary.
**4.** The school board could randomly call parents by placing their names in a hat and drawing names.
**5.** Students should be selected randomly from each grade level, proportional to the number of students in each grade.
**6.** The store could ask every tenth customer for an opinion.
**7. a)** number of students of each age **b)** number of days of sunlight **c)** price **d)** frequency of a letter
**8. a)** bar graph **b)** bar graph **c)** broken-line graph
**d)** bar graph

**9. a)** 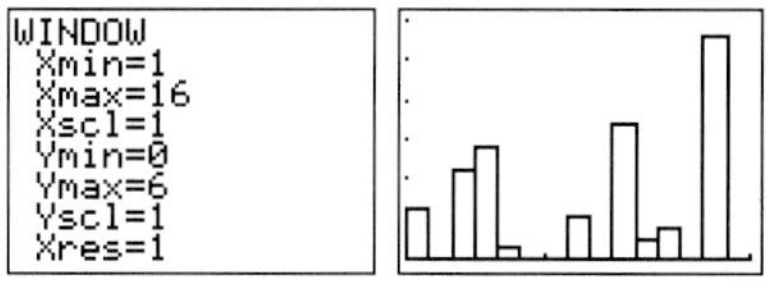


**d)** The graph shows the amount of snow that fell each day during a two-week period in January.
**e)** A bar graph was used because there is no connection between the amount of snow that falls from day to day.
**10. a)** mean 3, median 3, mode 3 **b)** mean
**11. a)** mean 3.76 kg, median 3.6 kg, mode 3.6 kg **b)** mean

**12. a)** no relationship **b)** As variable 1 increases, variable 2 decreases. **c)** no relationship

**13. a)** no outliers **b)** no outliers **c)** no outliers

**14. a)** distance, because flight time depends on it

**b)**

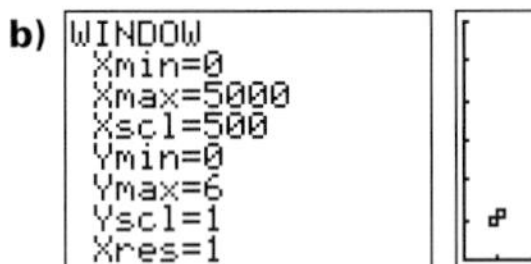


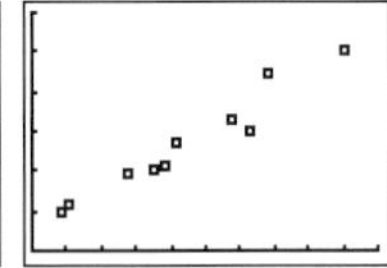

**c)** As distance increases, flight time increases.

## Practice Test, pages 164–165

**1.** B **2.** D **3.** C

**4. a)** primary **b)** secondary **c)** secondary **d)** primary

**5. a)** non-random **b)** simple random **c)** stratified random **d)** systematic random

**6. a)** mean \$21.50, median \$20, mode \$0 **b)** mean

# CHAPTER 5

## Get Ready, pages 168–171

**1. a)** 6 **b)** –3 **c)** 0 **d)** 5

**2.** Answers may vary.

**3. a)** –3 –2 –1 0 1 2 3 4 5 6 7 8 9 10 11 12

**b)**

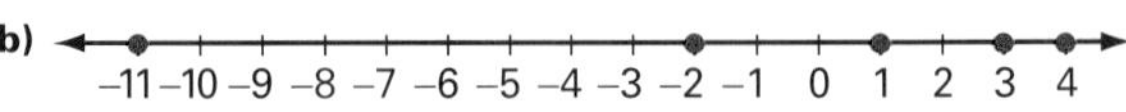


**4.** 8 7 6 5 4 3 2 1 0 –1 –2 –3 –4 –5 –6

**5. a)** 34 **b)** 16 **c)** 21 **d)** 16 **e)** 19 **f)** 21 **g)** 22 **h)** 30 **i)** 32

**6. a)** $\frac{3}{8}$ **b)** $\frac{3}{2}$; $1\frac{1}{2}$ **c)** $\frac{11}{3}$; $3\frac{2}{3}$

**9. a)** 10 **b)** 12 **c)** 20 **d)** 12

**10. a)** $\frac{5}{10}+\frac{8}{10}=\frac{13}{10}$

**b)** $\frac{4}{12}+\frac{9}{12}=\frac{13}{12}$

**c)** $\frac{5}{20}+\frac{6}{20}=\frac{11}{20}$

**d)** $\frac{10}{12}+\frac{9}{12}=\frac{19}{12}$

**e)** $\frac{6}{15}+\frac{5}{15}=\frac{11}{15}$

**f)** $\frac{4}{8}+\frac{3}{8}=\frac{7}{8}$

**g)** $\frac{9}{12}-\frac{8}{12}=\frac{1}{12}$

**h)** $\frac{10}{12}-\frac{3}{12}=\frac{7}{12}$

**11. a)** $\frac{1}{2}$ **b)** $\frac{4}{5}$ **c)** $\frac{3}{10}$ **d)** $\frac{9}{20}$ **e)** $\frac{8}{25}$ **f)** $\frac{3}{4}$ **g)** $\frac{7}{25}$ **h)** $\frac{19}{20}$ **i)** $\frac{13}{40}$ **j)** $\frac{27}{40}$

## 5.1 Adding and Subtracting Integers, pages 175–178

**1. a)** D **b)** B **c)** A **d)** C

**2. a)** 15 **b)** 3 **c)** –4 **d)** –2 **e)** 3 **f)** –10

**3. a)** 10 **b)** –2 **c)** 5 **d)** 2 **e)** 5 **f)** –5

**4. a)** 6°C **b)** 0°C **c)** –11°C **d)** 6°C

**5. a)** 5 **b)** –11 **c)** –2 **d)** 4 **e)** –4 **f)** 0

**6. a)** –4 **b)** +6 **c)** +12 **d)** –15

**7. a)** 7 **b)** –2 **c)** –8 **d)** 6

**8. a)** 16 **b)** –15 **c)** –8 **d)** –26 **e)** 3 **f)** 12 **g)** –2 **h)** –4 **i)** 16 **j)** –6 **k)** –7 **l)** 13

**9. a)** −17 **b)** −31 **c)** −122 **d)** −29 **e)** 21 **f)** −222 **g)** 22 **h)** 101

**10. a)** No, because the lowest value is 6. **b)** No; the answer is 18 and the line only extends to 15.

**c)**

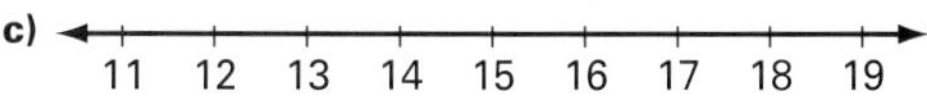


**d)**

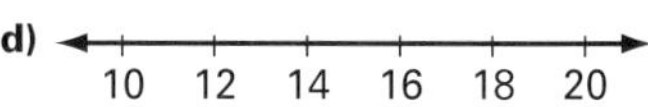


**11.** −13.5°C

**12.** lower by 64¢

**13.** net loss of $83

**14.** $132

**15. a)** 4:00 p.m. **b)** 3 h **c)** 6:00 a.m.

**16.** China 02:00 or 2:00 a.m., Israel 08:00 or 8:00 a.m., Morocco 10:00 or 10:00 a.m., New Zealand 22:00 or 10:00 p.m.

## 5.2 Multiplying and Dividing Integers, pages 182–183

**1. a)** − **b)** − **c)** + **d)** − **e)** − **f)** +

**2. a)** 18 **b)** −32 **c)** 15 **d)** −24

**3. a)** −28 **b)** 40 **c)** −90 **d)** 36 **e)** 126 **f)** 55 **g)** −80 **h)** 48

**4. a)** −21 ÷ (−7) = 3; −21 ÷ 3 = −7

**b)** −18 ÷ 2 = −9; −18 ÷ (−9) = 2

**c)** 35 ÷ (−5) = −7; 35 ÷ (−7) = −5

**5. a)** 2 **b)** 16 **c)** −25 **d)** −20 **e)** −25 **f)** 3

**6. a)** −27 **b)** −16 **c)** 50 **d)** −2 **e)** −31 **f)** −37

**7.** Answers may vary.

**8. a)** 3 × (−$2) **b)** 3 × $5

**9. a)** −$6 **b)** $15

**10. a)** −$60 ÷ 3 **b)** $125 ÷ 5

**11. a)** −$20 **b)** $25

**12. a)** 25 × 30 **b)** $10 × (25 × 30)

**13. a)** $50 **b)** 30

## 5.3 Plotting Points on the Cartesian Plane, pages 188–190

**1. a)** B **b)** G **c)** A **d)** D **e)** C **f)** E **g)** F

**2. a)**

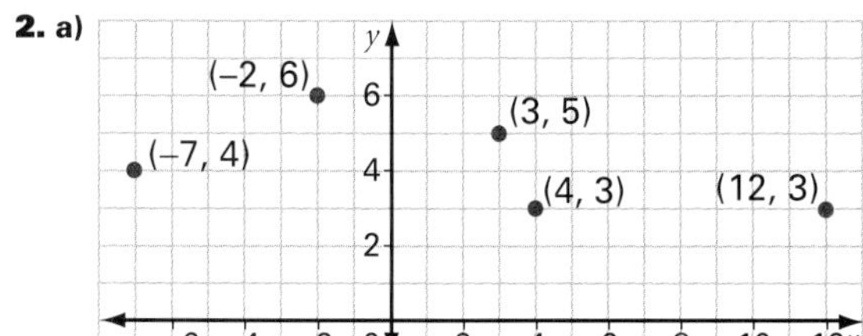


**b)** **c)** **d)**

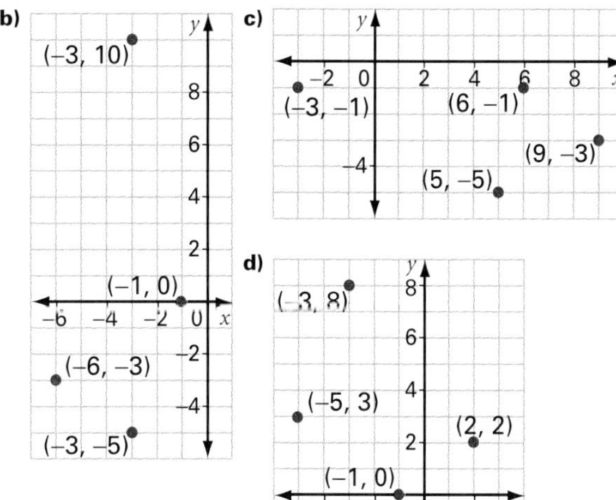


**3. a)** 1st quadrant **b)** 3rd quadrant **c)** 4th quadrant **d)** 2nd quadrant

**4.** A(−3, 1), B(5, 0), C(3, 3), D(−2, −3), E(0, 4), F(4, −2)

**5.** It keeps the points organized and helps to identify them easily.

**6. a)**

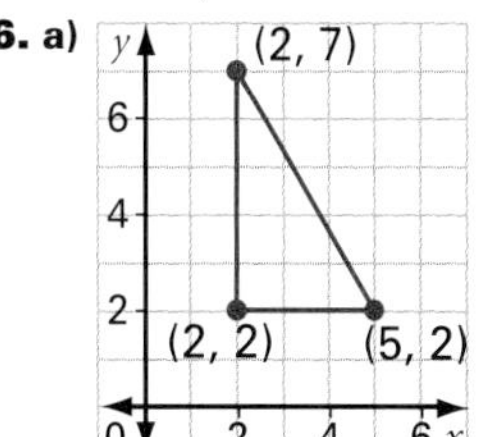


right triangle
7.5 square units

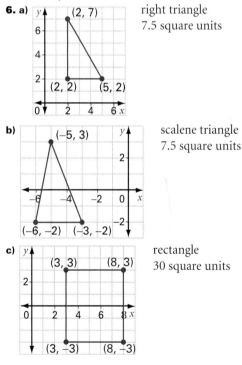

**b)**

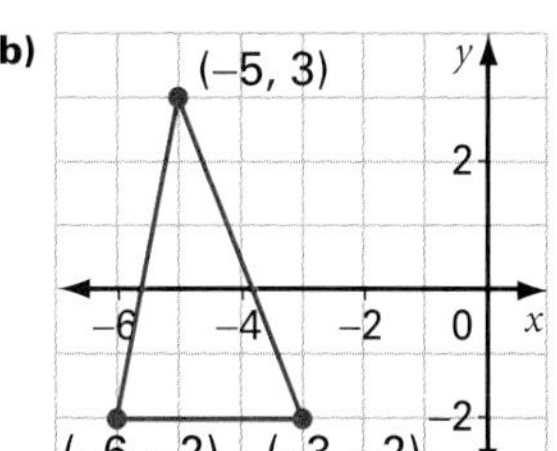


scalene triangle
7.5 square units

**c)**

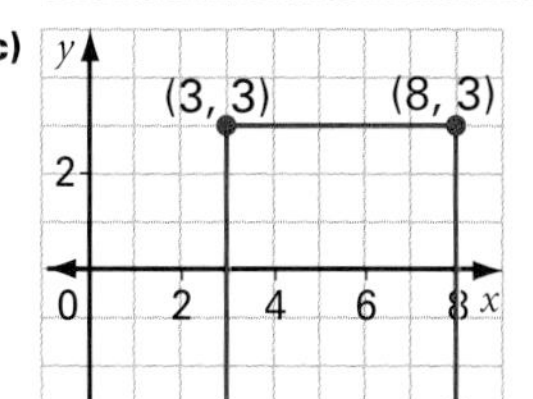


rectangle
30 square units

**d)** 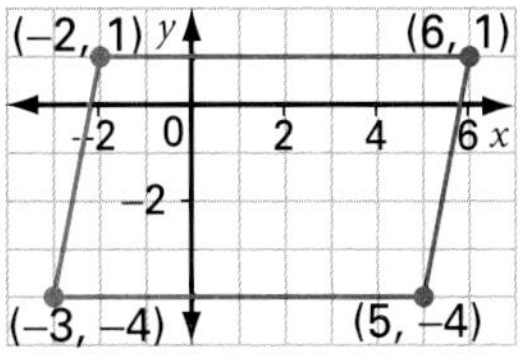

parallelogram
40 square units

**e)** 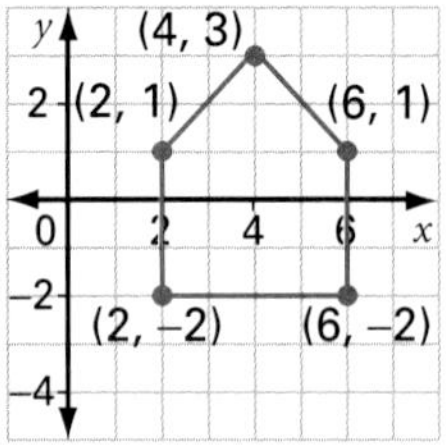

pentagon
16 square units

**7. a)** 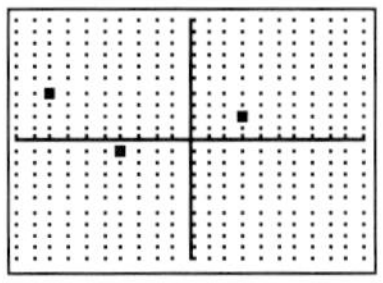

**b)** Points plotted using the dot symbol will not show if the grid is turned on.
**8.** A (3, 0), B (1, 3), C(1, −4), D(0, 5), E(0, −3), F(−3, 2), G(−4, −4)
**9.** A (5, 10), B (10, 2), C(−6, −10), D(−9, 20), E(−10, 0), F(−15, 18), G(15, −4)
**10.** One block on the *x*-axis represents 2 units. One block on the *y*-axis represents 10 units.
**11.** 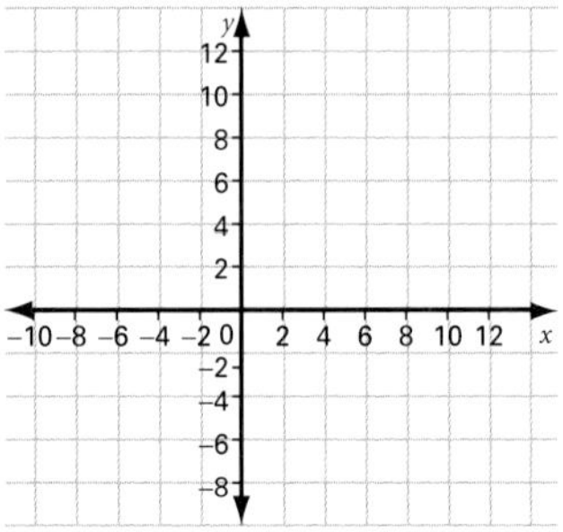

**12.** Answers may vary.

## 5.4 Exploring Rational Numbers, pages 195–197

**1. a)** C **b)** A **c)** E **d)** B **e)** D
**2. a)** 0.3 **b)** 3.25 **c)** −1.3 **d)** −4.4 **e)** 2.375 **f)** −5.8
**3. a)** $\frac{2}{5}$ **b)** $-\frac{3}{2}$ **c)** $\frac{1}{4}$ **d)** $-\frac{3}{4}$ **e)** $-\frac{5}{8}$ **f)** $2\frac{4}{5}$
**4. a)** $\frac{11}{4}$ **b)** $-\frac{10}{3}$ **c)** $\frac{13}{8}$ **d)** $-\frac{14}{5}$ **e)** $-\frac{17}{3}$ **f)** $\frac{23}{5}$

**5.** 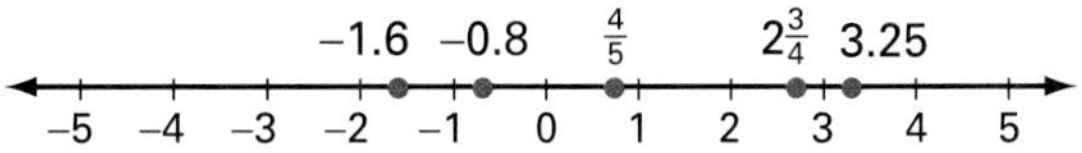


**6. a)** < **b)** > **c)** > **d)** =
**7. a)** $0.\dot{3}$ **b)** $0.1\dot{6}$ **c)** $-0.\dot{6}$ **d)** $-3.8\dot{3}$ **e)** $-0.41\dot{6}$
**8.** Answers may vary.
**9. a)** $\frac{1}{4}, \frac{5}{16}$
**10. a)** A, C, E, D, B
**11.** potassium, water, bromine, mercury, krypton
**12. a)** $3 \times \frac{3}{4}$ **b)** $3 \times \left(-\frac{2}{3}\right)$ **c)** $4 \times \left(-\frac{3}{8}\right)$
**13. a)** $-\frac{1}{2}$ **b)** −2 **c)** $1\frac{1}{4}$
**14. a)** 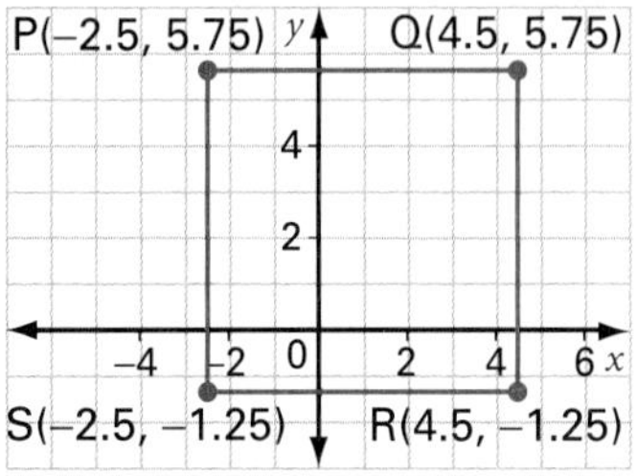


**b)** square **c)** 49 square units

## 5.5 Operations With Rational Numbers, pages 203–205

**1. a)** $\frac{3}{10}$ **b)** $-\frac{1}{2}$ **c)** $-\frac{49}{20}$ **d)** $\frac{9}{4}$
**2. a)** $\frac{4}{3}$ **b)** $-\frac{4}{5}$ **c)** $-\frac{2}{9}$ **d)** $\frac{15}{64}$
**3. a)** $\frac{4}{5}$ **b)** $\frac{1}{3}$ **c)** $\frac{1}{4}$ **d)** $-\frac{1}{2}$ **e)** $-\frac{1}{3}$ **f)** $\frac{1}{6}$
**4. a)** $\frac{7}{6}$ **b)** $-\frac{1}{6}$ **c)** $\frac{7}{20}$ **d)** $-\frac{1}{8}$ **e)** $-\frac{17}{15}$ **f)** $-\frac{1}{12}$
**5. a)** $\frac{1}{4}$ **b)** $-\frac{1}{15}$ **c)** $-\frac{3}{4}$ **d)** $-\frac{11}{8}$ **e)** $-\frac{5}{6}$ **f)** $\frac{5}{3}$
**6. a)** −6.3 **b)** −7.2 **c)** −3 **d)** −84 **e)** 2 **f)** 0.5 **g)** −0.4 **h)** −3 **i)** −3.6
**7. a)** $\frac{1}{16}$ **b)** $\frac{3}{8}$
**8. a)** The fractions are cancelled before inverting the second fraction and multiplying it by the first fraction. $\frac{4}{9} \div \frac{3}{4} = \frac{4}{9} \times \frac{4}{3} = \frac{16}{27}$ **b)** The numerators are added instead of multiplied. $\frac{2}{5} \times \frac{3}{7} = \frac{6}{35}$

**9. a)** You cannot cancel fractions when adding. You must find a common denominator first.
$\frac{4}{5} + \frac{5}{7} = \frac{28}{35} + \frac{25}{35} = \frac{53}{35}$
**b)** You must multiply the numerators by the same factor as the denominators.
$\frac{2}{9} - \frac{1}{6} = \frac{4}{18} - \frac{3}{18} = \frac{1}{18}$
**10.** B and D must be wrong because negative ÷ positive = negative. C must be wrong because the answer can not be an integer.
**11.** length, $74\frac{1}{4}$ in.; width, $30\frac{3}{8}$ in.
**12.** 8 cups of popped corn, $\frac{1}{2}$ cup of peanuts (optional), 1 cup of brown sugar, $\frac{1}{2}$ cup of butter, $\frac{1}{4}$ cup light corn syrup, $\frac{1}{2}$ tsp. salt, $\frac{1}{4}$ tsp. soda
**13.** \$21.83
**14.** −\$39
**15.** $-2\frac{1}{3}$°C/h
**16.** yes
**17.** Move the negative to the numerator.
**18. a)** 1.875 ohms **b)** 15 ohms

## 5.6 Ratio and Rate, pages 209–211

**1. a)** 4:7 **b)** 1:5 **c)** 7:30
**2. a)** 4:3 **b)** 3:4:5 **c)** 14:5
**3. a)** 1:11 **b)** 9:11 **c)** 5:6 **d)** 2:1 **e)** 14:1 **f)** 1:3 **g)** 1:2:5 **h)** 12:5:11
**4. a)** 6 **b)** 12 **c)** 24 **d)** 9 **e)** 2 **f)** 15
**5. a)** 80 km/h **b)** \$22/h **c)** 30 customers per hour **d)** 5 cm/h **e)** \$2.08 per rose **f)** −3.2°C/h
**6. a)** \$0.2292 per bun or \$0.2113 per bun **b)** \$0.25 per orange or \$0.2625 per orange **c)** \$2.18/L or \$1.0475/L
**7. a)** bulk store **b)** grocery store **c)** grocery store
**8. a)** 2:2:1 **b)** Butter is measured in grams, not cups. **c)** 2 cups white flour, 2 cups brown sugar, 1 cup of rolled oats, 400 g butter
**9. a)** 2:5:1:1 **b)** 10 cups almonds, 25 cups peanuts, 5 cups raisins, 5 cups dried apples
**10. a)** 1:40 **b)** 200 mL
**11. a)** car B **b)** X, 5.83 L/100 km; Y, 7 L/100 km; Z, 5.13 L/100 km **c)** Y, X, Z
**12. a)** 1:2300 **b)** Answers may vary.

## Review, pages 212–213

**1. a)**
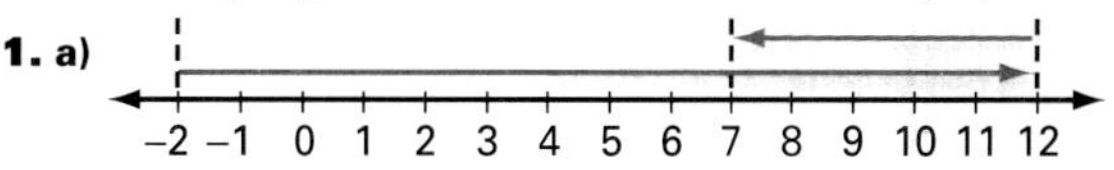


**b)**
−8 −7 −6 −5 −4 −3 −2 −1 0

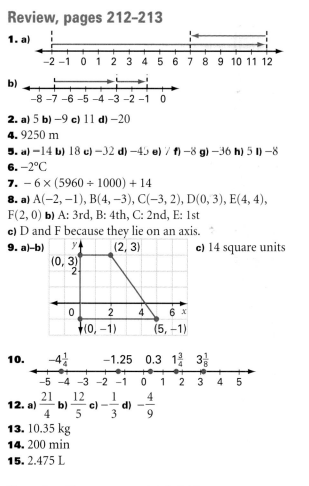

**2. a)** 5 **b)** −9 **c)** 11 **d)** −20
**4.** 9250 m
**5. a)** −14 **b)** 18 **c)** −32 **d)** −45 **e)** 7 **f)** −8 **g)** −36 **h)** 5 **i)** −8
**6.** −2°C
**7.** $-6 \times (5960 \div 1000) + 14$
**8. a)** A(−2, −1), B(4, −3), C(−3, 2), D(0, 3), E(4, 4), F(2, 0) **b)** A: 3rd, B: 4th, C: 2nd, E: 1st **c)** D and F because they lie on an axis.
**9. a)–b)**
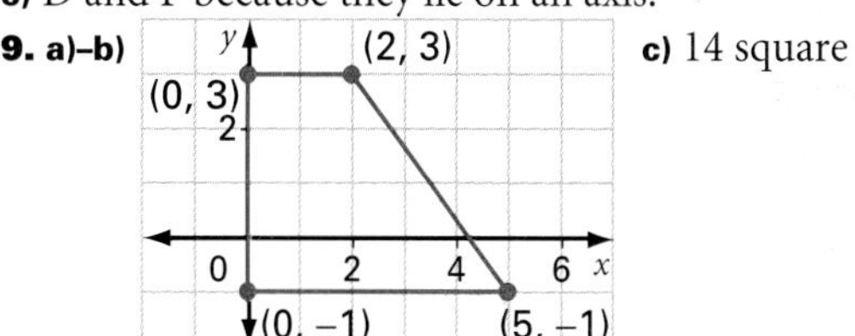

**c)** 14 square units

**10.**
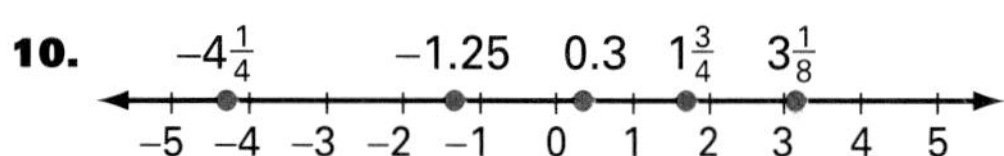


**12. a)** $\frac{21}{4}$ **b)** $\frac{12}{5}$ **c)** $-\frac{1}{3}$ **d)** $-\frac{4}{9}$
**13.** 10.35 kg
**14.** 200 min
**15.** 2.475 L

## Practice Test, pages 214–215

**1.** C **2.** B **3.** A **4.** B **5.** B **6.** C **7.** C
**8.** Answers may vary.
**9. a)** A(3, −1), B(2, 2), C(−4, −1), D(4, 0), E(0, −1), F(−2, 5) **b)** A: 4th, B: 1st, C: 3rd, F: 2nd **c)** D and E because they lie on an axis.
**10. a)** 2 **b)** $-\frac{1}{20}$ **c)** $-\frac{20}{3}$ **d)** $\frac{53}{12}$
**11.** $-3\frac{1}{3}$°C/h
**12.** $\frac{1}{4}$ cup sour cream, $\frac{1}{8}$ cup butter
**13. a)** The student's mark is 20% lower than it could be if the student did not watch any TV. **b)** −37.5% **c)** −84%

## Cumulative Review: Chapters 4 and 5, pages 216–217

**1. a)** secondary **b)** primary **c)** primary

**2. a)** Answers may vary.

**b)**

| Juice Type | Tally | Frequency |
|---|---|---|
| Orange | 卌 ||| | 8 |
| Apple | 卌 | | 6 |
| Grape | 卌 | 5 |
| Cranberry | ||| | 3 |
| Grapefruit | || | 2 |

**c)** survey **d)** Orange and apple because most students prefer these two.

**3. a)** students enrolled in the school **b)** Canadians **c)** newspaper readers

**4.** Students are randomly selected from each grade level, proportional to the number of students in each grade.

**5.** Stand in a park and ask every 10th jogger how many kilometres a week are jogged.

**6. a)** 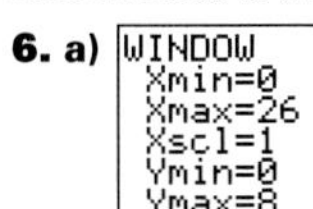

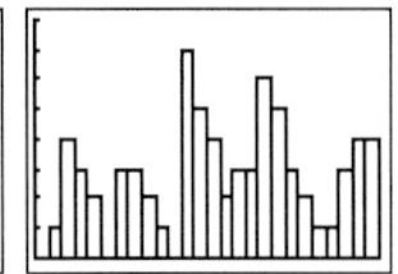

**b)** Answers may vary.

**7. a)** mean 46.3, median 48.5, mode 70, outlier 11 **b)** mean 16.2, median 13, mode 6 and 14, outlier 51 **c)** mean 28.4, median 27.5, mode 29, outliers 4 and 62 **d)** mean 26.8, median 27, mode 27

**8. a)** 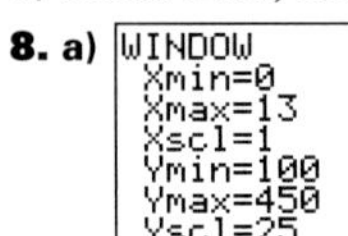

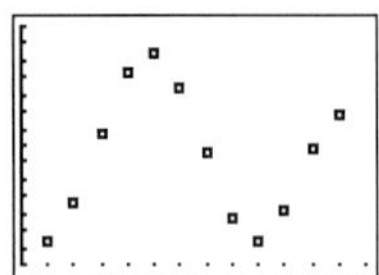

**b)** The population increases, then decreases, and then increases again. **c)** Answers may vary.

**9.** 2°C

**10. a)** −56 **b)** 7 **c)** 36 **d)** −7

**11.** −8°C

**12. a)–b)** 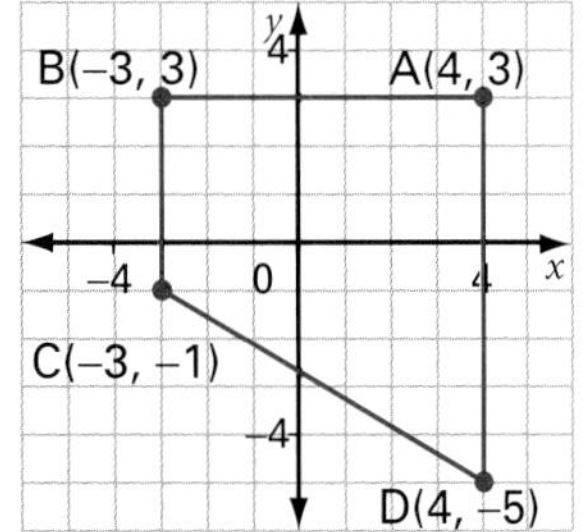


**c)** 42 square units

**13. a)** $-\frac{18}{5}$ **b)** 2 **c)** $\frac{45}{14}$ **d)** $\frac{3}{7}$ **e)** $\frac{1}{8}$ **f)** $-\frac{7}{6}$

**14.** $\frac{1}{4}+\frac{1}{2}=\frac{3}{4}$, $1-\frac{1}{4}=\frac{3}{4}$, $\frac{1}{4}+\frac{1}{4}+\frac{1}{4}=\frac{3}{4}$

# Chapter 6

## Get Ready, pages 222–223

**1. a)** 2.5 m/s **b)** \$7.50/h c) \$0.995/L

**2. a)** \$9.50/h **b)** \$380

**3. a)** 21 **b)** −30 **c)** −14 **d)** −2 **e)** 11 **f)** 6

**4. a)** 10 **b)** −8 **c)** 2 **d)** −2

**5.** P(3, 2), Q(−3, 0), R(2, −4), S(0, 0), T(−2, −2), V(−1, 4)

**6.** 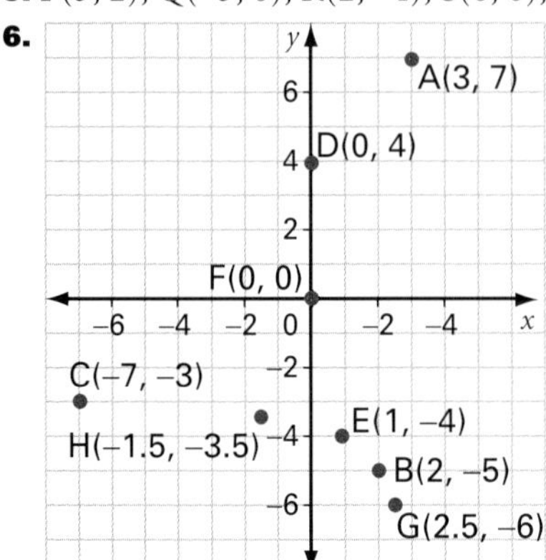


## 6.1 Direct Variation, pages 229–231

**1. a)** $C = kn$ **b)** $C = kr$

**2. a)** 8 **b)** 90 **c)** 36

**3. a)** 82; Claude travels at 82 km/h **b)** $d = 82t$ **c)** 123 km **d)** 3.05 h or 3 h 3 min **e)** Claude will travel at a constant rate.

**4. a)**

| Time (h) | Cost (\$) |
|---|---|
| 1 | 2.50 |
| 2 | 5.00 |
| 3 | 7.50 |

**b)** 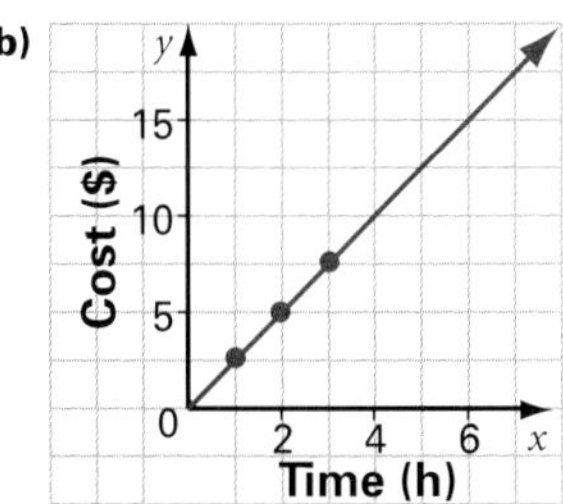

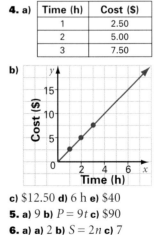

**c)** \$12.50 **d)** 6 h **e)** \$40

**5. a)** 9 **b)** $P = 9t$ **c)** \$90

**6. a) a)** 2 **b)** $S = 2n$ **c)** 7

## 6.2 Partial Variation, pages 237–239

**1. a)** A partial variation because the line does not start at the origin. **b)** A partial variation because the line does not start at the origin. **c)** Neither, because the graph is not linear.

**2. a)** A direct variation because the equation has no constant term. **b)** A partial variation because the equation has a constant term, 30. **c)** A partial variation because the equation has a constant term, 4. **d)** A direct variation because the equation has no constant term.

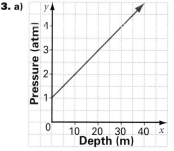

**3. a)**

**b)** A partial variation because at 0 m, the scuba diver starts at 1 atm. **c)** 3.5 atm **d)** 40 m

**4. a)**

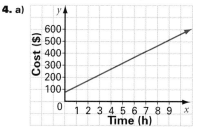

**b)** \$420 **c)** 8.6 h **d)** Round down because you do not have the extra money to pay for the rental if you round up. **e)** fixed cost \$70, variable cost \$50 **f)** The line would move up \$30 but have the same slope. **g)** The slope of the graph would be steeper.

**5. a)** \$15; Find the difference between the second and the first day. **b)** fixed 40, variable $15d$ **c)** $C = 15d + 40$ **d)** \$145

**6. a)** fixed 50, variable $2t$ **b)** 80 km/h **c)** 25 s. Substitute 100 into the left side of the equation and solve for $t$.

**7. a)**

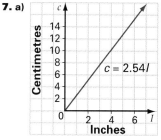

**b)** A direct variation because the graph passes through (0, 0). **c)** Answers may vary.

**8. a)** This is a partial variation, because if you finish in 30 s or less, you are rewarded with 10 points straight away. **b)** $P = 10 + 2n$ **c)** 16

**9. b)** \$700

## 6.3 Graphing Linear Relations From a Table of Values, pages 246–247

**1. a)**
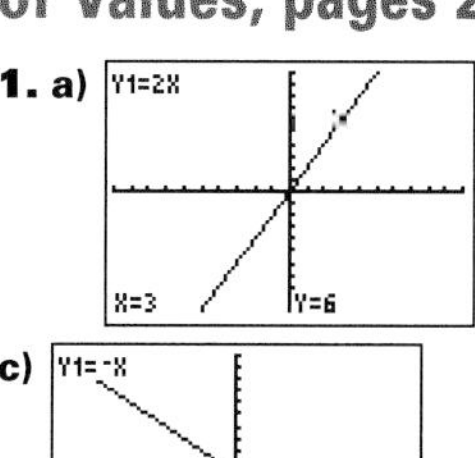


**b)**
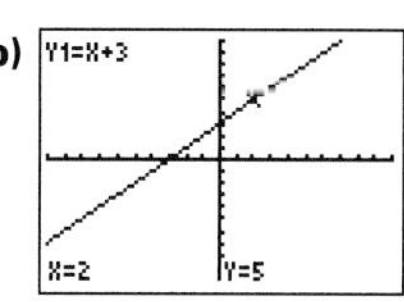


**c)**
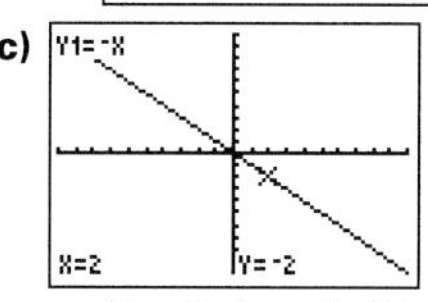


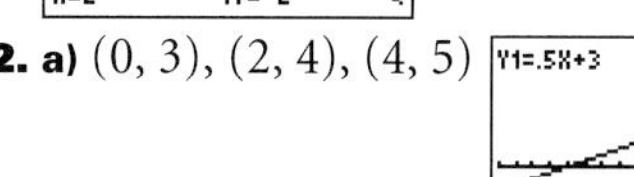
**2. a)** (0, 3), (2, 4), (4, 5)
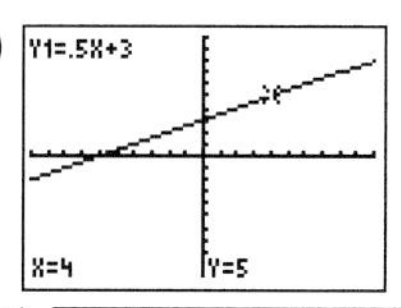


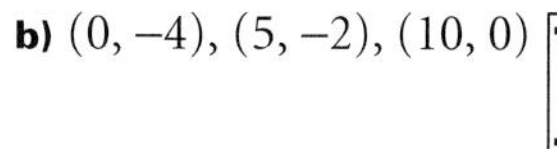
**b)** (0, −4), (5, −2), (10, 0)
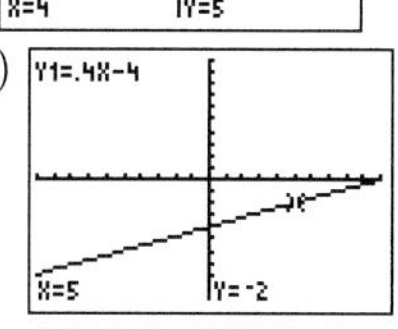


**3. a)**
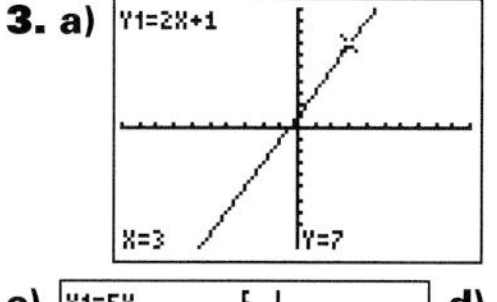


**b)**
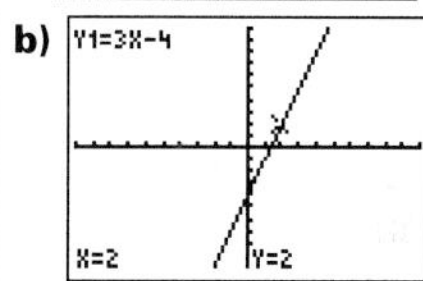


**c)**
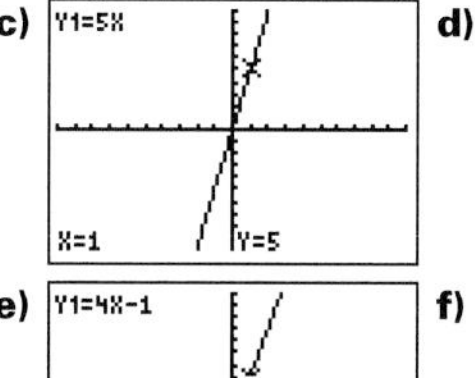


**d)**
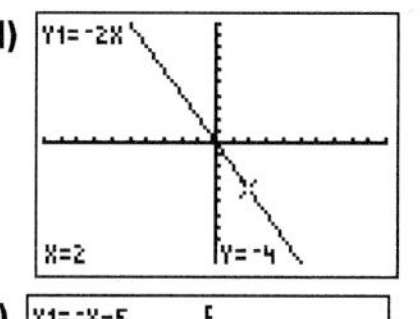


**e)**
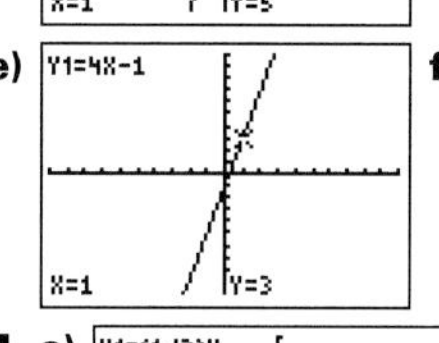


**f)**
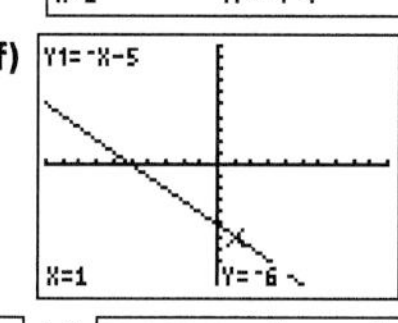


**4. a)**
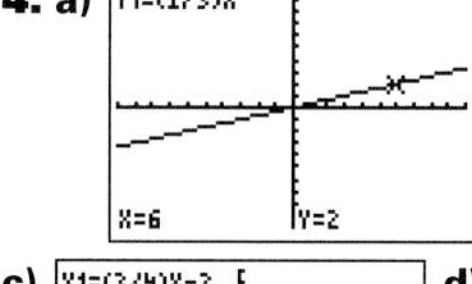


**b)**
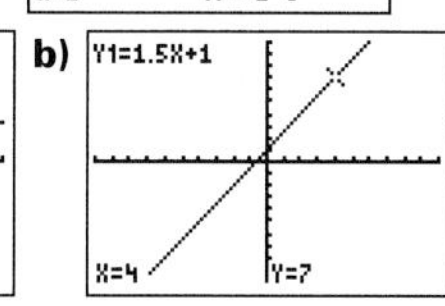


**c)**
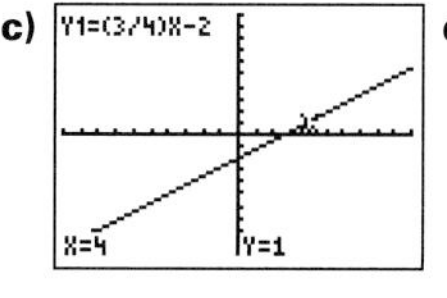


**d)**
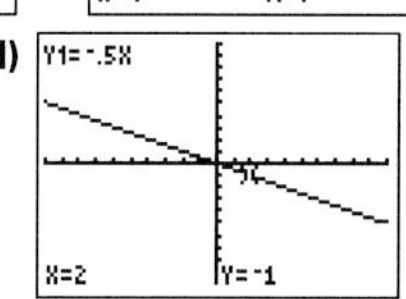

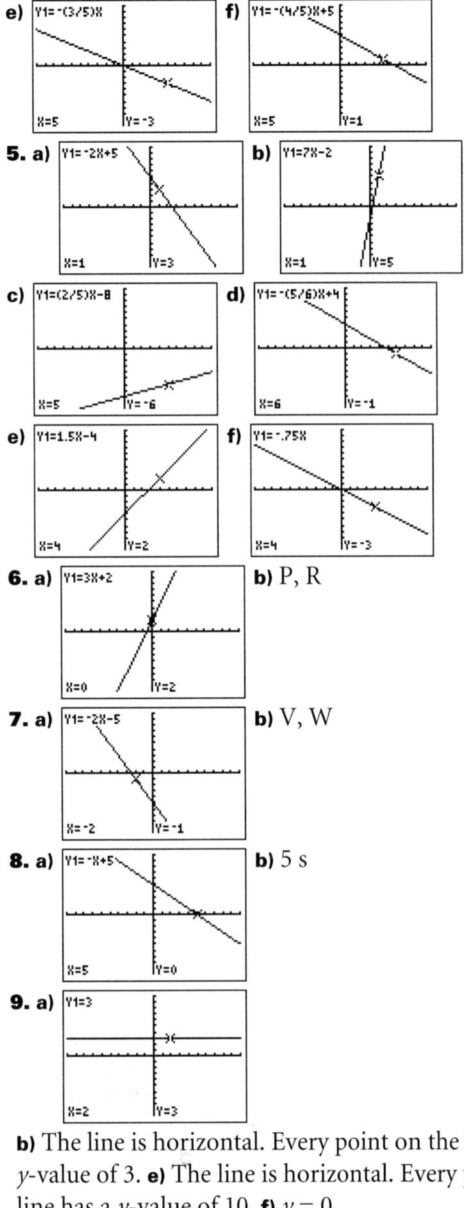


**6. b)** P, R

**7. b)** V, W

**8. b)** 5 s

**b)** The line is horizontal. Every point on the line has a $y$-value of 3. **e)** The line is horizontal. Every point on the line has a $y$-value of 10. **f)** $y = 0$

**10. a)**

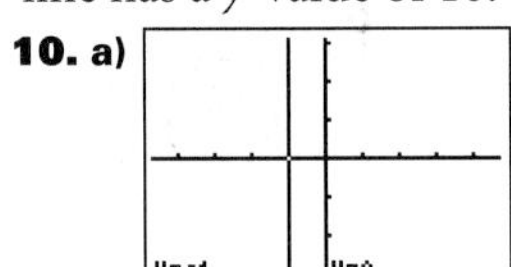


**b)** The line is vertical. Every point on the line has an $x$-value of –1.

**d)**

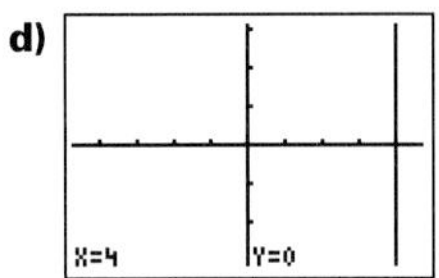


**e)** $x = 0$ **f)** The line is vertical. Every point on the line has an $x$-value of –3.

## 6.4 Graphing Non-Linear Relations, pages 255–257

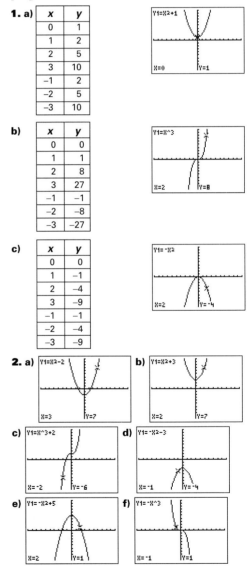

**1. a)**

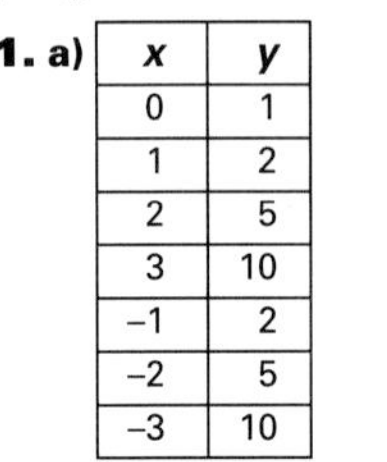

| $x$ | $y$ |
|---|---|
| 0 | 1 |
| 1 | 2 |
| 2 | 5 |
| 3 | 10 |
| –1 | 2 |
| –2 | 5 |
| –3 | 10 |

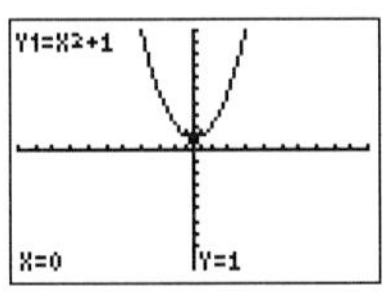


**b)**

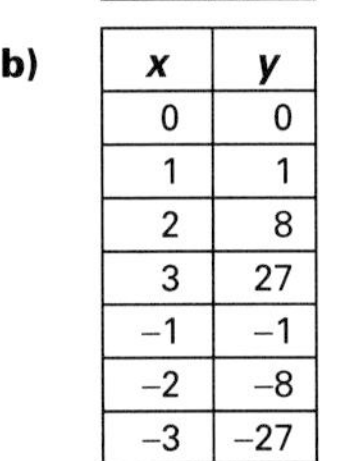

| $x$ | $y$ |
|---|---|
| 0 | 0 |
| 1 | 1 |
| 2 | 8 |
| 3 | 27 |
| –1 | –1 |
| –2 | –8 |
| –3 | –27 |

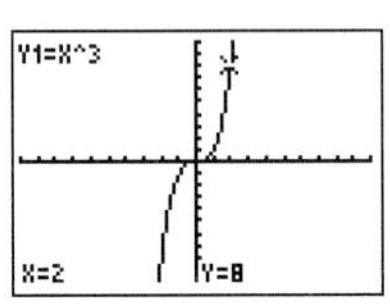


**c)**

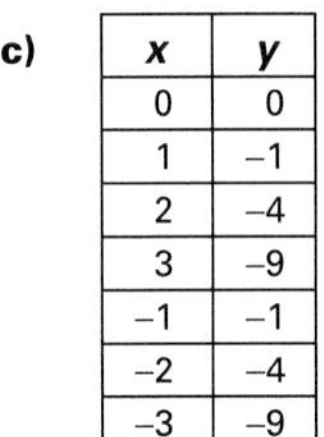

| $x$ | $y$ |
|---|---|
| 0 | 0 |
| 1 | –1 |
| 2 | –4 |
| 3 | –9 |
| –1 | –1 |
| –2 | –4 |
| –3 | –9 |

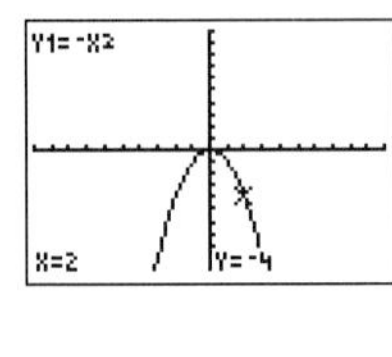


**2. a)**

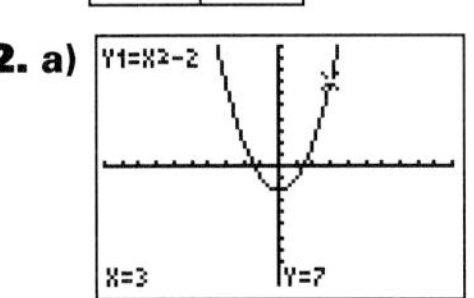


**b)**

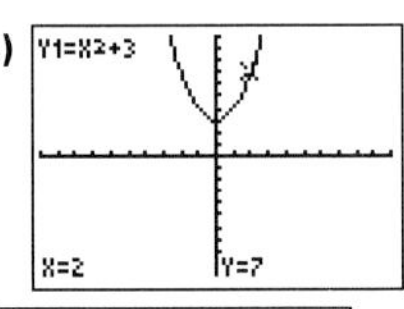


**c)** **e)**

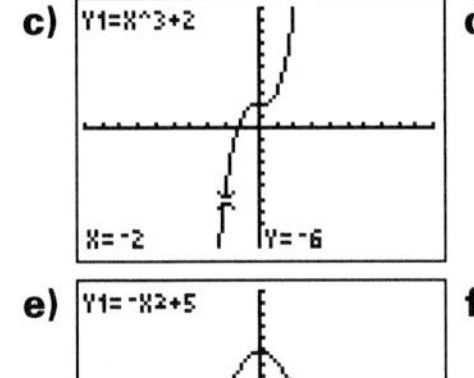


**d)** **f)**

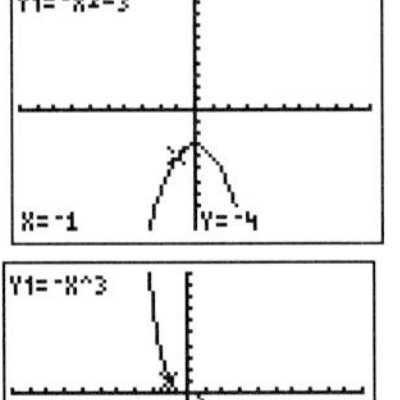

**3. a)** 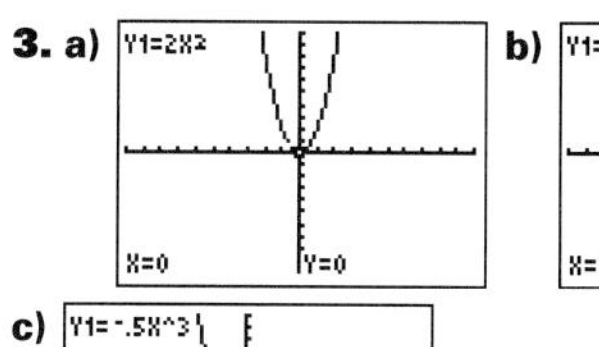


**b)** 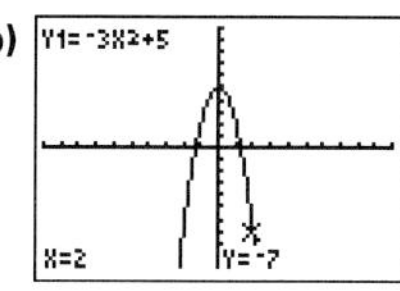


**c)** 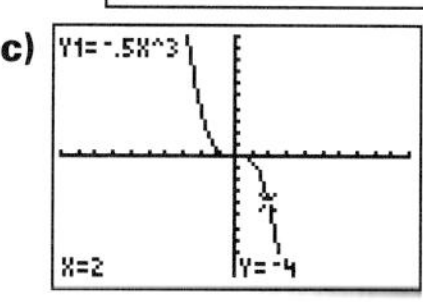


**4.** Vina should expand her existing yard.

**5. b)**

| Radius (cm) | Area (cm$^2$) |
|---|---|
| 2 | 13 |
| 4 | 50 |
| 5 | 79 |
| 6 | 113 |
| 7 | 154 |

**c)** 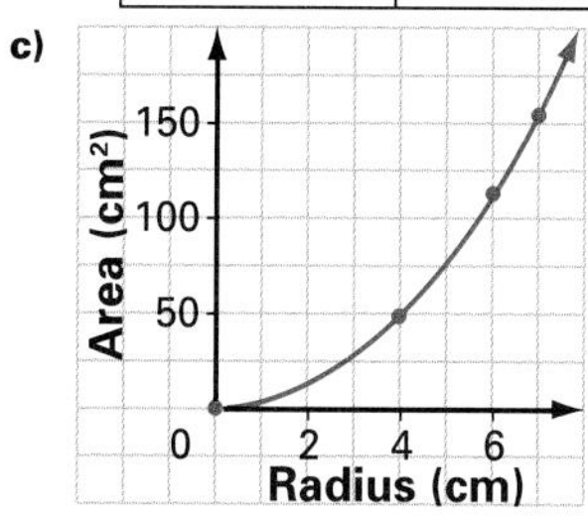

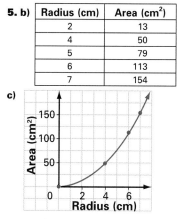

**d)** non-linear **e)** Answers may vary. **f)** 452 cm$^2$
**g)** 5 cm

**6. a)** (3, 7.6), (4, 8.8), (5, 9.8), (6, 10.8)

**b)** 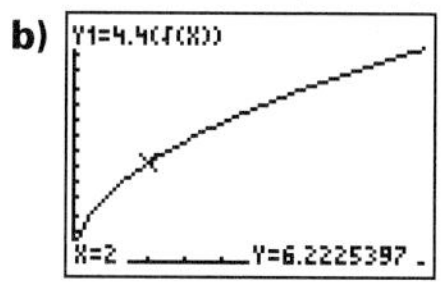


**c)** non-linear **d)** 8.2 m/s **e)** 13.9 m/s **f)** No, because air resistance will slow the styrofoam ball.

**7. a)** (0.4, 0.6), (0.6, 0.3), (0.8, –0.3), (1.0, –1.4)

**b)** 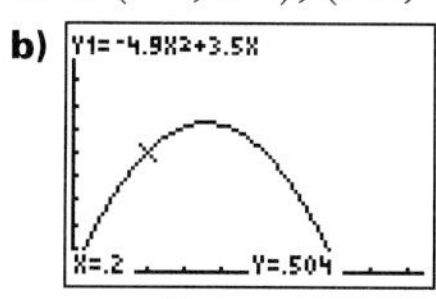


**c)** non-linear **d)–e)** Answers may vary.

## 6.5 First Differences, pages 263–265

**1. a)** Yes because the independent variable increases by a constant amount. **b)** No because the independent variable does not increase by a constant amount.
**c)** Yes because the independent variable increases by a constant amount.

**2. a)** first differences are all 4; linear **b)** first differences: 4, 12, 20, 28; non-linear **c)** first differences are all –3; linear

**3. a)** linear **b)** non-linear **c)** non-linear **d)** linear

**4. a)** (1, 8.50), (2, 17.00), (3, 25.50), (4, 34.00) **b)** first differences are all 8.50 **c)** This is a linear relationship because first differences are constant. **d)** First differences match Jay's rate of pay, \$8.50/h. **e)** This is a direct variation because for 0 h, Jay is paid \$0. **f)** 8.50

**5. a)** first differences are all –2; linear **b)** $F = -0.1v + 25$, where $F$ is fuel consumption and $v$ is speed **c)** 20 km/L
**d)** Answers may vary.

**6. a)** Vanessa: first differences are constant, 90. Ally: first differences are 60, 70, 80, 90, 100. **b)** Vanessa: linear, Ally: non-linear **c)** Answers may vary.

**7. a)** 1.23, 3.67, 6.13, 8.57, 11.03 **b)** non-linear

**c)** 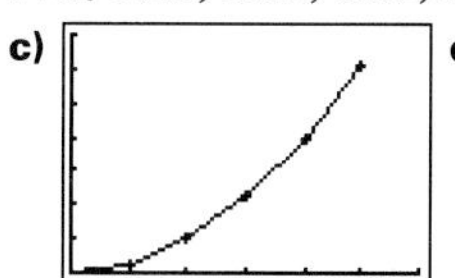

**e)** 62 m

## 6.6 Characteristics of Linear and Non-Linear Relations, pages 269–271

**1. a)** non-linear **b)** linear **c)** linear **d)** non-linear

**2. a)** linear **b)** non-linear **c)** non-linear **d)** linear

**3. a)** linear **b)** non-linear **c)** linear

**4. a)** linear **b)** non-linear **c)** non-linear **d)** linear
**e)** non-linear **f)** non-linear

**5.** Queenston non-linear, Ivytown linear, Neuville non-linear

**6. a)** linear **b)** non-linear **c)** linear

**7. a)** 5, 14, 23, 32, 41 **b)** Non-linear, because the first differences are not constant. **c)** an upward curve

**d)** 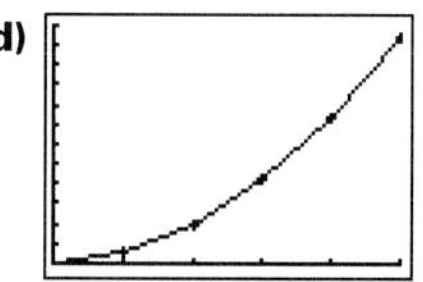

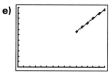

**8. a)** all 41 **b)** Linear because the first differences are constant. **c)** No, because Question 7 was non-linear.
**d)** a line

**e)**

**9. a)** Answers may vary.

b)
```
WINDOW
 Xmin=0
 Xmax=150
 Xscl=25
 Ymin=0
 Ymax=500
 Yscl=50
 Xres=1
```

**c)** Vanessa linear, Ally non-linear **d)** Ally **e)** You must assume that Ally continues to increase her speed at the same rate, and Vanessa continues at a steady rate.

**10. a)** non-linear **b)**

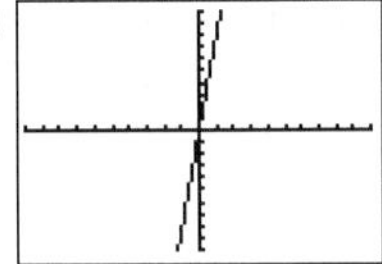

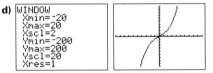

**c)** The graph looks linear but the equation has $x^3$, so it is a non-linear relation.

**d)**
```
WINDOW
 Xmin=-20
 Xmax=20
 Xscl=2
 Ymin=-200
 Ymax=200
 Yscl=20
 Xres=1
```

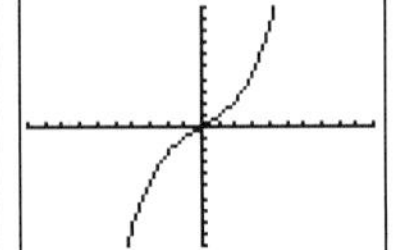

## Review, pages 272–273

**1. a)** \$9/h, \$9/h, \$9/h; This is a linear relationship because the rate of pay is constant.

**b)**

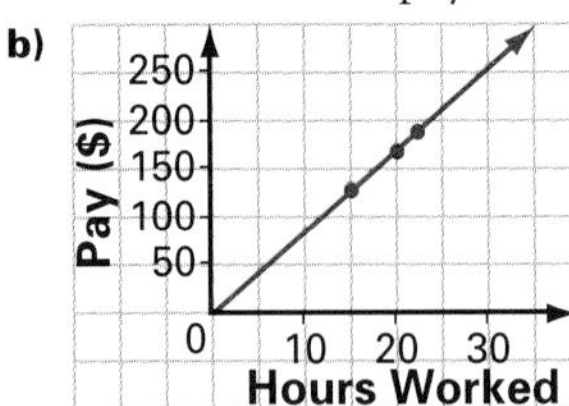


**c)** Yes, because the graph of the line goes through the origin. **d)** \$90, \$225 **e)** 27.8 h

**2. a)**

| Distance (km) | Cost ($) |
|---|---|
| 0 | 60 |
| 50 | 85 |
| 100 | 110 |
| 200 | 160 |
| 500 | 310 |

**b)**

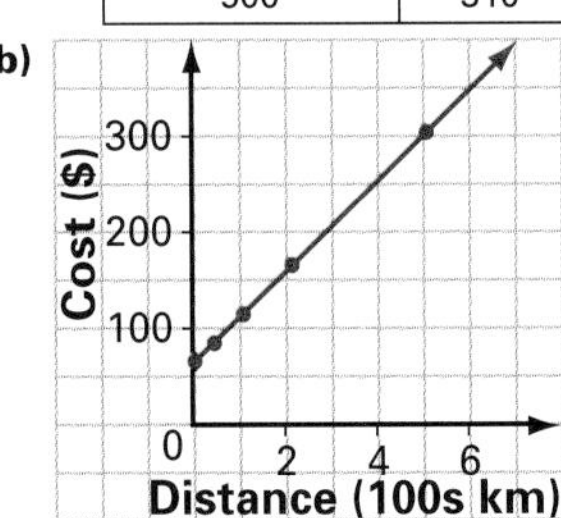


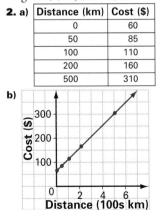

**c)** A partial variation because the graph does not go through the origin. **d)** \$185 **e)** 640 km

**3. a)** fixed 400, variable $5n$ **b)** $p = 400 + 5n$ **c)** \$560, \$650

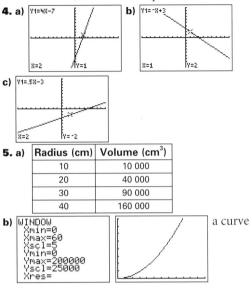

**4. a)** Y1=4X−7 **b)** Y1=−X+3

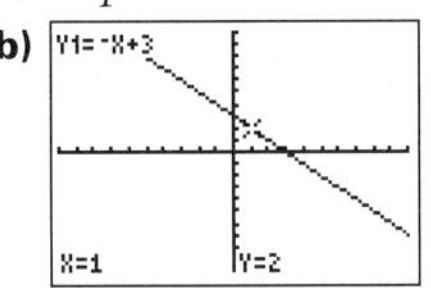

**c)** Y1=.5X−3

**5. a)**

| Radius (cm) | Volume ($cm^3$) |
|---|---|
| 10 | 10 000 |
| 20 | 40 000 |
| 30 | 90 000 |
| 40 | 160 000 |

**b)**
```
WINDOW
 Xmin=0
 Xmax=60
 Xscl=5
 Ymin=0
 Ymax=200000
 Yscl=25000
 Xres=
```

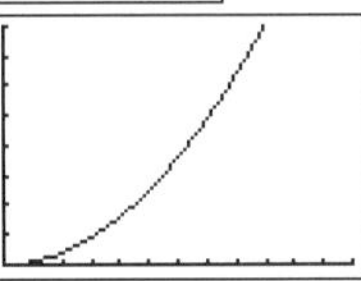

a curve

**c)** 302 500 $cm^3$ **d)** 16 cm

**6. a)** simple linear, compound non-linear

| Simple Interest Account | | |
|---|---|---|
| Number of Years | Amount ($) | First Differences |
| 0 | 1000 | 100 |
| 1 | 1100 | 100 |
| 2 | 1200 | 100 |
| 3 | 1300 | |

| Compound Interest Account | | |
|---|---|---|
| Number of Years | Amount ($) | First Differences |
| 0 | 1000 | 100 |
| 1 | 1100 | 110 |
| 2 | 1210 | 121 |
| 3 | 1331 | |

**b)**

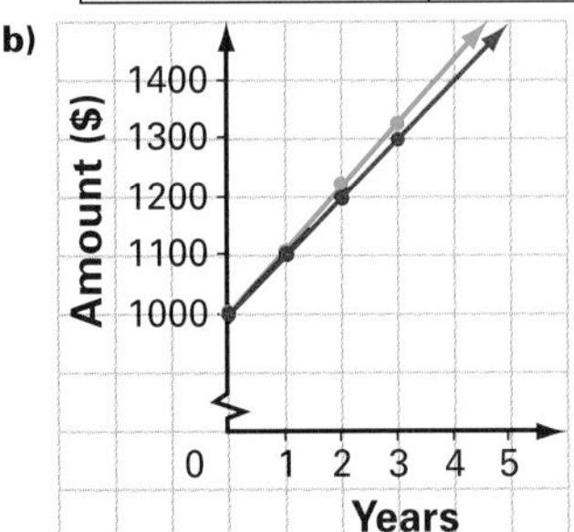


**c)** The compound interest account seems to be a better savings account because the money accumulates faster than in the simple interest account.

**7. a)** linear **b)** linear **c)** linear **d)** non-linear

**8. a)** linear **b)** non-linear **c)** non-linear

## Practice Test, pages 274–275

**1.** D **2.** B **3.** A **4.** C **5.** B **6.** C **7.** B

**8. a)** linear 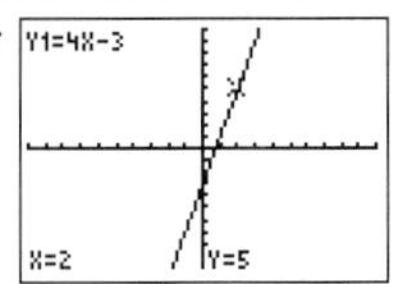


**b)** non-linear 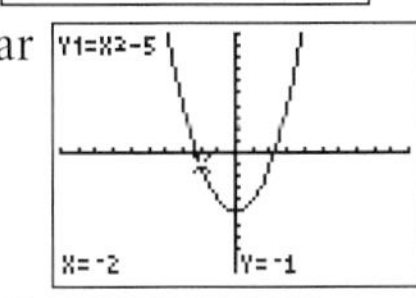


**c)** linear 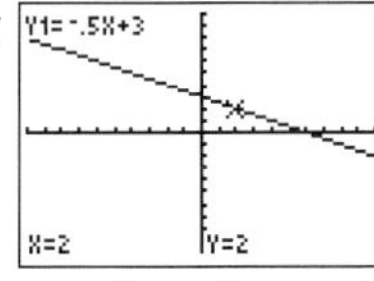


**9. a)** The $x$-values do not increase by a fixed amount. **b)** non-linear, reasons may vary

**10. a)** It is a partial variation because when no one attends, the cost is $225.

**b)**

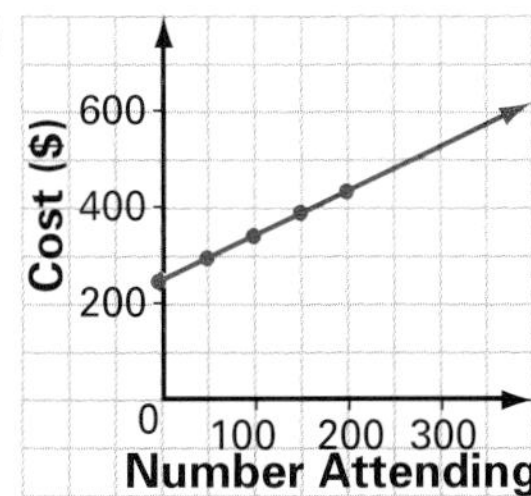


**c)** $C = 225 + n$ **d)** $550 **e)** Santino can afford this banquet hall because it costs only $725 to invite 500 people.

# Chapter 7

## Get Ready, pages 278–279

**1. a)** $\frac{1}{4}$ **b)** $\frac{3}{5}$ **c)** $\frac{1}{5}$ **d)** $\frac{7}{2}$ **e)** $\frac{8}{3}$ **f)** $\frac{10}{3}$

**2. a)** 2 **b)** −2 **c)** 3 **d)** $-\frac{1}{2}$ **e)** $-\frac{3}{2}$ **f)** $-\frac{5}{2}$

**3. a)** 12 **b)** −20 **c)** 2 **d)** −1

**4. a)** −2 **b)** −5 **c)** 1 **d)** −14

**5. a)** −7 **b)** 1 **c)** −3 **d)** −15 **e)** 2 **f)** −1

**6. a)** 4 **b)** 3 **c)** −6 **d)** −7

**7. a)** 5 **b)** 2 **c)** 4 **d)** −8

## 7.1 Motion Sensors and Distance-Time Graphs, pages 285–287

**1.** b, d, c, a

**2. a)** D **b)** C **c)** A **d)** B

**3. a)**

**b)**

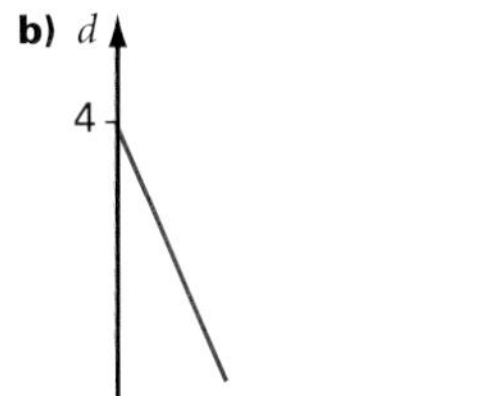


**c)**

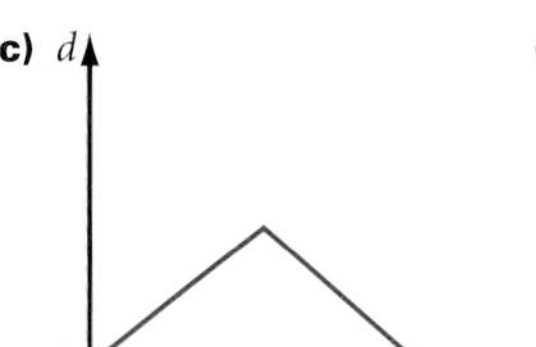


**d)**

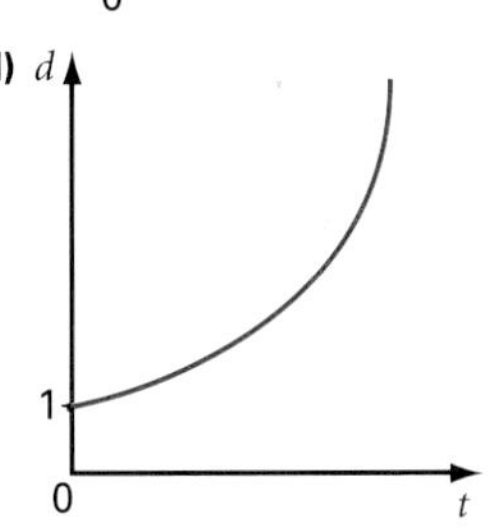


**e)**

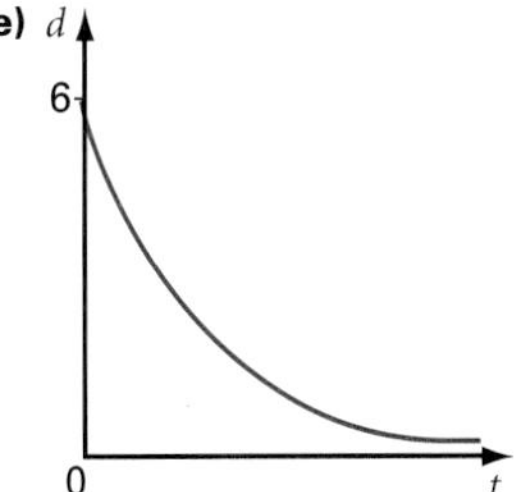

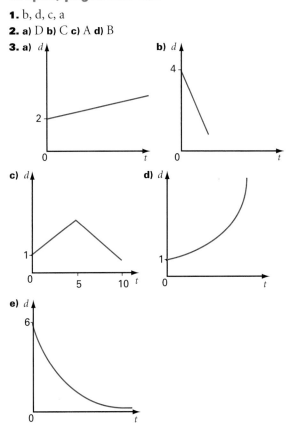


**4. a)** linear **b)** linear **c)** non-linear **d)** non-linear **e)** non-linear

**5. a)** Team Papa: linear, Team Koko: linear, Team Susie: non-linear **b)** Team Koko **c)** Team Susie

**6.** During Interval A, the car begins from a stop and gradually picks up speed. During Interval B, it is travelling at a constant speed. During Interval C, it is slowing down. During Interval D it is stopped.

## 7.2 Slope, pages 291–293

**1. a)** 1.38 **b)** 0.14
**2. a)** 1, 2, $\frac{1}{2}$ **b)** −2, 1, −2 **c)** −1, 1, −1 **d)** 2, 1, 2
**3. a)** D, B, A, C **b)** A away, B away, C toward, D not walking
**4.** 3000 Steps: 1.15, Camel Path: 0.58
**5.** Starting 2 m from the sensor, walk away from the sensor at 0.5 m/s for 2 s. Stop for 3 s. Then, walk toward the sensor at 0.67 m/s.
**6. a)**

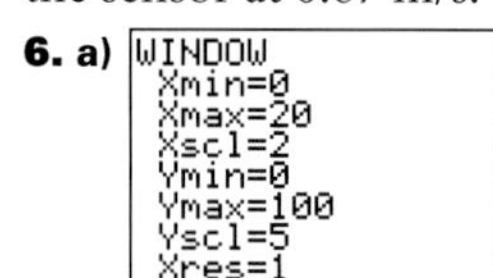


Naomi

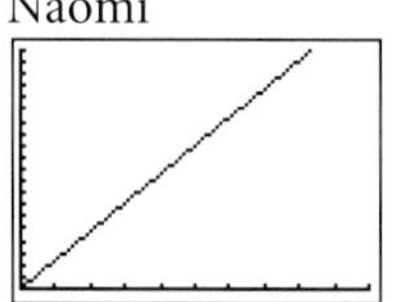

Pinder

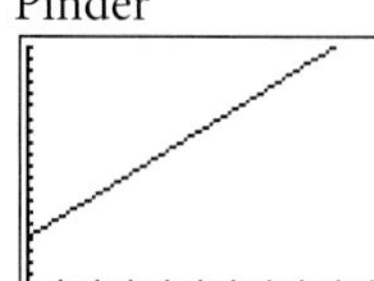

**b)** Naomi will win the race because she will finish slightly before 17 s, while Pinder will finish slightly before 18 s.

## 7.3 Applying the Slope Formula, pages 297–298

**1. a)** 2 **b)** 2 **c)** −1 **d)** $-\frac{3}{4}$
**2. a)** −1 **b)** $\frac{5}{4}$ **c)** $-\frac{6}{5}$ **d)** $\frac{5}{3}$ **e)** $\frac{5}{7}$ **f)** $-\frac{3}{4}$
**3. a)** A(−3, 0), B(0, 2), C(4, 5) **b)** $\frac{2}{3}$ **c)** Answers may vary. **d)** $\frac{2}{3}$, $\frac{2}{3}$ **e)** The two points chosen do not matter because the slope is the same anywhere on a given line.
**4.** 0.5 m/s
**5. a)** Team Koko **b)** 87.5 km/h **c)** 5 h **d)** Team Papa could have started the race heading in the right direction, and then at 3 h, they could have travelled backward. After 1 h, they continued travelling in the right direction.
**e)** 100 km/h travelling forward, 60 km/h travelling backward, 60 km/h travelling forward **f)** 7.2 h

**6. a)** AB: $-\frac{2}{3}$, PQ: $-\frac{2}{3}$, UV: $-\frac{2}{3}$ **b)** All the slopes are equal. **c)** Answers may vary.
**d)**

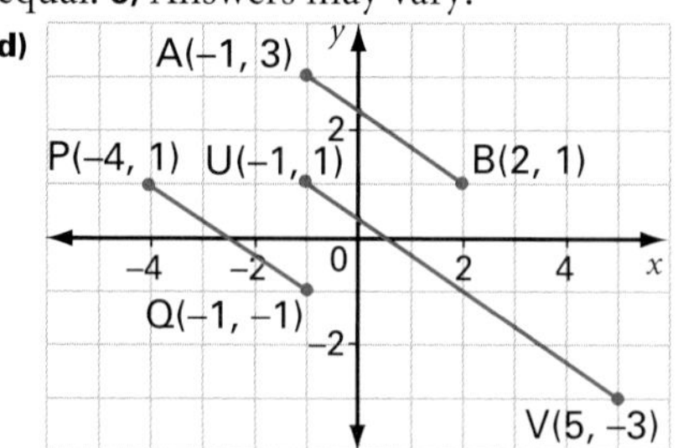


**e)** The line segments are parallel.

## 7.4 Graphing Lines Using Intercepts, pages 303–305

**1. a)** $x$-intercept −4, $y$-intercept 5 **b)** $x$-intercept −6, $y$-intercept −3 **c)** $x$-intercept 7, $y$-intercept −3.5
**2.**

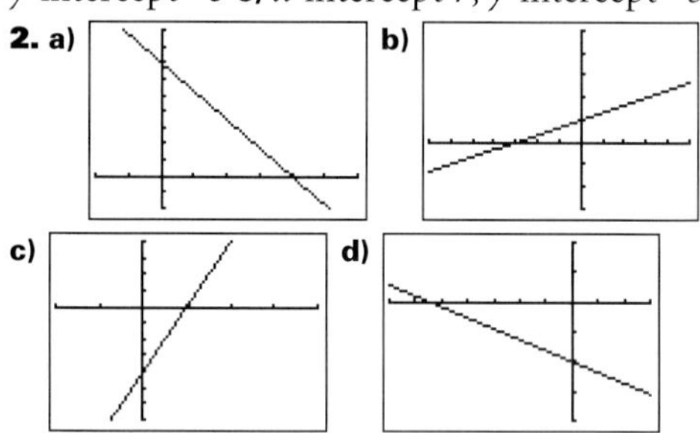


**3. a)** $x$-intercept 5, $y$-intercept 2
**b)** $x$-intercept −6, $y$-intercept −4
**c)** $x$-intercept −3, $y$-intercept $-\frac{3}{2}$
**d)** $x$-intercept $\frac{3}{2}$, $y$-intercept 6

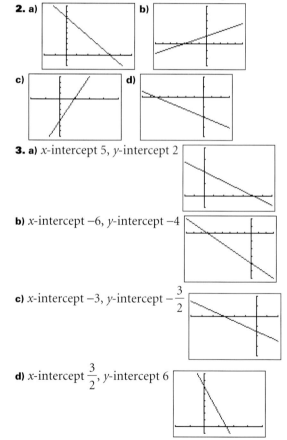

**e)** $x$-intercept $-3$, $y$-intercept 7

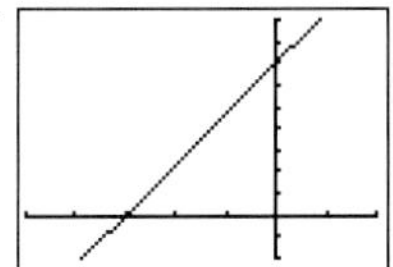

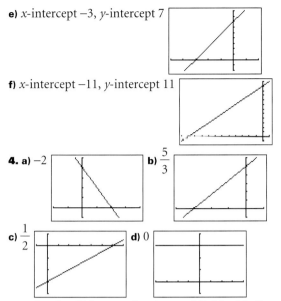

**f)** $x$-intercept $-11$, $y$-intercept 11

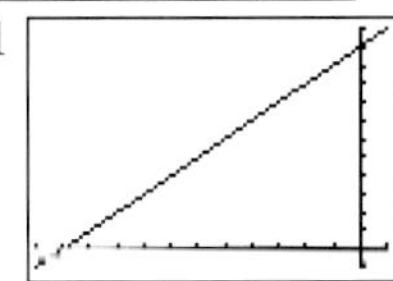

**4. a)** $-2$

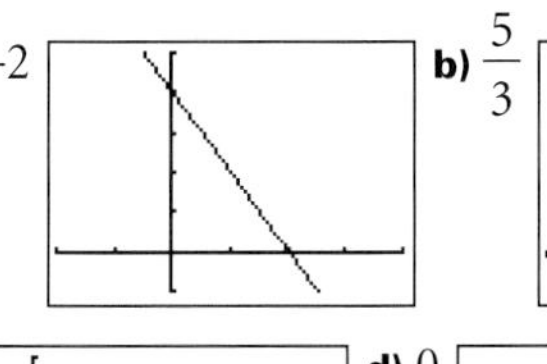

**b)** $\frac{5}{3}$

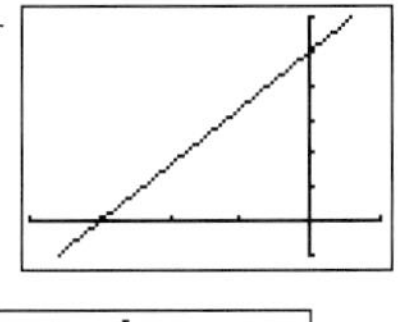

**c)** $\frac{1}{2}$ **d)** 0

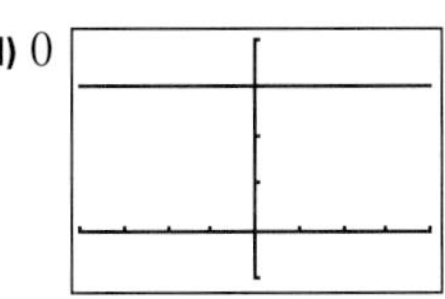

**5. a)** 4 **b)** 5 **c)** Kyla started at 4 m and finished in 5 s.
**d)** 0.8 m/s

**6. a)**

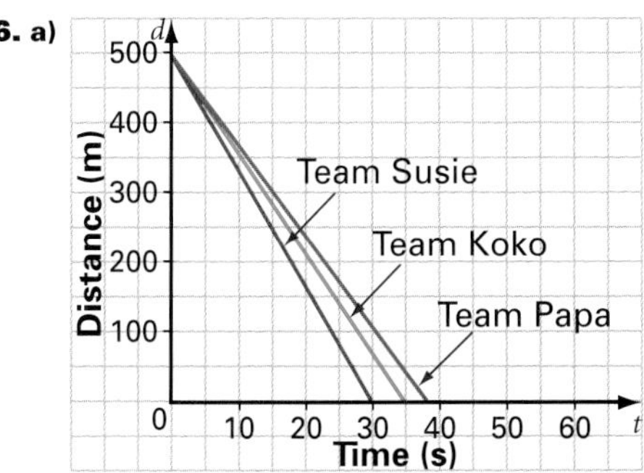


**b)** Team Susie was the fastest. Team Papa was the slowest.

**7. a)** $x$-intercept 3, $y$-intercept 6
**b)** and **d)**

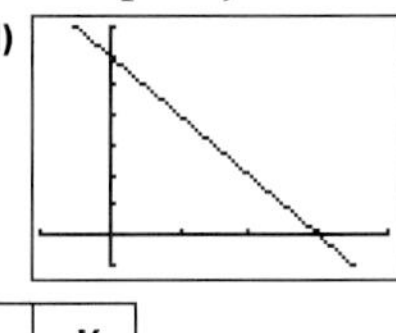

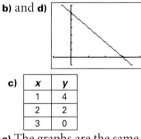

**c)**

| $x$ | $y$ |
|---|---|
| 1 | 4 |
| 2 | 2 |
| 3 | 0 |

**e)** The graphs are the same. **f)** Answers may vary.

**8. a)** independent: time, dependent: length
**b)**

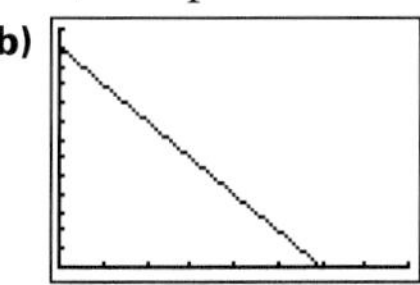

**e)** The $l$-intercept at 12 cm tells us that the candle started at that length at 0 s.
**f)** The $t$-intercept at 6 h tells us that the candle burned out at that time.
**g)** There is no meaning below the $t$-axis because the lowest the candle can burn to is 0 cm.
**h)** There is no meaning to the left of the $l$-axis because time is always positive.

**9. a)** two $x$ intercepts, $-3$, 3 **b)** one $y$-intercept, $-9$
**c)**

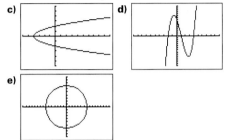

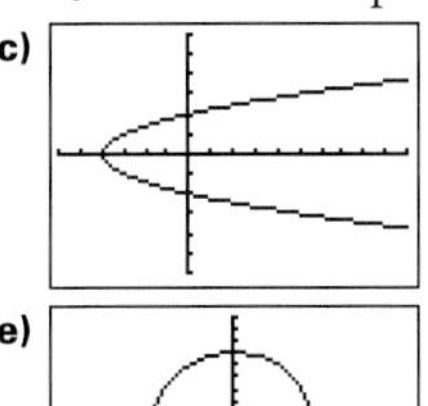

**d)**

**e)**

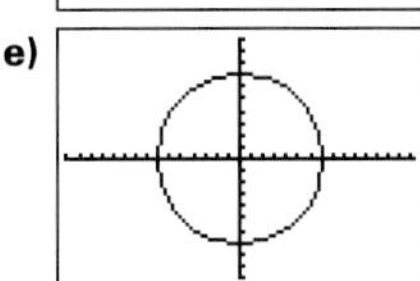

**10. a)** Yes. **b)** Yes. **c)** No.

## 7.5 The Equation of a Line: $y = mx + b$, pages 312–313

**1. a)** slope 6, $y$-intercept 5 **b)** slope $-\frac{3}{4}$, $y$-intercept 3
**c)** slope 1, $y$-intercept $-4$ **d)** slope $-1$, $y$-intercept 0

**2. a)** slope 3, $y$-intercept $-4$, $y = 3x - 4$ **b)** slope $-\frac{3}{4}$, $y$-intercept $-2.5$, $y = -\frac{3}{4}x - 2.5$

**3. a)** $y = 2x - 5$

**b)** $y = \frac{1}{3}x + 2$

**c)** $y = -\frac{3}{4}x$

**4. a)** \$11 is the cost per person, and \$250 is the base fee charged. **b)** The slope would be the same, but the $y$-intercept would be at 350 instead of 250.
**c)** $y = 20x + 250$

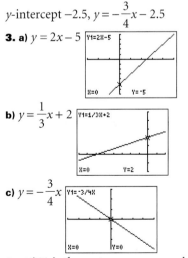

**5. a)** Answers may vary.

**b)**



**c)** Team Papa $d = -2t + 20$, Team Koko $d = -3t + 25$, Team Susie $d = -2.5t + 30$ **d)** Team Papa 10, Team Koko 8.3, Team Susie 12 **e)** Team Koko won the race because $t$-intercept is the smallest, at 8.3 s.

**6. a)** $y = 3$ **b)** $x = -2$ **c)** $y = 0$

**7. a)** $x = 0$ **b)** undefined **c)** All points on $x = 0$ are $y$-intercepts.

**8. a)**

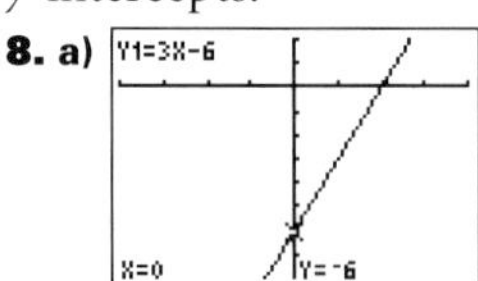


**b)** and **c)** Answers may vary.

## 7.6 Constructing Linear Models: The Line of Best Fit, pages 319–321

**1. a)**

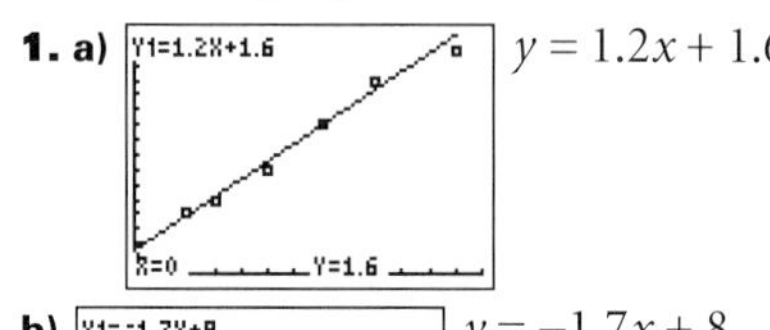


$y = 1.2x + 1.6$

**b)**

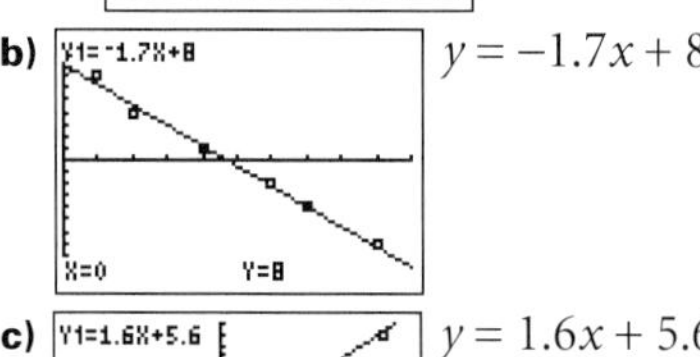


$y = -1.7x + 8$

**c)**

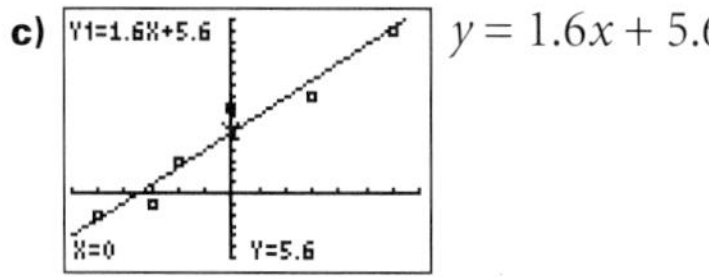


$y = 1.6x + 5.6$

**2.** Answers may vary.

**3. a)** Keep $m$ the same, but increase $b$ to shift the $y$-intercept up. **b)** Decrease $m$ to make the line steeper and increase $b$ to shift the $y$-intercept up.

**4. a)**

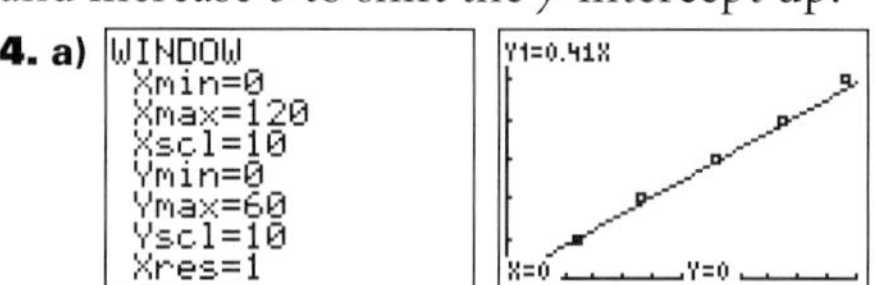


**b)** $y = 0.41x$ **c)** 85 s **d)** 170 s

**5. a)**

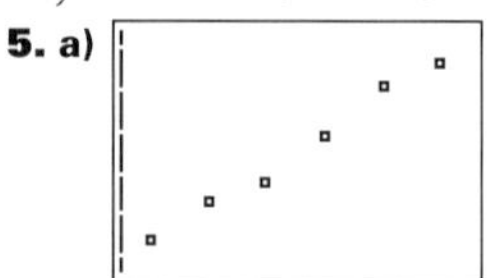

**b)** Answers may vary.

**c)**

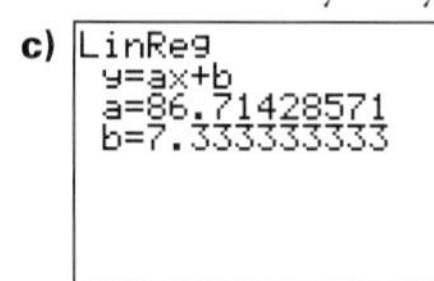


**e)** and **g)** Answers may vary.

## Review, pages 326–327

**1. a)** Moving toward the motion sensor at a constant pace. **b)** Moving away from the sensor at a constant pace. **c)** Moving toward the sensor at a fast pace. **d)** Moving towards the sensor, gradually picking up speed.

**2. a)** **b)**

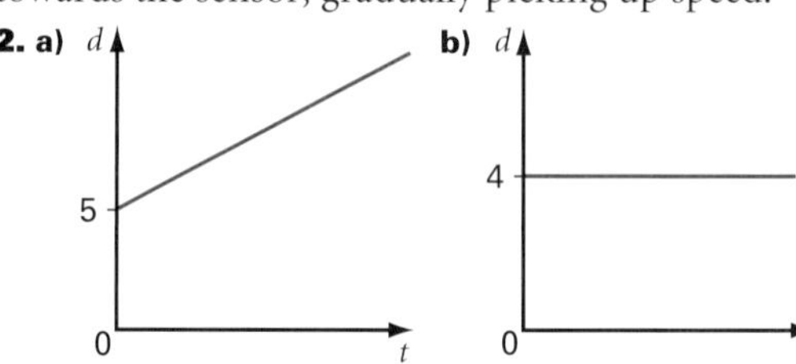


**c)**

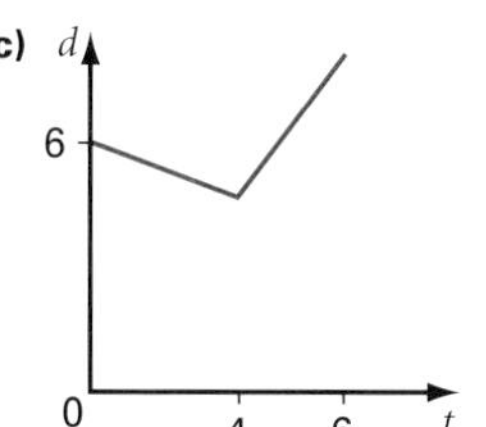


**3. a)** 0.23 **b)** 0.42

**4.** Start at 4 m and walk toward the sensor at a speed of 1 m/s for 2 s. Stop for 3 s. Then, walk away from the sensor at a speed of 0.2 m/s.

**5. a)** 1 **b)** $-\frac{1}{2}$

**6. a)** $x$-intercept 3, $y$-intercept 5

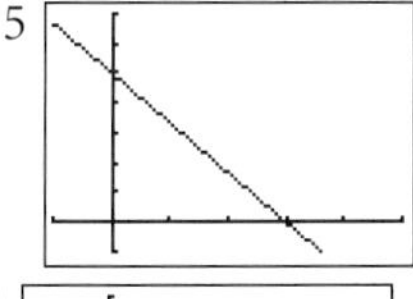

**b)** $x$-intercept 6, $y$-intercept −4

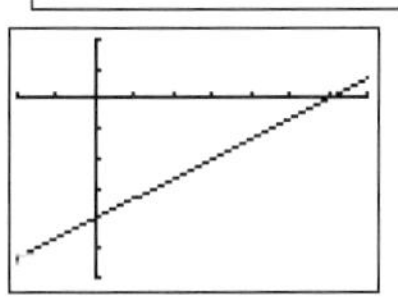

**c)** $x$-intercept −2, $y$-intercept 6

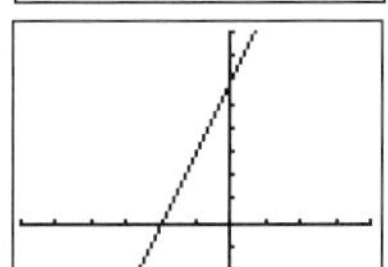

**7. a)** $y = \frac{1}{5}x - 4$

**b)** $y = -3x$

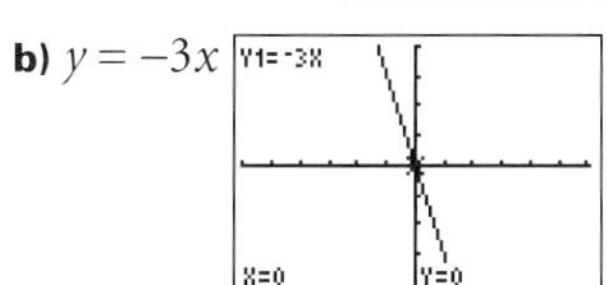


**8. a)** Yes, because the graph is linear. **b)** slope 4, $A$-intercept 40 **c)** The slope tells us that she eats 4 g of cat food every minute. The $A$-intercept tells us that Nala starts with 40 g of cat food. **d)** The $t$-intercept tells us that Nala finishes her food after 10 min.

**9. a)** Team Papa: $d = -5t + 50$, Team Susie: $d = -5t + 60$, Team Koko: $d = -5t + 65$

**b)**

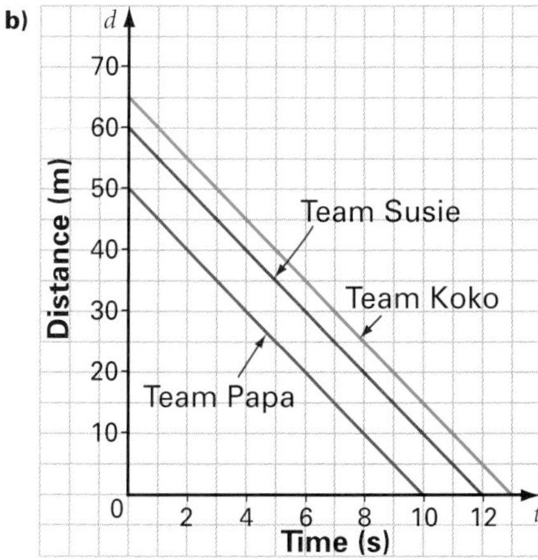


**c)** Team Papa **d)** Team Susie will finish 2 s behind and Team Koko will finish 3 s behind. **e)** Team Susie must run at 6 m/s, or 60 m ÷ 10 s. **f)** Team Koko must run at 6.5 m/s, or 65 m ÷ 10 s.

**10. a)**

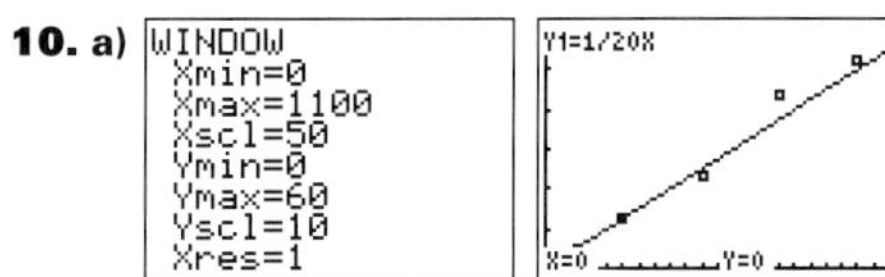


**c)** $y = \frac{1}{20}x$ **d)** 30 cm **e)** 500 cm

## Practice Test, pages 328–329

**1.** B **2.** B **3.** D **4.** C **5.** B

**6. a)** Sheila could have found the $x$- and $y$-intercepts, connected them and graphed the line.

**b)**

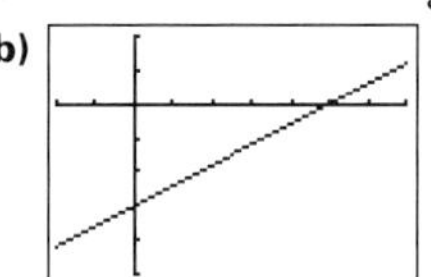

**7. a)** Rocco: slope 1, $d$-intercept 0, Biff: slope $\frac{4}{5}$, $d$-intercept 3 **b)** Biff got a head start of 3 m. **c)** Rocco: 1 m/s, Biff: $\frac{4}{5}$ m/s **d)** Biff will win because he will finish in 9 s while Rocco will finish in 10 s. **e)** Rocco will win because he will finish in 20 s while Biff will finish in 21 s. **f)** Both bears will tie at 15 m because they will both reach that distance in 15 s.

**8. a)**

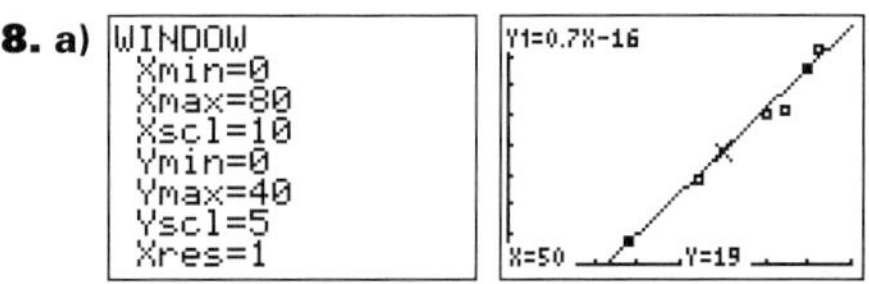


**c)** $y = 0.7x - 16$ **d)** 19 **e)** 41 **f)** 51

## Cumulative Review, Chapters 6 and 7, pages 330–331

**1. a)** This is a direct variation because when the length is 0 cm, the perimeter is also 0 cm. **b)** $P = 6s$ **c)** 48 cm

**2. a)** This is a partial variation because when the distance towed is 0 km, the cost is \$40. **b)** $C = d + 40$

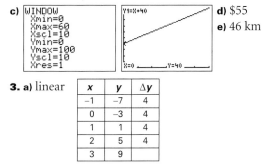

**c)**

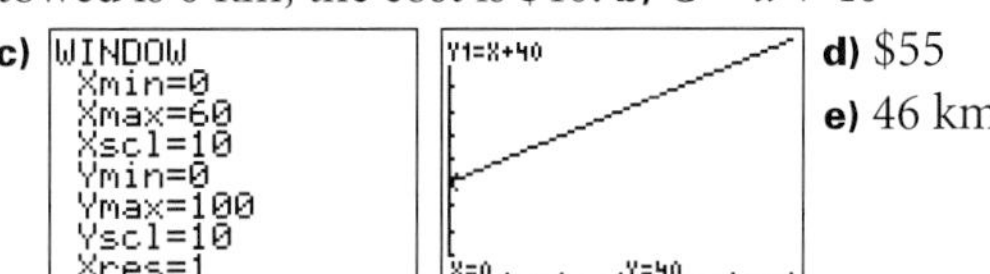


**d)** \$55 **e)** 46 km

**3. a)** linear

| $x$ | $y$ | $\Delta y$ |
|---|---|---|
| −1 | −7 | 4 |
| 0 | −3 | 4 |
| 1 | 1 | 4 |
| 2 | 5 | 4 |
| 3 | 9 | |

**b)** non-linear

| *x* | *y* | Δ*y* |
|---|---|---|
| −2 | 1 | 3 |
| −1 | −2 | 1 |
| 0 | −3 | 1 |
| 1 | −2 | 3 |
| 2 | 1 | |

**c)** linear

| *x* | *y* | Δ*y* |
|---|---|---|
| −4 | 3 | 1 |
| −2 | 2 | 1 |
| 0 | 1 | 1 |
| 2 | 0 | 1 |
| 4 | −1 | |

**4. a)**

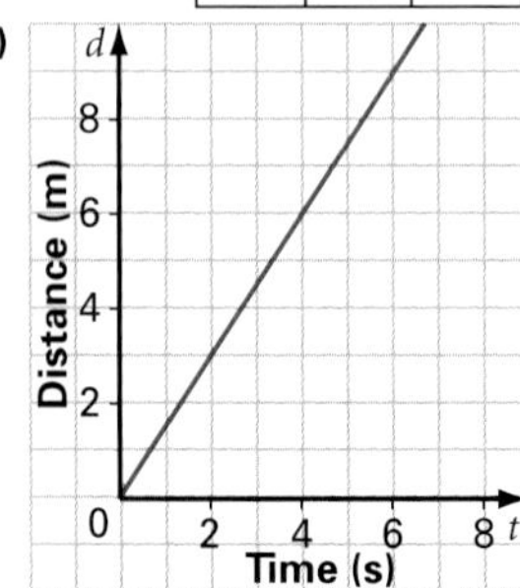


**b)**

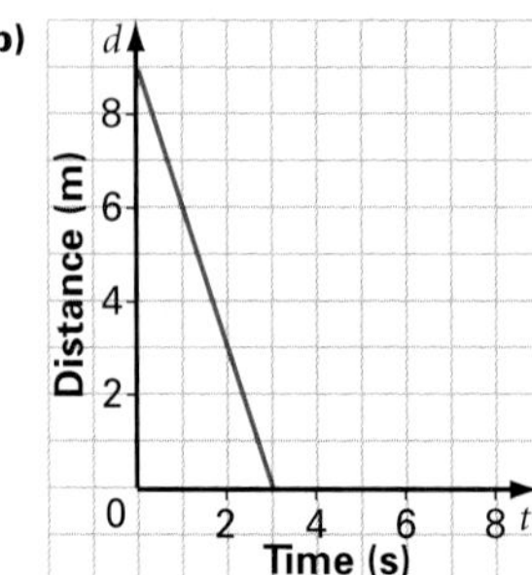


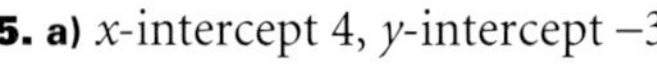

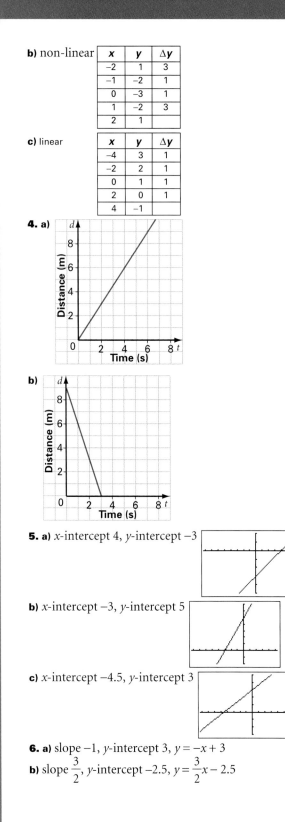

**5. a)** $x$-intercept 4, $y$-intercept −3

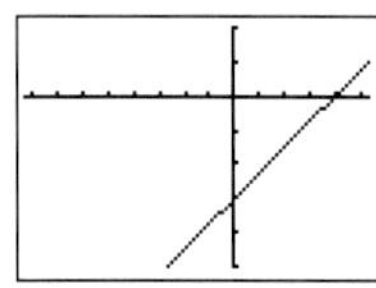

**b)** $x$-intercept −3, $y$-intercept 5

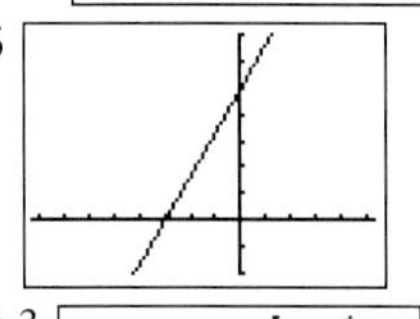

**c)** $x$-intercept −4.5, $y$-intercept 3

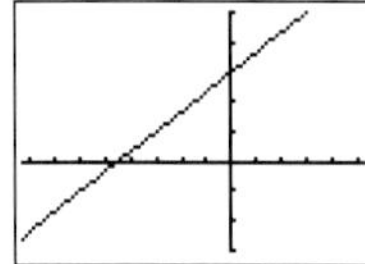

**6. a)** slope −1, $y$-intercept 3, $y = -x + 3$

**b)** slope $\frac{3}{2}$, $y$-intercept −2.5, $y = \frac{3}{2}x - 2.5$

**7. a)** slope undefined, no $y$-intercept

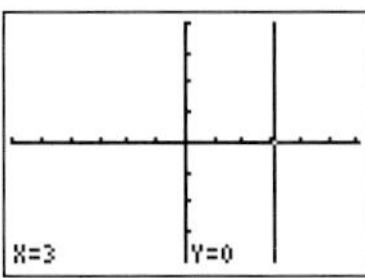

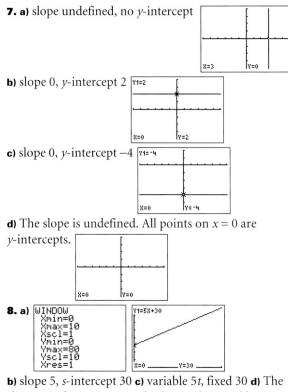

**b)** slope 0, $y$-intercept 2

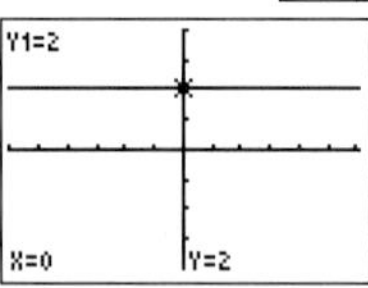


**c)** slope 0, $y$-intercept −4

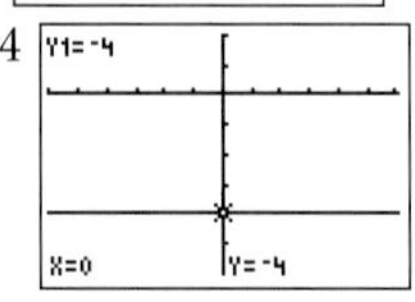


**d)** The slope is undefined. All points on $x = 0$ are $y$-intercepts.

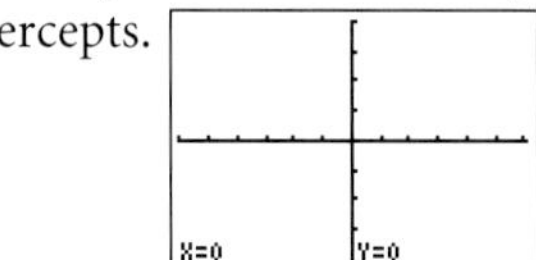


**8. a)**

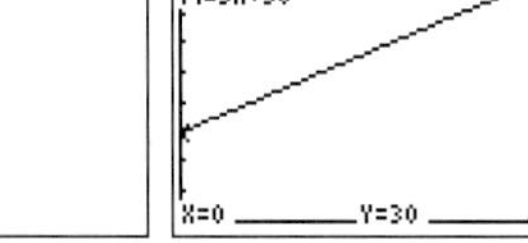


**b)** slope 5, $s$-intercept 30 **c)** variable $5t$, fixed 30 **d)** The slope 5, is the constant multiplier in the variable part. **e)** The $s$-intercept 30, is the fixed part.

**9. a)**

| Distance (km) | Cost ($) |
|---|---|
| 100 | 75 |
| 200 | 100 |
| 300 | 125 |

**b)**

WINDOW
Xmin=0
Xmax=350
Xscl=50
Ymin=0
Ymax=150
Yscl=25
Xres=1

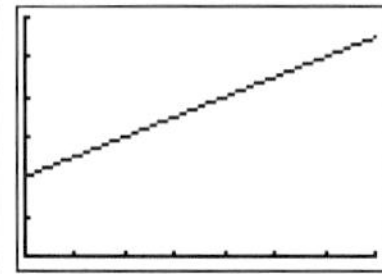

**c)** 50 **d)** slope 0.25, $C$-intercept 50, $C = 0.25d + 50$

**e)** $93.75 **f)** $162.50

**10. a)**

WINDOW
Xmin=0
Xmax=12
Xscl=1
Ymin=0
Ymax=15
Yscl=1
Xres=1

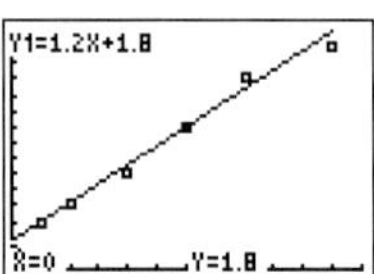


slope 1.2, $y$-intercept 1.8, $y = 1.2x + 1.8$

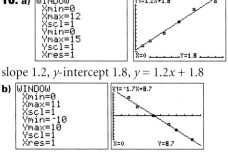

**b)**

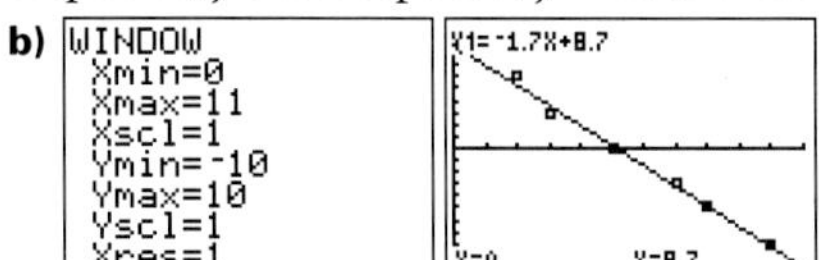


slope −1.7, $y$-intercept 8.7, $y = -1.7x + 8.7$

# CHAPTER 8

## Get Ready, pages 336–337

**1. a)** 8 **b)** 25 **c)** 10 000 **d)** 512 **e)** 2401 **f)** 243 **g)** 64 **h)** 36 **i)** 729

**2. a)** 100 **b)** 11 **c)** 200 **d)** −15 **e)** 87 **f)** 9 **g)** 7 **h)** 4 **i)** 40 **j)** 16

**3. a)** −4 **b)** −9 **c)** 8 **d)** −5 **e)** −8 **f)** −7 **g)** −15 **h)** −8 **i)** 3

**4. a)** $\frac{9}{16}$ **b)** $\frac{1}{27}$ **c)** $\frac{16}{25}$ **d)** $\frac{16}{81}$ **e)** $\frac{1}{32}$ **f)** $\frac{343}{512}$

## 8.1 Powers With Rational Bases, pages 340–341

**1. a)** $\frac{1}{4} \times \frac{1}{4} = \frac{1}{16}$ **b)** $\frac{1}{6} \times \frac{1}{6} \times \frac{1}{6} = \frac{1}{216}$

**c)** $\frac{2}{11} \times \frac{2}{11} \times \frac{2}{11} \times \frac{2}{11} = \frac{16}{14\,641}$ **d)** $\frac{3}{10} = \frac{3}{10}$

**e)** $\frac{4}{15} \times \frac{4}{15} \times \frac{4}{15} = \frac{64}{3375}$

**f)** $\frac{2}{9} \times \frac{2}{9} \times \frac{2}{9} \times \frac{2}{9} \times \frac{2}{9} = \frac{32}{59\,049}$

**2. a)** $\frac{4^3}{5^3} = \frac{64}{125}$ **b)** $\frac{1^5}{5^5} = \frac{1}{3125}$ **c)** $\frac{5^6}{12^6} = \frac{15\,625}{2\,985\,984}$

**d)** $\frac{2^1}{7^1} = \frac{2}{7}$ **e)** $\frac{9^5}{4^5} = \frac{59\,049}{1024}$ **f)** $\frac{8^3}{3^3} = \frac{512}{27}$

**3. a)** $\frac{1}{4}$ **b)** $\frac{1296}{625}$ **c)** $\frac{16}{625}$ **d)** $\frac{25}{9}$ **e)** $\frac{343}{8}$ **f)** $\frac{625}{16}$

**5. a)** $\frac{p^2}{q^2}$ **b)** $\frac{m^3}{n^3}$ **c)** $\frac{x^5}{y^5}$

**6. a)** 1 kg **b)** 0.5 kg **c)** 0.125 kg **d)** 0.004 kg

**7. a)** 4 **b)** $\frac{4}{9}$ **c)** $\frac{4}{9}$ **d)** −125 **e)** $-\frac{125}{8}$ **f)** $-\frac{125}{8}$ **g)** $\frac{9}{25}$

**h)** $-\frac{27}{64}$ **i)** $-\frac{32}{243}$

## 8.2 Exponent Rules, pages 345–346

**1. a)** $5^5$ **b)** $8^9$ **c)** $7^6$ **d)** $3^6$ **e)** $4^{27}$ **f)** $10^4$

**2. a)** $b^{10}$ **b)** $y^7$ **c)** $w^3$ **d)** $x$ **e)** $n^8$ **f)** $c^{15}$

**3. a)** $2^7 = 128$ **b)** $5^3 = 125$ **c)** $4^5 = 1024$ **d)** $6^3 = 216$

**e)** $10^3 = 1000$ **f)** $11^3 = 1331$ **g)** $5^6 = 15\,625$

**h)** $2^{20} = 1\,048\,576$

**4. a)** 8 **b)** 1 **c)** 6 **d)** 6

**5. a)** 13 **b)** 2 **c)** 8 **d)** 8

**6. a)** 42 **b)** 4 **c)** 3 **d)** 3

**7. a)** 2 **b)** 36 **c)** $x^{13}$ **d)** 1 **e)** $k$ **f)** $n^6$

**8.** 8 times

**9. a)** 4 **b)** −32 **c)** −128 **d)** −8 **e)** 729 **f)** −16

**10. a)** $5 \times \frac{1}{2^{12}}$ **b)** $\frac{1}{15} \times 2^{22}$ **c)** $\frac{1}{3} \times 2^{10}$ **d)** $\frac{1}{3} \times 2^{11}$

## 8.3 Zero and Negative Exponents, pages 349–351

**1. a)** $\frac{1}{6^2}$ **b)** $\frac{1}{9^5}$ **c)** $\frac{1}{4^1}$ **d)** $\frac{1}{7^3}$ **e)** $\frac{1}{15^6}$ **f)** $\frac{1}{1^4}$

**2. a)** $\frac{1}{49}$ **b)** $\frac{1}{27}$ **c)** $\frac{1}{8}$ **d)** 1 **e)** $\frac{1}{1024}$ **f)** $\frac{1}{9}$ **g)** 1 **h)** $\frac{1}{10}$

**3. a)** −4 **b)** −6 **c)** 0 **d)** 3 **e)** 2 **f)** 0

**4. c)** The graph is a curve that gets steeper as you move to the right. **d)** The value of $2^x$ decreases by half each time as you scroll to the left. **e)** no

**5. a)** $3^1 = 3, 3^2 = 9, 3^3 = 27, 3^4 = 81, 3^5 = 243$

**b)** $3^{-1} = \frac{1}{3}, 3^{-2} = \frac{1}{9}, 3^{-3} = \frac{1}{27}, 3^{-4} = \frac{1}{81}, 3^{-5} = \frac{1}{243}$

**c)** The number in the denominator is the same as the answer to the positive exponent.

**6. b)** $10^{-2}, \frac{1}{100}, 0.01$ **c)** $10^{-3}, \frac{1}{1000}, 0.001$

**d)** $10^{-4}, \frac{1}{10\,000}, 0.0001$ **e)** $10^{-5}, \frac{1}{100\,000}, 0.000\,01$

**f)** $10^{-6}, \frac{1}{1\,000\,000}, 0.000\,001$; The exponent value indicates how many zeros are in the denominator of the fraction as well as the number of zeros in decimal form.

**7. b)** $5^4 \times 5^{-2}, (5 \times 5 \times 5 \times 5) \times \left(\frac{1}{5} \times \frac{1}{5}\right), 5^2, 25$

**c)** $7^6 \div 7^8, \frac{7 \times 7 \times 7 \times 7 \times 7 \times 7}{(7 \times 7 \times 7 \times 7 \times 7 \times 7 \times 7 \times 7)}, 7^{-2}, \frac{1}{49}$

**d)** $10^6 \times 10^{-9}, 10 \times 10 \times 10 \times 10 \times 10 \times 10 \times \left(\frac{1}{10} \times \frac{1}{10} \times \frac{1}{10} \times \frac{1}{10} \times \frac{1}{10} \times \frac{1}{10} \times \frac{1}{10} \times \frac{1}{10} \times \frac{1}{10}\right), 10^{-3}, \frac{1}{1000}$ **e)** $8^2 \times 8^{-3}, (8 \times 8) \times \left(\frac{1}{8} \times \frac{1}{8} \times \frac{1}{8}\right), 8^{-1}, \frac{1}{8}$

**f)** $\frac{6^5}{6^8}, \frac{6 \times 6 \times 6 \times 6 \times 6}{6 \times 6 \times 6 \times 6 \times 6 \times 6 \times 6 \times 6}, 6^{-3}, \frac{1}{216}$

**8. a)** $4^3 = 64$ **b)** $5^{-3} = \frac{1}{125}$ **c)** $2^{-1} = \frac{1}{2}$ **d)** $3^{-1} = \frac{1}{3}$ **e)** $2^{-4} = \frac{1}{16}$

**f)** $4^2 = 16$ **g)** $12^0 = 1$ **h)** $125^{-1} = \frac{1}{125}$ **i)** $10^1 = 10$

**j)** $10^{-2} = \frac{1}{100}$ **k)** $10^{-9} = \frac{1}{1\,000\,000\,000}$ **l)** $10^{-3} = \frac{1}{1000}$

**9.** $\frac{1}{49}, \frac{1}{216}, \frac{1}{625}, \frac{1}{1024}, \frac{1}{729}, \frac{1}{128}$; $\frac{1}{1024}, \frac{1}{729}, \frac{1}{625}, \frac{1}{216}, \frac{1}{128}, \frac{1}{49}$

**10. a)** $-8$ **b)** $-\frac{1}{8}$ **c)** 1 **d)** 1 **e)** $\frac{1}{9}$ **f)** $-\frac{1}{5}$ **g)** 1 **h)** $-\frac{1}{125}$

**11. a)** $\frac{1}{8}$ **b)** $\frac{1}{2^{30}}$ **c)** $2^{-4}, 2^{-30}$

## 8.4 Scientific Notation, pages 355–357

**1. a)** 3 **b)** 8 **c)** 16 **d)** $-1$ **e)** $-7$ **f)** $-13$

**2. a)** $5.6884 \times 10^3$ m **b)** $2.788\,166\,4 \times 10^7$ km$^2$ **c)** $2 \times 10^{-4}$ g **d)** $3.51 \times 10^{-10}$ mg **e)** $3.41 \times 10^{17}$ km **f)** $8 \times 10^{-21}$ mm

**3. a)** 3 400 000 cm **b)** 6000 L **c)** 9 112 000 000 000 km **d)** 0.000 045 mm **e)** 0.000 000 01 g **f)** 0.000 000 000 673 25 mg

**4. a)** 778 000 000 km **b)** 0.000 12 m **c)** 340 m/s **g)** 3 500 000 000 years

**5. a)** $2.7631 \times 10^5$, 276 310 **b)** $5.41 \times 10^{12}$, 5 410 000 000 000 **c)** $1.19 \times 10^{-2}$, 0.0119 **d)** $8.005 \times 10^{-11}$, 0.000 000 000 080 05

**6. a)** $8.05 \times 10^7$ **b)** $8.05 \times 10^7$ **c)** $8.05 \times 10^7$; All answers are the same because the order of multiplication does not matter.

**7. a)** $3.213 \times 10^{10}$ **b)** $2.0655 \times 10^{11}$ **c)** $6.48 \times 10^{-8}$ **d)** $3.366 \times 10^{-6}$ **e)** $3.936 \times 10^4$ **f)** $3.366 \times 10^8$ **g)** $5.0 \times 10^3$ **h)** $9.0 \times 10^{-9}$ **i)** $8.3 \times 10^{-17}$

**8. a)** $2.583\,1443 \times 10^7$ mm **b)** $2.583\,1443 \times 10^6$ cm **c)** $2.583\,1443 \times 10^4$ m **d)** $2.583\,1443 \times 10$ km

**9.** 3.48 people per square kilometre

**10.** $1.0 \times 10^{24}$

**11. a)** 91 200, $9.12 \times 10^4$ **b)** 14 400, $1.44 \times 10^4$ **c)** 19 200 000, $1.92 \times 10^7$ **d)** 139 200 000, $1.392 \times 10^8$ **e)** 144 000, $1.44 \times 10^5$

**12. a)** No, because $(9.0 \times 10^{-4}) \times 100 = 9.0 \times 10^{-6}$ m is not as wide as $2.0 \times 10^{-4}$ m. **b)** No, because $(9.0 \times 10^{-8}) \times 1000 = 9.0 \times 10^{-5}$ m is not as wide as $2.0 \times 10^{-4}$ m. **c)** $\frac{9.0 \times 10^{-8}}{2.0 \times 10^{-4}}$ or $4.5 \times 10^{-4}$

**13. a)** 8 min 20 s, 500 s **b)** 5 h 33 min, 333 min

## Review, pages 358–359

**1. a)** $\frac{8}{27}$ **b)** $\frac{16}{25}$ **c)** $\frac{27}{1000}$ **d)** $\frac{1}{256}$ **e)** $\frac{243}{32}$ **f)** $\frac{343}{512}$

**2. a)** $\frac{16}{25}$ **b)** $\frac{64}{125}$

**3. a)** $4^3$, 64 **b)** $2^5$, 32 **c)** $5^4$, 625 **d)** $8^2$, 64 **e)** $5^3$, 125 **f)** $10^5$, 100 000 **g)** $2^8$, 256 **h)** $3^4$, 81 **i)** $4^0$, 1

**4. a)** $5^{15}$ **b)** $7^5$ **c)** $m^{11}$ **d)** $x^3$ **e)** $g^4$ **f)** $a^1$

**6. a)** $-3$ **b)** 6 **c)** $-5$ **d)** 7

**7. a)** $\frac{1}{9}$ **b)** $\frac{1}{125}$ **c)** $\frac{1}{7}$ **d)** 1 **e)** $\frac{1}{1000}$ **f)** $\frac{1}{9}$ **g)** $\frac{1}{625}$ **h)** 1 **i)** $\frac{1}{3125}$

**8. a)** 9 **b)** 1 **c)** $\frac{1}{25}$ **d)** $\frac{1}{49}$ **e)** $\frac{1}{36}$ **f)** 49 **g)** $\frac{1}{8}$ **h)** $\frac{1}{10^{24}}$ **i)** $\frac{1}{125}$

**9. a)** 530 000 000 m **b)** 71 200 g **c)** 39 901 000 000 L **d)** 0.000 62 L **e)** 0.000 000 000 3 m **f)** 0.000 000 040 01 g

**10. a)** $6 \times 10^8$ m **b)** $5.6 \times 10^{10}$ L **c)** $6.519 \times 10^{15}$ m$^2$ **d)** $3 \times 10^{-5}$ m **e)** $6.7 \times 10^{-8}$ L **f)** $9.1 \times 10^{-17}$g

**11. a)** 30 because you have to account for the one covered by 9. **b)** 41 because there are no more non-zero digits after the 1 to account for.

**12.** 55 people per square kilometre

## Practice Test, pages 360–361

**1.** D **2.** B **3.** C **4.** D

**5. a)** $\frac{3}{5} \times \frac{3}{5} = \frac{9}{25}$ **b)** $\frac{7}{3} \times \frac{7}{3} \times \frac{7}{3} = \frac{343}{27}$ **c)** $\frac{5}{8} \times \frac{5}{8} \times \frac{5}{8} \times \frac{5}{8} \times \frac{5}{8} \times \frac{5}{8} = \frac{15\,625}{262\,144}$

**6. a)** $\frac{1}{8^1} = \frac{1}{8}$ **b)** $\frac{1}{5^2} = \frac{1}{25}$ **c)** $\frac{1}{4^3} = \frac{1}{64}$ **d)** $\frac{1}{10^5} = \frac{1}{100\,000}$

**7. a)** $2.488\,75 \times 10^8$ **b)** $7.349 \times 10^{12}$ **c)** $2.0 \times 10^{-7}$ **d)** $4.3 \times 10^{-17}$

**8. a)** $5^6 = 15\,625$ **b)** $7^2 = 49$ **c)** $12^{-1} = \frac{1}{12}$ **d)** $9^0 = 1$ **e)** $2^6 = 64$ **f)** $5^{-2} = \frac{1}{25}$

**9.** 22.7 times

**10.** 9091 hamburgers

# CHAPTER 9

## Get Ready, pages 364–365

**1. a)** $x^2 - 3$ **b)** $3x + 2$ **c)** $x^2 - x + 1$
**2.** Answers may vary.
**3. a)** $6x^2$ **b)** $y^3$ **c)** $-40k^2$ **d)** $15n^2$ **e)** $\frac{x^2}{y^2}$ **f)** $-30c^3$
**4.** 36 cm, 72 $\text{cm}^2$
**5.** 36 $\text{m}^2$
**6. a)** $S = 280\ \text{cm}^2$, $V = 300\ \text{cm}^3$ **b)** $S = 5400\ \text{mm}^2$, $V = 27\ 000\ \text{mm}^3$

## 9.1 Introducting Polynomials, pages 370–372

**1. a)** 1 **b)** 2 **c)** 2 **d)** 3, trinomial **e)** 5
**2. a)** 10 **b)** −3 **c)** 1 **d)** −1
**3. a)** 9 **b)** 3 **c)** −4 **d)** −14
**4. a)** 13 **b)** 26 **c)** 10 **d)** 34 **e)** 145
**5. a)** $5x + 15$ **b)** $3p - 4$ **c)** $7y + 4$ **d)** $-5x^2 + 12x - 4$ **e)** $7m^2 - 11m - 9$ **f)** $-7v^3 - 2v$
**6. a)** $A = lw$ **b)** $A = 8w$ **c)** $A = 3l$ **d)** $A = s^2$
**7. a)** Let $h$ be Andy's height. $h + 5$ **b)** Let $c$ be the cost of a chocolate bar. $3c$ **c)** Let $l$ be the length. $l^2$ **d)** Let $c$ be the cost of the phone call. $c - 3$ **e)** Let $x$ be the cost of the CD. $2x + 4$ **f)** Let $h$ be the hours Mae worked. $10h$
**8. a)** 1 m **b)** 6 m **c)** 1 m
**9. a)**

| Number of Days | 1 | 2 | 3 | 4 | 5 |
|---|---|---|---|---|---|
| Total Cost ($) | 3 | 5 | 7 | 9 | 11 |

**b)** $C = 1 + 2n$ **c)** $15 **d)** $29
**10. a)** 12, 14, 16; $2n$; 20 **b)** 13, 15, 17; $2n + 1$; 21 **c)** 36, 49, 64; $n^2$; 100
**11. a)** 2 **b)** 1, −6 **c)** −2

## 9.2 Adding and Subtracting Polynomials, pages 376–377

**1. a)** $7x$, $54x$, $9x$ **b)** $8k^3$, $k^3$; −10, 12; $6k$, $7k$
**2. a)** $5x + 12$ **b)** $13y - 4$ **c)** $13n^2 + 5n - 15$ **d)** $-c^2 - 9c - 6$ **e)** $2g^2 + 7g - 6$ **f)** $-5m^2 + 5m - 5$ **g)** $8x^3 - 4x^2 - 5x - 1$
**3. a)** $2x + 7$ **b)** $-2b + 9$ **c)** $-5d^2 + 13d + 14$ **d)** $5p^2 + p + 7$ **e)** $-9y + 1$ **f)** $13y^2 - 2y - 2$ **g)** $-w^3 + 10w^2 - 4w - 3$
**4. a)** $6c - 1$ **b)** $3x - 5$ **c)** $-3y^2 - 2y + 2$ **d)** $-2k^2 - 13k + 10$ **e)** $9x - 10$
**5. a)** 38, 20, 19; $P = 77$ **b)** $14x + 7$; 77 **c)** second method **d)** Answers may vary.
**6.** $x^2 + 5x + 5$
**7. a)** $20\ 700x - 19\ 500$ **b)** $1200 profit **c)** $228 900 profit
**8. a)** $4n^2 - 4000n - 90\ 000$ **b)** −$1 090 000, loss **c)** −$90 000, loss
**9.** composite, because the answer will always be an even number greater than 2

## 9.3 Multiplying a Monomial and a Polynomial, pages 380–381

**1. a)** $3x + 18$ **b)** $7k + 28$ **c)** $4d + 40$ **d)** $-2y - 10$ **e)** $-9c - 27$ **f)** $5m - 20$ **g)** $2w - 12$ **h)** $-3g + 15$ **i)** $-5y + 15$
**2. a)** $x^2 + 6x$ **b)** $c^2 + 8c$ **c)** $m^2 + 3m$ **d)** $y^2 - 5y$ **e)** $k^2 - 4k$ **f)** $-x^2 - 5x$ **g)** $-a^2 - 2a$ **h)** $-b^2 + 3b$ **i)** $-x^2 + x$
**3. a)** $2x^2 + 6x$ **b)** $5y^2 + 35y$ **c)** $3k^2 + 24k$ **d)** $4m^2 - 24m$ **e)** $5w^2 - 20w$ **f)** $-6p^2 - 6p$ **g)** $-x^2 - 25x$ **h)** $-3y^2 + 27y$ **i)** $-2h^2 + 16h$
**4. a)** $8y^2 + 20y$ **b)** $21c^2 + 24c$ **c)** $12m^2 + 24m$ **d)** $-40a^2 + 15a$ **e)** $35h^2 - 5h$ **f)** $-12d^2 - 28d$ **g)** $-16j^2 + 14j$ **h)** $0.3x^2 - 0.6x$ **i)** $-x^2 - 4x$
**5. a)** $20x^2 + 15x - 10$ **b)** $x^3 + 3x^2 + 7x$ **c)** $4y^3 - 5y^2 + 2y$ **d)** $-m^3 - 2m^2 + 4m$ **e)** $4k^3 + 28k^2 + 12k$ **f)** $6w^3 - 10w^2 - 12w$
**6. a)** $2x^2 + 6x$; 36 $\text{cm}^2$ **b)** $5x^2 + 35x$; 150 $\text{cm}^2$ **c)** $12x^2 + 24x$; 180 $\text{cm}^2$
**7. a)** $100m^2 + 150m$ **b)** 16 200 **c)** 61 200 **d)** Answers may vary.
**8. a)** $30(x + 30)$, $30(2x + 50)$, $(x + 30)(2x + 50)$ **b)** $30x + 900$, $60x + 1500$, $2x^2 + 110x + 1500$ **c)** 1080 $\text{cm}^2$, 1860 $\text{cm}^2$, 2232 $\text{cm}^2$ **d)** 8484 $\text{cm}^2$
**9. a)** $-2t^2 + 40t$ **b)** 38 m, 200 m, 0 m **c)** Answers may vary.

## 9.4 Expanding and Simplifying Polynomial Expressions, pages 384–385

**1. a)** $3x + 12$ **b)** $-10y + 16$ **c)** $k^2 + 3k$ **d)** $12n^2 - 15n$ **e)** $-4x^2 + 7x$ **f)** $18y^2 - 24y$
**2. a)** $9x + 52$ **b)** $8y - 44$ **c)** $3m + 6$ **d)** $-14g^2 + 8$ **e)** $14y - 27$ **f)** $-11n^2 - 16n + 5$
**3. a)** $2y^2 - y$ **b)** $2b^2 - 7b$ **c)** $-5x$ **d)** $-14c$ **e)** $10f$ **f)** $-2p^2 - p$
**4. a)** $7x^2 + 6x$ **b)** $-c^2 + 7c$ **c)** $-5y$ **d)** $5x^2 + 29x$ **e)** $k^2 + 17k$ **f)** $-a^2 + 18a$
**5. a)** $16x^2 + 19x$ **b)** $31y^2 - 40y$ **c)** $3m^2 + 17m$ **d)** $18g^2 + 11g$ **e)** $2a^2 + 10a$ **f)** $-18k^2 + 50k - 24$
**6. a)** $5x^2 + 19x - 6$ **b)** $-9y^2 + 3y$ **c)** $6x^3 + 23x^2$
**7. a)** Draw a horizontal line to separate the shape into two rectangles. **b)** $3x(x + 4) - 3(2x)$ **c)** $3x^2 + 6x$

**8. a)** $(3x - 1)(3x) + (2x)(x - 1)$, $11x^2 - 5x$, 34 cm$^2$ **b)** $(8x + 7)(3x + 3x + 1) - (3x + 1)(3x + 7)$, $39x^2 + 26x$, 208 cm$^2$ **c)** $(5x + 6)(8x) - (2x)(x + 9)$, $38x^2 + 30x$, 212 cm$^2$
**9. a)** $3y^2$ **b)** $6y^2 + 15y$ **c)** $2y^2 + 5y$ **d)** $22y^2 + 40y$ **e)** 1728 cm$^2$
**10. a)** Ahmed $6x^2 + 12x + 1$, Briana $5x^2 + 15x + 25$, Chi $18x + 1$, Dawn $5x^2 + 15x + 25$ **b)** Ahmed $6x^2 + 8x - 5$, Briana $5x^2 + 15x + 25$, Chi $10x - 11$, Dawn $x^2 + 3x + 5$ **c)** Answers may vary.

## Review, pages 386–387

**1. a)** 2 b) 1 **c)** 4 **d)** 3 **e)** 1 **f)** 2; d) is a trinomial
**2. a)** $6a + 11$ **b)** $8x + 19$ **c)** $7y - 5$ **d)** $6n^2 + 7n + 7$ **e)** $3x^2 + 2x + 3$ **f)** $-2w - 1$
**3. a)** 11 m **b)** 2 m **c)** The diver enters the water, at 0 m.
**4. a)** $5x + 13$ **b)** $7y + 7$ **c)** $3k^2 + 6k - 6$ **d)** $5a^2 + 3a + 8$ **e)** $13x^2 - 2x + 5$ **f)** $y^2 + 6$
**5. a)** $4x^2 + 6x - 2$ **b)** 53 cm, 111 cm, 128 cm
**6. a)** Multiply both terms inside the bracket by the term outside the bracket. **b)** Multiply both terms inside the bracket by the term outside the bracket.
**7. a)** $3x + 12$ **b)** $2x - 10$ **c)** $y^2 + 5y$ **d)** $y^2 - y$ **e)** $7c^2 - 21c$ **f)** $-5a^2 - 10a$ **g)** $16w^2 + 24w$ **h)** $-20n^2 - 8n$ **i)** $-21v^2 + 18v$
**8. a)** $3x^2 + 15x - 3$ **b)** $2x^3 + 4x^2 + 3x$ **c)** $7g^3 - 3g^2 + 5g$ **d)** $-y^3 - 5y^2 + 2y$ **e)** $3a^3 + 9a^2 + 12a$ **f)** $10m^3 - 15m^2 - 25m$
**9. a)** $4x^2 + 8x$, 140 cm$^2$ **b)** $3x(2x - 5)$, $6x^2 - 15x$, 75 cm$^2$
**10. a)** $8x + 13$ **b)** $7x - 47$ **c)** $2y^2 + 12y$ **d)** $-2d$ **e)** $7a^2 - 14a$ **f)** $-k^2 - 43k$ **g)** $-6k^2 + 24k + 10$ **h)** $-45n^2 + 46n - 28$ **i)** $10x^2 + 22x - 5$ **j)** $-10y^3 + 16y^2 + 22y$
**11. a)** $5x(4x - 2 + x - 2) - 2x(x - 2)$; $5x(4x - 2) + 3x(x - 2)$ **b)** $23x^2 - 16x$ **c)** 159 cm$^2$

## Practice Test, pages 388–389

**1.** C **2.** D **3.** B **4.** D
**5. a)** Multiply the number outside the bracket by both the variables inside the bracket. **b)** The signs are opposite.
**6. a)** $h - 6$ **b)** $2a$ **c)** $c + 10$ **d)** $0.5p$
**7. a)** $5x - 15$ **b)** $-12y - 24$ **c)** $6a^2 - 8a$ **d)** $-20k^2 + 10k$ **e)** $6n^2 + 18n - 24$ **f)** $-10c^2 - 12c + 4$
**8. a)** $8x + 4$ **b)** $5y^2 - 12y + 5$ **c)** $10x + 13$ **d)** $2h^2 + h$ **e)** $-x^2 + 8x$ **f)** $11c^2 + 21c - 24$
**9. a)** $P = 22x - 4$, $S = 28x^2 - 8x$ **b)** $P = 24x + 6$, $S = 30x^2 + 11x$
**10 a)** $P = 84$ cm, $A = 416$ cm$^2$ **b)** $P = 102$ cm, $A = 524$ cm$^2$
**11.** Answers may vary.

# CHAPTER 10

## Get Ready, pages 392–393

**1. a)** $7x + 7$ **b)** $2y - 1$ **c)** $4c - 4$ **d)** $3d$
**2. a)** $3x - 24$ **b)** $8k + 20$ **c)** $-6f - 2$ **d)** $-27h + 63$
**3. a)** B **b)** D **c)** A **d)** C
**4. a)** $-1$ **b)** $-2$ **c)** $-3$ **d)** $\frac{3}{2}$
**5. a)** $y = -x + 2$ **b)** $y = -\frac{1}{2}x + 1$

## 10.1 Solving One- and Two-Step Equations, pages 397–398

**1. a)** 5 **b)** 9 **c)** 8 **d)** 5 **e)** $-1$ **f)** $-12$
**2. a)** 7 **b)** 9 **c)** 4 **d)** 20 **e)** 1.5 **f)** 16
**3. a)** yes **b)** no
**4. a)** 6 **b)** 1 **c)** 3 **d)** 5
**5. a)** 22 **b)** $-6$ **c)** $-3$ **d)** 2 **e)** $-15$ **f)** 28
**6. a)** 7 **b)** $-1$ **c)** 3 **d)** $-8$ **e)** 0 **f)** 3
**7. a)** Answers may vary. **b)** 480 **c)** algebra
**8. a)** Subtract 6 from both sides to get $-2x = 2$. Next, divide both sides by $-2$ to get $x = -1$. **b)** Substitute $x = -1$ into the original equation to see if the two sides are equal. $6 - 2(-1) = 8$ is true so the value is correct.
**9.** 4.5 h
**10. a)** 32 m **b)** Create an equation using the perimeter formula, $P = 2l + 2w$. Substitute in the known values and solve for $w$.

## 10.2 Solving Multi-Step Equations, pages 402–403

**1. a)** 2 **b)** 2 **c)** $-2.5$ **d)** $-2$ **e)** 3 **f)** 7
**2. a)** 10.5 **b)** 0 **c)** 3 **d)** 9 **e)** $-4$ **f)** 0.75
**3. a)** yes **b)** No, because the left side equals $-9$ while the right side equals $-10$.
**4. a)** 5 **b)** 9 **c)** $-1$ **d)** 3 **e)** 0 **f)** $-1$
**5. a)** 10 **b)** 2.5 **c)** 0 **d)** $-1$ **e)** $-1$ **f)** 0.5
**6.** Answers may vary.
**7. a)** $30 = \frac{4}{2}(2x + x)$ **b)** 5 **c)** The length of the shorter side is $-2$. **d)** 5 cm, 10 cm
**8. a)** 30 **b)** 60
**9. a)** 20 years **b)–d)** Answers may vary.

## 10.3 Modelling With Formulas, pages 408–410

**1. a)** $w = \frac{A}{l}$ **b)** $I = A - P$ **c)** $st = d$ **d)** $d = \frac{C}{\pi}$ **e)** $b = \frac{A}{h}$
**f)** $w = \frac{V}{lh}$ **g)** $b = y - mx$ **h)** $l = \frac{P}{2} - w$ **i)** $R = \frac{P}{I^2}$
**2.** $h = \frac{S - 2\pi r^2}{2\pi r}$
**3. a)** $P = A - I$ **b)** \$5250
**4. a)** $I = \frac{V}{R}$, 3 A **b)** $R = \frac{V}{I}$, 36 Ω
**5.** Answers may vary.
**6. a)** 1.7 cm **b)** 1.7 cm
**c)** 1.7 cm 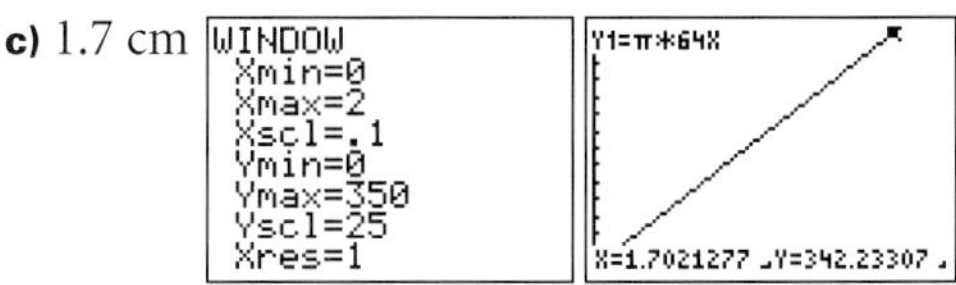

**d)** Answers may vary.
**7. a)** $m = \frac{1}{2}$ **b)** $m = \frac{1}{2}$ **c)** $m = \frac{1}{2}$ **d)** Answers may vary.
**8. a)** $x = \frac{F}{k}$ **b)** 5
**9. a)** $L = \frac{V}{\pi ab}$ **b)** 1.2 m
**10. a)** $t = \frac{d}{s}$ **b)** 500 s **c)** $5.3 \times 10^{12}$ s, or about 170 000 years

## 10.4 Modelling With Algebra, pages 416–417

**1. a)** $4n$ **b)** $n - 3$ **c)** $2n + 9$
**2. a)** $5n = 30$ **b)** $l - 10 = 2$ **c)** $2n + 3 = 25$
**3.** Donna 39, Sophie 13
**4.** Luke 14, André 18
**5. a)** 240 m by 80 m **b)** Answers may vary.
**6. a)** 40 cm, 80 cm, 160 cm **b)** Let $x$ be the first side, then the second side is $2x$, and the third side is $4x$. Write an equation for the perimeter. $P = x + 2x + 4x$. Substitute $P = 280$ and solve for $x$.
**7. a)** height 5.2 cm, base 10.4 cm **b)** 27.2 cm
**8. a)** 644 h **b)** 322 h
**9.** 28, 29, 30
**10.** Answers may vary.
**11. a)** 4.8 m, 9.6 m, 10.6 m **b)** Use the Pythagorean theorem to find that the hypotenuse is $2.2x$. Write an equation for the perimeter and solve.

## 10.5 Equation of a Line, Given Slope and a Point, pages 421–423

**1. a)** 1 **b)** –8 **c)** –5
**2. a)** 0 **b)** $y = 2x$
**3. a)** $y = 2x - 3$ **b)** $y = -3x + 5$ **c)** $y = \frac{2}{3}x - 1$
**d)** $y = -\frac{1}{2}x - 9$ **e)** $y = -6x$ **f)** $y = -2$
**4.** $y = \frac{2}{3}x$
**5. a)** $y = 2x - 3$ **b)** $y = 3x + 14$ **c)** $y = -x + 5$ **d)** $y = x + 3$
**e)** $y = 5x + 13$ **f)** $y = -2x - 1$
**6. a)** $y = \frac{1}{2}x - 4$ **b)** $y = -\frac{1}{4}x - \frac{11}{2}$ **c)** $y = -\frac{3}{5}x - 4$
**7. a)** $\frac{3}{2}$ **b)** $y = \frac{3}{2}x + 3$
**8. a)** \$200 represents the fixed cost for producing T-shirts **b)** $C = 8n + 200$
**c)** 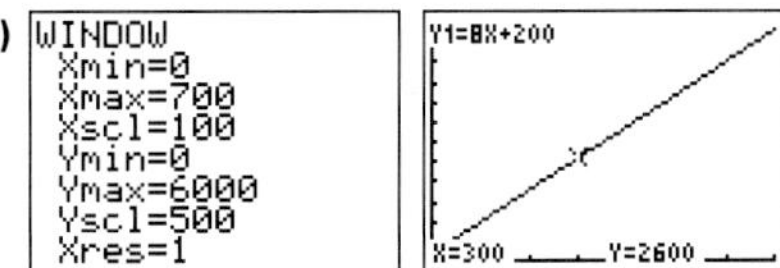

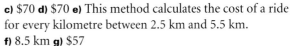

**d)** \$4200 **e)** 660, algebra
**9. a)** $C = 10d + 15$
**b)** 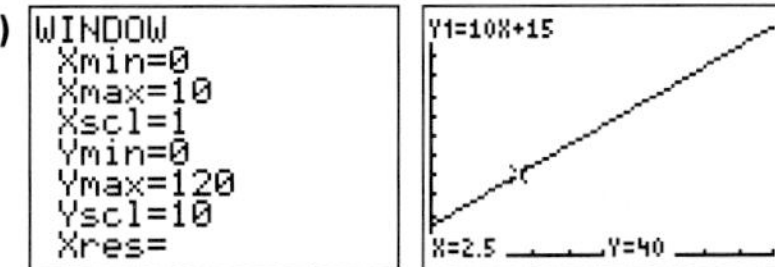

**c)** \$70 **d)** \$70 **e)** This method calculates the cost of a ride for every kilometre between 2.5 km and 5.5 km.
**f)** 8.5 km **g)** \$57
**10. a)** The point (8, 1900) means that at 8 s, Kara is at an altitude of 1900 m. **b)** 1500 **c)** $A = 50t + 1500$ **d)** 1500 m
**e)** 30 s
**11. a)** The ordered pair (2, 250) means that in 2 h he will be 250 km from Windsor. **b)** The value of –90 means that he travels at 90 km/h towards Windsor. It is negative because his distance to Windsor is decreasing.
**c)** 430 **d)** $d = -90t + 430$
**e)** 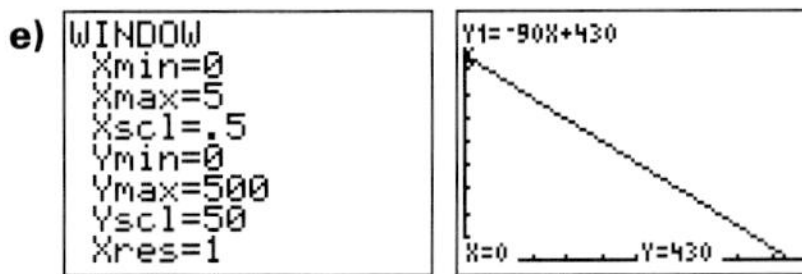

The $d$-intercept means that he started 430 km away from Windsor. **f)** 4.8 h **g)** No, because the entire trip is 430 km but he has only travelled 180 km so far.

**12. a)**

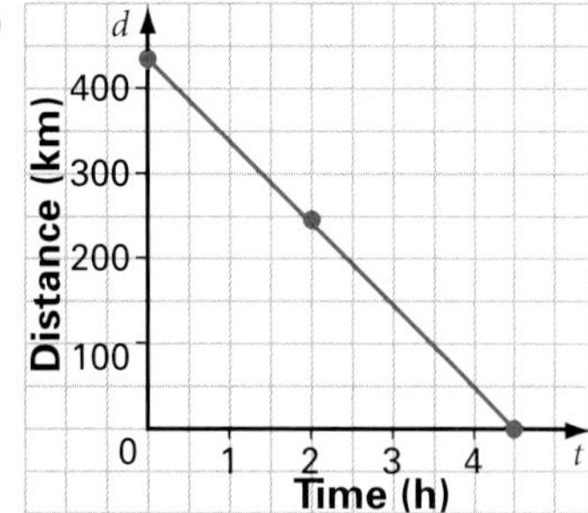


**b)** 4.5 h; No, because the entire trip is 430 km but he has only travelled for 180 km so far. **c)** Answers may vary.

## 10.6 Equation of a Line, Given Two Points, pages 427–429

**1. a)** $\frac{4}{5}$ **b)** $-\frac{1}{3}$

**2. a)** $\frac{1}{10}$ **b)** $-\frac{1}{2}$ **c)** 2 **d)** 1

**3. a)** 18 **b)** 1 **c)** –4

**4. a)** $y = -x + 4$ **b)** $y = 5x - 1.5$ **c)** $y = \frac{3}{4}x - 2$

**5. a)** $y = 2x - 1$ **b)** $y = -\frac{1}{2}x + 5$ **c)** $y = x - 4$

**d)** $y = -\frac{1}{3}x - 3$ **e)** $y = \frac{1}{4}x - \frac{1}{2}$ **f)** $y = -3x - 3$

**6. a)** $y = \frac{3}{5}x - 3$ **b)** $y = -x - 4$

**7. a)** (5, 16.25) represents the point where at 5 years, Kathy is making $16.25/h. (2, 11.75) represents the point where at 2 years, Juan is making $11.75/h. **b)** 1.5 **c)** 8.75 **d)** $w = 1.5n + 8.75$ **e)** $19.25 **f)** $46.25; Answers may vary.

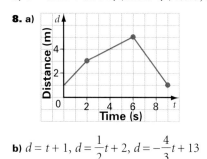

**8. a)**

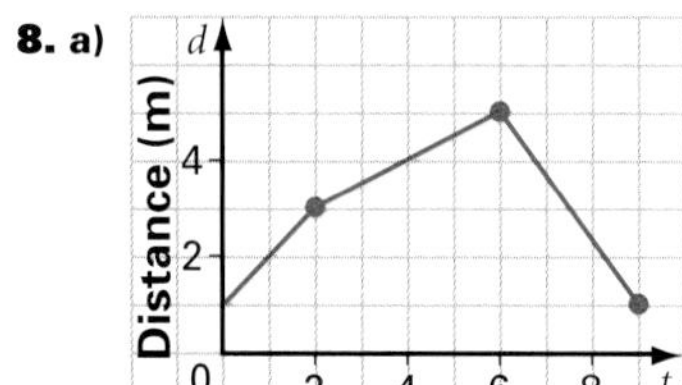


**b)** $d = t + 1$, $d = \frac{1}{2}t + 2$, $d = -\frac{4}{3}t + 13$

**9. a)** The point (2, 3000) means that after 2 h in the air, the plane is 3000 km from Calgary. The point (3.5, 1500) means that after 3.5 h in the air, the plane is 1500 km from Calgary.

**b)**

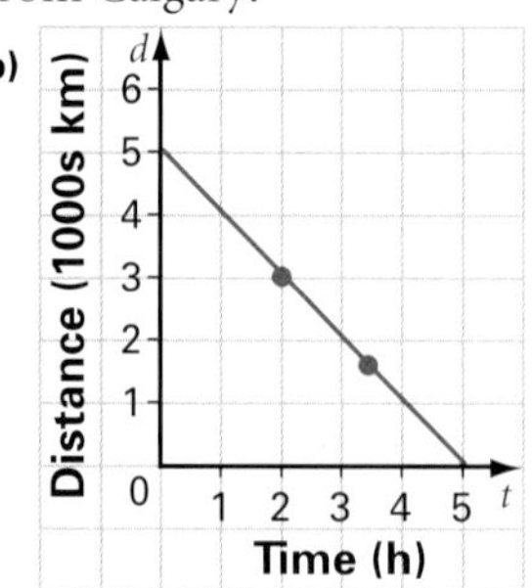


The slope is –1000. This means that the plane travels at 1000 km/h towards Calgary. The slope is negative because the distance to Calgary is decreasing.

**c)** 5000 **d)** $d = -1000t + 5000$ **e)** 5000 km **f)** 5 h

## Review, pages 430–431

**1. a)** 5 **b)** 4 **c)** –6 **d)** –18

**2. a)** 2 **b)** $\frac{3}{2}$ **c)** –7 **d)** 2

**3.** 11 km

**4. a)** 7 **b)** –2 **c)** –3 **d)** 2

**5. a)** 15 **b)** 30 **c)** 45

**6. a)** $w = \frac{A}{l}$ **b)** $r = \sqrt{\frac{A}{\pi}}$ c) $h = \frac{P - 2b}{2}$ **d)** $k = \frac{E + P}{x}$

**7. a)** 147 m **b)** Isolate the $h$ variable to get $h = \frac{3V}{b^2}$. Substitute the values for $V = 2\ 600\ 000$ and $b = 230$. Then, solve for $h$.

**8. a)** $6n = 48$ **b)** $\frac{1}{3}n = 7$ **c)** $n + 8 = 22$

**9. a)** 42 cm, 84 cm, 84 cm **b)** Let each longer side be $2x$ and each shorter side be $x$. Add the sides together to get $5x$ and set equal to 210. Solve for $x$.

**10. a)** 10 m by 2.5 m **b)** Let the width be $x$ and the length be $4x$. Write an equation for the perimeter: $4x + x + 4x + x = 25$ and solve for $x$.

**11.** $y = -3x + 21$

**12. a)** $3.50 **b)** $C = 2.2d + 3.5$ **c)** $29.90

**13.** $y = -2x + 7$

**14. a)** 1.25 m/s **b)** $d = -1.25t + 4$ **c)** 3 m

## Practice Test, pages 432–433

**1.** B **2.** A **3.** C **4.** D **5.** B **6.** D **7.** C

**8. a)** $-\frac{1}{2}$

**9.** 11 m

**10.** $y = x - 5$

**11. a)** $-1.5$ m/s **b)** Chuck is walking towards the sensor because he is getting closer to it as time passes.
**c)** $d = -1.5t + 7$
**d)**

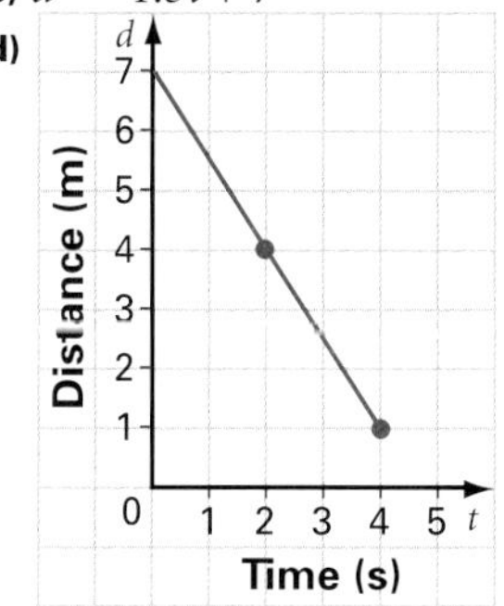


**e)** 7 m **f)** 3 s

## Cumulative Review, Chapters 8 to 10, pages 434–435

**1. a)** $\frac{1}{9}$ **b)** $\frac{625}{16}$ **c)** $\frac{16}{625}$ **d)** $\frac{25}{9}$
**2. a)** 10 **b)** 12 **c)** 18 **d)** 4
**3. a)** $\frac{1}{25}$ **b)** 4096 **c)** $\frac{1}{128}$ **d)** 1
**4.** $\frac{1}{8}$
**5. a)** $3.27 \times 10^4$ kg **b)** $7.120\ 357 \times 10^6$ m
**c)** $2 \times 10^{-3}$ s **d)** $4.05 \times 10^{-10}$ g
**6. a)** 0.000 000 000 000 005 635 88 m
**b)** 11 500 000 000 **c)** 0.000 02 m
**7. a)** $3.0 \times 10^{-5}$ kg **b)** 0.15 carats
**8. a)** $6n + 9$ **b)** $-3n + 4$ **c)** $4h^2 - 8h - 9$
**9. a)** $12t + 30$ **b)** $-2a^2 - 6$ **c)** $5m + 7$ **d)** $3n^2 - 5n$
**e)** $8x^2 - 28x - 21$
**10. a)** $14x + 6$ **b)** $8x^2 + 9x - 4$
**11. a)** 13 **b)** 9 **c)** 3 **d)** $-\frac{5}{3}$ **e)** 11
**12. a)** $C = 10 + 0.75n$ **b)** 15
**13. a)** $t = \frac{d}{s}$ **b)** $c = \sqrt{\frac{E}{m}}$ **c)** $t = \frac{A - P}{t} = \frac{A - P}{rP}$
**14.** $y = \frac{3}{2}x + 1$

# Chapter 11

## Get Ready, pages 438–439

**1. a)** 3 **b)** 5 **c)** 4
**2. a)** obtuse **b)** right **c)** acute
**3. a)** scalene **b)** equilateral **c)** isosceles
**4. a)** rectangle **b)** trapezoid **c)** square **d)** parallelogram
**e)** rhombus **f)** parallelogram
**5. a)** 140°, obtuse **b)** 26°, acute **c)** 90°, right
**6.** $a = 28°$, opposite angles
**7. a)** $a = 141°$ **b)** $b = 65°$ **c)** $c = 90°$
**8. a)** $a = 38°$ **b)** $b = 65°$ **c)** $c = 57°$
**9. a)** ∠BAC **b)** ∠DFG
**10. a)** PS **b)** BC

## 11.1 Investigating Angles of Triangles and Quadrilaterals, pages 448–449

**1. a)** $a = 30°$, $b = 75°$ **b)** a = 60°, $b = 60°$, $c = 60°$
**c)** $a = 65°$, b = 65° **d)** $d = 43°$ **e)** $e = 20°$ **f)** $f = 135°$
**2. a)** $a = 90°$ **b)** $b = 45°$ **c)** $c = 120°$
**3. a)** $a = 25°$ **b)** $b = 140°$ **c)** $c = 102°$ **d)** $d = 125°$
**e)** $e = 55°$ **f)** $f = 140°$
**4. a)** The student did not the extend all the sides in the same direction.
**b)**

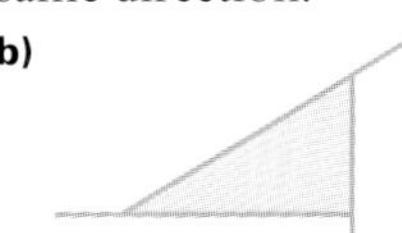

**5. a)**

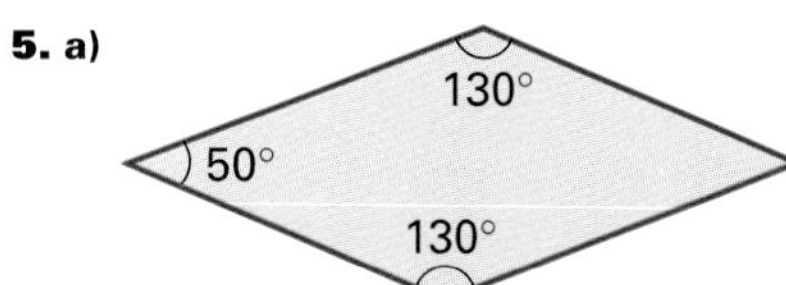


**b)** 50°
**6. a)** 80° **b)** 35°

## 11.2 Investigating Angles and Parallel Lines, pages 456–457

**1. a)** $m$ and $p$, $r$ and $t$, $s$ and $u$, $n$ and $q$ **b)** alternate angles
**c)** $m$ and $s$, $r$ and $n$, $p$ and $u$, $t$ and $q$ **d)** two
**2.** $a = 75°$, $b = 75°$, $c = 105°$, $d = 75°$, $e = 105°$, $f = 105°$, $g = 75°$

**3. a)** $a = 80°$, $b = 80°$, $c = 25°$, $d = 55°$ **b)** $a = 70°$, $b = 110°$, $c = 70°$, $d = 105°$, $e = 75°$, $f = 75°$, $g = 105°$, $h = 70°$, $i = 110°$, $j = 110°$, $k = 70°$, $l = 75°$, $m = 75°$, $n = 105°$ **c)** $a = 60°$, $b = 120°$, $c = 120°$, $d = 60°$ **d)** $a = 80°$, $b = 20°$, $c = 80°$, $d = 62°$, $e = 38°$, $f = 142°$
**4.–5.** Answers will vary.
**6.** 115°
**7.** $\angle A = 59°$, $\angle B = 121°$
**8.** Answers may vary.

## 11.3 Investigating Angle Bisectors, Medians, and Altitudes of Triangles, pages 465–466

**1. a)** altitude **b)** centroid **c)** orthocentre **d)** incentre
**2. a)** altitude **b)** angle bisector **c)** median
**5.** 5 cm

## Review, pages 474–475

**1. a)** 180° **b)** 360° **c)** 360° **d)** 360°
**2.** An exterior angle of a triangle is equal to the sum of the two opposite interior angles.
**3. a)** $a = 54°$, $b = 72°$ **b)** $c = 40°$, $d = 45°$ **c)** $e = 60°$, $f = 110°$
**4.**

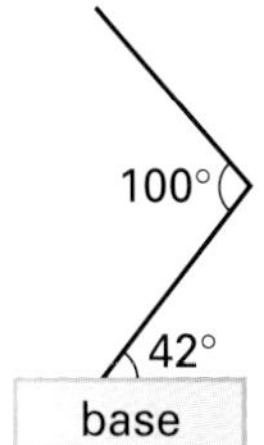


**5.** Answers may vary. Refer to page 455, section 11.2.
**6. a)** $a = 120°$, $b = 60°$, $c = 60°$, $d = 120°$ **b)** $e = 58°$, $f = 25°$, $g = 33°$, $h = 122°$
**7. a)** inside **b)** outside **c)** neither
**8.** 2 cm

## Practise Test, pages 476–477

**1.** B **2.** D **3.** C **4.** D **5.** C **6.** C **7.** A **8.** C **9.** D
**10.** $a = 50°$, $b = 130°$, $c = 50°$
**11.** The student did not extend all the sides in the same direction (clockwise or counterclockwise).
**12. a)** $a = 52°$, $b = 128°$ **b)** $c = 113°$, $d = 114°$ **c)** $e = 67°$
**13.** Answers may vary. Refer to section 11.2.

## Course Review, pages 478–481

**1. a)** $a = 32$ cm, $b = 49$ cm **b)** 261 cm
**2. a)** He should use the side of the house.
**b)**

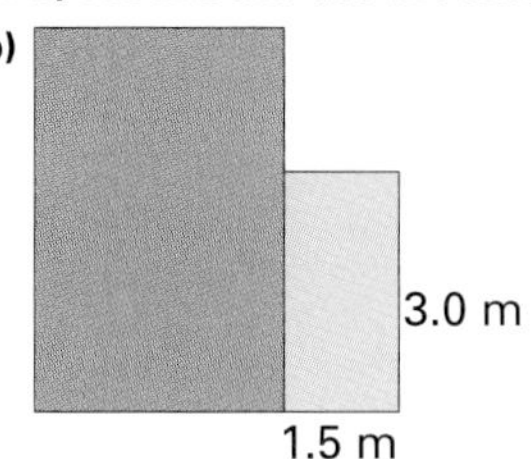


**3. a)** 1.1 cm$^2$ **b)** 2
**4. a)**

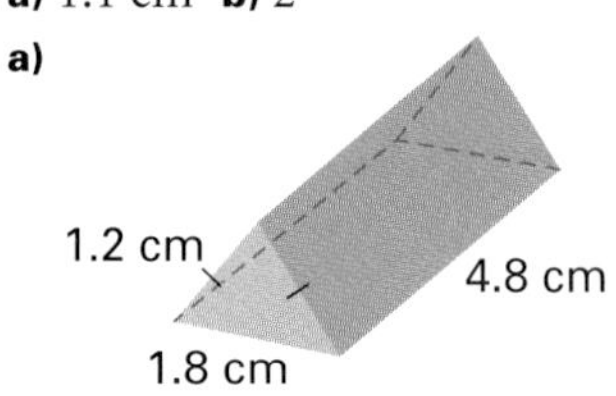


**b)** 0.8 cm **c)** 0.71 cm$^2$ **d)** 3.5 cm$^3$
**5. a)** Answers may vary. **b)** Answers may vary.
**c)** Use stratified random sampling to survey the students in proportion to their grade levels.
**6. a)** \$20.22 **b)** mean \$2.89, median \$1.85, mode \$3.50
**c)** The mean because the lunch box is an outlier.
**7. a)**

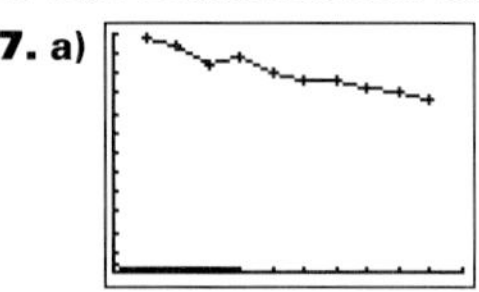

**b)** Enrolment is decreasing during the ten-year period.
**c)** Answers may vary.
**8. a)** $\frac{3}{8}$ **b)** $\frac{6}{5}$ **c)** $\frac{5}{7}$ **d)** $\frac{4}{3}$ **e)** $\frac{9}{8}$ **f)** $\frac{3}{8}$ **g)** $\frac{19}{24}$ **h)** $5\frac{7}{8}$
**9. a)** 9 packs per minute **b)** 6480
**10. a)**

| Nights | Cost (\$) |
|---|---|
| 1 | 1200 |
| 2 | 1550 |
| 3 | 1900 |
| 4 | 2250 |

**b)** 3
**11. a)**

| *t* (s) | *h* (m) |
|---|---|
| 0 | 9.5 |
| 0.5 | 11.6 |
| 1.0 | 11.3 |
| 1.5 | 8.5 |
| 2.0 | 3.3 |

**b)** 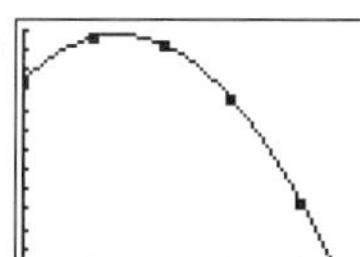 Non-linear because the points do not lie on a line.

**c)** You can use first differences or the fact that the equation has a $t^2$ term.

**12. a)–b)** 

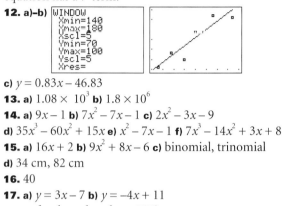

**c)** $y = 0.83x - 46.83$

**13. a)** $1.08 \times 10^3$ **b)** $1.8 \times 10^6$

**14. a)** $9x - 1$ **b)** $7x^2 - 7x - 1$ **c)** $2x^2 - 3x - 9$
**d)** $35x^3 - 60x^2 + 15x$ **e)** $x^2 - 7x - 1$ **f)** $7x^3 - 14x^2 + 3x + 8$

**15. a)** $16x + 2$ **b)** $9x^2 + 8x - 6$ **c)** binomial, trinomial
**d)** 34 cm, 82 cm

**16.** 40

**17. a)** $y = 3x - 7$ **b)** $y = -4x + 11$

**18. a)** $f$ and $c$ **b)** $b$ and $c$ **c)** 107°

# Glossary

## A

**accuracy** The number of digits given in the answer to a calculation when multiplication or division of measurements is used. For example, if a rectangle is 12.5 m long and 11.3 m wide, then its area is 141 $m^3$, to three digits of accuracy.

**acute angle** An angle whose measure is less than 90°.

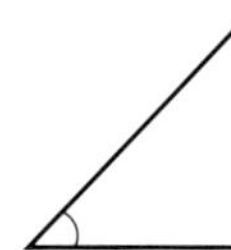

**acute triangle** A triangle in which each of the three interior angles is less than 90°.

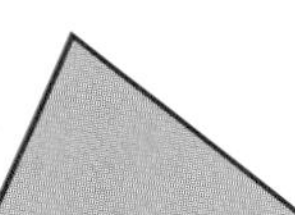

**algebraic expression** An expression that has at least one variable.

$x - 3$, $5y$, and $6 + 2k$ are algebraic expressions.

**algebraic modelling** The process of representing a relationship by an equation or a formula, or representing a pattern of numbers by an algebraic expression.

**alternate angles** Pairs of equal angles formed on either side of a transversal crossing a pair of parallel lines.

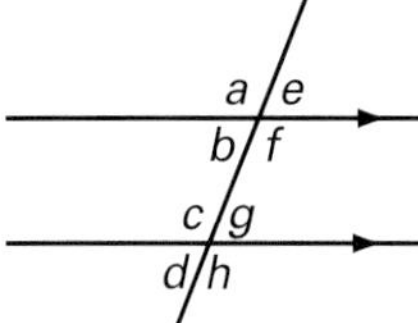


$b = g$
$c = f$

**altitude** The height of a geometric figure.

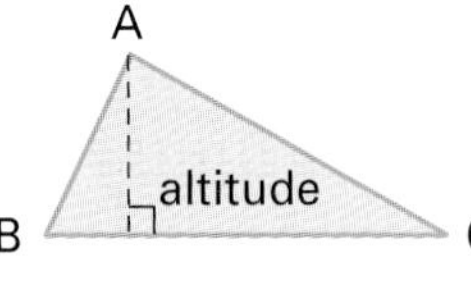


**angle bisector** A line that divides an angle into two equal parts.

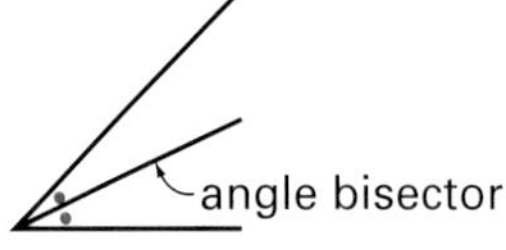


**approximate** A rounded answer or measurement.

**area** The number of square units contained in a two-dimensional region.

**average (also known as the mean)** The sum of a set of values divided by the number of values.

The mean of 1, 5, and 6 is $\frac{1 + 5 + 6}{3}$, or 4.

## B

**bar graph** A graph that uses bars to represent data.

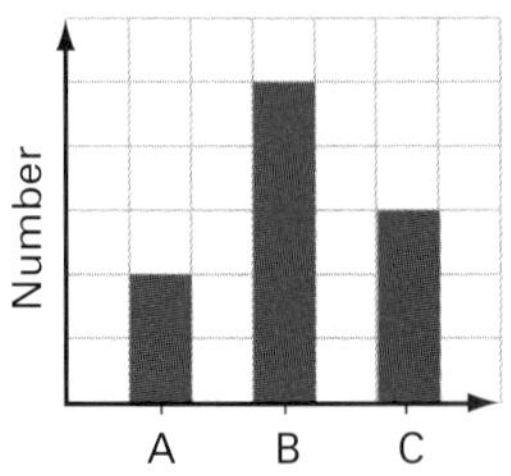


**base (of a power)** The number used as a factor for repeated multiplication.

In $6^3$, the base is 6.

**BEDMAS** A way of remembering the order of operations. BEDMAS stands for **B**rackets, **E**xponents, **D**ivision, **M**ultiplication, **A**ddition, **S**ubtraction.

**binomial** A polynomial that has two terms.

$3x + 4$ is a binomial.

**bisect (a line segment)** Divide a line segment into two equal parts.

**broken-line graph** A graph that relates two variables as ordered pairs, with consecutive points joined by line segments.

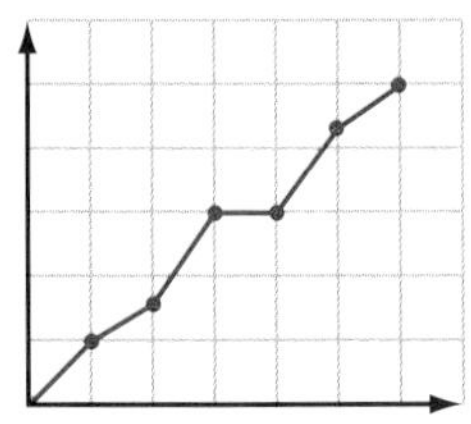

# C

**Calculator-Based Ranger™ (CBR™)** A device that can be attached to a graphing calculator to collect data such as distance.

**capacity** The greatest volume that a container can hold, usually measured in litres, or millilitres.

**Cartesian coordinate system** The system developed by René Descartes for graphing points as ordered pairs on a grid, using two perpendicular number lines. Also referred to as the Cartesian plane, the coordinate grid, or the *xy*-plane.

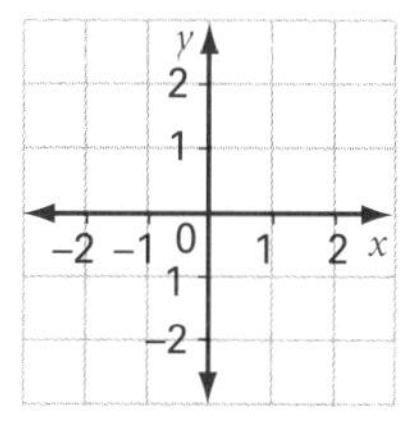


**CBR™** See Calculator-Based Ranger.

**census** A survey of an entire population.

**centroid** The point where the three medians of a triangle intersect.

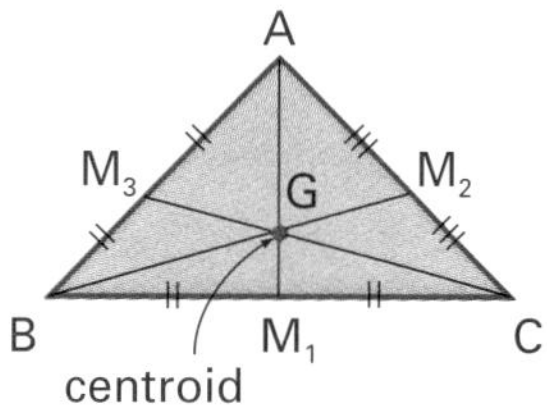


**circle** The set of all points in the plane that are equidistant from a fixed point called the centre.

**circle graph** A graph using sectors of a circle to represent data.

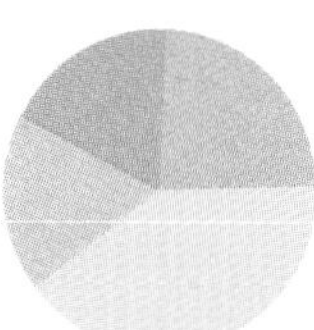

**circumference** The perimeter of a circle.

**coefficient** The number by which a variable is multiplied.

In the term $8y$, the coefficient is 8.

**co-interior angles** Pairs of supplementary angles formed between a pair of parallel lines by a transversal. Refer to the diagram shown for corresponding angles.

$b + c = 180°$
$f + g = 180°$

**collecting like terms** Simplifying an expression containing like terms by adding their coefficients.

**commission** Pay based on a percent of the amount of sales or business done.

**common factor** A number that is a factor of (divides evenly into) the given numbers.

3 is a common factor of 6, 12, and 15.

**complementary angles** Angles whose sum is 90°.

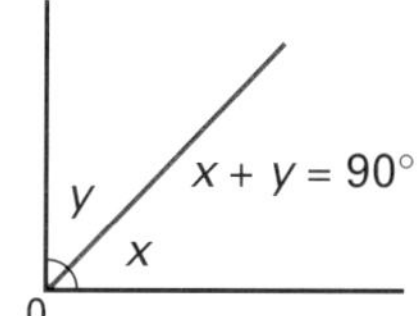


**composite figure** A figure made up of two or more simple shapes.

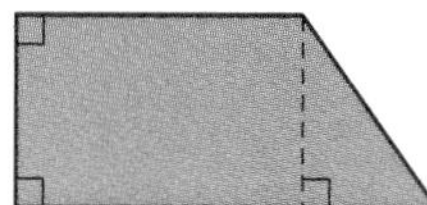

**composite number** A number that has factors other than itself and 1.

$24 = 2 \times 2 \times 2 \times 3$ is a composite number.

**cone** A three-dimensional object with a circular base and a curved surface.

**constant of variation** In a direct variation, the ratio of corresponding values of the variables. Refer to section 6.1.

**constant term** A term that contains no variables. Its value does not change.

In $2x + 5$, the constant term is 5.

**corresponding angles** Pairs of equal angles, in corresponding positions, formed by a transversal crossing a pair of parallel lines.

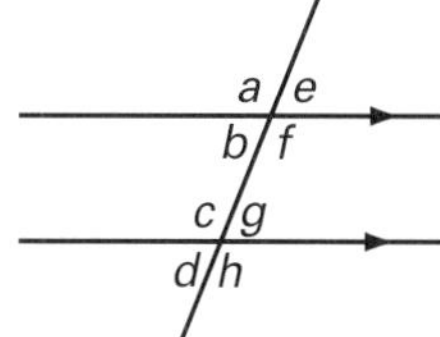


$a = c \quad b = d$
$e = g \quad f = h$

**cube** A prism with six congruent square faces.

**cylinder** A three-dimensional object with two parallel circular bases.

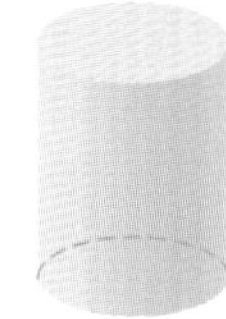

# D

**denominator** The number of equal parts in the whole or the group.

$\frac{3}{4}$ has denominator 4.

**dependent variable** In a relation, the variable whose value depends on the value of the other variable (the independent variable). On a coordinate grid, the values of the dependent variable are on the vertical axis.

In $d = 85t$, $d$ is the dependent variable.

**diagonal** A line segment joining two non-adjacent vertices of a polygon.

**diameter** A line segment, joining two points on the circumference, that passes through the centre of a circle.

**direct variation** A relationship between two variables in which one variable is a constant multiple of the other.

# E

**equation** A statement formed by two expressions related by an equal sign.

$3x + 3 = 2x - 1$ is an equation.

**equilateral triangle** A triangle with all three sides equal.

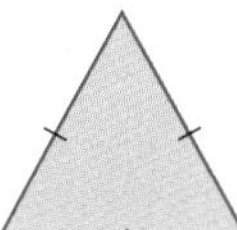

**equivalent expressions** Algebraic expressions that are equal for all values of the variable.

$7a - 3a$ and $4a$ are equivalent expressions.

**equivalent fractions** Fractions such as $\frac{1}{3}$, $\frac{2}{6}$, and $\frac{3}{9}$ that represent the same part of a whole or group.

**equivalent ratios** Ratios such as 1:3, 2:6, and 3:9 that represent the same division of the whole.

**equivalent rational numbers** Numbers such as $-1\frac{1}{2}$ and $-1.5$ that represent the same rational number.

**estimate** A guess at a measurement based on known comparisons, or a rough calculation using approximate numbers.

**evaluate** To determine a value for an expression or formula.

**exponent** The use of a raised number to denote repeated multiplication of a base.

In $3^4$, the exponent is 4.

**exponential form** A shorthand method for writing numbers expressed as repeated multiplications.

$3^4$ is the exponential form for $3 \times 3 \times 3 \times 3$ or 81.

**exponential notation** The notation used by scientific calculators to display numbers that are too large or too small to fit onto the screen of the calculator. For example, the number 1 500 000 000 might appear as 1.5 $^{9}$. The number 9 indicates the number of places that the decimal point should be moved to express the number in standard form.

**expression** A mathematical phrase made up of numbers and variables, connected by operators.

$3x + 2$ is an expression.

**exterior angle** An angle contained between one side of a polygon and the extension of an adjacent side.

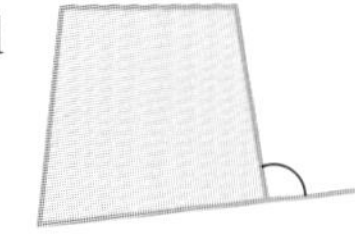

**extrapolate** Estimate values lying outside the given data. To extrapolate from a graph means to estimate coordinates of points beyond those that are plotted.

# F

**face** A plane surface of a polyhedron.

**first differences** Differences between consecutive $y$-values in tables of values with evenly spaced $x$-values. Refer to section 6.5.

**frequency** The number of times a measure occurs in a data set.

# G

**GST** Goods and Services Tax.

**graphing calculator** A hand-held device capable of a wide range of mathematical operations, including graphing from an equation, and constructing a scatter plot and a bar graph. Many graphing calculators will attach to scientific probes that can be used to gather data involving physical measurements, such as distance or temperature.

**graphing software** Computer software that provides features similar to those of a graphing calculator.

**greatest common factor (GCF)** The greatest number that is a factor of two or more numbers.

The GCF of 12 and 8 is 4.

# H

**hexagon** A polygon with six sides.

**hypotenuse** The longest side of a right triangle.

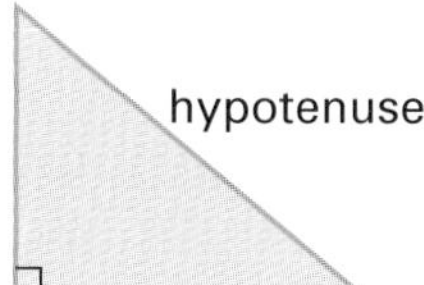


**hypothesis** A possible answer to a question.

# I

**improper fraction** A fraction in which the numerator is greater than the denominator, such as $\frac{8}{5}$.

**incentre** The point at which the three angle bisectors of a triangle meet.

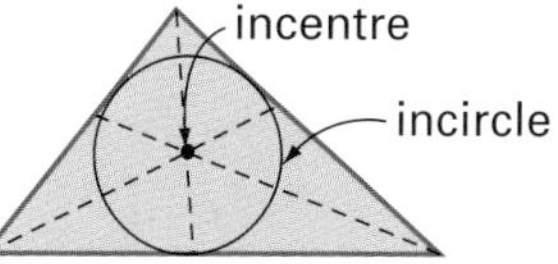


**incircle** The circle with centre at the incentre that just touches all three sides of a triangle.

**independent variable** In a relation, the variable that you need to know first. Its value determines the value of the dependent variable. On a coordinate grid, the values of the independent variable are on the horizontal axis.

In $d = 85t$, $t$ is the independent variable.

**integer** A number in the sequence …, −3, −2, −1, 0, 1, 2, 3,….

**intercept** The distance from the origin of the $xy$-plane to the point at which a line or curve crosses a given axis.

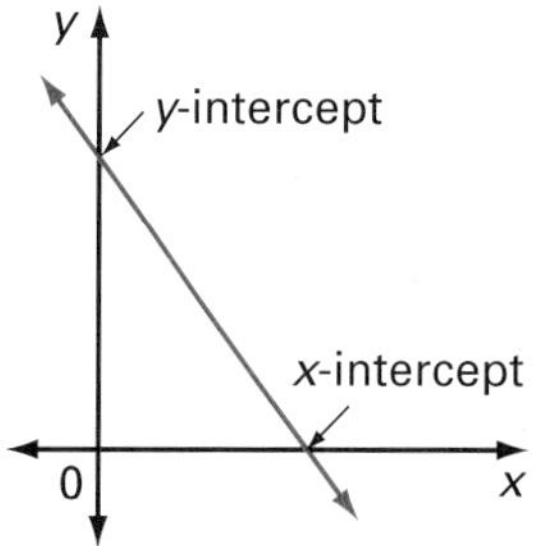


**interest rate** The percent of the principal that is earned, or paid, as interest.

**interior angle** An angle that is formed inside a polygon by two adjacent sides.

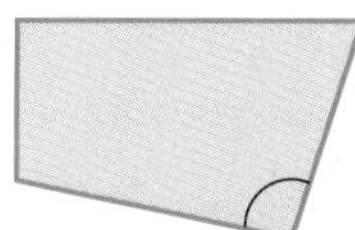

**interpolate** To estimate values lying between given data. To interpolate from a graph means to estimate coordinates of points between those that are plotted.

**isosceles triangle** A triangle with exactly two equal sides.

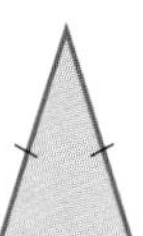

## K

**kite** A quadrilateral with two pairs of adjacent sides equal.

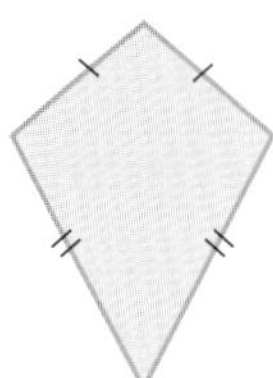

## L

**like terms** Terms that have the same variable(s) raised to the same exponent(s).

$3xy$, $-xy$, and $2.5xy$ are like terms.

**line of best fit** The straight line that passes through or as near as possible to the points on a scatter plot.

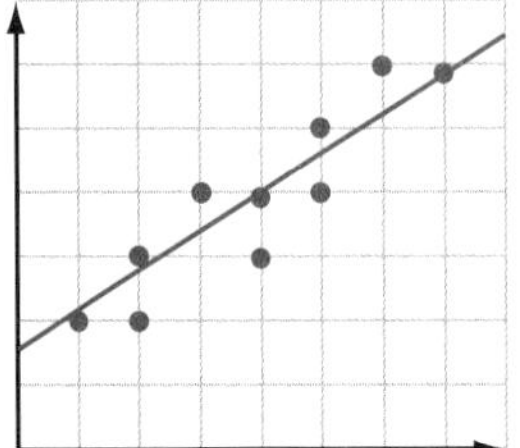

**line segment** The part of a line that joins two points.

**linear equation** An equation that relates two variables in such a way that ordered pairs satisfying the equation would form a straight line pattern on a graph.

**linear regression** A mathematical process used by graphing calculators and graphing software to find the line of best fit.

**linear relation** A relation between two variables that appears as a straight line when graphed on the coordinate plane.

**lowest common denominator (LCD)** The least common multiple of the denominators of two or more rational numbers.

The LCD of $\frac{3}{4}$ and $-\frac{2}{3}$ is 12.

**lowest common multiple (LCM)** The least multiple that two or more numbers have in common.

The LCM of 6 and 15 is 30.

## M

**mass** A measure of the quantity of matter in an object, measured in grams, kilograms, milligrams, or tonnes.

**mathematical model** A mathematical description of a real situation. The description may be a diagram, a graph, a table of values, an equation, a formula, a physical model, or a computer model.

**mathematical modelling** The process of describing a real situation in a mathematical form.

**mean** The sum of a set of values divided by the number of values. See Example 1 on page 144.

**measure of central tendency** A value that represents the "average" of a set of data. It can be the mean, median, or mode.

**median (data)** The middle value when data are arranged in order from least to greatest. If there is an even number of pieces of data, then the median is the average of the two middle values.

The median of 1, 1, 3, 5, 6 is 3.
The median of 1, 1, 3, 5 is 2.

**median (geometry)** A line segment that joins a vertex of a triangle to the midpoint of the opposite side.

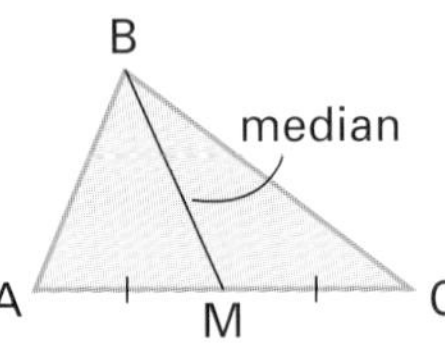


BM is a median of $\triangle ABC$.

**mixed number** A number that is part whole number and part fraction, such as $3\frac{1}{2}$.

**mode** The value that occurs most frequently in a set of data.

For 1, 2, 3, 3, 8, the mode is 3.

**monomial** A polynomial with one term, such as $7x$.

## N

**natural number** A number in the sequence 1, 2, 3, 4, … .

**negative slope** On a graph, a line that rises to the left has a negative slope.

The line shown has slope –1.

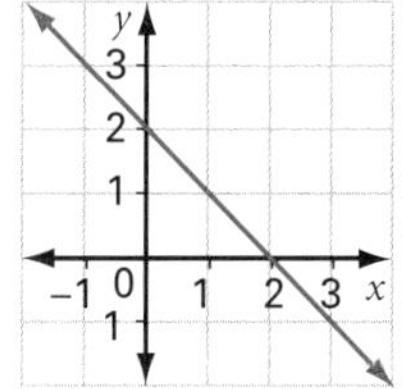

**net** A two-dimensional (flat) pattern that can be cut out, folded, and taped to form a three-dimensional shape. A net for a cube is shown.

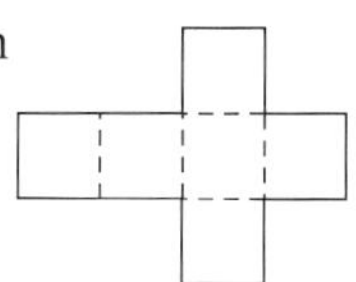

**non-linear relation** A relationship between two variables that is not a straight line when graphed.

**non-random sample** A sample in which participants volunteer or are selected by convenience.

**numerator** The number of equal parts being considered in the whole or the group.

$\frac{3}{4}$ has numerator 3.

## O

**obtuse angle** An angle that measures more than 90° but less than 180°.

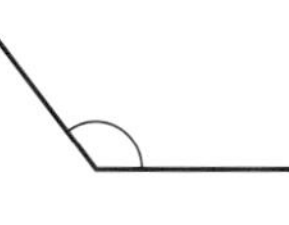

**obtuse triangle** A triangle containing one obtuse angle.

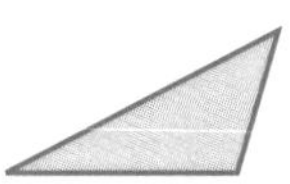

**octagon** A polygon with eight sides.

**opposite angles** When two lines cross, the pairs of angles formed on either side.

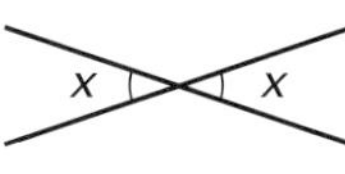


**opposite integers** Two integers, such as 5 and –5, that are an equal distance either side of 0. Their sum is 0.

**ordered pair** A pair of numbers, such as (2, 5), used to locate a point on the coordinate plane.

**origin** The point of intersection of the $x$-axis and the $y$-axis on a coordinate grid. The point (0, 0).

**orthocentre** The point where the altitudes of a triangle intersect.

**outlier** A data point that does not fit the pattern of the other data.

## P

**PST** Provincial Sales Tax.

**parallel lines** Lines in the same plane that never meet. On a graph, parallel lines have the same slope.

**parallelogram** A quadrilateral with two pairs of opposite sides that are parallel.

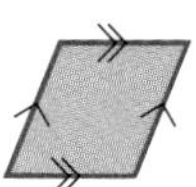

**partial variation** A relationship between two variables in which one variable equals a constant multiple of the other, plus a constant value.

**pentagon** A five-sided polygon.

**percent** A fraction in which the denominator is 100.

72% means $\frac{72}{100}$.

**perimeter** The distance around the outside of a shape.

**period (of a pendulum)** The time it takes to complete one back-and-forth swing.

**perpendicular lines** Two lines that cross at 90°. On a graph, perpendicular lines have the slopes that are negative reciprocals (their product is –1).

**point of intersection** The point where two lines cross.

**polygon** A two-dimensional closed figure whose sides are line segments.

**polyhedron** A three-dimensional object with faces that are polygons.

**polynomial** An algebraic expression formed by adding or subtracting terms.

**polynomial expression** An algebraic expression made up of terms separated by addition or subtraction.

**population** In data analysis, the entire group that is being studied.

**positive slope** On a graph, a line that rises to the right has a positive slope.

The line shown has slope $\frac{2}{3}$.

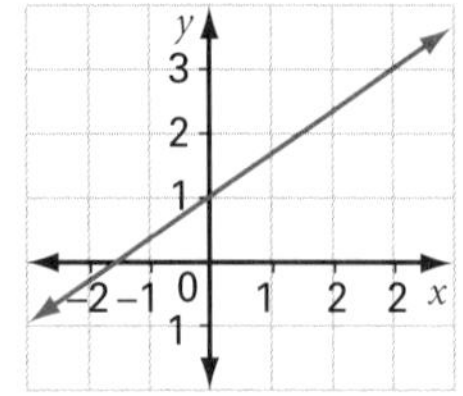

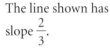

**power** A short form of writing repeated multiplication of the same number by itself.

$5^3$, $x^2$, and $10^7$ are powers.

**precision** The place value of the last digit in a measurement.

The precision of 8.6 cm is tenths.

**primary source of data** Use of a survey or an experiment to collect your own data.

**prime number** A number with exactly two factors—itself and 1.

2, 5, and 13 are prime numbers.

**principal** The original money invested or borrowed.

**prism** A three-dimensional object with two parallel, congruent polygonal bases. A prism is named by the shape of its bases, for example, rectangular prism, triangular prism.

**product** The result of multiplication.

**Pythagorean theorem** In a right triangle, the square of the length of the hypotenuse is equal to the sum of the squares of the two shorter side lengths.

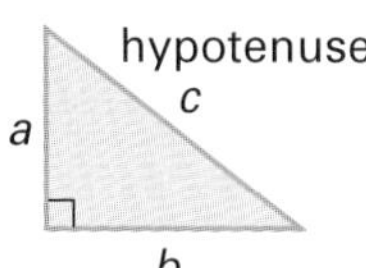


$c^2 = a^2 + b^2$

# Q

**quadrant** One of the four regions formed by the intersection of the $x$-axis and the $y$-axis.

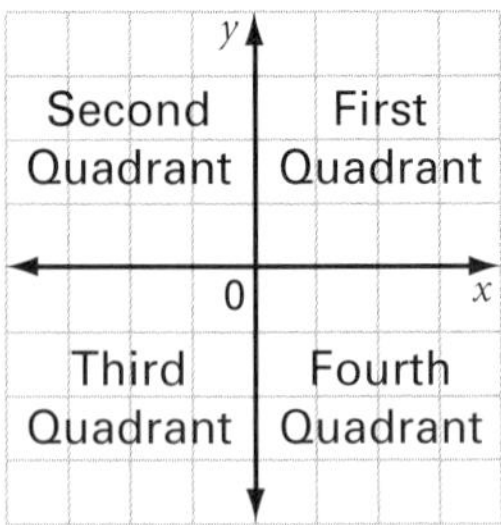


**quadrilateral** A polygon that has four sides.

**quotient** The result of division.

# R

**radius** A line segment joining the centre of a circle to a point on the circumference, or the length of this line segment.

**random sample** A sample in which every member of a population has an equally likely chance of being selected.

**rate** A comparison of two quantities expressed in different units.

60 km/h and $12.95/kg are rates.

**ratio** A comparison of two quantities with the same units.

**rational number** A number that can be expressed as the quotient of two integers, where the divisor is not zero.

0.75, $\frac{3}{4}$, and $-2$ are rational numbers.

**ray** A part of a line, with one end point.

**reciprocals** Two numbers that have a product of 1.

3 and $\frac{1}{3}$ are reciprocals.

**rectangle** A quadrilateral with two pairs of equal opposite sides and four right angles.

**rectangular prism** The mathematical name for a box with right angles at every corner.

**reflex angle** An angle that measures more than 180° but less than 360°.

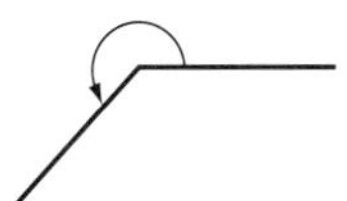

**regular polygon** A polygon with all sides equal and all angles equal.

**relation** An identified pattern, or relationship, between two variables. It may be expressed as ordered pairs, a table of values, a graph, or an equation.

**rhombus** A quadrilateral in which the lengths of all four sides are equal.

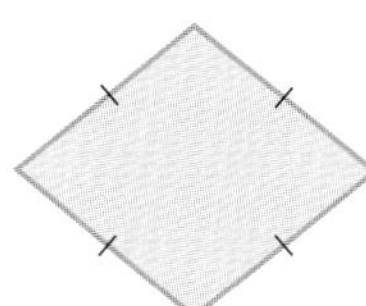

**right angle** An angle that measures 90°.

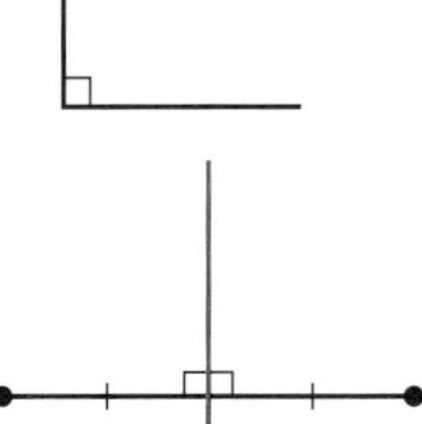

**right bisector of a line segment** A line that is perpendicular to a line segment and divides the line segment into two equal parts.

**right prism** A three-dimensional object with two parallel, congruent polygonal bases and side faces that are perpendicular to the bases.

**right triangle** A triangle containing a 90° angle.

**rise** The vertical distance between two points.

**run** The horizontal distance between two points.

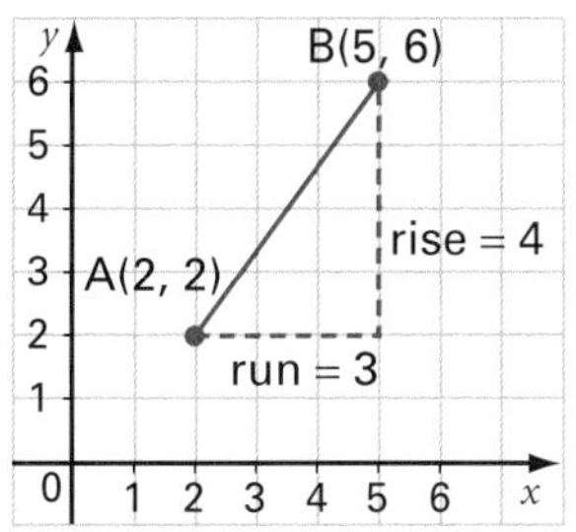


# S

**sample** A small group chosen from a population and examined in order to make predictions about the population.

**sampling error** The difference between the results of a survey and the truth.

**scalene triangle** A triangle with no sides equal.

**scatter plot** A graph showing two-variable data as points plotted on a coordinate grid. See **line of best fit**.

**scientific notation** A method of writing large or small numbers that contain many zeros. The decimal is placed to the right of the first non-zero digit and the exponent on base 10 tells how the decimal point is moved.

$123\ 000 = 1.23 \times 10^5$
$0.000\ 000\ 085 = 8.5 \times 10^{-8}$

**secondary source of data** Information that has been collected by someone else.

**semicircle** Half a whole circle.

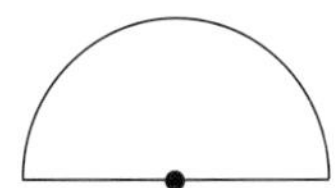

**sequence** An ordered list of numbers.

**simple interest** Interest calculated only on the original principal using the formula $I = Prt$.

**simple random sample** A method of choosing a fixed number of people from a population. Each person has the same chance of being chosen. For example, drawing names from a hat.

**simplest form (of a fraction)** A fraction whose numerator and denominator have no common factors other than 1.

$\frac{2}{3}$ is in simplest form, $\frac{8}{12}$ is not.

**simplest form (of a ratio)** The terms of the ratio are whole numbers that have no common factors other than 1.

**simplest form (of an algebraic expression)** An expression with no like terms. For example, $2x + 7$ is in simplest form, $5x + 1 + 6 - 3x$ is not.

**single-variable data** Data in which there is just one data list.

**slope** A measure of the steepness of a line.

$$\text{slope} = \frac{\text{rise}}{\text{run}}$$

**slope formula** The slope, $m$, of a line containing the points $A(x_A, y_A)$ and $B(x_B, y_B)$ is

$$m_{AB} = \frac{\text{vertical change}}{\text{horizontal change}}$$

$$m_{AB} = \frac{y_B - y_A}{x_B - x_A}, x_B \neq x_A$$

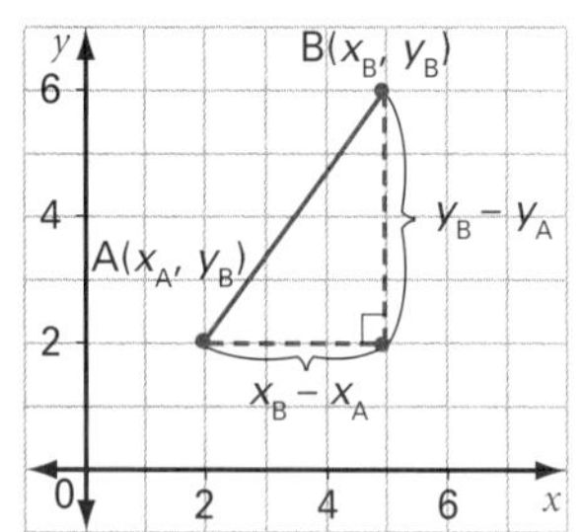


**slope-intercept form of a linear equation** The equation of a line with slope $m$ and $y$-intercept $b$ is $y = mx + b$.

**speed** The rate of change in distance compared to change in time. The slope of a distance-time graph.

**sphere** A round ball-shaped object. All points on its surface are the same distance from a fixed point called the centre.

**square** A rectangle in which the lengths of all four sides are equal.

**square root** A number that is multiplied by itself to give another number. For example, $\sqrt{36} = 6$.

**straight angle** An angle that measures 180°.

180°

**stratified random sample** A population is divided into groups, and proportional samples are randomly selected from within each group. Refer to Example 1 on page 132.

**substitution** Replacing a variable by a value.

**supplementary angles** Angles whose sum is 180°.

$a + b = 180°$

**surface area** The number of square units needed to cover the surface of a three-dimensional object.

**survey** A question or questions asked of a sample of a population.

**systematic random sampling** A method of choosing, in a predetermined way, a fixed number of people from a population. For example, choosing every tenth person on a list. Refer to section 4.2.

# T

**table of values** A table used to record the coordinates of points in a relation. For example,

| $y = x + 3$ | |
|---|---|
| $x$ | $y$ |
| 0 | 3 |
| 1 | 4 |
| 2 | 5 |

**term** A number or a variable, or the product of numbers and variables.

The expression $5x + 3$ has two terms: $5x$ and 3.

**transversal** A line that crosses or intersects two or more lines.

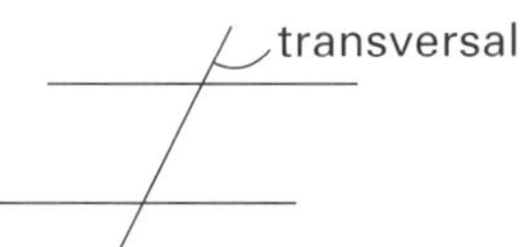


**trapezoid** A quadrilateral with one pair of parallel sides.

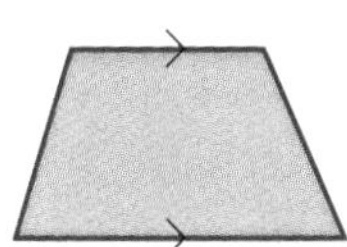

**triangle** A three-sided polygon.

**triangular prism** A prism with triangular bases.

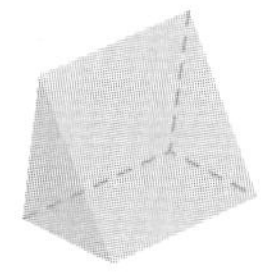

**trinomial** A polynomial with three terms.

$x^2 + 3x - 1$ is a trinomial.

**two-variable data** A set of data with two lists of data. Each entry in one list is related in some way to an entry in the other list.

## U

**unit price** The cost for one item or for one unit of measurement.

**unit rate** A comparison of two quantities in which the second term is 1. For example, $5 per ticket, or 30 km/h.

**unlike terms** Terms that have different variables, or the same variable but different exponents.

$2x$, $5y$, and $x^2$ are unlike terms.

## V

**variable** A letter used to represent a value that can change or vary. For example, $t$ is the variable in the expression $2t + 3$.

**variable term** A term that contains a variable. Its value changes when the value of the variable changes.

**vertex** A point at which two sides of a polygon meet.

**volume** The amount of space that an object occupies, measured in cubic units.

## W

**whole number** A number in the sequence 0, 1, 2, 3, 4, 5, … .

## X

***x*-axis** The horizontal number line in the Cartesian coordinate system.

***x*-coordinate** The first number in the ordered pair describing a point on a Cartesian plane.

The point P(2, 5) has $x$-coordinate 2.

***x*-intercept** The $x$-coordinate of the point where a line or curve crosses the $x$-axis. At this point $y = 0$.

***xy*-plane** A coordinate system based on the intersection of two perpendicular lines called axes. The horizontal axis is the $x$-axis, and the vertical axis is the $y$-axis. The point of intersection of the axes is called the origin.

## Y

***y*-axis** The vertical number line in the Cartesian coordinate system.

***y*-coordinate** The second number in the ordered pair describing a point on a Cartesian plane.

The point Q(–3, 4) has $y$-coordinate 4.

***y*-intercept** The $y$-coordinate of the point where a line or curve crosses the $y$-axis. At this point $x = 0$.

# Index

# O



# P



# Q



# R



# S

## T



## U



## V



## W

## Y

# Credits

## Photo Credits

**Pages iv, v, vi, vii** Roland W. Meisel; **page viii** Photodisk/Getty Images; **page ix top** Comstock Images, **bottom** Tom Dart; **page x top** ©Rommel/Masterfile, **bottom** Don Ford; **page xi** Ian Crysler; **page xii** Jeff Curtes/CORBIS/MAGMA; **page xiv** © Peter Griffith/Masterfile; **pages 4, 5** Roland W. Meisel; **page 6** Tom Dart; **page 9** Roland W. Meisel; **page 10** V.C.L./Getty Images; **pages 11, 16-17, 21, 22** Roland W. Meisel; **page 23** © W. Deuter/Zefa; **page 25** © Lloyd Sutton/ Masterfile; **pages 27, 28** Roland W. Meisel; **pages 32-33** Peter Gridley/Getty Images; **page 36** Roland W. Meisel; **page 41** Jake Rajs/Getty Images; **pages 42, 46, 54** Roland W. Meisel; **page 57** Court Mast/Getty Images; **pages 62, 64** Kevin Fleming/ CORBIS/MAGMA; **pages 76-77** © Roy Ooms/Masterfile; **pages 80, 81, 86, 88, 92** Roland W. Meisel; **page 100 top** © Klemm/Masterfile, **bottom** Roland W. Meisel; **page 106** Roland W. Meisel; **page 118** Jeff Curtes/CORBIS/MAGMA; **page 119** Roland W. Meisel; **pages 120-121** J. Silver/ Superstock; **page 124** © Ron Fehling/Masterfile; **pages 130-131** Charles Gupton/Getty Images; **page 135** Digital Vision/Getty Images; **page 149** John Perret/Getty Images; **pages 154-155** Roland W. Meisel; **page 156** Comstock Images; **pages 158, 161** Roland W. Meisel; **pages 166-167** Alexander Walter/Getty Images; **pages 172, 179, 184** Roland W. Meisel; **page191** Jim Tinios & Ted Sheppard/firstlight.ca; **pages 193, 196** Roland W. Meisel; **page 198** Dan Sherwood/ Getty Images; **page 204** Roland W. Meisel; **page 206** Jens Haas/CORBIS/MAGMA; **page 207** Photodisk/Getty Images; **page 219** Roland W. Meisel; **pages 220-221** Nils-Johan Norenlind; **page 224** acestock/firstlight.ca; **page 230** Anne-Marie Weber/Getty Images; **page 232** Jeff Zaruba/CORBIS/ MAGMA; **page 236** Getty Images; **page 238** Roland W. Meisel; **page 240** Alan Marsh/firstlight.ca; **page 248** Heatons/ firstlight.ca; **page 258** Roland W. Meisel; **page 260** Paramount Canada's Wonderland, Paramount Parks. All Rights Reserved; **page 266** Roland W. Meisel; **pages 276-277** © Mark Tomalty/ Masterfile; **page 280** © Ed Gifford/Masterfile; **pages 281, 287** Roland W. Meisel; **page 288** © Bryan Reinhart/Masterfile; **page 291** Roland W. Meisel; **page 293** Roland W. Meisel; **page 294** Roy Ooms/Masterfile; **page 299** Bill Losh/Getty Images; **pages 304, 306, 314** Roland W. Meisel; **page 322** © Bryan Sytnyk/Masterfile; **page 333** Roland W. Meisel; **pages 334-335** Photodisk/Getty Images; **page 338** Roland W. Meisel; **page 342** Digital Vision/ Getty Images; **page 347** David Burder/Getty Images; **page 352** NASA; **page 357 left** Harry Sieplinga/Getty Images, **right** Lester V. Bergman/CORBIS/MAGMA; **pages 362-363** © Ken Davies/Masterfile; **page 366** Doug Menuez/Getty Images; **page 372** Lew Long/CORBIS/MAGMA; **page 373** Lester Lefkowitz/Getty Images; **page 378** Pascal Rondeau/Getty Images; **page 381, 382, 385** Roland W. Meisel; **page 386** © Peter Griffith/Masterfile; **pages 390-391** Larry MacDougal/firstlight.ca; **page 394** imagestate/firstlight.ca; **page 398** Ron Watts/firstlight.ca; **page 399** Roland W. Meisel; **page 404** Royalty-Free/CORBIS/MAGMA; **page 410** Roland W. Meisel; **page 411** G. K. & Vikki Hart/Getty Images; **page 418** Roland W. Meisel; **page 424** © Masterfile; **page 430** Roland W. Meisel; **pages 436-437** Tom Kitchin/firstlight.ca; **pages 440, 446** Roland W. Meisel; **page 449 top** ©Rommel/Masterfile, **bottom** Don Ford; **pages 450, 457, 458, 459** Roland W. Meisel; **page 466** Ken Straiton/firstlight.ca; **page 467** Roland W. Meisel; **pages 482-483** Roland W. Meisel; **page 492** Ian Crysler.

The authors and editors would like to extend a special thank you to the students of Central Peel Secondary School, Peel District School Board, who allowed their photographs to be taken for some of the visuals found in this text.

## Text Credits

**Page 125, Example 1** Adapted from Statistics Canada CANSIM database, *http://cansim2.statcan.ca/cgi-win/CNSMCGI.EXE*, Table 110-0006, September 2002; **page 128, Question 4** Adapted from Statistics Canada CANSIM database, *http://cansim2.statcan.ca/cgi-win/CNSMCGI.EXE*, Table 358-0006, September 2002.

Statistics Canada information is used with the permission of the Minister of Industry, as Minister responsible for Statistics Canada. Information on the availability of the wide range of data from Statistics Canada can be obtained from Statistics Canada's Regional Offices, its World Wide Web site at *http://www.statcan.ca*, and its toll-free access number 1-800-263-1136.

## Screen Captures

Calculator templates, Texas Instruments Incorporated; *The Geometer's Sketchpad®*, Key Curriculum Press.

## Illustration

**Page 143**, Ben Hodson

## Technical Art

Greg Duhaney, Claire Milne, Adam Wood, and Tom Dart of First Folio Resource Group, Inc.